M000098232

Finite Mathematics

Finite

Mathematics

N. A. Weiss

Arizona State University

M. L. Yoseloff

Arizona State University

WORTH PUBLISHERS, INC.

Finite Mathematics

Copyright © 1975 by Worth Publishers, Inc.
All rights reserved. No part of this publication
may be reproduced, stored in a retrieval system, or
transmitted in any form or by any means,
electronic, mechanical, photocopying, recording,
or otherwise, without the prior written permission
of the copyright holder.
Printed in the United States of America
Library of Congress Catalog Card No. 74-20001
ISBN: 0-87901-039-8

6 7 8 9 – 92 91

Worth Publishers, Inc.
33 Irving Place
New York, New York 10003

Preface

This book is intended primarily for use in an introductory course in finite mathematics for students in the life, social, and management sciences. A year of high school algebra is sufficient prerequisite.

In writing the book we have tried to keep four important factors in mind: readability; motivation through examples; interesting, relevant, and varied applications; and extensive exercise sets.

We have introduced key concepts by first presenting examples that illustrate and motivate the material to follow. In this way the student will always have a concrete example to consider while proceeding through the general development of the subject matter. This technique has been used successfully in our own classes.

The applications have been drawn from a wide variety of subject areas. In general, we have simplified the applications in order that students will not have to become involved in the technicalities of a specific subject matter. However, a few applications are included which delve more deeply into specialized subject areas.

We have been particularly careful in the construction and composition of the exercises. A wide range of exercises is included: computational, theoretical, and exercises dealing with applications. Generally, the first few exercises in a set will be relatively routine, and students should have no difficulty with them. As one progresses through an exercise set, more difficult and varied types of problems will be encountered. The more challenging exercises are marked with an asterisk.

The answers to the odd-numbered exercises are given in the back of the text.

At the present time, there is considerable disagreement among instructors of finite mathematics courses as to whether it is appropriate to cover a chapter on symbolic logic. This text has been designed in such a way that the chapter on logic (Chapter 1) can be omitted. Of course, the instructor also has the option of covering only a few parts of the chapter (e.g., Sections 1.1 and 1.2).

Throughout the book we have attempted to write a text that offers a great deal of flexibility in the choice of material to be covered. To simplify selection of material for your particular course, we include on the following pages a short description of each chapter, a flowchart showing the organization and structure of the text, and some possible course outlines.

Chapter 1 Logic   The fundamentals of symbolic logic are introduced. The main topics include propositions, connectives, and valid arguments. The instructor may omit part or all of this chapter.

Chapter 2 Set Theory   The basic concepts of set theory needed for the remainder of the text are presented: sets, elements, subsets, set operations, and the number of elements in a set.

Chapter 3 Combinatorial Analysis We introduce the fundamental counting principles. Permutations and combinations are presented, and charts and diagrams are utilized to aid in the discussion.

Chapter 4 Probability The basic concepts of finite sample spaces are discussed in detail: sample spaces, events, laws of probability, uniform sample spaces, conditional probability, independence, Bayes' formula, the binomial distribution, and expected value. Those wishing a briefer treatment of probability may omit Sections 4.11 and 4.12.

Chapter 5 Descriptive Statistics Some of the topics included are measures of central tendency, measures of dispersion, organization of data in large samples, and descriptive measures for grouped data.

Chapter 6 Linear Equations, Vectors, and Matrices We present the Gaussian elimination method for solving systems of linear equations, introduce vectors and matrices, discuss systems of linear equations in vector-matrix form, and apply these methods in order to develop an algorithm for determining the inverse of a matrix. This chapter is prerequisite for the remaining chapters.

Chapter 7 Geometric Linear Programming This chapter presents the geometric method for solving linear programming problems. All of the required geometric concepts are contained in the chapter and the student is not assumed to have any background knowledge in geometry.

Chapter 8 The Simplex Method for Linear Programming Here we develop the algebraic method for solving linear programming problems; namely, the simplex algorithm. The steps in the algorithm are carefully motivated by the detailed discussion of an example (Section 8.4).

Chapter 9 Markov Chains Among the topics covered are the transition matrix and distribution of a Markov chain, regular Markov chains and equilibrium distributions, and absorbing Markov chains.

Chapter 10 Applications of Probability and Markov Chains Several interesting and relevant applications of probability and Markov chains are presented. Applications are given to genetics, queuing theory, psychology, and gambling.

Chapter 11 Matrix Games We introduce and develop the theory of two-person, zero-sum, matrix games. Topics presented include strictly determined games, 2×2 matrix games, $m \times n$ matrix games, and von Neumann's minimax theorem (which is optional). Several applications are also included.

The prerequisites for the various chapters are given in the following flowchart. A line from one chapter to another below it indicates that the previous chapter is a prerequisite for the latter. A dashed line indicates an optional prerequisite.

Acknowledgments The entire list of people whom we should like to acknowledge for their helpful comments, suggestions, and contributions is too long to present here. However, we are pleased to express our appreciation to the many reviewers

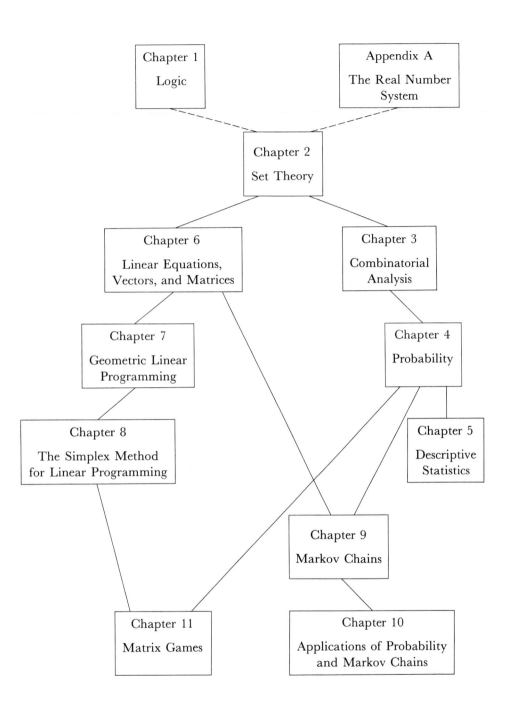

Suggested Course Outline

Time allotted	Chapters to be covered
1 semester, 3 credits	2, 3, 4, 6, 7*, *or* 1, 2, 3, 4, 5, *or* 1, 2, 3, 4, 6, *or* 2, 3, 4, 5, 6, *or* 1, 2, 3, 6, 7, 8
1 quarter, 4 credits	2, 3, Sections 4.1–4.10, 4.13, 6, 7*, *or* 1, 2, 3, 4, 5, *or* 2, 3, 4, 6, *or* 2, 3, 6, 7, 8, *or* 1, 2, 3, 6, 7
1 semester, 4 credits, *or* 2 quarters, 6 credits	2, 3, 4, 6, 7, 9*, *or* 2, 3, 4, 6, 7, 8, 11*, *or* 1, 2, 3, 4, 6, 7, 8, *or* 1, 2, 3, 4, 5, 6, 7, *or* 2, 3, 4, 5, 6, 7, 8
1 semester, 5 credits	2, 3, 4, 6, 7, 8, 9, 10*, *or* 2, 3, 4, 6, 7, 8, 9, 11*, *or* 1, 2, 3, 4, 5, 6, 7, 8, 11, *or* 1, 2, 3, 4, 6, 7, 8, 9
2 semesters, *or* 3 quarters	Entire text

*Our personal preferences.

whose considerable efforts were crucial to the improvement of several aspects of the book: Professor Yousef Alavi, Western Michigan University; Professor David G. Cantor, University of California, Los Angeles; Professor Garret J. Etgen, University of Houston; Professor Louis Friedler, University of Missouri; Professor Michael Gartenberg, Baruch College—The City University of New York; Professor Gustav B. Hensel, Catholic University of America; Professor Elizabeth B. Hesch, University of Richmond; Professor Donald E. Ramirez, University of Virginia; Professor David A. Schedler, Virginia Commonwealth University; Professor Michael W. Varano, Villanova University.

We also thank Professors Michael Driscoll, Matthew Hassett, Gustav Levine, and Fred Sansone for many useful consultations. Professor Greg Nielson helped make possible the many parts of the book that involved the computer. And our special thanks go as well to Robert Cranwell for his assistance in preparing and solving many of the exercises.

Ethel Bauer, Verna Campbell, and Gay Daugherty did a superb job of typing. Finally, we should like to express our appreciation to everyone at Worth Publishers for their help in the publication of the book.

Neil Weiss
Mark Yoseloff

January, 1975

Contents

Applications

Examples and Exercises Related to the Social Sciences

Subject	Examples	Exercises
Classification		3.2.4
Number of Offspring		4.2.8, 4.3.5, 4.4.8
Voting Percent by Religion	4.11.2	4.5.4
Judicial System		4.12.8
Accidents/Sex/Intoxication		4.13.13
Union Affiliation		4.14.11
ESP		4.15.7, 5.4.6, 5.5.11
Scholastic Aptitude Tests		5.4.1, 5.6.13
Color Preference		6.5.18
Social Mobility	9.2.1, 9.3.1, 9.3.4, 9.4.1, 9.7.1, 9.8.1, 9.10.1, 9.11.2	9.2.9, 9.5.12, 9.6.6, 9.9.5, 9.11.8, 9.13.6
Maze Experiment		9.3.6
Spread of Rumors		9.4.10, 9.6.5, 9.8.4, 9.10.6
Urban vs. Rural Population		9.6.8
Word Structure	9.2.2, 9.4.3	9.8.3, 9.10.2
Study Habits		9.10.5
Graduating vs. "Flunking Out"		9.12.7, 9.13.7
Behavioral Patterns	3.4.5	
Political Sampling	3.7.3, 5.1.1	
Birth Months	4.1.4	
Incomes	5.2.2, 5.2.4, 5.2.7, 5.3.2, 5.3.5	
Effect of Diet on Learning	6.1.1	
Paired-Associate Learning	Sections 10.4, 10.5	10.4.1–10.4.5, 10.5.1–10.5.6

Examples and Exercises Related to Biology and Medicine

Subject	Examples	Exercises
Blood Types		2.5.8, 2.6.10, 2.7.4
Reproduction	4.9.2	4.6.1, 4.8.1, 4.8.10, 4.14.7, 4.15.14
Smoking and Heart Attack		4.12.7
Skull Sizes		5.2.9, 5.3.14
Life Expectancy	5.4.1, 5.5.1	5.6.12
Vaccine Effectiveness	4.14.2	6.5.17
Dieting		8.7.9
Eye Color		9.7.10
Genetics	3.3.3, 4.7.4, 9.12.2, 9.13.2, 10.1.1, 10.1.3, 10.2.1	10.1.1–10.1.9, 10.2.1–10.2.8
Effect of Diet on Learning	6.1.1	6.1.10, 6.2.8, 6.5.14
Toxicity of Snakes	2.7.1, 4.13.2	
Botany	4.8.1	

Examples and Exercises Related to Business and Economics

Subject	Examples	Exercises
Stock Purchases		2.1.14, 3.3.3, 3.5.6, 3.6.7, 4.8.11
Sales	4.15.2	2.3.8, 2.3.9
Taxes and Labor		2.4.10
Insurance		2.4.12
Committee Organization		2.5.10
Survey Analysis	2.6.7, 3.4.2	2.6.7, 2.6.8, 2.7.3
Officer Selection	3.1.5, 3.3.4	3.2.10, 4.10.7, 4.11.13
Screening Exams		4.5.6
Job Assignments		3.5.4
Sampling	4.7.1	4.7.1, 4.9.12, 4.11.3, 4.11.11, 4.13.8
Personnel	4.3.2	4.7.4
Automobile Manufacturing		4.12.13, 4.15.13
Union Affiliation		4.14.11
Investments		4.15.15
Business Failures		4.16.11
Misprints		5.2.8, 5.3.13
Phone Conversation Duration		5.2.12
Mean Salary		5.2.13
Customer Interarrival Times		5.4.4, 5.5.9
Quality Control	5.1.3	5.5.8, 5.6.15
Advertising Expenditures	6.1.2	6.1.11, 6.5.15
Cost of Automobiles		6.30
Building Contracting		6.7.23, 7.7.6, 8.7.8
Oil Refineries		6.9.22, 7.7.7, 8.7.10
Fabric Manufacturing	7.1.2	7.1.7, 7.2.16, 7.4.23
Feed Mixtures	7.1.3	7.1.8, 7.4.24, 7.7.5
Net Profits		7.2.22
Income Tax Returns		7.4.21, 7.5.13, 7.7.3, 8.7.4
Carton Manufacturing		7.4.22, 7.5.14, 7.7.4, 8.7.7
Cabinet Making	8.1.3	8.1.16
Rental Service	8.1.4	8.1.17, 8.7.5
Restaurant Problem	4.15.4	7.7.1, 8.7.1
Stereo Manufacturing		7.7.2, 8.7.2
Calculator Manufacturing		8.7.3
Carpentry Problem		8.7.6
Inventory		8.7.11
Machine Breakdowns		9.3.3, 9.4.7, 9.5.10, 9.10.12
Car Leasing		9.4.9, 9.10.15
Supermarket Problem		9.5.15
Telephone Switchboards	5.4.2, 5.5.2, 5.5.4 5.6.4, 9.6.1, 9.10.3 9.7.3, 9.10.2	9.6.1
Business Trends		9.6.6, 9.6.11
Television Commercials		9.7.7
Business Location	11.7.1	11.1.6, 11.1.7, 11.2.14, 11.2.15, 11.7.2
Advertising Strategies		11.7.5
Territorial Assignments	3.5.1	
Queuing Theory	10.3.1	10.3.1, 10.3.2

Logic

1

Some of the fundamental notions of symbolic logic are presented in this chapter. Principles of logic are often useful toward understanding the precise meanings of statements, and they are also helpful in the development of important methods of reasoning. Although symbolic logic is not used explicitly in subsequent chapters, many readers will find it useful to have a working knowledge of the subject.

Section 1.1 Propositions and Connectives

We begin this section with an example that illustrates the various types of sentences that may be encountered in the English language.

Example 1.1.1

1. Los Angeles is in California.
2. Today is the fourth of July.
3. Close the door!
4. Which city in the United States has the largest population?
5. The price of gold went up today.
6. The rate of inflation this year was 8 percent.
7. Why did you walk to work today?

In studying these sentences we see that they can be divided into two main types: (1) those which can be classified as either true or false, and (2) those which cannot be so classified.

Definition
A sentence that can be meaningfully classified as either true or false is called a *proposition.*

This chapter is optional.

For instance, sentences 1, 2, 5, and 6 in Example 1.1.1 are propositions, whereas the other sentences are not propositions.

In our day-to-day writing and conversation we often combine two or more propositions. For example, the two propositions

1. John is taking English 101.
2. John is taking Math 119.

can be combined into the proposition "John is taking English 101 *and* John is taking Math 119." They can also be combined into the proposition "John is taking English 101 *or* John is taking Math 119."

The combination of two or more propositions is called a *compound proposition*, and the words used to combine the propositions in a compound proposition are called *connectives*. For example, "and" and "or" are connectives.

In the study of logic it is convenient to let letters stand for propositions. We shall use the letters p, q, r, and s to denote propositions.

Definition

Let p and q denote propositions. Then the compound proposition "p and q" is called the *conjunction* of p and q. We use the symbolism

$$p \wedge q$$

to denote the conjunction of p and q.

Example 1.1.2   Consider the two propositions

p: Los Angeles is in California.
q: Chile is south of the equator.

Then the conjunction of p and q is the proposition

$p \wedge q$: Los Angeles is in California, and Chile is south of the equator.

Example 1.1.3   Let p and q denote the propositions

p: Phoenix is in Arizona.
q: England is south of the equator.

Then the conjunction of p and q is the proposition

$p \wedge q$: Phoenix is in Arizona, and England is south of the equator.

Consider the compound proposition of Example 1.1.2. Since each of the propositions comprising the conjunction is true, we are willing to say that the conjunction itself is true. On the other hand, consider the compound proposition of Example 1.1.3. Although the first proposition in the conjunction is true, the second one is not. Therefore, we would say that the conjunction is false.

Definition

Let p and q be propositions. Then the proposition $p \wedge q$ (the conjunction of p and q) is said to be *true* when both p and q are true, and it is said to be *false* otherwise.

We next consider the connective "or." As in the case of the connective "and," we employ a symbolic representation.

Definition
Let p and q denote propositions. Then the compound proposition "p or q" is called the *disjunction* of p and q and is written symbolically as

$$p \vee q$$

In discussing whether or not a disjunction is true, we need to be a little careful.

Example 1.1.4 Consider again the propositions of Example 1.1.3. Then the disjunction of p and q is

$p \vee q$: Phoenix is in Arizona, or England is south of the equator.

Although the proposition q is false, we certainly would not hesitate in saying that the disjunction $p \vee q$ is true. This is because the proposition p *is* true.

Example 1.1.5 Consider again the propositions of Example 1.1.2. Then the disjunction of p and q is the proposition

$p \vee q$: Los Angeles is in California, or Chile is south of the equator.

Since both p and q are true propositions, it is not exactly clear whether or not we should consider the disjunction $p \vee q$ to be true. Indeed, if by the "or" we mean that one or the other, *but not both*, of the propositions is true, then in this case $p \vee q$ will be false. On the other hand, if by the "or" we mean that one or the other *or both* of the propositions is (are) true, then in this case $p \vee q$ will be true. We shall adopt the latter convention.

Definition
Let p and q denote propositions. Then the proposition $p \vee q$ (the disjunction of p and q) is said to be *true* if either p is true or q is true or both are true; and it is said to be *false* otherwise.

The disjunctions in both Examples 1.1.4 and 1.1.5 are true propositions.
    The final concept to be considered in this section is that of negation.

Definition
Let p denote a proposition. Then the proposition "not p" is called the *negation* of p and is denoted symbolically by

$$\sim p$$

Example 1.1.6 Let p be the proposition

p: Los Angeles is in California.

Then the negation of p is the proposition

~*p*: Los Angeles is *not* in California.

Note that since *p* is true, the negation of *p* is false.

Example 1.1.7 Consider the proposition

p: England is south of the equator.

Then the negation of *p* is the proposition

~*p*: England is *not* south of the equator.

Note that since *p* is false, the negation of *p* is true.

Definition

Let *p* denote a proposition. Then the proposition ~*p* (the negation of *p*) is said to be *false* if *p* is true and is said to be *true* if *p* is false.

Exercises for 1.1

1. Which of the following sentences are propositions?
   (a) Tomorrow will be Wednesday.   (b) All birds can fly.
   (c) This dog is lazy.   (d) Stand up!
   (e) Are you leaving today?   (f) Bill has black hair.
   (g) Jack, please close the door.   (h) The sun is shining.
2. Write the conjunction of each of the following propositions.
   (a) Every number is even. Seven is odd.
   (b) Smith is a teacher. Jones is a lawyer.
   (c) Some summers are hot. All winters are cold.
   (d) All circles are round. This rectangle is a square.
   (e) Fred has brown eyes. Mary has red hair.
3. Write the disjunction of each of the following propositions.
   (a) All roses are red. Some tulips are yellow.
   (b) Some lines are parallel. These lines intersect.
   (c) Philadelphia is in New Jersey. Texas is one of the New England states.
   (d) Ray has gone fishing. Judy is swimming.
   (e) This is a good steak. He is hungry.
4. Indicate whether the following conjunctions are true or false.
   (a) Reno is in Nevada, and Denver is the capitol of Colorado.
   (b) All roses are red, and some tulips are yellow.
   (c) Zero is a multiple of seven, and all numbers are even.
   (d) All rectangles are squares, and all lines are parallel.
5. Indicate whether the following disjunctions are true or false.
   (a) Washington, D.C., is the capital of the United States, or Lincoln is the capital of Nebraska.
   (b) All circles are round, or all lines are straight.
   (c) All ripe apples are red, or some oranges have no seeds.
   (d) All rectangles are square, or no two triangles are similar.
6. Let *p* and *q* be propositions. Determine the truth value of *p* given the truth values in each of the following.
   (a) *q* is true and $p \land q$ is true.   (b) *q* is false and $p \lor q$ is true.
   (c) *q* is true and $p \land q$ is false.   (d) *q* is true and $p \land \sim q$ is false.
   (e) ~*q* is true and $p \land \sim q$ is false.

7. Write the negation of each of the following propositions.
    (a) He is a good student.
    (b) The steak was tender.
    (c) All stocks are listed on the New York Stock Exchange.
    (d) Some people own two cars.
    (e) No one enjoyed the book.
    (f) Everyone is different.
8. In each of the following problems, two statements are given. Determine whether the second is the negation of the first.
    (a) I am hungry. I am not hungry.
    (b) Some cats are black. Some cats are white.
    (c) Everyone liked the book. Exactly one person did not like the book.
    (d) All houses are red. Some houses are yellow.
    (e) No one likes him. Some people like him.
    (f) Sometimes I am wrong. I am right all the time.
9. Let p be the proposition "The sun is shining," and let q be the proposition "It is cold." Write a verbal statement that describes each of the following.
    (a) $p \wedge q$ (b) $p \vee q$
    (c) $\sim p$ (d) $p \vee \sim q$
    (e) $\sim p \wedge q$ (f) $\sim p \wedge \sim q$
10. Let p be the proposition "She is pretty" and let q be the proposition "She is intelligent." Write each of the following statements in symbolic form; use p and q.
    (a) She is pretty and intelligent.
    (b) She is intelligent but not pretty.
    (c) Either she is pretty or she is intelligent.
    (d) She is neither pretty nor intelligent.
    (e) She is intelligent, or she is pretty and not intelligent.
    (f) It is not true that she is pretty or intelligent.
    (g) It is not true that she is not pretty and intelligent.
11. Let p be a true proposition, and let q be a false proposition. Determine which of the following propositions are true and which are false.
    (a) $\sim q$ (b) $p \wedge q$
    (c) $p \vee \sim q$ (d) $\sim p \wedge q$
    (e) $\sim p \vee \sim q$ (f) $\sim (p \vee q)$
    (g) $\sim (\sim p \vee q)$ (h) $\sim (p \wedge \sim q)$
    (i) $\sim (\sim p \wedge \sim q)$ (j) $\sim (\sim p)$
12. Suppose it is true that the sun is shining but it is not cold. Which of the six propositions in problem 9 are true and which are false?
13. Let p and q be propositions. Write a compound proposition that symbolically states "p or q, but not p and q"; use only the symbols $\sim$, $\vee$, and $\wedge$.

Section 1.2   Truth Tables

When determining the truth value of a compound proposition (i.e., whether it is true or false), it is convenient to utilize a schematic representation. This representation is exhibited in what is called a *truth table*.

Example 1.2.1   Let p and q denote propositions. Then there are four possible combinations of truth values for p and q:

1. p is true and q is true.
2. p is true and q is false.

3. p is false and q is true.

4. p is false and q is false.

The definition of the truth value of $p \land q$ (the conjunction of p and q) can be summarized as in Figure 1.2.1. It is immediately clear from the figure that the conjunction of p and q ($p \land q$) is true exactly when both p and q are true.

Figure 1.2.1

p	q	$p \land q$
T	T	T
T	F	F
F	T	F
F	F	F

Example 1.2.2 We exhibit the definition of the truth value of the disjunction of two propositions via a truth table, Figure 1.2.2. The figure makes it perfectly clear that the disjunction of two propositions is false exactly when both propositions in the disjunction are false.

Figure 1.2.2

p	q	$p \lor q$
T	T	T
T	F	T
F	T	T
F	F	F

Example 1.2.3 The truth table for the negation of a proposition p is as shown in Figure 1.2.3.

Figure 1.2.3

p	$\sim p$
T	F
F	T

By continued use of the connectives "and" and "or" and the word "not," we can construct significantly more complex propositions than the ones considered previously. It is in these more complicated situations that the value of the truth-table representation really becomes evident. However, to effectively use the technique for obtaining the truth values of a compound proposition, it is necessary to have a precise method for the construction of such tables. The method is as follows:

1. List the possible truth-value combinations for the individual propositions that constitute the compound proposition.

2. Using step 1, determine the truth values of the main components of the compound proposition.
3. Using step 2, determine the truth value of the compound proposition.

This procedure is illustrated in the following examples.

Example 1.2.4 Construct the truth table for the compound proposition

$$\sim p \wedge q$$

At step 1 we have the table shown in Figure 1.2.4. Then at step 2 we use column

Figure 1.2.4

p	q	$\sim p$	$\sim p \wedge q$
T	T		
T	F		
F	T		
F	F		

1 of the figure together with the definition of the truth value for the negation of a proposition to obtain Figure 1.2.5. Finally, using the third and second columns of this figure along with the definition of the truth value for the conjunction of two propositions, we get the truth table of Figure 1.2.6. From this figure it is clear that the compound proposition $\sim p \wedge q$ is true exactly when p is false and q is true (see the third row of the table).

Figure 1.2.5

p	q	$\sim p$	$\sim p \wedge q$
T	T	F	
T	F	F	
F	T	T	
F	F	T	

Figure 1.2.6

p	q	$\sim p$	$\sim p \wedge q$
T	T	F	F
T	F	F	F
F	T	T	T
F	F	T	F

Generally, we will carry out steps 1–3 for the truth-table construction by using one truth table instead of, for example, the three used in Example 1.2.4.

Example 1.2.5 Find the truth table for the compound proposition

$$(p \wedge \sim q) \vee q$$

Figure 1.2.7

p	q	$\sim q$	$p \wedge \sim q$	$(p \wedge \sim q) \vee q$
T	T	F	F	T
T	F	T	T	T
F	T	F	F	T
F	F	T	F	F

It is evident from Figure 1.2.7 that the compound proposition $(p \wedge {\sim} q) \vee q$ is true unless both p and q are false.

Example 1.2.6 Determine the truth table for the compound proposition

$$\sim (p \vee {\sim} q) \wedge ({\sim} p \vee q) \tag{1.2.1}$$

As you can see from Figure 1.2.8, the compound proposition given by Eq. (1.2.1) is true exactly when p is false and q is true. (See if you can determine this fact without a truth table!)

Figure 1.2.8

p	q	${\sim}p$	${\sim}q$	$p \vee {\sim}q$	$\sim(p \vee {\sim}q)$	${\sim}p \vee q$	$\sim(p \vee {\sim}q) \wedge ({\sim}p \vee q)$
T	T	F	F	T	F	T	F
T	F	F	T	T	F	F	F
F	T	T	F	F	T	T	T
F	F	T	T	T	F	T	F

We conclude this section with an example concerning a compound proposition that contains three individual propositions: p, q, and r.

Example 1.2.7 Find the truth table for the compound proposition

$$({\sim}p \vee r) \wedge {\sim}q \tag{1.2.2}$$

Since three individual propositions are involved here, there will be eight possible combinations of truth values. In view of Figure 1.2.9, the compound proposition given in Eq. (1.2.2) is true if both p and q are false or if q is false and r is true. Otherwise the proposition in Eq. (1.2.2) is false.

Figure 1.2.9

p	q	r	${\sim}p$	${\sim}q$	${\sim}p \vee r$	$({\sim}p \vee r) \wedge {\sim}q$
T	T	T	F	F	T	F
T	T	F	F	F	F	F
T	F	T	F	T	T	T
T	F	F	F	T	F	F
F	T	T	T	F	T	F
F	T	F	T	F	T	F
F	F	T	T	T	T	T
F	F	F	T	T	T	T

Exercises for 1.2

1. Construct a truth table for each of the following compound propositions.
   (a) ${\sim}p \vee q$
   (b) ${\sim}p \wedge {\sim}q$
   (c) ${\sim}p \vee {\sim}q$
   (d) $\sim(p \wedge {\sim}q)$
   (e) $({\sim}p \vee q) \wedge q$
   (f) $({\sim}p \vee q) \wedge p$

(g) $\sim p \vee (p \wedge \sim q)$ (h) $(q \wedge \sim p) \vee \sim q$

(i) $(p \vee q) \vee (p \wedge \sim q)$ (j) $(p \wedge \sim q) \vee (\sim p \wedge q)$

2. Construct truth tables for the following two compound propositions.

    (a) $p \wedge \sim p$ (b) $p \vee \sim p$

3. Construct a truth table for each of the following compound propositions involving the three individual propositions p, q, and r.

    (a) $(p \wedge q) \wedge r$ (b) $(p \wedge q) \vee r$

    (c) $(\sim p \vee q) \wedge \sim r$ (d) $\sim p \vee (\sim q \wedge r)$

    (e) $(\sim p \wedge q) \vee r$ (f) $(p \wedge q) \vee (p \wedge r)$

    (g) $(p \vee \sim r) \wedge (q \vee \sim r)$ (h) $\sim(\sim p \vee q) \wedge (\sim q \vee r)$

4. (a) How many combinations of truth values are necessary in constructing the truth table of a compound proposition that involves four individual propositions?

    (b) How many combinations are necessary if the compound proposition involves n individual propositions?

5. Show that the compound propositions $(p \wedge q) \wedge r$ and $p \wedge (q \wedge r)$ have the same last columns in their truth tables.

6. Let $p \veebar q$ denote the *exclusive disjunction* of p and q, where we define $p \veebar q$ to be true exactly when one or the other, but not both, of propositions p and q are true. Construct a truth table for each of the following compound propositions involving the exclusive disjunction.

    (a) $p \veebar q$ (b) $p \veebar \sim q$

    (c) $(p \vee q) \veebar (\sim p)$ (d) $(p \veebar q) \wedge (p \vee q)$

    (e) $(p \veebar q) \vee (p \wedge \sim q)$ (f) $(\sim p \veebar q) \wedge (p \wedge \sim q)$

7. (a) Let p be the proposition "It is raining" and let q be the proposition "It is cold." Write in symbolic form, using p and q, the compound proposition "It is not true that it is raining and not cold," and construct a truth table for this compound proposition.

    (b) Describe verbally the circumstances under which the compound proposition in (a) is true.

8. Find a compound proposition involving p and q which has the truth values listed in the third column of each of the following truth tables.

(a)

p	q	
T	T	T
T	F	T
F	T	F
F	F	T

(b)

p	q	
T	T	T
T	F	T
F	T	F
F	F	F

9. Let p and q denote propositions. The *joint denial* of p and q, denoted $p \downarrow q$, is defined to be true exactly when both p and q are false. Construct a truth table for $p \downarrow q$.

Section 1.3 Equivalence of Propositions

It is often the case that a proposition is stated in such a way that it is difficult to determine its meaning as it stands. In these situations it is convenient to find an "equivalent" alternative statement of the proposition which is easier to understand.

Example 1.3.1 Consider the proposition obtained by *negating* the compound proposition "Jim plays poker or Jim does not play bridge." That is, "It is not the case that Jim plays poker or Jim does not play bridge." This proposition, as it stands, is a bit confusing as to its meaning. We shall use the notion of the equivalence of two propositions to restate this proposition so that its meaning is perfectly clear.

The formal way to express the fact that two propositions have the same meaning is as follows.

Definition

Two propositions are said to be *equivalent* if they have the same truth values in every possible case. We use the notation $p \equiv q$ to denote the fact that p and q are equivalent.

Example 1.3.2 Consider the two propositions

$$\sim(p \vee \sim q) \quad \text{and} \quad \sim p \wedge q$$

We can obtain the truth tables for both propositions using a single truth table, Figure 1.3.1. In the last column we obtain the truth values of the proposition $\sim p \wedge q$ for

Figure 1.3.1

p	q	$\sim p$	$\sim q$	$p \vee \sim q$	$\sim(p \vee \sim q)$	$\sim p \wedge q$
T	T	F	F	T	F	F
T	F	F	T	T	F	F
F	T	T	F	F	T	T
F	F	T	T	T	F	F

the various possibilities of the truth values for p and q. In the second-to-last column appear the truth values of the proposition $\sim(p \vee \sim q)$ for the various possibilities of the truth values for p and q. Note that these two columns are identical and therefore, by definition, the propositions $\sim(p \vee \sim q)$ and $\sim p \wedge q$ are equivalent. In our notation we have

$$\sim(p \vee \sim q) \equiv \sim p \wedge q \tag{1.3.1}$$

We can use this fact to clarify the meaning of the proposition "It is not the case that Jim plays poker or Jim does not play bridge," which was introduced in Example 1.3.1. Let p and q be the propositions

p: Jim plays poker.
q: Jim plays bridge.

Then the proposition in quotes is simply $\sim(p \vee \sim q)$. But we have just seen that $\sim(p \vee \sim q) \equiv \sim p \wedge q$. Therefore, the proposition in quotes can be restated as follows: "Jim does not play poker and Jim plays bridge." This last proposition, whether true or false, is perfectly clear.

The example above illustrates the usefulness of the concept of the equivalence of two propositions. There are certain basic equivalences in logic. We shall exhibit some of these in the way of giving additional illustrations.

Example 1.3.3 Commutative Law   The propositions $p \wedge q$ and $q \wedge p$ are equivalent. To see this, observe that the last two columns in Figure 1.3.2 are identical. Thus

$$p \wedge q \equiv q \wedge p$$

Figure 1.3.2

p	q	$p \wedge q$	$q \wedge p$
T	T	T	T
T	F	F	F
F	T	F	F
F	F	F	F

A similar argument shows that

$$p \vee q \equiv q \vee p$$

Example 1.3.4   Associative Law   The propositions $(p \vee q) \vee r$ and $p \vee (q \vee r)$ are equivalent since the last two columns in Figure 1.3.3 are the same. Therefore,

$$(p \vee q) \vee r \equiv p \vee (q \vee r)$$

Figure 1.3.3

p	q	r	$p \vee q$	$q \vee r$	$(p \vee q) \vee r$	$p \vee (q \vee r)$
T	T	T	T	T	T	T
T	T	F	T	T	T	T
T	F	T	T	T	T	T
T	F	F	T	F	T	T
F	T	T	T	T	T	T
F	T	F	T	T	T	T
F	F	T	F	T	T	T
F	F	F	F	F	F	F

A similar argument reveals that

$$(p \wedge q) \wedge r \equiv p \wedge (q \wedge r)$$

Example 1.3.5   Distributive Law   The following equivalences illustrate the ways in which the connectives "and" and "or" interact with one another:

$$p \wedge (q \vee r) \equiv (p \wedge q) \vee (p \wedge r) \qquad (1.3.2)$$
$$p \vee (q \wedge r) \equiv (p \vee q) \wedge (p \vee r)$$

Figure 1.3.4

p	q	r	$q \vee r$	$p \wedge q$	$p \wedge r$	$p \wedge (q \vee r)$	$(p \wedge q) \vee (p \wedge r)$
T	T	T	T	T	T	T	T
T	T	F	T	T	F	T	T
T	F	T	T	F	T	T	T
T	F	F	F	F	F	F	F
F	T	T	T	F	F	F	F
F	T	F	T	F	F	F	F
F	F	T	T	F	F	F	F
F	F	F	F	F	F	F	F

We prove the first equivalence; the proof of the second equivalence is similar. Since the last two columns of Figure 1.3.4 are identical, we see that Eq. (1.3.2) holds.

Example 1.3.6 De Morgan's Laws The following equivalences illustrate the ways in which the connectives "and" and "or" interact with negation:

$$\sim(p \wedge q) \equiv \sim p \vee \sim q \qquad (1.3.3)$$
$$\sim(p \vee q) \equiv \sim p \wedge \sim q \qquad (1.3.4)$$

We prove Eq. (1.3.3) and leave Eq. (1.3.4) as an exercise for the reader. Since the last two columns of Figure 1.3.5 are identical, we see that Eq. (1.3.3) holds.

Figure 1.3.5

p	q	$\sim p$	$\sim q$	$p \wedge q$	$\sim(p \wedge q)$	$\sim p \vee \sim q$
T	T	F	F	T	F	F
T	F	F	T	F	T	T
F	T	T	F	F	T	T
F	F	T	T	F	T	T

As an application of De Morgan's laws we establish Eq. (1.3.1) without resorting to truth tables. Replacing q by $\sim q$ in Eq. (1.3.4) we obtain

$$\sim(p \vee \sim q) \equiv \sim p \wedge \sim(\sim q) \qquad (1.3.5)$$

However, since $\sim(\sim q) \equiv q$ (see problem 4, Exercises 1.3) we conclude from Eq. (1.3.5) that

$$\sim(p \vee \sim q) \equiv \sim p \wedge q$$

which is Eq. (1.3.1).

As we have already indicated in the previous example, an advantage of having the above-established equivalences at our disposal is that we can often eliminate the need for using truth tables to verify equivalences. This is especially useful when there are a large number of propositions and connectives involved.

Example 1.3.7 Use the equivalences established above to prove that

$$\sim[p \vee \sim(q \vee \sim r)] \equiv \sim(p \vee r) \vee (\sim p \wedge q)$$

The steps in the proof are

$$\sim[p \vee \sim(q \vee \sim r)] \equiv \sim p \wedge \sim[\sim(q \vee \sim r)]$$
$$\equiv \sim p \wedge (q \vee \sim r) \equiv (\sim p \wedge q) \vee (\sim p \wedge \sim r)$$
$$\equiv (\sim p \wedge q) \vee \sim(p \vee r) \equiv \sim(p \vee r) \vee (\sim p \wedge q)$$

and the reader is asked to state which of the equivalences previously cited justify the steps in this proof.

Remark: In Example 1.3.7 and the last half of Example 1.3.6 we have tacitly used the fact that a proposition occurring in a compound proposition may be replaced by any equivalent proposition and the resulting compound proposition will be equivalent to the original. This is called the *law of substitution*.

For example, since

$$\sim[\sim(p \wedge q)] \equiv p \wedge q$$

we have by the law of substitution that

$$r \vee (s \wedge \sim[\sim(p \wedge q)]) \equiv r \vee [s \wedge (p \wedge q)]$$

Exercises for 1.3

1. Show that the propositions $p \vee q$ and $q \vee p$ are equivalent.
2. Show that the propositions $p \vee (q \wedge r)$ and $(p \vee q) \wedge (p \vee r)$ are equivalent.
3. Prove Eq. (1.3.4): $\sim(p \vee q) \equiv \sim p \wedge \sim q$.
4. Prove that $\sim(\sim p) \equiv p$.
5. Verify the following:
   (a) $p \vee p \equiv p$ (b) $p \wedge p \equiv p$
   (These are sometimes referred to as the *idempotent laws*.)
6. Verify the following:
   (a) $p \vee (p \wedge q) \equiv p$ (b) $p \wedge (p \vee q) \equiv p$
7. Prove that $(p \vee q) \wedge \sim p \equiv \sim p \wedge q$.
8. Prove that $\sim(p \vee q) \vee (\sim p \wedge q) \equiv \sim p$.
9. Let p be a proposition, t be a proposition that is true, and f be a proposition that is false. Verify the following.
   (a) $p \wedge t \equiv p$ (b) $p \wedge f \equiv f$
   (c) $p \vee t \equiv t$ (d) $p \vee f \equiv p$
   (e) $p \vee \sim p \equiv t$ (f) $p \wedge \sim p \equiv f$
10. Use the results of this chapter to write an equivalent statement to each of the following statements.
    (a) It is not true that he is 25 or his brother is 34.
    (b) It is not true that her hair is black but her eyes are not brown.
    (c) It is not true that prices are decreasing and employment is increasing.
    (d) It is not true that it is cold or it is snowing.
11. Justify the steps in the proof of Example 1.3.7:

$$\begin{aligned} \sim[p \vee \sim(q \vee \sim r)] &\equiv \sim p \wedge \sim[\sim(q \vee \sim r)] && \text{Why?} \\ &\equiv \sim p \wedge (q \vee \sim r) && \text{Why?} \\ &\equiv (\sim p \wedge q) \vee (\sim p \wedge \sim r) && \text{Why?} \\ &\equiv (\sim p \wedge q) \vee \sim(p \vee r) && \text{Why?} \\ &\equiv \sim(p \vee r) \vee (\sim p \wedge q) && \text{Why?} \end{aligned}$$

12. Prove the following without using truth tables. Be sure to justify each step.
    (a) $\sim(p \vee \sim q) \equiv \sim p \wedge q$
    (b) $\sim(\sim p \wedge q) \equiv p \vee \sim q$
    (c) $\sim(\sim p \vee \sim q) \equiv p \wedge q$
13. Prove without using truth tables that $\sim p \wedge \sim(\sim q \wedge r) \equiv \sim[(p \vee \sim q) \wedge (p \vee r)]$. Be sure to justify each step.
14. Use a truth table to prove that $p \veebar q \equiv (p \vee q) \wedge \sim(p \wedge q)$. (See problem 6, Exercises 1.2, for the definition of $p \veebar q$.)
15. Use truth tables to prove the following:
    (a) $\sim p \wedge \sim q \equiv p \downarrow q$ (b) $\sim p \equiv p \downarrow p$
    (c) $p \wedge q \equiv (p \downarrow p) \downarrow (q \downarrow q)$ (d) $p \vee q \equiv (p \downarrow q) \downarrow (p \downarrow q)$
    (See problem 9, Exercises 1.2, for the definition of $p \downarrow q$.)
16. Let p and q be propositions such that q is equivalent to the negation of p. Prove that p is equivalent to the negation of q.

Section 1.4   Conditional Propositions

In this section we consider propositions of a different type than the ones previously considered. These are the conditional propositions or implications. They are propositions of the form "if . . ., then . . ." and various rearrangements of this form.

Example 1.4.1   Some examples of conditional propositions are as follows:

1. If it is raining, then we are in the house.
2. If he stays in the sun too long, then he gets sunburned.
3. If you buy groceries at Smith's market, then you get Green Stamps.

As you would expect, implications are extremely important propositions in mathematics. However, their frequent occurrence in day-to-day language also makes them significant outside mathematics.

Definition

Let p and q denote propositions. Then the proposition "if p, then q" is called an *implication* or *conditional proposition* and is denoted symbolically by

$$p \rightarrow q$$

For example, if p is the proposition "It is raining" and q is the proposition "We are in the house," $p \rightarrow q$ is the proposition "If it is raining, then we are in the house."

To obtain the truth values for $p \rightarrow q$ for the various possibilities of truth values for p and q, we first consider the following example. Suppose that p is the proposition "You buy groceries at Smith's Market" and q is the proposition "You get Green Stamps." Then $p \rightarrow q$ is the proposition "If you buy groceries at Smith's Market, then you get Green Stamps." Now, if you buy groceries at Smith's Market and you do *not* get Green Stamps, you would certainly say that the implication $p \rightarrow q$ is false. So, if p is true and q is false, we say that $p \rightarrow q$ is false.

On the other hand, if you buy groceries at Smith's Market and you *do* get Green Stamps, you would definitely say that the implication $p \rightarrow q$ is true. So, if p is true and q is true, we say that $p \rightarrow q$ is true.

Keeping the example above in mind, we can fill in the first two rows of the truth table for $p \rightarrow q$, Figure 1.4.1. Hence, when p is true, the truth value of $p \rightarrow q$ is true if q is true, and is false if q is false.

Figure 1.4.1

p	q	$p \rightarrow q$
T	T	T
T	F	F
F	T	
F	F	

When p is false, it turns out to be convenient to define $p \rightarrow q$ to be true, regardless of the truth value of q. Therefore, if p is false, we say that the implication $p \rightarrow q$

is true.[1] The complete truth table for $p \to q$ is as shown in Figure 1.4.2. The figure gives the definition of the truth value of the conditional proposition $p \to q$. Thus $p \to q$ is false when p is true and q is false, and is true otherwise.

Figure 1.4.2

p	q	$p \to q$
T	T	T
T	F	F
F	T	T
F	F	T

For example, consider the proposition "If there is an elephant in this room, then the sun is shining." Then, if there is no elephant in this room, we say that the implication is true regardless of whether or not the sun is shining.

Example 1.4.2 An implication can be restated in terms of negation and the connective "or." For example, the proposition "If it is raining, then we are in the house" can be rephrased as "It is not raining or we are in the house." If either proposition is true, so is the other.

More generally, Figure 1.4.3 shows that

$$p \to q \equiv {\sim}p \vee q$$

Figure 1.4.3

p	q	${\sim}p$	${\sim}p \vee q$	$p \to q$
T	T	F	T	T
T	F	F	F	F
F	T	T	T	T
F	F	T	T	T

Implications can be "turned around" in several ways. It is quite important to understand the precise meanings of these variations, because people often read into implications things that are not there.

Example 1.4.3 Consider the proposition "If it is raining, then we are in the house." Some variations on this implication are the following:

1. If we are in the house, then it is raining.
2. If we are not in the house, then it is not raining.
3. If it is not raining, then we are not in the house.

In terms of the symbolism introduced, if we define the propositions p and q by

p: It is raining.
q: We are in the house.

---

[1] It is common for students to find this convention difficult to accept. Perhaps the best justification for this convention is that it is consistent with accepted mathematical thought.

then the original proposition is $p \rightarrow q$. The propositions in 1–3 become

1'. $q \rightarrow p$.
2'. $\sim q \rightarrow \sim p$.
3'. $\sim p \rightarrow \sim q$.

The problem at hand is to determine how the propositions in 1'–3' are related (if they are related) to the original proposition $p \rightarrow q$.

Definition
Let p and q denote propositions. Then the proposition

$$q \rightarrow p$$

is called the *converse* of the proposition $p \rightarrow q$.

Taking a look at Example 1.4.3, it appears that an implication and its converse are *not* equivalent. In this case $p \rightarrow q$ is the proposition "If it is raining, then we are in the house," whereas its converse is the proposition "If we are in the house, then it is raining." Certainly the former proposition could be true without the latter being true. For example, we may be in the house whenever it is colder than 30°.

We can rigorously prove that an implication and its converse are *not* equivalent by examining Figure 1.4.4. Since the last two columns of this truth table are *not* identical, this means that the propositions $p \rightarrow q$ and $q \rightarrow p$ are *not* equivalent.

Figure 1.4.4

p	q	$p \rightarrow q$	$q \rightarrow p$
T	T	T	T
T	F	F	T
F	T	T	F
F	F	T	T

Next, we consider the relation between the implications $p \rightarrow q$ and $\sim q \rightarrow \sim p$.

Definition
Let p and q denote propositions. Then the proposition

$$\sim q \rightarrow \sim p$$

is called the *contrapositive* of the proposition $p \rightarrow q$.

Returning, for a moment, to Example 1.4.3 we see that the contrapositive of the proposition "If it is raining, then we are in the house" is the proposition "If we are not in the house, then it isn't raining." If we study these two propositions carefully, it appears that they have the same meaning.

As a matter of fact, Figure 1.4.5 shows that

$$\sim q \rightarrow \sim p \equiv p \rightarrow q \tag{1.4.1}$$

Figure 1.4.5

p	q	$\sim p$	$\sim q$	$p \to q$	$\sim q \to \sim p$
T	T	F	F	T	T
T	F	F	T	F	F
F	T	T	F	T	T
F	F	T	T	T	T

Finally, we consider the relationship between the two implications $p \to q$ and $\sim p \to \sim q$.

Definition

Let p and q denote propositions. Then the proposition

$$\sim p \to \sim q$$

is called the *inverse* of the proposition $p \to q$.

There is a great tendency to consider an implication and its inverse to be equivalent propositions.

In Example 1.4.3 the inverse of the proposition "If it is raining, then we are in the house" is the proposition "If it isn't raining, then we are not in the house." It is quite clear that the former proposition does not say anything about what happens "if it isn't raining." Hence the two propositions are certainly not equivalent.

In general, we can see that $\sim p \to \sim q$ is *not* equivalent to $p \to q$ by noting that the last two columns in Figure 1.4.6 are *not* identical.

Figure 1.4.6

p	q	$\sim p$	$\sim q$	$p \to q$	$\sim p \to \sim q$
T	T	F	F	T	T
T	F	F	T	F	T
F	T	T	F	T	F
F	F	T	T	T	T

What is true is that the inverse and converse of an implication are equivalent. That is,

$$\sim p \to \sim q \equiv q \to p$$

This follows because the inverse of an implication is the contrapositive of the converse of an implication and we have already seen in Eq. (1.4.1) that the contrapositive of an implication is equivalent to that implication.

In summary, then, we have the equivalences

$$\sim q \to \sim p \equiv p \to q$$
$$\sim p \to \sim q \equiv q \to p$$

That is, the contrapositive of an implication is equivalent to the implication, while the inverse of an implication is equivalent to the converse of the implication.

We also have seen that neither the converse nor the inverse of an implication is equivalent to the implication. That is,

$$q \to p \not\equiv p \to q$$
$$\sim p \to \sim q \not\equiv p \to q$$

Exercises for 1.4

1. Let p be the proposition "Productivity increases." and let q be the proposition "Wages rise." Write the following conditional propositions in symbolic form.
   (a) If productivity increases, then wages rise.
   (b) If wages rise, then productivity increases.
   (c) If productivity does not increase, then wages do not rise.
   (d) If wages do not rise, then productivity does not increase.
   (e) Wages do not rise when productivity increases.

2. Let p be the proposition "He runs fast" and q the proposition "He wins." Give a verbal statement for each of the following conditional propositions.
   (a) $p \to q$ (b) $p \to \sim q$
   (c) $\sim p \to q$ (d) $\sim p \to \sim q$

3. Let p be the proposition "It is snowing," q the proposition "The roads are icy," and r the proposition "He does *not* drive his car." Write the following propositions in symbolic form; use p, q, and r.
   (a) If it is snowing and the roads are icy, then he does not drive his car.
   (b) If it is snowing or the roads are icy, then he does not drive his car.
   (c) If he drives his car, then it is not snowing or the roads are not icy.
   (d) If he does not drive his car, then it is snowing or the roads are icy.
   (e) If it is not snowing or the roads are not icy, then he drives his car.
   (f) If the roads are icy but it is not snowing, then he does not drive his car.

4. Construct truth tables for each of the following.
   (a) $(p \to q) \land (q \to p)$ (b) $p \to (p \lor q)$
   (c) $(p \land q) \to q$ (d) $(p \to p) \lor (p \to \sim p)$

5. Construct truth tables for the following two conditional propositions.
   (a) $(p \to q) \to (p \lor q)$ (b) $\sim q \to (p \to q)$

6. Construct truth tables for each of the following.
   (a) $p \to (q \land r)$
   (b) $(p \land r) \lor (q \to p)$
   (c) $r \to (p \lor \sim q)$

7. Write the converse of each of the following conditional propositions.
   (a) If it is snowing, then I wear my coat.
   (b) If productivity does not increase, then wages do not rise.
   (c) Whenever I am taking an examination, I get nervous.
   (d) If 2 is larger than 3, then -1 is larger than 0.
   (e) If a triangle is equilateral, then it is equiangular.

8. Write the contrapositive and the inverse of each of the conditional propositions in problem 7.

9. Write the converse, contrapositive, and the inverse of each of the following. [Simplify as much as possible by using the fact that $\sim(\sim r) \equiv r$.]
   (a) $p \to \sim q$ (b) $\sim p \to q$
   (c) $\sim p \to \sim q$ (d) $\sim q \to \sim p$

10. Prove that the contrapositive of the contrapositive of $p \to q$ is (equivalent to) $p \to q$.

11. Prove that the contrapositive of the converse of $p \to q$ is the inverse of $p \to q$.

12. Use a truth table to show that $p \to q$ is equivalent to $(p \land \sim q) \to \sim p$.

13. Use a truth table to show that $p \to (q \land r) \equiv (p \to q) \land (p \to r)$.

14. Prove that $\sim(p \to q) \equiv p \land \sim q$.

Section 1.5   Biconditional Propositions

Recall that a conditional proposition is one of the form "if p, then q," which we denote symbolically by $p \rightarrow q$. In Section 1.4 we showed that the converse, $q \rightarrow p$, of the implication $p \rightarrow q$ is not equivalent to $p \rightarrow q$.

It is often desirable to consider an implication and its converse together as a single proposition. This is accomplished by using the biconditional connective "if and only if."

Example 1.5.1   The proposition, "We are in the house *if and only if* it is raining" contains two implications:

1. If we are in the house, then it is raining.
2. If it is raining, then we are in the house.

Symbolically, if we let p and q be the propositions

p: We are in the house.
q: It is raining.

then proposition 1 is the implication $p \rightarrow q$ and proposition 2 is the converse of this implication, $q \rightarrow p$. The biconditional proposition "We are in the house if and only if it is raining" has the symbolic representation $(p \rightarrow q) \wedge (q \rightarrow p)$.

Definition
Let p and q denote propositions. Then the proposition "p if and only if q" is called a *biconditional proposition*. It is defined to be the conjunction of the implication $p \rightarrow q$ and its converse $q \rightarrow p$. Thus "p if and only if q" means

$$(p \rightarrow q) \wedge (q \rightarrow p)$$

We use the notation

$$p \leftrightarrow q$$

to represent the proposition "p if and only if q."

Example 1.5.2   Let p and q denote the propositions

p: I am hiking.
q: The sun is shining.

Then the implication $p \rightarrow q$ is "If I am hiking, then the sun is shining" and its converse, $q \rightarrow p$, is the implication "If the sun is shining, then I am hiking." The biconditional proposition $p \leftrightarrow q$ is, "I am hiking if and only if the sun is shining" and means that "If I am hiking, then the sun is shining, *and* if the sun is shining, then I am hiking."

To obtain the truth table for the proposition $p \leftrightarrow q$ we simply use the fact that this is a shorthand notation for

$$(p \rightarrow q) \wedge (q \rightarrow p)$$

We see in Figure 1.5.1 that $p \leftrightarrow q$ is true if either both p and q are true or both are false. Otherwise, $p \leftrightarrow q$ is false. In other words, the biconditional proposition $p \leftrightarrow q$ is true exactly when both p and q have the same truth values.

Figure 1.5.1

p	q	$p \rightarrow q$	$q \rightarrow p$	$p \leftrightarrow q$ or $(p \rightarrow q) \wedge (q \rightarrow p)$
T	T	T	T	T
T	F	F	T	F
F	T	T	F	F
F	F	T	T	T

We now present a few examples involving biconditional propositions whose components are compound propositions.

Example 1.5.3   Determine the truth table for the proposition

$$(p \vee \sim q) \leftrightarrow q \tag{1.5.1}$$

We see from Figure 1.5.2 that the proposition in Eq. (1.5.1) is true if both p and q are true and is false otherwise.

Figure 1.5.2

p	q	$\sim q$	$p \vee \sim q$	$(p \vee \sim q) \leftrightarrow q$
T	T	F	T	T
T	F	T	T	F
F	T	F	F	F
F	F	T	T	F

Example 1.5.4   Determine the truth table for the proposition

$$(\sim p \wedge q) \leftrightarrow (\sim p \vee q) \tag{1.5.2}$$

We see from Figure 1.5.3 that the proposition in Eq. (1.5.2) is true when p and q have opposite truth values and is false when p and q have the same truth values.

Figure 1.5.3

p	q	$\sim p$	$\sim p \wedge q$	$\sim p \vee q$	$(\sim p \wedge q) \leftrightarrow (\sim p \vee q)$
T	T	F	F	T	F
T	F	F	F	F	T
F	T	T	T	T	T
F	F	T	F	T	F

Example 1.5.5 Determine the truth table for the proposition

$$(\sim p \wedge r) \leftrightarrow (\sim r \rightarrow q) \tag{1.5.3}$$

(It is shown in Figure 1.5.4.)

Figure 1.5.4

p	q	r	$\sim p$	$\sim r$	$\sim p \wedge r$	$\sim r \rightarrow q$	$(\sim p \wedge r) \leftrightarrow (\sim r \rightarrow q)$
T	T	T	F	F	F	T	F
T	T	F	F	T	F	T	F
T	F	T	F	F	F	T	F
T	F	F	F	T	F	F	T
F	T	T	T	F	T	T	T
F	T	F	T	T	F	T	F
F	F	T	T	F	T	T	T
F	F	F	T	T	F	F	T

One final remark concerning the biconditional connective bears mentioning. Recall that the converse of the implication $p \rightarrow q$ is the implication $q \rightarrow p$. We have seen that these two propositions are not equivalent (i.e., they do not have the same meaning). However, we have seen that

$$\sim p \rightarrow \sim q \equiv q \rightarrow p \tag{1.5.4}$$

Since $p \leftrightarrow q$ means $(p \rightarrow q) \wedge (q \rightarrow p)$, we have, in view of Eq. (1.5.4), that it also means $(p \rightarrow q) \wedge (\sim p \rightarrow \sim q)$.

For example, let p and q denote the propositions

p: Jim goes to a movie.
q: Jim drives his car.

Then $p \leftrightarrow q$ means that "Jim goes to a movie if and only if Jim drives his car." That is,

1. If Jim goes to a movie, then Jim drives his car, and
2. If Jim drives his car, then Jim goes to a movie.

In view of Eq. (1.5.4), proposition 2 can be replaced by

2′. If Jim doesn't go to a movie, then Jim doesn't drive his car.

In other words, in this situation, $p \leftrightarrow q$ also means "If Jim goes to a movie, then Jim drives his car, *and* if Jim doesn't go to a movie, then Jim doesn't drive his car."

Exercises for 1.5

1. Let p be the proposition "I will come" and let q be the proposition "It is *not* raining." Give a verbal statement for each of the following biconditional propositions.
   (a) $p \leftrightarrow q$ (b) $p \leftrightarrow \sim q$
   (c) $\sim p \leftrightarrow q$ (d) $\sim p \leftrightarrow \sim q$

2. Let p be the proposition "I am wearing my coat" and let q be the proposition "It is snowing." Write the following biconditional propositions in symbolic form.

(a) I am wearing my coat if and only if it is snowing.

(b) I am not wearing my coat if and only if it is snowing.

(c) It is not snowing if and only if I am not wearing my coat.

(d) If I am wearing my coat, then it is snowing, and if I am not wearing my coat, then it is not snowing.

3. Determine the truth table for each of the following propositions.

(a) $(p \wedge \sim q) \leftrightarrow p$　　　　　　　　　　(b) $\sim q \leftrightarrow (p \vee q)$

(c) $(p \rightarrow \sim q) \leftrightarrow q$　　　　　　　　　　(d) $(\sim p \vee q) \leftrightarrow \sim p$

(e) $\sim p \leftrightarrow (p \wedge q)$　　　　　　　　　　(f) $(\sim p \vee \sim q) \rightarrow (p \leftrightarrow q)$

(g) $(p \rightarrow q) \wedge \sim(\sim p \leftrightarrow q)$　　　　　(h) $(p \leftrightarrow \sim q) \leftrightarrow (q \rightarrow p)$

4. Determine the truth table for each of the following biconditional propositions.

(a) $(p \vee q) \leftrightarrow r$　　　　　　　　　　(b) $q \leftrightarrow (p \wedge r)$

(c) $(p \vee \sim q) \leftrightarrow \sim r$　　　　　　　　(d) $\sim q \leftrightarrow (p \wedge \sim r)$

5. Show that $p \leftrightarrow q \equiv (\sim p \vee q) \wedge (\sim q \vee p)$.

6. Prove that $\sim(p \leftrightarrow q) \equiv \sim p \leftrightarrow q$.

Section 1.6　Tautologies and Valid Arguments

We begin this section by introducing three examples that illustrate an important concept.

Example 1.6.1　Determine the truth table for the proposition

$$p \vee \sim p \tag{1.6.1}$$

(It is shown in Figure 1.6.1.) We see that regardless of the truth value for p, the compound proposition of Eq. (1.6.1) is true. In English, Eq. (1.6.1) states that "either p is true or p is false."

Figure 1.6.1

p	$\sim p$	$p \vee \sim p$
T	F	T
F	T	T

Example 1.6.2　Determine the truth table for the proposition

$$(p \wedge q) \rightarrow p \tag{1.6.2}$$

As shown in Figure 1.6.2, Eq. (1.6.2) is true regardless of the choice of truth values for p and q.

Figure 1.6.2

p	q	$p \wedge q$	$(p \wedge q) \rightarrow p$
T	T	T	T
T	F	F	T
F	T	F	T
F	F	F	T

Example 1.6.3 Determine the truth table for

$$[(p \rightarrow q) \wedge p] \rightarrow q \tag{1.6.3}$$

As in the previous two examples, Figure 1.6.3 shows that the proposition in Eq. (1.6.3) is always true.

Figure 1.6.3

p	q	$p \rightarrow q$	$(p \rightarrow q) \wedge p$	$[(p \rightarrow q) \wedge p] \rightarrow q$
T	T	T	T	T
T	F	F	F	T
F	T	T	F	T
F	F	T	F	T

As we have seen in the last three examples, there are compound propositions that are always true, regardless of the truth values of the component propositions that make up the compound proposition. Such propositions are given a special name.

Definition
A compound proposition that is always true (regardless of the truth values of its component propositions) is called a *tautology*.[2]

In Examples 1.6.1–1.6.3 we determined that each of the propositions

$$p \vee \sim p$$
$$(p \wedge q) \rightarrow p$$

and

$$[(p \rightarrow q) \wedge p] \rightarrow q$$

is a tautology.

There are, of course, propositions that are always false. Such a proposition is called a *contradiction*.

Example 1.6.4 Determine the truth table for the proposition

$$p \wedge \sim p \tag{1.6.4}$$

Figure 1.6.4 shows that $p \wedge \sim p$ is a contradiction.

Figure 1.6.4

p	$\sim p$	$p \wedge \sim p$
T	F	F
F	T	F

---

[2] There are texts in which the words "logically true" are used to describe tautologies. However, in a more advanced treatment the reader discovers that there are "logically true" sentences which are not tautologies according to the above definition (i.e., sentences involving "there exists" and "for all").

Example 1.6.5 Determine the truth table for the proposition

$$(p \wedge q) \wedge (p \to \sim q) \qquad (1.6.5)$$

From Figure 1.6.5 we deduce that Eq. (1.6.5) is a contradiction.

Figure 1.6.5

p	q	$\sim q$	$p \to \sim q$	$p \wedge q$	$(p \wedge q) \wedge (p \to \sim q)$
T	T	F	F	T	F
T	F	T	T	F	F
F	T	F	T	F	F
F	F	T	T	F	F

We now introduce the extremely important concept of valid arguments. An argument consists of a set of propositions $p_1, p_2, \ldots, p_n$, called the *premises,* and a proposition q, called the *conclusion.* An argument is called *valid* if, whenever all the premises are true, the conclusion is true. In particular, an argument with premises $p_1, p_2, \ldots, p_n$ and conclusion q is valid if the proposition

$$(p_1 \wedge p_2 \wedge \cdots \wedge p_n) \to q$$

is a *tautology.*[3]

Example 1.6.6   The Law of Detachment   The law of detachment is an argument of the form

Premises: $p \to q$, p
Conclusion: q

To show that this is a valid argument, we must prove that the proposition

$$[(p \to q) \wedge p] \to q \qquad (1.6.6)$$

is a tautology. This was done in Example 1.6.3.

As an illustration of this argument, let p and q denote the propositions

p: It is raining today.
q: We will stay in the house (today).

Assume it is true that

Premises: $(p \to q)$: If it is raining today, then we will stay in the house.
$\qquad\qquad\ \ p$: It is raining today.

Then by the law of detachment we may conclude that

Conclusion: q: We will stay in the house (today).

---

[3] Again, as footnote 2, there are valid arguments involving the phrases "there exists" and "for all" in which the above implication is not a tautology. However, such arguments will not be considered in this text.

Example 1.6.7   Show that the argument

Premises: $p \to q$, q
Conclusion: p

(1.6.7)

is *not* valid.

The problem is to show that the proposition

$$[(p \to q) \land q] \to p$$

is *not* a tautology. To do this, just observe that the last column in Figure 1.6.6 contains an F. In other words, if p is false and q is true, then although both premises in Eq. (1.6.7) will be true, the conclusion will be false. Thus, the argument is not valid.

Figure 1.6.6

p	q	$p \to q$	$(p \to q) \land q$	$[(p \to q) \land q] \to p$
T	T	T	T	T
T	F	F	F	T
F	T	T	T	F
F	F	T	F	T

As an example of this *invalid* line of reasoning (argument), let p and q denote the propositions

p: It is raining today.
q: We will stay in the house.

and assume it is true that

Premises: $(p \to q)$: If it is raining today, then we will stay in the house.
              q: We will stay in the house (today).

Then the invalid argument of Eq. (1.6.7) leads us to the

Invalid Conclusion: p: It is raining today.[4]

Example 1.6.8   The Transitive Law   The transitive law is an argument of the form

Premises: $p \to q$, $q \to r$
Conclusion: $p \to r$

To show that this is a valid argument, we must prove that the proposition

$$[(p \to q) \land (q \to r)] \to (p \to r)$$

(1.6.8)

is a tautology. This is accomplished by observing that the last column in Figure 1.6.7 consists only of Ts.

To illustrate the transitive law, let p, q, and r be the propositions

p: It is raining today.
q: We will stay in the house (today).
r: We will play chess (today).

---

[4]It may, in fact, be true that "It is raining today," but it is not valid to conclude this from the information given (premises).

Figure 1.6.7

p	q	r	$p \rightarrow q$	$q \rightarrow r$	$(p \rightarrow q) \wedge (q \rightarrow r)$	$p \rightarrow r$	$[(p \rightarrow q) \wedge (q \rightarrow r)] \rightarrow (p \rightarrow r)$
T	T	T	T	T	T	T	T
T	T	F	T	F	F	F	T
T	F	T	F	T	F	T	T
T	F	F	F	T	F	F	T
F	T	T	T	T	T	T	T
F	T	F	T	F	F	T	T
F	F	T	T	T	T	T	T
F	F	F	T	T	T	T	T

Assume it is true that

Premises: $(p \rightarrow q)$: If it is raining today, then we will stay in the house.
$(q \rightarrow r)$: If we stay in the house, then we will play chess.

Then by the transitive law we can conclude that

Conclusion: $(p \rightarrow r)$: If it is raining today, then we will play chess.

If we *add* the additional premise

p: It is raining today.

we can use the transitive law along with the law of detachment to conclude that

r: We will play chess (today).

Symbolically this involves proving that the argument

Premises: $p, p \rightarrow q, q \rightarrow r$
Conclusion: r

is valid. That is,

$$[p \wedge (p \rightarrow q) \wedge (q \rightarrow r)] \rightarrow r \tag{1.6.9}$$

is a tautology. This is left as an exercise for the reader.

Example 1.6.9 Suppose it is true that

1. We go to the movie or we don't drive the car.
2. We get the tickets early or we don't go to the movie.
3. We drive the car.

Is it valid to conclude that "We get the tickets early."? The answer is, yes. There are several ways to see this. One way is to let p, q, and r denote the propositions:

p: We drive the car.
q: We go to the movie.
r: We get the tickets early.

Then the premises are

Premises: $q \vee \sim p, r \vee \sim q, p$

and we desire the conclusion

Conclusion: r.

The argument will be valid if we can show that the proposition

$$[(q \lor \sim p) \land (r \lor \sim q) \land p] \to r \qquad\qquad (1.6.10)$$

is a tautology. We leave it to the reader to verify this fact.

Exercises for 1.6

1. Show that the following compound propositions are tautologies.
   (a) $\sim(p \land \sim p)$ (b) $p \lor \sim(p \land q)$
2. Show that the following conditional propositions are tautologies.
   (a) $p \to (p \lor q)$ (b) $\sim p \to \sim(p \land q)$
   (c) $[p \land (p \to q)] \to q$ (d) $[(p \to q) \land \sim q] \to \sim p$
   (e) $[(p \to q) \land (q \to r)] \to (p \to r)$
3. Show that the following biconditional propositions are tautologies.
   (a) $[p \land (p \lor q)] \leftrightarrow p$ (b) $[p \lor (p \land q)] \leftrightarrow p$
   (c) $(\sim p \leftrightarrow \sim q) \leftrightarrow [(p \to q) \land (q \to p)]$ (d) $[p \lor (q \lor r)] \leftrightarrow [(p \lor q) \lor r]$
4. Show that the biconditional proposition $\sim(p \land q) \leftrightarrow (\sim p \lor \sim q)$ is a tautology without the use of a truth table.
5. Show that the following compound propositions are contradictions.
   (a) $\sim(p \lor \sim p)$
   (b) $\sim(p \lor q) \land p$
   (c) $(p \land q) \land \sim(p \lor q)$
6. Show that the proposition $\sim[(p \land \sim p) \to q]$ is a contradiction.
7. Determine which of the following arguments are valid.
   (a) *Premises:* $p \leftrightarrow q$, q (b) *Premises:* $p \to q$, $\sim q$
        Conclusion: p *Conclusion:* $\sim p$
   (c) *Premises:* $p \lor q$, $\sim q$ (d) *Premises:* $\sim p \to q$, p
        Conclusion: p *Conclusion:* $\sim q$
   (e) *Premises:* $p \land q$, $p \to \sim q$
        Conclusion: $p \land \sim q$
8. Determine which of the following arguments are valid.
   (a) *Premises:* $\sim p \lor \sim q$, $p \lor \sim r$ (b) *Premises:* $p \to q$, $q \lor r$
        Conclusion: $r \to q$ *Conclusion:* $r \to \sim p$
   (c) *Premises:* $p \lor \sim q$, $p \lor r$, $q \to r$ (d) *Premises:* $p \to r$, $q \lor \sim r$, $\sim q$
        Conclusion: $q \lor r$ *Conclusion:* $\sim p$
9. Determine which of the following arguments are valid.
   (a) *Premises:* If the wind blows, then I will not ride my bicycle. The wind did not blow.
        Conclusion: I rode my bicycle.
   (b) *Premises:* If I like this course, then I will study. Either I study or I fail.
        Conclusion: If I fail, then I do not like this course.
   (c) *Premises:* If Boston is not in Texas, then Phoenix is not in Arizona. Phoenix is in Arizona.
        Conclusion: Boston is in Texas.
   (d) *Premises:* On our anniversary, I bring my wife flowers. Either it's our anniversary or I play golf. I did not bring my wife flowers today.
        Conclusion: Today I played golf.
   (e) *Premises:* If income increases, then consumers' buying increases. Either income increases or investments increase. Investments increased.
        Conclusion: Consumers' buying increased.
10. Suppose that the following premises are given: Productivity is low or wages are high; if sales are good, then productivity is not low; wages are not high. Give a valid argument to answer the question: Are sales good?

11. Supply the missing reasons for the following proof that the argument:

Premises: $p \rightarrow \sim q$, q

Conclusion: $\sim p$

is a valid argument.

Proof:

q is true.	Given
$p \rightarrow \sim q$ is true.	Given
Thus $q \rightarrow \sim p$ is true.	Why?
Therefore, $\sim p$ is true.	Why?

12. Prove that Eq. (1.6.9) is a tautology.
13. Verify that Eq. (1.6.10) is a tautology.
14. Prove that the following argument is valid:

Premises: $p \rightarrow \sim q$, $r \rightarrow q$, r

Conclusion: $\sim p$

Set Theory

2

Mathematics has been referred to as the "Language of Science." By this it is meant that within the framework of mathematics, scientific concepts can be formally expressed without the possibility of ambiguity that exists in everyday speech. In recent times this formalism has been brought into play in the life, social, and management sciences, and students in these areas must acquaint themselves with certain basic mathematical notions.

In this chapter we examine the area of mathematics known as *set theory*.

Section 2.1 Definitions and Basic Properties

A *set* is a collection of objects or elements. This is a notion that is used constantly in everyday thought. For example, consider the set S of residents of the United States. Each individual is either a member of this set or is not a member of this set. We indicate that an individual i is a member of the set S by writing

$$i \in S$$

which is read "i is a member of S." So, for example,

Gerald Ford $\in S$

To indicate that an element (individual) i is not a member of S, we write

$$i \notin S$$

So Queen Elizabeth $\notin S$.

Following are additional examples that illustrate these ideas.

Example 2.1.1 Days of the Week Let W be the set consisting of the days of the week. Then W contains 7 elements. For example,

Tuesday $\in W$

On the other hand,

January $\notin W$

Example 2.1.2 States in the United States Let S be the set consisting of the states in the United States. Then S contains 50 elements. For example,

Alaska $\in S$

but

Washington, D.C. $\notin S$

Example 2.1.3 Digits Let D denote the set of digits, that is, the integers between 0 and 9, inclusive. Then S has 10 elements. We have, for example, that

$2 \in D$ but $15 \notin D$

There are several ways to define or describe sets. One way is to give a *verbal statement* that describes the elements of the set. This was the method used in all the preceding examples.

Another common method of defining sets is to *list the elements* of the set in braces. For example, the set D of digits introduced in Example 2.1.3 can also be described by writing

$$D = \{0, 1, 2, 3, 4, 5, 6, 7, 8, 9\}$$

As another example, the set V of vowels in the English alphabet can be described as

$$V = \{a, e, i, o, u\}$$

To get a complete description of a set, it is not always necessary to list all the elements. In these cases a *partial listing* suffices to establish a pattern that describes the set completely.

For example, the set L, consisting of the letters in the English alphabet, can be described by writing

$$L = \{a, b, c, d, \ldots, x, y, z\}$$

The three dots indicate that certain members of the set have not been listed but that it should be clear what the missing members are. As another example, the set

$$M = \{\text{January, February}, \ldots, \text{December}\}$$

is just the set of months of the year, although a complete list of the elements of M was not given.

The final method that we shall use to define or describe sets is a combination of the preceding two methods. It utilizes what is called *set builder notation*.

Example 2.1.4 Digits Consider again the set D of digits introduced in Example 2.1.3. We write this in set builder notation as

$$D = \{x \,|\, x \text{ is a digit}\}$$

which is read "D is the set of elements x such that x is a digit." Alternatively, we could use set builder notation to describe D as

$$D = \{x \,|\, x \text{ is an integer and } 0 \leq x \leq 9\}$$

which is read "D is the set of elements x such that x is an integer and x is greater than or equal to 0 but less than or equal to 9."

Example 2.1.5 Here is another example to illustrate set builder notation. We read the statement

$$E = \{x \,|\, x^2 = 1\}$$

as "E is the set of elements x such that $x^2 = 1$." In this case it is also quite easy to use the listing method to describe the set E:

$$E = \{-1, 1\}$$

Sometimes it is not only inconvenient to describe a set by listing its elements but it is, in fact, impossible to do so. For example, consider the set N of positive integers. Then a direct listing of the elements of N is impossible. However, N can either be described by a partial listing,

$$N = \{1, 2, 3, 4, \ldots\}$$

or by use of set builder notation:

$$N = \{x \,|\, x \text{ is a positive integer}\}$$

Example 2.1.6 Even Integers Let E be the set of all even integers. Then we can use the partial-listing method to write

$$E = \{\ldots, -6, -4, -2, 0, 2, 4, 6, \ldots\}$$

or the set builder notation to write

$$E = \{x \,|\, x \text{ is an even integer}\}$$

Exercises for 2.1

1. Fill in the blanks with the appropriate symbol, $\in$ or $\notin$.
   (a) 2 ——— $\{1, 3, 7, 2, 11\}$
   (b) a ——— $\{c, d, e, b, g\}$
   (c) 5 ——— $\{x \,|\, x \text{ is an even integer}\}$
   (d) 0 ——— $\{x \,|\, x \text{ is a multiple of 7}\}$
   (e) Dwight Eisenhower ——— set of Presidents of the United States.
2. Let M be the set consisting of the months of the year. Answer true or false.
   (a) March $\in M$ (b) December $\in M$
   (c) April $\notin M$ (d) Monday $\in M$
3. Use set notation to rewrite the following statements.
   (a) d is not a member of the set B.
   (b) a is a member of the set A.
   (c) The set S does not include x as a member.
   (d) The set E has e as a member.
4. Let $S = \{a, b, c\}$. State whether each of the following statements is correct or incorrect.
   (a) $b \in S$ (b) $w \notin S$
   (c) $c \in S$ (d) $a \notin S$
   (e) $2 \in S$
5. Let $N = \{1, 2, 3, 4, \ldots\}$; that is, N is the set of positive integers. Indicate which of the following statements are true and which are false.
   (a) $3 \in N$ (b) $16 \in N$
   (c) $157 \notin N$ (d) $\frac{2}{3} \in N$
   (e) $-7 \notin N$ (f) $\pi \in N$

6. Let $C = \{x \mid x$ is a city in the state of California$\}$. Answer true or false.
    (a) Los Angeles $\in C$ (b) San Francisco $\in C$
    (c) San Diego $\notin C$ (d) Boston $\in C$

*7. Answer true or false to the following statements.
    (a) Detroit $\in \{x \mid x$ is a city in the state of Michigan$\}$.
    (b) $5 \in \{\{x\} \mid x$ is an integer$\}$.
    (c) Wednesday $\in \{$days of the week$\}$.

8. Let $A = \{1, 2, \{3\}, 4\}$. Which statements are correct and which are incorrect?
    (a) $2 \in A$ (b) $3 \in A$
    (c) $4 \notin A$ (d) $\{3\} \in A$

9. Let $B = \{a, b, \{c, d\}, d\}$. Indicate which of the following statements are true and which are false.
    (a) $\{c\} \in B$ (b) $d \notin B$
    (c) $b \in B$ (d) $\{d\} \in B$
    (e) $\{c, d\} \in B$ (f) $c \in B$

10. Give a verbal statement that describes the elements of each of the following sets.
    (a) $\{a, b, c, d, e\}$
    (b) $\{$Maine, New Hampshire, Vermont, Massachusetts, Connecticut, Rhode Island$\}$
    (c) $\{$violet, blue, green, yellow, orange, red$\}$
    (d) $\{\ldots, -12, -8, -4, 0, 4, 8, 12, \ldots\}$
    (e) $\{$Denver, Sacramento, Phoenix, Boise, Helena, Atlanta, $\ldots\}$

11. Either list or give a partial listing of the elements in each of the following sets.
    (a) the set of positive even integers less than or equal to 4
    (b) the set of states in the United States beginning with the letter C
    (c) $\{x \mid x$ is a letter in the word "vanilla"$\}$
    (d) the set of playing positions on a baseball field
    (e) the set of integers less than 2
    (f) $\{x \mid x$ is an integer multiple of 3$\}$
    (g) $\{x \mid x^2 - 4 = 0\}$

12. Use set builder notation to rewrite each of the following sets.
    (a) $I = \{-1, -2, -3, -4, \ldots\}$
    (b) $T = \{\ldots, -20, -15, -10, -5, 0, 5, 10, 15, 20, \ldots\}$
    (c) the set of integers greater than or equal to 100
    (d) the set of all positive real numbers less than or equal to 20

13. Give an example of a set that can only be described by a verbal statement or by using set builder notation; that is, a listing or partial listing of the elements would not be feasible.

14. A man is planning to purchase eight shares of stock. He wants a distribution among cosmetics, drugs, and electronics. Each distribution is to be purchased in multiples of two. Construct two sets of possible distributions of purchases.

15. Two red balls and two white balls are in an urn. Three balls are selected, one at a time, and are not returned to the urn after being selected. Let r and w represent red and white, respectively. Write the set of all possible draws in this situation.

16. A family of four, consisting of the father, the mother, a son, and a daughter, is having a family portrait taken. They want to line up so that males and females alternate. List the set of all possible arrangements.

Section 2.2   Set Equality and Subsets

We begin this section by considering the concept of the equality of two sets.

Definition

Two sets are said to be *equal* if they contain the same elements. In other words, the sets S and T are equal if each element of S is an element of T and vice versa. If S and T are equal sets, we write

$$S = T$$

For example,

$$\{x \mid x \text{ is an integer}, 0 < x < 9\} = \{1, 2, 3, 4, 5, 6, 7, 8\}$$
$$\{x \mid x^2 = 1\} = \{-1, 1\}$$

As another example, if P is the set of states in the United States bordering the Pacific Ocean and $C = \{$Alaska, California, Hawaii, Oregon, Washington$\}$, then

$$P = C$$

The elements of a set are considered independently of any repetitions or the order in which they appear. That is, in considering a set we are only interested in whether or not an element is contained in the set. The number of times an element is listed or the position in which it is listed in writing the set is unimportant. Hence

$$\{1, 2, 3, 4\} = \{2, 3, 4, 1\} = \{4, 1, 3, 2\}$$
$$\{1, 5, 2, 1, 1, 7, 3, 2\} = \{1, 2, 3, 5, 7\} = \{7, 2, 3, 5, 1\}$$

Now consider the sets V and L defined by

$$V = \{x \mid x \text{ is a vowel in the English alphabet}\}$$
$$L = \{x \mid x \text{ is a letter in the English alphabet}\}$$

Note that each element of V is an element of L. However, it is *not true* that each element of L is an element of V. For example, $b \in L$ but $b \notin V$. Thus in this case V and L are not equal, and we write $V \neq L$.

Next we consider the notion of one set being a subset of another set.

Definition

Let S and T be two sets and assume that each element of S is also an element of T. Then S is said to be a *subset* of T and we write

$$S \subset T$$

For example, if V and L are the sets defined above, then $V \subset L$, because every vowel in the English alphabet is also a letter in the English alphabet. Note, however, that $L \not\subset V$ (i.e., L is not a subset of V), because there are letters in the English alphabet that are not vowels.

Some additional examples of the subset relationship are as follows:

$$\{1, 2, 3\} \subset \{1, 2, 3, 4, 5\}$$
$$\{\text{Ohio, Idaho}\} \subset \{x \mid x \text{ is a state in the United States}\}$$
$$\{\text{English, French, Spanish}\} \subset \{x \mid x \text{ is a language}\}$$

Given two sets S and T, it may be the case that neither set is a subset of the other. For example, if $S = \{1, 2, 3, 4\}$ and $T = \{1, 2, 3, 5\}$, then $S \not\subset T$ and $T \not\subset S$.

Next note that from the definition of subset, every set is a subset of itself. A subset S of a set T that is not equal to T is called a *proper subset* of T. If it is to be emphasized that S is a proper subset of T, we write

$$S \subsetneq T$$

in place of the notation

$$S \subset T$$

For example, let V (= vowels) and L (= letters) be defined as before. Then $V \subset L$; but if we want to emphasize the fact that there are letters that are not vowels, we write $V \subsetneq L$.

The relationship between the concepts of set equality and subset is expressed in the following proposition.

Proposition 2.2.1

If two sets S and T satisfy the conditions that

$$S \subset T \tag{2.2.1}$$

and

$$T \subset S \tag{2.2.2}$$

then

$$S = T$$

PROOF

This follows directly from the definition of subset, since by Eq. (2.2.1), every element of S is also an element of T, and by Eq. (2.2.2), every element of T is also an element of S.

Next, we emphasize the distinction between sets and elements, as this can often be confusing. From the point of view of mathematics, a set is a higher-order structure than its individual elements, and the set and the elements are not comparable. For example, the element 1 is not equal to the set containing the element 1. Symbolically,

$$1 \neq \{1\} \tag{2.2.3}$$

In this case, the 1 on the left-hand side of Eq. (2.2.3) is a number, whereas the object on the right-hand side is a set containing that number. An intuitive analogy can be drawn by thinking of a room in a building. If one person is in the room, it is not true that the person and the room containing the person are the same. Note, for example, that $1 \in \{1, 2, 3\}$, but $1 \not\subset \{1, 2, 3\}$. Also $\{1\} \subset \{1, 2, 3\}$, but $\{1\} \notin \{1, 2, 3\}$.

Finally, we consider a set that plays an important role in mathematics. It is the set that contains no elements and is referred to as the *empty set* or *null set*. It is denoted by the symbol $\emptyset$. From the definition of a subset, the empty set is a subset of every set. As an example, let

$$S = \{x \mid x^2 = 1 \text{ and } x > 2\}$$

Then $S = \emptyset$, because there is no number greater than 2 which when squared yields 1. As another example, if T is the set of all people 30 feet tall, then $T = \emptyset$.

Exercises for 2.2

1. Which of the following sets are equal: $\{a, b, c\}$, $\{c, b, a, c\}$, $\{b, c, b, a\}$, $\{c, a, c, b\}$?
2. State whether each pair of sets is equal or not.
   (a) $\{1, 2, 3, 4\}$; $\{2, 3, 1, 4\}$
   (b) the set of all licensed cars in the United States; the set of all licensed vehicles in the United States
   (c) $\{x \mid x^2 - 16 = 0\}$; $\{4, -4\}$
   (d) $\{a, b, \{c\}, d\}$; $\{a, b, c, d\}$
   (e) $\{x \mid x$ is a letter in the word "correct"$\}$; $\{x \mid x$ is a letter in the word "erect"$\}$
3. Fill in the blanks with the appropriate symbol, $=$ or $\subsetneq$.
   (a) $\{1, 7\}$ —— $\{1, 2, 7\}$
   (b) $\varnothing$ —— $\{9, 11\}$
   (c) $\{x, y, z\}$ —— $\{x, x, y, z\}$
   (d) $\{3\}$ —— $\{x \mid x^2 - 9 = 0\}$
   (e) $\{x \mid x$ is an integer$\}$ —— $\{x \mid -x$ is an integer$\}$
   (f) $\{0, 1, 2, 3, 4\}$ —— $\{x \mid x$ is an integer and $-1 < x < 5\}$
4. Let $A = \{a\}$, $B = \{a, b\}$, $C = \{b, c, d\}$, $D = \{c, d\}$, and $E = \{a, c, d\}$. Determine which of the following statements are true and which are false.
   (a) $D \subset C$ (b) $B \neq E$
   (c) $A \subset E$ (d) $A \subset C$
   (e) $B = C$ (f) $B \subset D$
5. List all possible subsets of the following sets.
   (a) $\{x \mid x^2 = 4\}$ (b) $\{a, b, c\}$
   (c) $\{1, 2, 3, 4\}$ *(d) $\{1, \{2, 3\}, 4\}$
   (e) $\varnothing$
6. Let $R = \{x \mid x$ is a rectangle$\}$
   $S = \{x \mid x$ is a square$\}$
   $P = \{x \mid x$ is a parallelogram$\}$
   $Q = \{x \mid x$ is a quadrilateral$\}$
   Determine which sets are proper subsets of the others.
7. Which of the following correctly relate the sets $A = \{a, b, c, d\}$ and $B = \{a, b, d, e\}$?
   (a) $A \subset B$ (b) $B \subsetneq A$
   (c) $A = B$ (d) $B \not\subset A$
8. (a) How many subsets does a set with one element have?
   (b) Answer the same question for a set with two elements.
   (c) Answer the same question for a set with three elements.
   (d) Answer the same question for a set with four elements.
   (e) From your answers to (a)–(d), what would you guess to be the number of subsets of a set containing n elements, where n is an arbitrary positive integer?
9. Does every set have a proper subset?
10. Let $A = \{a, b, c, d, e, f\}$, $B = \{d, e, f, g, h, i\}$, $C = \{b, d, h, i\}$, $D = \{d, e\}$, $E = \{b, d\}$, and $F = \{b\}$. Which of the sets A, B, C, D, E, or F can equal the set X if we are given the following information?
    (a) $X \subset A$ and $X \subset B$ (b) $X \not\subset B$ and $X \subset C$
    (c) $X \subset B$ and $X \not\subset C$ (d) $X \not\subset A$ and $X \not\subset C$
11. Prove that the set $A = \{1, 2, 3, 4\}$ is not a subset of the set $B = \{x \mid x$ is an odd integer$\}$.
12. Prove that if $A \subset B$ and $B \subset C$, then $A \subset C$.
13. Prove that if $A = B$ and $B = C$, then $A = C$.
14. Indicate which of the following statements are true and which are false.
    (a) $\{7\} \subsetneq \{7, 8, 9\}$
    (b) $a = \{a\}$
    (c) $\{a\} \notin \{a, b, c, d\}$
    (d) $u \subset \{u, v, w\}$

(e) $-7 \in \{\{x\} \,|\, x$ is a negative integer$\}$

(f) The set $A = \{\{1, 2\}\}$ is a set containing two elements

15. Let $S = \{x \,|\, 3x = 12\}$. Does $S = 4$?

16. Which of the following sets represents the empty set?

(a) The set of all even numbers with last digit 5

(b) $\{x \,|\, x^2 = -1$ and x is a real number$\}$

(c) $\{\varnothing\}$

(d) The set of all odd integers whose square is even

*17. Indicate which of the following statements are true and which are false.

(a) $\varnothing \subset \{\varnothing\}$ (b) $\varnothing \in \{\varnothing\}$

(c) $\varnothing = \{\varnothing\}$ (d) $\varnothing \nsubseteq \{\varnothing\}$

(e) $\{\varnothing\} \subset \{\{\varnothing\}\}$

18. Prove that if S is a subset of the empty set $\varnothing$, then $S = \varnothing$.

Section 2.3   Operations Involving Sets

In this section we consider certain operations that can be performed on sets. The following example will illustrate the pertinent ideas.

Example 2.3.1   **Residents of the United States**   Let U be the set consisting of all residents of the United States. Define the sets F and Y by

$$F = \{x \,|\, x \text{ is a female resident of the United States}\} \tag{2.3.1}$$
$$Y = \{x \,|\, x \text{ is a resident of the United States under 25 years old}\} \tag{2.3.2}$$

Notice that F and Y are both subsets of the set U. Considering for the moment just the set F, each element of U can be classified according to whether or not it is a member of F. This classification gives rise to a new set, the set of all elements of U that are not elements of F. This new set is referred to as the *complement* (in U) of F and is denoted by

$$\tilde{F}$$

In this case, $\tilde{F}$ is the set of nonfemale (male) residents of the United States. Notice that the phrase "in U" has been written parenthetically in defining the complement. Generally, the set in which the complement is taken will be understood from the context of the problem under consideration and this phrase may be omitted.

Typically, we begin, as we did above, with a set U that contains all the elements that we shall want to consider for a given problem. This is referred to as the *universal set* for that problem. All the sets that are considered subsequently will be subsets of this universal set. When we refer to the complement of a set in that context, we shall mean the complement in the universal set.

Definition

Let U be a specified universal set and let $S \subset U$. Then the *complement* (in U) of S is defined to be the set of elements in U that are *not* elements of S. It is denoted by $\tilde{S}$. In set builder notation

$$\tilde{S} = \{x \,|\, x \in U \text{ and } x \notin S\}$$

Following are additional examples of this concept.

Example 2.3.2 The Complement of a Set

1. Let Y be the set defined by Eq. (2.3.2) in Example 2.3.1. Then

$$\tilde{Y} = \{x \mid x \text{ is a resident of the United States at least 25 years old}\}$$

2. Let L be the set of letters in the English alphabet and V the set of vowels. Then the complement of V (in L) is the set of consonants in the English alphabet:

$$\tilde{V} = \{x \mid x \text{ is a consonant in the English alphabet}\}$$

3. Let U denote the set of integers between 1 and 10 inclusive. That is,

$$U = \{1, 2, 3, \ldots, 9, 10\}$$

Also, let T consist of the integers between 1 and 10 that are a multiple of 3:

$$T = \{3, 6, 9\}$$

Then the complement of T (in U) is

$$\tilde{T} = \{1, 2, 4, 5, 7, 8, 10\}$$

Example 2.3.3 Consider again the sets F and Y defined in Example 2.3.1. We can use these two sets to form another set, which consists of those elements that are members of both F and Y (i.e., those elements which the two sets have in common). This is just the set that consists of residents of the United States who are female *and* under 25 years old. It is denoted by $F \cap Y$ (read "F intersect Y"). Thus

$$F \cap Y = \{x \mid x \text{ is a female resident of the United States under 25 years old}\}$$

Definition

Let U be a specified universal set and let A and B be subsets of U. Then the *intersection* of A and B is defined to be the set consisting of all elements that are members of both A *and* B. This set is denoted by $A \cap B$. In set builder notation,

$$A \cap B = \{x \mid x \in A \text{ and } x \in B\}$$

Example 2.3.4 The Intersection of Two Sets

1. Let U denote the set of positive integers less than 16, A the subset of U that consists of the multiples of 2, and B the subset of U that consists of the multiples of 3:

$$U = \{1, 2, 3, 4, \ldots, 14, 15\}$$
$$A = \{2, 4, 6, 8, 10, 12, 14\}$$
$$B = \{3, 6, 9, 12, 15\}$$

Then $A \cap B$ consists of all positive integers less than 16 which are multiples of both 2 and 3. We have

$$A \cap B = \{6, 12\}$$

so $A \cap B$ can also be described as the set of all positive integers less than 16 which are a multiple of 6.

We can also consider the set $\tilde{A} \cap B$. This consists of all elements which are not a multiple of 2 but which are a multiple of 3. Since

$$\tilde{A} = \{1, 3, 5, 7, 9, 11, 13, 15\}$$

we have that

$$\bar{A} \cap B = \{3, 9, 15\}$$

2. Let U denote the set consisting of the months of the year, J the set of those months beginning with the letter J, and T the set of months with 31 days. Then

$$J \cap T = \{\text{January, July}\}$$

Also, the set $J \cap \bar{T}$ consists of the months of the year that begin with the letter J and do not have 31 days. Thus

$$J \cap \bar{T} = \{\text{June}\}$$

Finally, the set $\bar{J} \cap \bar{T}$ consists of the months of the year that do not begin with the letter J and do not have 31 days. So

$$\bar{J} \cap \bar{T} = \{\text{February, April, September, November}\}$$

3. Let U denote the set of states in the United States, A the set of states beginning with the letter A, and B the set of states south of Vancouver which border the Pacific Ocean. Then

$$A = \{\text{Alabama, Alaska, Arizona, Arkansas}\}$$
$$B = \{\text{California, Hawaii, Oregon, Washington}\}$$

Notice that A and B have no elements in common. This means that the intersection of A and B does not have any members. Thus

$$A \cap B = \emptyset$$

The final set operation that we shall consider is the union operation.

Definition

Let U be a specified universal set and let A and B be subsets of U. Then the *union* of A and B is defined to be the set consisting of all elements that are either members of A or members of B (or members of both A and B). This set is denoted by $A \cup B$ (read "A union B"). Thus

$$A \cup B = \{x \mid x \in A \text{ or } x \in B\}$$

As we pointed out in Section 2.2, the number of times that an element appears in listing the elements of a set is of no consequence. So, if an element is a member of both A and B, it will still be counted only once in forming $A \cup B$.

Example 2.3.5 The Union of Two Sets

1. Consider the sets F and Y defined in Example 2.3.1. Then $F \cup Y$ consists of all residents of the United States who are either female or under 25 years old.
2. Let U denote the set of positive integers less than 16, A denote the subset of U consisting of the multiples of 2, and B the subset of U consisting of the multiples of 3. Then

$$U = \{1, 2, 3, 4, \ldots, 14, 15\}$$
$$A = \{2, 4, 6, 8, 10, 12, 14\}$$
$$B = \{3, 6, 9, 12, 15\}.$$

The set

$$A \cup B = \{2, 3, 4, 6, 8, 9, 10, 12, 14, 15\}$$

consists of all positive integers less than 16 that are either a multiple of 2 or a multiple of 3 (or both). Note that the elements 6 and 12 appear only once in $A \cup B$, even though they are contained in both A and B.

3. Let U denote the set of letters in the English alphabet, S denote the subset of U that consists of the first six letters, and V denote the vowels. Then

$$S = \{a, b, c, d, e, f\}$$
$$V = \{a, e, i, o, u\}$$

Consequently,

$$S \cup V = \{a, b, c, d, e, f, i, o, u\}$$

Exercises for 2.3

1. Let $U = \{1, 3, 5, 7, 8, 10, 11, 15, 21, 45\}$. Find $\bar{A}$ (the complement of A in U) if
   (a) $A = \{3, 7, 15, 21\}$
   (b) $A = \{1, 5, 8, 10, 7, 21, 11\}$
   (c) $A = \{x \mid x \in U$ and x is even$\}$
   (d) $A = \{x \mid x \in U$ and $3x \in U\}$
   (e) $A = U$

2. Let $U = \{3, 8, 9, 14, 27\}$. Find the complement (in U) of each of the following sets.
   (a) $A = \{x \mid x \in U$ and x is odd$\}$
   (b) $B = \{x \mid x \in U$ and $2x \in U\}$
   (c) $C = \{x \mid x \in U$ and $x + 5 \in U\}$
   (d) $D = \{x \mid x \in U$ and $x^2 \in U\}$

3. Let $U = \{1, 2\}$ and S be a subset of U. Find the complement of S given
   (a) $S = \{x \mid 1 \le x \le 2\}$
   (b) $S = \{x \mid 1 < x < 2\}$

4. Let $A = \{a, b, c, d\}$, $B = \{b, d, f, h\}$, and $C = \{a, c, e\}$. Find
   (a) $A \cap B$
   (b) $A \cap C$
   (c) $B \cap C$
   (d) $C \cap C$

5. Let $A = \{1, 2, 3, 4\}$, $B = \{2, 4, 6, 8\}$, and $C = \{3, 4, 5, 6\}$. Find
   (a) $A \cup B$
   (b) $A \cup C$
   (c) $B \cup C$
   (d) $B \cup B$

6. Let $U = \{a, b, c, d, e, f, g\}$, $A = \{a, b, c, d, e\}$, $B = \{a, c, e, g\}$, and $C = \{b, e, f, g\}$. Find
   (a) $A \cap \bar{B}$
   (b) $\bar{A} \cup C$
   (c) $\bar{A} \cap \bar{B}$
   (d) $\overline{A \cup B}$
   (e) $\bar{B} \cup \bar{C}$
   (f) $\overline{B \cap C}$

7. Let U be the set of states in the United States, E the set of New England states, B the set of states bordering the Pacific Ocean, and C the set of states beginning with the letter C. Find
   (a) $C \cap E$
   (b) $C \cap B$
   (c) $E \cap \bar{C}$
   (d) $E \cup B$
   (e) $B \cap E$
   (f) $B \cap \bar{E}$

8. Company C is a multiproduct firm that makes and sells a variety of products. Suppose that they have sales divisions in the United States and in foreign countries. Let $A = \{x \mid x$ is a product made by C and on which the profit margin is greater than 20 percent$\}$ and $B = \{x \mid x$ is a product made by C and sold abroad$\}$. Find
   (a) $A \cap B$
   (b) $A \cup B$
   (c) $\bar{A} \cap B$
   (d) $\bar{A} \cap \bar{B}$

9. In problem 8, what accusations can be made against company C if $A \cap B \ne \emptyset$ but $A \cap \bar{B} = \emptyset$?

10. Let A and B be any two sets. Prove the following two statements.
    (a) $A \cap B \subset A$ (with a similar result for B)
    (b) $B \subset A \cup B$ (with a similar result for A)

11. Let A and B be sets such that $A \subset B$. Prove that $A \cap B = A$ and $A \cup B = B$. (*Hint:* Since $A \cap B \subset A$ and $B \subset A \cup B$, you need only show that $A \subset A \cap B$ and $A \cup B \subset B$.)

12. Let A and B be subsets of the universal set U. Determine the most general conditions on the sets A and B so that the following hold.
    (a) $A \cap \emptyset = A$
    (b) $A \cup U = U$
    (c) $A \cap B = A \cup B$
    (d) $A \cup B = \emptyset$

13. Prove that if $A \subset B$, then $\tilde{B} \subset \tilde{A}$.

14. Prove that $\tilde{\tilde{A}} = A$.

Problems 15–20 pertain to the difference of two sets.

   Definition: Let A and B be subsets of a universal set U. Then we define the *difference* of A and B, denoted $A - B$, as the set of elements that belong to A but do not belong to B. That is, $A - B$ is the (relative) complement of B in A.

15. Let $A = \{1, 2, 3, 4\}$, $B = \{2, 4, 6, 8\}$, and $C = \{3, 4, 5, 6\}$. Find
    (a) $A - B$
    (b) $B - A$
    (c) $B - C$
    (d) $C - A$
    (e) $A - A$

16. Let U be the set of integers, $A = \{0, 2, 3, 5, -11\}$, and $B = \{0, 2, 5\}$. Find
    (a) $A - B$
    (b) $B - A$
    (c) $A - \tilde{B}$
    (d) $\tilde{A} - \tilde{B}$
    (e) $(A - B) \cap (B - A)$
    (f) $(A - B) \cup (B - A)$

17. Prove that $A - B \subset A$.

18. Prove that $(A - B) \cap B = \emptyset$.

19. Prove that $A - B = A \cap \tilde{B}$.

20. Find the most general conditions on the sets A and B so that the following hold.
    (a) $A - B = A$
    (b) $A - B = B - A$
    (c) $A - B = B$

21. Prove that
    (a) $A \cup B = B \cup A$
    (b) $A \cap B = B \cap A$

22. Prove that $\tilde{A} - \tilde{B} = B - A$.

Section 2.4   Venn Diagrams and De Morgan's Laws

Before examining the interrelationships among the operations that have been introduced, it might benefit the reader to summarize our definitions.

   Let U be a specified universal set and let A and B be subsets of U. Then

1. $\tilde{A} = \{x \mid x \in U \text{ and } x \notin A\}$.
2. $A \cap B = \{x \mid x \in A \text{ and } x \in B\}$.
3. $A \cup B = \{x \mid x \in A \text{ or } x \in B\}$.

   To facilitate further examination of these three operations we use a method of graphically illustrating set-theoretic notions. We employ what are called *Venn diagrams*. The universal set is portrayed as a rectangle with its various subsets drawn as disks inside the rectangle. The simplest situation is that of a universal set U and one set $A \subset U$. For this, we have the Venn diagram of Figure 2.4.1, where the unshaded portion represents those elements of U that are not in A. Hence, from the definition of $\tilde{A}$, this represents $\tilde{A}$, as noted in the diagram.

   If we consider subsets A and B of U, the general situation is portrayed by the Venn diagram of Figure 2.4.2. Here the sets A and B are shown as two shaded disks, and their intersection is the heavily shaded region indicated in the diagram. The union of A and B is represented by the total shaded area in the diagram.

Figure 2.4.1

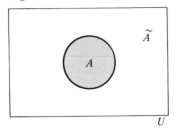

Figure 2.4.2

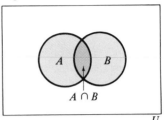

Venn diagrams are quite useful in visualizing sets formed by use of the various operations that have been introduced. They are also useful in giving informal proofs of set-theoretic results. Here they will be used to demonstrate two fundamental identities that relate to the set operations now at our disposal. These identities are known as *De Morgan's laws*. The following examples illustrate these laws.

Example 2.4.1 Let U denote the set of positive integers less than 16, A the subset of U that consists of the multiples of 2, and B the subset of U that consists of the multiples of 3. Then

$$U = \{1, 2, 3, 4, \ldots, 14, 15\}$$
$$A = \{2, 4, 6, 8, 10, 12, 14\}$$
$$B = \{3, 6, 9, 12, 15\}$$

$A \cap B$ consists of all positive integers less than 16 which are multiples of both 2 and 3:

$$A \cap B = \{6, 12\}$$

Now, $\widetilde{A \cap B}$ denotes the set of elements in U which are not in $A \cap B$:

$$\widetilde{A \cap B} = \{1, 2, 3, 4, 5, 7, 8, 9, 10, 11, 13, 14, 15\} \tag{2.4.1}$$

In words, $\widetilde{A \cap B}$ is the set of elements of U that are not multiples of both 2 and 3. Putting it another way, $\widetilde{A \cap B}$ is the set of elements of U that either are *not* a multiple of 2 *or* are *not* a multiple of 3. But that set is just the union of $\tilde{A}$ and $\tilde{B}$. The argument just given indicates that

$$\widetilde{A \cap B} = \tilde{A} \cup \tilde{B} \tag{2.4.2}$$

Of course, we can check the validity of Eq. (2.4.2) in this case by determining $\tilde{A} \cup \tilde{B}$. We have

$$\tilde{A} = \{1, 3, 5, 7, 9, 11, 13, 15\}$$
$$\tilde{B} = \{1, 2, 4, 5, 7, 8, 10, 11, 13, 14\}$$

Consequently,

$$\tilde{A} \cup \tilde{B} = \{1, 2, 3, 4, 5, 7, 8, 9, 10, 11, 13, 14, 15\}$$

This set is the same as the one given in Eq. (2.4.1) and hence Eq. (2.4.2) holds as asserted. Formula (2.4.2) illustrates the first of De Morgan's laws.

Example 2.4.2 Months of the Year Let U denote the set consisting of the months of the year, J the set of months beginning with the letter J, and T the set of months with 31 days. Then

$$J = \{\text{January, June, July}\}$$
$$T = \{\text{January, March, May, July, August, October, December}\}$$

The set $J \cup T$ consists of all months of the year that begin with the letter J or have 31 days.

$$J \cup T = \{\text{January, March, May, June, July, August, October, December}\}$$

Now, the set $\widetilde{J \cup T}$ consists of all elements in U that are not in $J \cup T$.

$$\widetilde{J \cup T} = \{\text{February, April, September, November}\} \tag{2.4.3}$$

In words, $\widetilde{J \cup T}$ is the set of months that neither begin with the letter J nor have 31 days. Putting it another way, $\widetilde{J \cup T}$ is the set of months that do *not* begin with the letter J *and* do *not* have 31 days. But that set is just the intersection of $\tilde{J}$ and $\tilde{T}$. Hence it appears that

$$\widetilde{J \cup T} = \tilde{J} \cap \tilde{T} \tag{2.4.4}$$

The validity of this equality can be verified by determining explicitly the set $\tilde{J} \cap \tilde{T}$. We have

$$\tilde{J} = \{\text{February, March, April, May, August, September, October, November,}$$
$$\text{December}\}$$
$$\tilde{T} = \{\text{February, April, June, September, November}\}$$

Consequently,

$$\tilde{J} \cap \tilde{T} = \{\text{February, April, September, November}\}$$

This set is the same as the one given in Eq. (2.4.3), and hence Eq. (2.4.4) is true. Formula (2.4.4) illustrates the second of De Morgan's laws.

With these examples in mind we now state and demonstrate the validity of De Morgan's laws.

Theorem 2.4.1 De Morgan's Laws
Let U be a specified universal set and let A and B be subsets of U. Then the following hold:

1. $\widetilde{(A \cap B)} = \tilde{A} \cup \tilde{B}$; the set consisting of those elements not common to A and B consists of the elements not in A and the elements not in B.
2. $\widetilde{(A \cup B)} = \tilde{A} \cap \tilde{B}$; the set consisting of those elements not in A or B consists of the elements common to the complement of A and the complement of B.

PROOF

To demonstrate rule 1, first observe that $A \cap B$ is the shaded portion of Figure 2.4.3. From this it follows that $\widetilde{A \cap B}$ is the *unshaded* portion of this same diagram. Now, $\tilde{A}$ and $\tilde{B}$ are the shaded portions of Figures 2.4.4 and 2.4.5. The union of these two sets consists of the shaded portions in either of the two diagrams. Consequently, $\tilde{A} \cup \tilde{B}$

Figure 2.4.3

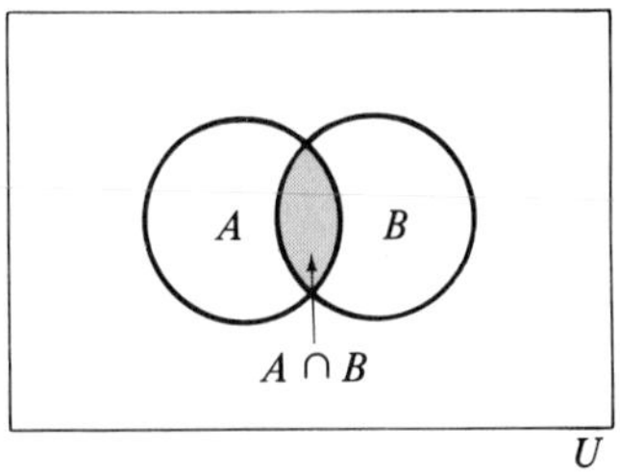

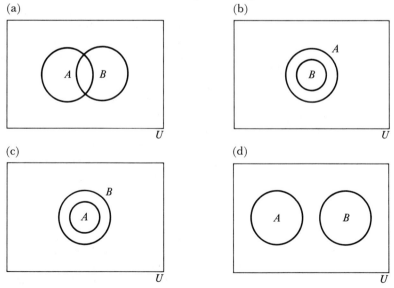

Figure 2.4.4

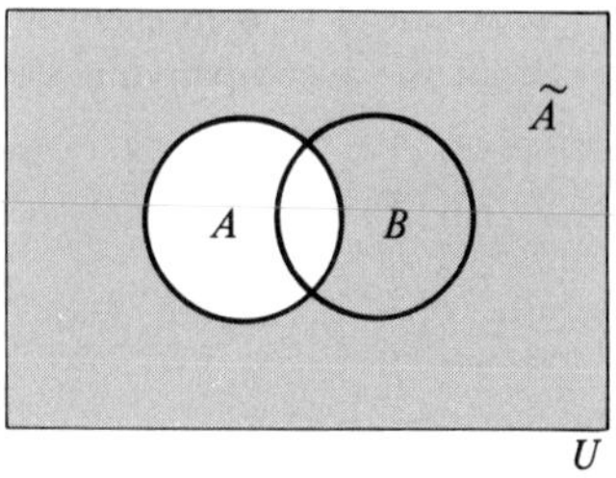

Figure 2.4.5

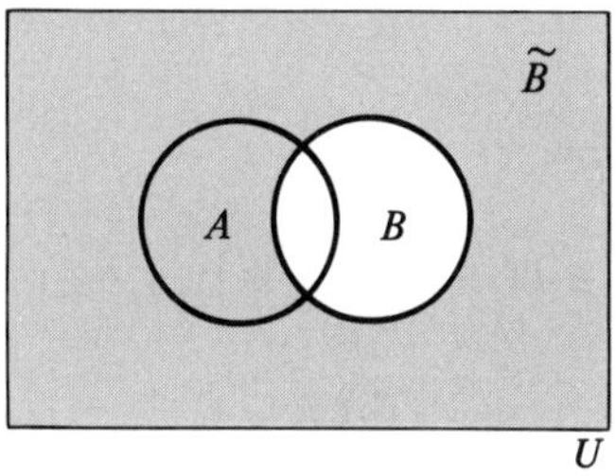

Figure 2.4.6

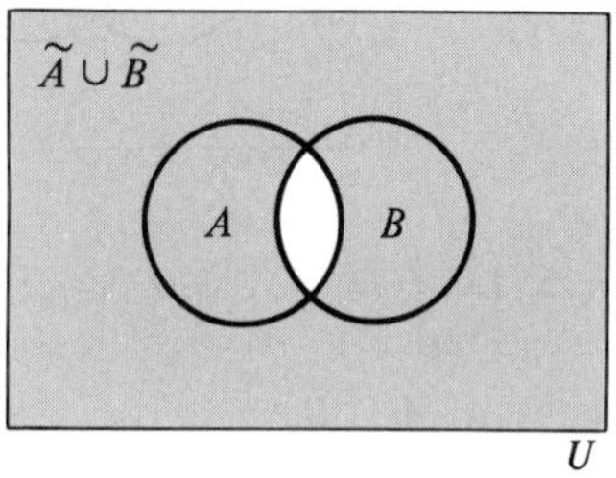

is the shaded portion of Figure 2.4.6. Note that the shaded portion here, corresponding to $\tilde{A} \cup \tilde{B}$, is precisely the same as the unshaded portion of Figure 2.4.3, which corresponds to $\widetilde{A \cap B}$. Thus we have demonstrated the first of De Morgan's laws. The second identity can be demonstrated using Venn diagram arguments similar to those which were just employed.

Exercises for 2.4

Note: Several of these problems employ the concept of the difference of two sets. This concept is defined directly preceding problem 15, Exercises 2.3.

1. Shade $A \cap B$ in each of the following Venn diagrams.

(a)

(b)

(c)

(d)

2. Shade $A \cup B$ in each of the Venn diagrams in problem 1.

3. Shade $A - B$ in each of the Venn diagrams in problem 1.

4. In the accompanying Venn diagram, shade

(a) $\widetilde{A - B}$ (b) $A \cup \tilde{B}$

(c) $\tilde{A} \cap B$ (d) $\tilde{A} - B$

(e) $\widetilde{\tilde{A} - B}$ (f) $A - \tilde{B}$

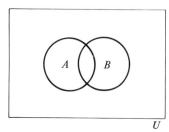

5. Let $U = \{1, 2, 3, 4, 5, 6, 7, 8, 9\}$, $A = \{1, 2, 3, 4\}$, $B = \{2, 4, 6, 8\}$, and $C = \{1, 3, 4, 5, 7\}$. Find

(a) $\widetilde{A \cap B}$ (b) $\widetilde{B \cup C}$

(c) $\widetilde{A - B}$ (d) $\widetilde{\tilde{A} - C}$

(e) $\widetilde{B - \tilde{C}}$ (f) $\tilde{A} - \tilde{B}$

6. Let A and B be subsets of a universal set U. Use Venn diagrams to illustrate the relationship between A and B if the following hold:

(a) $A \cap B = \emptyset$ (b) $A \cap B = B$

(c) $A \cup B = B$ (d) $B - A = \emptyset$

7. Use Venn diagrams to verify the second of De Morgan's laws: $\widetilde{(A \cup B)} = \tilde{A} \cap \tilde{B}$.

8. Let A and B be subsets of a universal set U. With the aid of a Venn diagram, list each of the distinct sets into which sets A and B partition U.

9. Let A and B be subsets of a universal set U. Use a Venn diagram to show that

$$(A \cap B) \cup (\tilde{A} \cap B) = B$$

10. A company is considering opening a new plant in one of the major cities in the United States. They have decided that they should locate in a city with a population of at least 200,000. Taxes and labor supply are being considered in the determination of the new location. Let U represent the set of all major cities with a population of at least 200,000. Let L be the subset of U that consists of cities with relatively low taxes, and let G be the subset of U that consists of cities with a good labor supply. Use a Venn diagram to illustrate the following classifications:

(a) Low taxes but labor supply is not good.

(b) Taxes are low or labor supply is good but not both.

(c) Taxes are low and labor supply is good.

(d) Labor supply is not good or taxes are high.

11. Prove that for any two sets A and B, $\widetilde{A - B} = \tilde{A} \cup B$.

12. Suppose that insurance companies are classified by the following two attributes: (1) those offering automobile insurance as opposed to those not offering automobile insurance, and (2) those offering coverages offered by only a few companies, as opposed to those offering only coverages offered by many companies. Let A represent the set of companies that offer automobile insurance and M represent the set of companies that offer only coverages offered by many companies. Use a Venn diagram to illustrate all the possibilities involved with intersections and complements of the sets A and M (e.g., a company that offers both automobile insurance and sky-diving insurance would be a member of $A \cap \tilde{M}$).

13. A survey is taken of the reactions of a number of people to a television show. Let U be

the set of all spectators of the show, M the set of males who watched the show, and L the set of spectators who liked the show. Use a Venn diagram to illustrate all the possibilities involved with intersections and complements of the sets M and L (e.g., females who do not like the show would be members of $\tilde{M} \cap \tilde{L}$).

14. Let A and B be subsets of a universal set U. Prove that if

$$(\tilde{A} \cap B) \cup (A \cap \tilde{B}) = \emptyset \qquad \text{then } A = B$$

Section 2.5 Interactions of the Set Operations

The concepts of union and intersection can be extended to more than two sets. First we consider intersections.

Example 2.5.1 Let U be the set of all positive integers less than 100:

$$U = \{x \mid x \text{ is an integer, } 1 \leq x \leq 99\}$$

Let A consist of the elements of U that are a multiple of 2, B the elements of U that are a multiple of 3, and C the elements of U that are a multiple of 5. Then

$$A = \{2, 4, 6, 8, \ldots, 96, 98\}$$
$$B = \{3, 6, 9, 12, \ldots, 96, 99\}$$
$$C = \{5, 10, 15, 20, \ldots, 90, 95\}$$

We have

$$A \cap B = \{6, 12, 18, 24, \ldots, 90, 96\}$$
$$B \cap C = \{15, 30, 45, 60, 75, 90\}$$

Thus $A \cap B$ consists of those elements of U which are a multiple of 6, and $B \cap C$ consists of those which are a multiple of 15.

Next we intersect the set $A \cap B$ with C to obtain

$$(A \cap B) \cap C = \{30, 60, 90\} \tag{2.5.1}$$

and the set A with $B \cap C$ to get

$$A \cap (B \cap C) = \{30, 60, 90\} \tag{2.5.2}$$

Comparing Eqs. (2.5.1) and (2.5.2) we see that

$$(A \cap B) \cap C = A \cap (B \cap C) \tag{2.5.3}$$

and that the members of this set are just the elements of U that belong to all three sets A, B, and C.

Equation (2.5.3) obtained in Example 2.5.1 for the three sets defined therein is typical of the general situation:

Proposition 2.5.1

Let U be a specified universal set and let A, B, and C be subsets of U. Then

$$(A \cap B) \cap C = A \cap (B \cap C) \tag{2.5.4}$$

and this set consists of the elements of U common to all three sets A, B, and C.

The validity of Eq. (2.5.4) can be demonstrated through Venn diagrams, and its verification is left to the reader as an exercise. Because of Eq. (2.5.4) we can use

$$A \cap B \cap C \tag{2.5.5}$$

to describe "the intersection of A, B, and C" without the possibility of ambiguity. The set $A \cap B \cap C$ is the set of elements of U that belong to all three sets. In set builder notation,

$$A \cap B \cap C = \{x \mid x \in A \text{ and } x \in B \text{ and } x \in C\}$$

In a similar manner, the idea of intersection can be extended to any number of sets without ambiguity. In every case, the intersection of any number of sets is the set of elements common to all the sets in the intersection.

The situation is the same for unions. That is,

$$(A \cup B) \cup C = A \cup (B \cup C)$$

and we write

$$A \cup B \cup C$$

to mean either of these equal sets. This is simply the set of elements contained in at least one of the sets A, B, or C. In set builder notation,

$$A \cup B \cup C = \{x \mid x \in A \text{ or } x \in B \text{ or } x \in C\}$$

More generally, the union of any number of sets is the set of elements belonging to at least one of the sets in the union.

Example 2.5.2 Let U denote the set of all people and

$$S = \{x \mid x \text{ is a resident of the United States}\}$$
$$F = \{x \mid x \text{ is a female}\}$$
$$Y = \{x \mid x \text{ is a person under 25 years old}\}$$
$$T = \{x \mid x \text{ is a person over 6 feet tall}\}$$

Then $S \cap F \cap Y$ denotes the set of female residents of the United States under 25 years old, and $S \cap Y \cap T$ denotes the set of residents of the United States who are under 25 years old and over 6 feet tall.

Also, $F \cup Y \cup T$ consists of all those people who are either female or under 25 years old or over 6 feet tall, and $S \cup F \cup T$ is the set consisting of all people who are either residents of the United States or female or over 6 feet tall.

Finally, $S \cap F \cap Y \cap T$ consists of the female residents of the United States who are under 25 years old and over 6 feet tall, and $S \cup F \cup Y \cup T$ is the set of all people who are either residents of the United States or female or under 25 years old or over 6 feet tall.

The following theorem and its corollaries will prove useful in calculating probabilities in Chapter 4. The theorem describes the ways in which the operations of union and intersection interact. These are called *distributive laws* for set operations.

Theorem 2.5.2

Let U be a specified universal set and let A, B, and C be subsets of U. Then the following distributive laws hold:

1. $A \cap (B \cup C) = (A \cap B) \cup (A \cap C)$.
2. $A \cup (B \cap C) = (A \cup B) \cap (A \cup C)$.

PROOF

We shall use Venn diagrams to prove rule 1. The set $B \cup C$ is shaded in Figure 2.5.1.

Figure 2.5.1

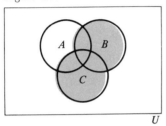

Intersecting this with the set A yields the shaded portion in Figure 2.5.2. Now, the

Figure 2.5.2

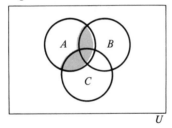

sets $A \cap B$ and $A \cap C$ are the shaded portions of Figures 2.5.3 and 2.5.4. The

Figure 2.5.3

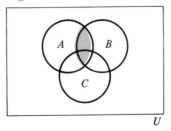

Figure 2.5.4

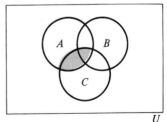

union, $(A \cap B) \cup (A \cap C)$, is then the portion of the diagram obtained by combining the shaded portions of Figures 2.5.3 and 2.5.4. But, this is just the shaded portion of Figure 2.5.2; consequently,

$$A \cap (B \cup C) = (A \cap B) \cup (A \cap C)$$

Rule 2 can be proved by a similar use of Venn diagrams.

We illustrate Theorem 2.5.2 in the following example.

Example 2.5.3 Let U be the set consisting of the positive integers less than 21, A those elements of U which are a multiple of 2, B those elements which are a multiple of 3, and C those elements which are a multiple of 5. Then

$$U = \{1, 2, 3, 4, \ldots, 19, 20\}$$
$$A = \{2, 4, 6, 8, 10, 12, 14, 16, 18, 20\}$$
$$B = \{3, 6, 9, 12, 15, 18\}$$
$$C = \{5, 10, 15, 20\}$$

Therefore,

$$A \cap (B \cup C) = A \cap \{3, 5, 6, 9, 10, 12, 15, 18, 20\}$$
$$= \{6, 10, 12, 18, 20\} \qquad (2.5.6)$$

But $A \cap B = \{6, 12, 18\}$ and $A \cap C = \{10, 20\}$; therefore,

$$(A \cap B) \cup (A \cap C) = \{6, 10, 12, 18, 20\} \qquad (2.5.7)$$

Comparing Eqs. (2.5.6) and (2.5.7) we see that

$$A \cap (B \cup C) = (A \cap B) \cup (A \cap C)$$

which illustrates rule 1 of Theorem 2.5.2.

To illustrate rule 2 of Theorem 2.5.2, first note that

$$A \cup (B \cap C) = A \cup \{15\}$$
$$= \{2, 4, 6, 8, 10, 12, 14, 15, 16, 18, 20\} \qquad (2.5.8)$$

and then that

$$A \cup B = \{2, 3, 4, 6, 8, 9, 10, 12, 14, 15, 16, 18, 20\}$$
$$A \cup C = \{2, 4, 5, 6, 8, 10, 12, 14, 15, 16, 18, 20\}$$

Consequently,

$$(A \cup B) \cap (A \cup C) = \{2, 4, 6, 8, 10, 12, 14, 15, 16, 18, 20\} \qquad (2.5.9)$$

and comparing Eq. (2.5.8) with Eq. (2.5.9) we see that

$$A \cup (B \cap C) = (A \cup B) \cap (A \cup C)$$

As corollaries to Theorem 2.5.2 we present two identities that are particularly useful in computing probabilities.

Corollary 2.5.3
Let U be a specified universal set and let A, B, and C be subsets of U. If $B \cup C = U$, then

$$A = (A \cap B) \cup (A \cap C)$$

PROOF

To prove this corollary, first observe that $A \cap U = A$. Now, from Theorem 2.5.2,

$$A \cap (B \cup C) = (A \cap B) \cup (A \cap C)$$

But $B \cup C = U$ and $A \cap U = A$, so

$$A \cap (B \cup C) = A \cap U$$
$$= A$$

and hence

$$A = (A \cap B) \cup (A \cap C)$$

Before we state our last corollary to Theorem 2.5.2, the following example is presented, to illustrate the reasoning involved.

Example 2.5.4 Let U be the set of all people, A the set of females, and B the people under 25 years old. Now, a female is either a female and under 25 *or* a female and not under 25. That is, an element of A is either an element of $A \cap B$ *or* an element of $A \cap \tilde{B}$. Hence the above argument suggests that

$$A = (A \cap B) \cup (A \cap \tilde{B})$$

Corollary 2.5.4
Let U be a specified universal set and let A and B be subsets of U. Then (see Figure 2.5.5)

$$A = (A \cap B) \cup (A \cap \tilde{B}) \tag{2.5.10}$$

and

$$(A \cap B) \cap (A \cap \tilde{B}) = \emptyset \tag{2.5.11}$$

PROOF

Observe that by definition of $\tilde{B}$, $B \cup \tilde{B} = U$. Letting $C = \tilde{B}$ in Corollary 2.5.3 yields Eq. (2.5.10). The proof of Eq. (2.5.11) is left to the reader as an exercise.

Figure 2.5.5

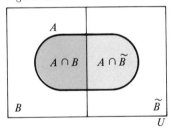

Exercises for 2.5

1. Let $U = \{1, 2, 3, 4, 5, 6, 7, 8, 9\}$, $A = \{1, 3, 4, 8\}$, $B = \{2, 4, 6, 7\}$, and $C = \{2, 3, 4, 5, 9\}$. Find
   (a) $(A \cap B) \cap C$
   (c) $A \cap (B \cup C)$
   (b) $A \cup (B \cup C)$
   (d) $A \cup (B \cap C)$
2. Let $U = \{1, 2, 3, 4, 5, 6, 7, 8, 9, 10, 11, 12\}$, $A = \{1, 4, 5\}$, $B = \{9, 10, 11, 12, 4\}$, and $C = \{4, 5, 6, 7, 8\}$. Find
   (a) $B \cup \widetilde{(A \cap C)}$
   (c) $\tilde{A} \cap B \cap C$
   (e) $\tilde{A} \cup (B \cap C)$
   (b) $\widetilde{(A \cup C)} \cap B$
   (d) $(\tilde{A} \cup \tilde{C}) \cap \tilde{B}$
   (f) $\widetilde{(A \cap B)} \cap \tilde{C}$

3. In the Venn diagram, shade

(a) $(\bar{A} \cap \bar{B}) \cup C$

(b) $(A \cup B) \cap \bar{C}$

(c) $\overline{(\bar{A} \cup C)} \cap B$

(d) $(A \cup C) \cup \bar{B}$

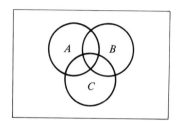

4. In each Venn diagram, what set describes the portion that is shaded?

(a)

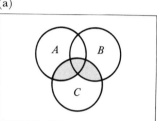

(b)

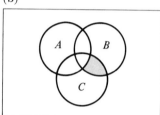

(c)

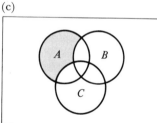

(d)

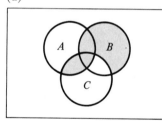

(e)

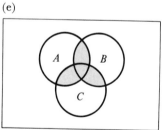

5. Let U denote the set of all people, and let

$R = \{x \mid x$ is a resident of the United States$\}$
$F = \{x \mid x$ is a female$\}$
$S = \{x \mid x$ is a person who smokes$\}$
$A = \{x \mid x$ is a person over the age of 65$\}$

Describe each of the following sets.

(a) $R \cap F \cap S$

(b) $R \cap S \cap A$

(c) $R \cap F \cap (S \cup A)$

(d) $F \cap S \cap A$

(e) $\bar{F} \cap S \cap A$

(f) $F \cup S \cup A$

(g) $F \cap A \cap \bar{S}$

(h) $R \cap F \cap S \cap A$

6. Use the distributive laws of Theorem 2.5.2 to find a set equal to each of the following expressions. (Also see problem 21, Exercises 2.3.)

(a) $A \cap (B \cup C)$ (b) $P \cup (N \cap M)$

(c) $(R \cup S) \cap T$ (d) $(A \cap B) \cup (B \cap C)$

(e) $(X \cup Y) \cap (X \cup Z)$ (f) $(R \cap S) \cup (T \cap S)$

7. Let A, B, and C be subsets of a universal set U. Simplify each of the following expressions.

(a) $(A \cup B) \cup \tilde{A}$ (b) $\widetilde{(A \cap B)} \cap B$

(c) $[\widetilde{(C \cup \emptyset)} \cup C]$ (d) $(A \cap B \cap C) \cup (A \cap B \cap \tilde{C})$

(e) $\widetilde{(A \cup B)} \cap \tilde{B}$

8. Blood types are determined in the following manner. Each person is doubly classified. If he has the Rh antigen, he is Rh positive. If he does not have the Rh antigen, he is Rh negative. If his blood contains A antigen but not B antigen, it is type A; if it has B antigen but not A antigen, it is type B; if it has both A and B antigens, it is type AB; and if it has neither antigen, it is type O. Let

$$P = \{x \mid x \text{ is a person whose blood contains the Rh antigen}\}$$
$$A = \{x \mid x \text{ is a person whose blood contains the A antigen}\}$$
$$B = \{x \mid x \text{ is a person whose blood contains the B antigen}\}$$

Determine the following persons' blood types.

(a) $P \cap A \cap B$ (b) $\tilde{P} \cap A \cap B$

(c) $P \cap (A \cap \tilde{B})$ (d) $P \cap B \cap \tilde{A}$

(e) $\tilde{P} \cap A \cap \tilde{B}$ (f) $\tilde{P} \cap (B \cap \tilde{A})$

(g) $P \cap \widetilde{(A \cup B)}$ (h) $\tilde{P} \cap \tilde{A} \cap \tilde{B}$

9. Let A, B, and C be subsets of a universal set U. Use a Venn diagram to illustrate the relationship between A, B, and C given that the following properties hold:

(a) $A \subset B$, $C \subset B$, $A \cap C = \emptyset$

(b) $A \subset B$, $C \not\subset B$, $B \not\subset C$, $A \cap C \neq \emptyset$

(c) $A \subset C$, $A \neq C$, $B \cap C = \emptyset$

(d) $A \subset (B \cap C)$, $B \subset C$, $C \neq B$, $A \neq B$

10. The members of a private organization use the following rules in determining the various committees:

1. The appropriations committee shall be chosen from the executive committee.
2. No member of the financial committee shall be on the appropriations committee.

Let U be the set of members of the organization, F the subset of U that consists of members of the financial committee, E the subset of U that consists of members of the executive committee, and A the subset of U that consists of members of the appropriations committee. Use a Venn diagram to illustrate the two rules.

11. Use Venn diagrams to verify Proposition 2.5.1.

12. Prove 2 of Theorem 2.5.2 by use of Venn diagrams.

13. Prove Eq. (2.5.11).

14. Let A and B be subsets of a universal set U. Prove that $A \subset B$ implies that $A \cup (B \cap \tilde{A}) = B$.

15. (a) Use Venn diagrams to show that

$$A \cap (B - C) = (A \cap B) - (A \cap C)$$

(b) Give an example to show that

$$A \cup (B - C) \neq (A \cup B) - (A \cup C)$$

(The definition of $A - B$ can be found directly before problem 15, Exercises 2.3.) Problems 16 and 17 pertain to the symmetric difference of two sets.

Definition: The *symmetric difference* $A \bigtriangleup B$ of two sets A and B is defined by $A \bigtriangleup B = (A \cup B) \cap \overline{(A \cap B)}$.

16. Let $U = \{1, 2, 3, 4, 5, 6, 7, 8, 9\}$, $A = \{1, 2, 3, 4, 5\}$, and $B = \{2, 4, 6, 8\}$. Find $A \bigtriangleup B$.
17. (a) Prove that $A \bigtriangleup B = (A \cap \bar{B}) \cup (B \cap \bar{A})$.
    (b) Is $A \bigtriangleup B = B \bigtriangleup A$?

Section 2.6 Cardinality of a Set

The cardinality of a set is simply the number of *distinct* elements contained in the set. All sets can be broadly characterized as being either finite sets or infinite sets. Basically, a set is finite if its cardinality is a positive integer. We shall use the notation

card S

to denote the cardinality of a set S. In this text we shall be concerned only with cardinalities of finite sets.

Example 2.6.1   The Cardinality of a Set

1. card $\{1, 2, 3\} = 3$
2. Let W be the set of days of the week. Then card $W = 7$.
3. card $\{x \mid x^2 = 1\} = 2$
4. If S denotes the set of U.S. Senators, card $S = 100$.
5. Since the empty set contains no elements, card $\emptyset = 0$.

We emphasize that the cardinality of a set is the number of *distinct* elements of the set. Hence, if an element is present more than once in the list of elements of a given set, it is still counted only once in determining the cardinality. For example,

card $\{1, 1, 2, 4, 2, 2, 1, 3\} = 4$

We are often given two sets A and B and asked to determine the cardinality of $A \cup B$. Since $A \cup B$ is the set of elements that belong to either A or B, it is often thought that card $(A \cup B) =$ card $A +$ card B. The following examples illustrate that this is not always the case.

Example 2.6.2   Let U denote the set of positive integers less than 20, A the elements of U that are a multiple of 2, and B the elements of U that are a multiple of 3. Then

$$A = \{2, 4, 6, 8, 10, 12, 14, 16, 18\}$$
$$B = \{3, 6, 9, 12, 15, 18\}$$

Consequently,

card $A = 9$
card $B = 6$

Also,

$$A \cup B = \{2, 3, 4, 6, 8, 9, 10, 12, 14, 15, 16, 18\}$$

so

card $(A \cup B) = 12$

Note that card A + card B = $9 + 6 = 15$; thus in this case,

$$12 = \text{card } (A \cup B) \neq \text{card } A + \text{card } B = 15$$

The problem here is that the elements 6, 12, and 18, which are common to both A and B (i.e., the elements in $A \cap B$), are *counted twice* in computing card A + card B, whereas these elements are to be counted only once in the determination of card $(A \cup B)$.

Example 2.6.3 Let U denote the set of cards in an ordinary deck of 52 playing cards. Let A denote the aces and B denote the hearts. Then

$$\text{card } A = 4$$
$$\text{card } B = 13$$

Now, a card is a member of $A \cup B$ if it is either an ace or a heart (or both). The set $A \cup B$ consists of the 4 aces (including the ace of hearts) together with the other 12 hearts. Thus

$$\text{card } (A \cup B) = 16$$

Consequently,

$$16 = \text{card } (A \cup B) \neq \text{card } A + \text{card } B = 17$$

As in Example 2.6.2, the problem is that the element in $A \cap B$ (i.e., the ace of hearts) is counted twice in computing card A + card B.

Using the examples above as motivation, the following result is now stated.

Theorem 2.6.1
Let A and B be two (finite) sets. Then

$$\text{card } (A \cup B) = \text{card } A + \text{card } B - \text{card } (A \cap B) \tag{2.6.1}$$

Thus to compute the cardinality of $A \cup B$, first add card A to card B and then subtract card $(A \cap B)$, because the elements of $A \cap B$ have been counted twice in the sum.

Example 2.6.4 Consider the sets A and B defined in Example 2.6.2. Then

$$\text{card } A = 9 \qquad \text{card } B = 6$$

Also, $A \cap B = \{6, 12, 18\}$, so

$$\text{card } (A \cap B) = 3$$

Thus, by Eq. (2.6.1),

$$\text{card } (A \cup B) = 9 + 6 - 3 = 12$$

which agrees with the direct counting in Example 2.6.2.

Example 2.6.5 Let A and B denote the sets defined in Example 2.6.3. Then

$$\text{card } A = 4 \qquad \text{card } B = 13$$

Also, $A \cap B = \{\text{ace of hearts}\}$, so

$$\text{card } (A \cap B) = 1$$

Hence, by Eq. (2.6.1),

$$\text{card } (A \cup B) = 4 + 13 - 1 = 16$$

and again this agrees with the direct count made in Example 2.6.3.

An important corollary to Theorem 2.6.1 is obtained when the sets A and B have no elements in common; that is, $A \cap B = \emptyset$. In this case, card $(A \cap B) = 0$.

Corollary 2.6.2

Let A and B be two sets with the property that $A \cap B = \emptyset$. Then

$$\text{card } (A \cup B) = \text{card } A + \text{card } B \qquad (2.6.2)$$

Example 2.6.6 The Congress Let S denote the U.S. Senators and R the members of the U.S. House of Representatives. Then

$$\text{card } S = 100 \qquad \text{card } R = 435$$

Since no person is both in the Senate and House, it follows that $S \cap R = \emptyset$. Consequently, by Eq. (2.6.2),

$$\begin{aligned}\text{card } (S \cup R) &= \text{card } S + \text{card } R \\ &= 100 + 435 = 535\end{aligned}$$

In other words, the number of members in the Senate and House combined is 535.

It is possible to develop formulas analogous to Eq. (2.6.1) for determining cardinalities when three or more sets are involved (see, for example, problem 6, Exercises 2.6). However, it is more instructive to utilize a method based on Venn diagrams.

Example 2.6.7 Survey Analysis A motorcycle company conducted a survey in which 100 people took part. Of these, 65 indicated that they were married, 78 indicated they owned an automobile, and 31 said they owned a motorcycle. Moreover, 60 people said they were married and owned an automobile, 11 said they were married and owned a motorcycle, and 13 indicated that they owned both a motorcycle and an automobile. Finally, 8 people said they were married and owned both an automobile and a motorcycle.

The company then posed the following questions:

1. How many people in the survey were not married and owned neither an automobile nor a motorcycle?
2. How many owned a motorcycle but were not married and did not own an automobile?
3. How many people in the survey were married and owned an automobile but did not own a motorcycle?
4. How many were married and owned a motorcycle but did not own an automobile?

At first glance these questions appear quite difficult to answer. However, by using Venn diagrams and taking the information piece by piece, it will be seen that the answers are quite easy to determine.

First we give names to the sets involved in the survey: The universal set U consists of the 100 people surveyed. Also set

$$M = \{x \,|\, x \text{ is married}\}$$
$$A = \{x \,|\, x \text{ owns an automobile}\}$$
$$C = \{x \,|\, x \text{ owns a motorcycle}\}$$

Then we have

1. card $M = 65$
2. card $A = 78$
3. card $C = 31$
4. card $(M \cap A) = 60$
5. card $(M \cap C) = 11$
6. card $(A \cap C) = 13$
7. card $(M \cap A \cap C) = 8$

This information is used in reverse order to obtain the answers to the four questions. Using statement 7, we place an 8 in the set $M \cap A \cap C$ (Figure 2.6.1). Next, by 6,

Figure 2.6.1

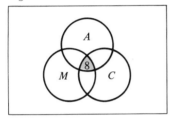

card $(A \cap C) = 13$. Hence a $5(= 13 - 8)$ must be placed in the remaining region of $A \cap C$ in the diagram (Figure 2.6.2). Using 5 and 4, we can fill in the remaining parts of $M \cap C$ and $M \cap A$ (Figure 2.6.3). Now, by 3, card $C = 31$. Taking a look

Figure 2.6.2

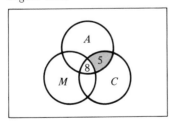

Figure 2.6.3

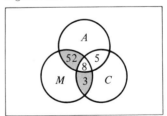

at Figure 2.6.3 reveals that 16 elements of C are already accounted for. Thus a $15 \,(= 31 - 16)$ must be placed in the remaining portion of C. Using 2 and 1, similar arguments yield the Venn diagram of Figure 2.6.4. Adding the numbers in the figure gives 98; consequently, a 2 $(= 100 - 98)$ must be placed in the portion of the Venn diagram lying outside the union of the three disks (Figure 2.6.5). With this figure

Figure 2.6.4

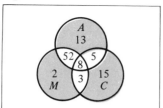

Figure 2.6.5

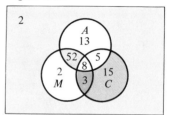

now at our disposal, it is a simple matter to answer the four questions posed by the motorcycle company. The answers to the questions are

1. 2

2. 15

3. 52

4. 3

Exercises for 2.6

1. Determine the cardinality of each of the following sets.
   (a) {1, 2, 7, 11}
   (b) {$x|x$ is a letter in the word "Mississippi"}
   (c) {$-1, 3, 4, 3, 9, 7, 2, -1, 7$}
   (d) {$x|x + 5 = 3$}
   (e) {$x|x$ is a positive integer and $x = -x$}
   (f) {$x|x$ is a state in the United States}
2. Let $U = \{1, 2, 3, 4, 5, 6, 7, 8, 9\}$, $A = \{1, 2, 3, 4, 5\}$, and $B = \{2, 4, 6, 8\}$. Find
   (a) card A (b) card B
   (c) card $(A \cap B)$ (d) card $(A \cup B)$
   (e) card $(A \cap \bar{B})$ (f) card $(B \cap \bar{A})$
3. Let U denote the set consisting of the months of the year, A be the set of those months beginning with the letter A, and S be the set of those months with 30 days. Find
   (a) card S (b) card A
   (c) card $(A \cup S)$ (d) card $(A \cap S)$
   (e) card $(A \cap \bar{S})$ (f) card $(\bar{A} \cap S)$
4. Let $U = \{a, b, c, d, e, f, g, h\}, A = \{a, b, c, d, e\}, B = \{a, c, e, g\},$ and $C = \{b, e, f, g\}$. Find
   (a) card A (b) card B
   (c) card C (d) card $(A \cap B)$
   (e) card $(A \cap C)$ (f) card $(B \cap C)$
   (g) card $(A \cap B \cap C)$ (h) card $(A \cup B \cup C)$
5. In problem 4, show that

$$\text{card } (A \cup B \cup C) = \text{card } A + \text{card } B + \text{card } C$$
$$- \text{card } (A \cap B) - \text{card } (A \cap C)$$
$$- \text{card } (B \cap C) + \text{card } (A \cap B \cap C)$$

6. Prove that the result of problem 5 holds in general. That is, for sets A, B, and C,

$$\text{card } (A \cup B \cup C) = \text{card } A + \text{card } B + \text{card } C$$
$$- \text{card } (A \cap B) - \text{card } (A \cap C)$$
$$- \text{card } (B \cap C) + \text{card } (A \cap B \cap C)$$

7. In promoting a new product, a company distributed free samples to 500 people at a local supermarket. The names of these people were taken and they were called 1 week later to see if they were using the product. Following this, there was an extensive advertising campaign. The same 500 people were called again and asked if they were using the product. Finally, to test the long-range effectiveness of the advertising, the same 500 people were called 1 month later and again asked if they were using the product.

Let U represent the set of people who were interviewed, F the set of people who said they were using the product on the first call, S the set of people who said they were using the product on the second call, and T the set of people who said they were using the product on the third call. The results of the survey were as follows:

card $F = 135$ card $(F \cap T) = 56$
card $S = 198$ card $(S \cap T) = 123$
card $T = 280$ card $(F \cap S \cap T) = 51$
card $(F \cap S) = 70$

Use a Venn diagram to aid in answering the following questions posed by the company.

(a) How many people in the survey did not use the product at all?

(b) How many of the people in the survey who were using the product at the time of the third call were not using it at the time of the first and second calls?

(c) How many people in the survey were using the product at the time of the first call but were not using it at the time of the second and third calls?

(d) How many people in the survey who were not using the product at the time of the first call were using it at the time of the second and third calls?

8. The report turned in on one survey of the 500 people of problem 7 showed the following results:

card $F = 132$ card $(F \cap T) = 70$
card $S = 167$ card $(S \cap T) = 135$
card $T = 285$ card $(F \cap S \cap T) = 60$
card $(F \cap S) = 95$

The person who turned in the report was fired by the company. Why?

9. In a survey of 100 students at a certain university, the numbers of students studying French, German, and Russian were found to be: French, 47; German, 32; Russian, 21; French and German, 11; French and Russian, 7; Russian and German, 6; and all three languages, 2. Use a Venn diagram to aid in answering the following questions.

(a) How many of the 100 students in the survey were not studying any of the three languages?

(b) How many of the students had Russian as their only language?

(c) How many of the students had French and German but not Russian?

(d) How many had German and Russian but not French?

10. Suppose that of 150 blood samples taken, 52 had A antigen, 45 had B antigen, 18 had both A and B antigens, 117 had Rh antigen, 41 had A and Rh antigens, 36 had B and Rh antigens, and 14 had all three antigens. Use a Venn diagram to answer the following questions. (Recall that a person is doubly classified in reference to type of blood.)

(a) How many of the 150 samples were Rh positive with type A?

(b) How many were Rh negative with type AB?

(c) How many were Rh positive with type O?

(d) How many of the 150 samples were Rh negative with type B?

(e) From the information gathered, what is the most common type of blood?

(f) What is the rarest type of blood?

Section 2.7[1] Application of Set Theory to Classification

We can now analyze an example in which the usefulness of sets in organizing information as well as their computational aspects are demonstrated.

Example 2.7.1 Toxicity of Snakes A biologist, after examining a large number of snakes of a certain poisonous variety, has observed that the toxicity of the snakes' venom varies from one snake to another but that the snakes divide about evenly into those whose venom is extremely toxic and those whose venom is only mildly toxic. He has also observed two easily identifiable physical characteristics of the snakes which seem to vary: (1) the presence or absence of a white streak on the snake's head, and (2) the color of the snake's stripes, which can be classified as either deep brown or greenish brown. Again, for both of these characteristics, there appear to be about an equal number of snakes in each category.

   The scientist feels that if either of these outward characteristics were related to the toxicity of the snakes' venom, this would be a great aid in identifying potentially dangerous snakes and could possibly also be useful in shedding some light on genetic links among these traits.

   To approach the problem he considers a breakdown of the snakes into the following sets:

$$T = \text{snakes with extremely toxic venom}$$
$$W = \text{snakes with a white streak on their heads}$$
$$G = \text{snakes with greenish-brown stripes}$$

It is understood in this breakdown that he is considering a universal set U consisting of all the snakes that he examines. Note that $T \subset U$, $W \subset U$, and $G \subset U$. He sets down the Venn diagram of Figure 2.7.1 and observes that this divides U into eight

Figure 2.7.1

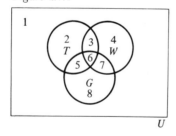

parts, numbered 1 through 8 in the diagram. Each of these portions of U represents one possible combination of the three traits. To list them:

1. $\tilde{T} \cap \tilde{W} \cap \tilde{G}$ = snakes with low toxicity, no white streak, and no green in stripes.
2. $T \cap \tilde{W} \cap \tilde{G}$ = snakes with high toxicity, no white streak, and no green in stripes.
3. $T \cap W \cap \tilde{G}$ = snakes with high toxicity, a white streak, and no green in stripes.
4. $\tilde{T} \cap W \cap \tilde{G}$ = snakes with low toxicity, a white streak, and no green in stripes.
5. $T \cap \tilde{W} \cap G$ = snakes with high toxicity, no white streak, and green in stripes.
6. $T \cap W \cap G$ = snakes with high toxicity, a white streak, and green in stripes.
7. $\tilde{T} \cap W \cap G$ = snakes with low toxicity, a white streak, and green in stripes.
8. $\tilde{T} \cap \tilde{W} \cap G$ = snakes with low toxicity, no white streak, and green in stripes.

[1]This section is optional.

After examining 128 snakes, he finds the following:

$$\text{card } (\check{T} \cap \check{W} \cap \check{G}) = 21$$

$$\text{card } (T \cap \check{W} \cap \check{G}) = 6$$

$$\text{card } (T \cap W \cap \check{G}) = 25$$

$$\text{card } (\check{T} \cap W \cap \check{G}) = 8$$

$$\text{card } (T \cap \check{W} \cap G) = 8$$

$$\text{card } (T \cap W \cap G) = 25$$

$$\text{card } (\check{T} \cap W \cap G) = 12$$

$$\text{card } (\check{T} \cap \check{W} \cap G) = 23$$

The biologist has determined that since each trait is as likely to occur as not, then if they were unrelated, there should be approximately 16 ($= \frac{1}{8} \cdot 128$) snakes in each of these eight sets (more about this in Chapter 4). This is not the case, so he continues his examination of the data. He reasons that if the white streak were related to toxicity, the sets $T \cap W$ and $\check{T} \cap \check{W}$ should have more than their share of snakes. If they were unrelated, that share would be approximately 32 ($= \frac{1}{4} \cdot 128$) snakes in each set. Similarly, if greenish stripes were related to toxicity, the sets $T \cap G$ and $\check{T} \cap \check{G}$ would have more than their expected share of snakes (also 32 for each set).

From the data,

$$\text{card } (T \cap W) = \text{card } (T \cap W \cap G) + \text{card } (T \cap W \cap \check{G})$$

$$= 50$$

$$\text{card } (\check{T} \cap \check{W}) = \text{card } (\check{T} \cap \check{W} \cap G) + \text{card } (\check{T} \cap \check{W} \cap \check{G})$$

$$= 44$$

$$\text{card } (T \cap G) = \text{card } (T \cap W \cap G) + \text{card } (T \cap \check{W} \cap G)$$

$$= 33$$

$$\text{card } (\check{T} \cap \check{G}) = \text{card } (\check{T} \cap W \cap \check{G}) + \text{card } (\check{T} \cap \check{W} \cap \check{G})$$

$$= 29$$

[These equations hold because

$$\text{card } (A \cap B) = \text{card } (A \cap B \cap C) + \text{card } (A \cap B \cap \check{C})$$

See problem 1, Exercises 2.7, for proof of this.]

From this information, the final conclusion is that high toxicity and the appearance of a white streak seem to be related, but high toxicity seems unrelated to the coloration of the stripes.

Exercises for 2.7

1. Let A, B, and C be subsets of a universal set U.
   (a) Prove that $A \cap B = (A \cap B \cap C) \cup (A \cap B \cap \check{C})$.
   (b) Prove that card $(A \cap B) = $ card $(A \cap B \cap C) + $ card $(A \cap B \cap \check{C})$.
2. For reasons of issuing scholarships, the athletic department of a large university ran a survey to determine if there was any correlation between an athlete's ability in the sports of

football, baseball, and basketball. A breakdown into sets of those athletes participating in all three sports was made as follows:

F = athletes earning a letter in football
B = athletes earning a letter in baseball
K = athletes earning a letter in basketball

It is understood in this breakdown that the universal set U is the set of all athletes surveyed who participated in all three sports. In a survey of 56 athletes participating in football, baseball, and basketball, the following facts were observed:

card $(\tilde{F} \cap \tilde{B} \cap \tilde{K}) = 10$

card $(F \cap \tilde{B} \cap \tilde{K}) = 4$

card $(F \cap B \cap \tilde{K}) = 12$

card $(\tilde{F} \cap B \cap \tilde{K}) = 2$

card $(F \cap \tilde{B} \cap K) = 2$

card $(F \cap B \cap K) = 11$

card $(\tilde{F} \cap B \cap K) = 6$

card $(\tilde{F} \cap \tilde{B} \cap K) = 9$

Use the techniques of this section to determine between which two sports—football and basketball, football and baseball, or baseball and basketball—the greatest correlation of an athlete's ability occurs, and also between which two the least correlation occurs.

3. In Example 2.6.7, suppose a survey by the motorcycle company of 100 people showed the following results:

card $(M \cap A \cap C) = 9$

card $(M \cap A \cap \tilde{C}) = 49$

card $(M \cap \tilde{A} \cap C) = 4$

card $(\tilde{M} \cap A \cap C) = 6$

card $(M \cap \tilde{A} \cap \tilde{C}) = 2$

card $(\tilde{M} \cap \tilde{A} \cap C) = 13$

card $(\tilde{M} \cap A \cap \tilde{C}) = 12$

card $(\tilde{M} \cap \tilde{A} \cap \tilde{C}) = 5$

(a) How many married people owned automobiles?
(b) How many people who owned motorcycles were not married?
(c) How many people did not own a car or a motorcycle?
(d) Does there appear to be a positive correlation between a person being married and not owning a motorcycle? Explain.

4. In problem 8, Exercises 2.5, suppose that an analysis of 150 blood samples showed the following results:

card $(R \cap A \cap B) = 13$

card $(R \cap A \cap \tilde{B}) = 30$

card $(R \cap \tilde{A} \cap B) = 21$

card $(\tilde{R} \cap A \cap B) = 3$

card $(R \cap \tilde{A} \cap \tilde{B}) = 51$

card $(\tilde{R} \cap \tilde{A} \cap B) = 6$

card $(\tilde{R} \cap A \cap \tilde{B}) = 8$

card $(\tilde{R} \cap \tilde{A} \cap \tilde{B}) = 18$

where the sets R, A, and B are defined by

$R =$ samples with Rh-positive blood
$A =$ samples of blood with A antigen
$B =$ samples of blood with B antigen

How many of the 150 samples are
(a) Rh positive and have blood containing the A antigen?
(b) Rh negative and have blood containing the B antigen?
(c) type AB?
(d) type O?
(e) type A?
(f) type B?
(g) Rh positive?

Combinatorial Analysis 3

In this chapter various counting techniques will be presented. These techniques are especially useful for certain problems in probability. Counting principles are used to determine the number of ways things can occur. In mathematical terms this means determining cardinalities of sets. Sometimes it is easy to do this: just list the members of the set explicitly and count the members. However, in most important cases the set will be "too big" to list its elements and additional counting procedures must be developed.

Section 3.1   Introduction

We begin this section by introducing several examples of the types of problems that will be encountered.

Example 3.1.1   Telephone Numbers Telephone numbers consist of seven integers. The first two numbers must be between 2 and 9, inclusive. The third number must be between 1 and 9, inclusive. Each of the remaining numbers may lie between 0 and 9, inclusive. How many possible telephone numbers are there?

Example 3.1.2   License Plates Suppose that a state's license plates consist of three letters followed by three numbers: for example, MFT 986. How many different license plates can be manufactured?

Example 3.1.3   Combination Locks A company produces combination locks. The combinations consist of three numbers from 0 to 39. Because of the construction of the lock, no number appears more than once in any combination. For example, 32–8–6 is a possible combination, but 32–8–32 is not. How many locks can be manufactured if they are all to have different combinations?

The solutions to these three problems and to those of a similar type are not difficult once some basic techniques are discussed. Let us begin with a somewhat easier example.

Example 3.1.4 Coin Tossing   A coin is tossed three times and the result recorded after each toss. How many possible outcomes are there?

For convenience we use H and T to represent head and tail, respectively. Then the outcome of a head on the first toss, a tail on the second, and a head on the third, can be represented simply as HTH. In this problem it is quite simple to list all the possibilities explicitly. They are:

$$\begin{array}{ll} \text{HHH} & \text{THH} \\ \text{HHT} & \text{THT} \\ \text{HTH} & \text{TTH} \\ \text{HTT} & \text{TTT} \end{array}$$

So there are eight possible outcomes. In general, it will be difficult to list all possibilities, and hence it is necessary to develop an alternative technique. This technique applied to the above problem is as follows: There are two possibilities for the first toss (H or T). To each of these possibilities there corresponds two possibilities for the second toss (H or T), and to each of these possibilities there corresponds two possibilities for the third toss (see Figure 3.1.1). Consequently, there are $2 \cdot 2 \cdot 2 = 8$

Figure 3.1.1

Toss:	1	2	3
	H or T	H or T	H or T

possible outcomes altogether. A *tree diagram* illustrates this technique nicely (Figure 3.1.2). The number of possibilities can be obtained by counting the number of "branches" at the end of the tree, as illustrated in the figure.

Figure 3.1.2

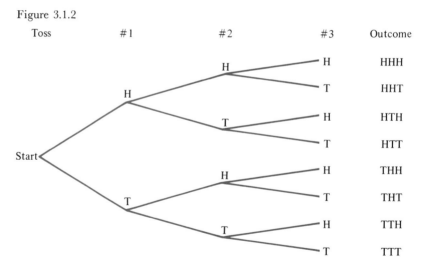

| Toss | #1 | #2 | #3 | Outcome |

To see why we *multiply* the possibilities at each toss ($2 \cdot 2 \cdot 2$), notice that there are two possibilities for the last toss, corresponding to each of the two possibilities for the second toss. Hence there are

$$2 + 2 = 2 \cdot 2$$

possibilities for the last two tosses (explicitly HH, HT, TH, TT). Then because there are two possibilities for the first toss, there are a total of

$$2 \cdot 2 + 2 \cdot 2 = 2(2 \cdot 2) = 2 \cdot 2 \cdot 2$$

possibilities altogether (simply, 2 possibilities for the first, 2 for the second, and 2 for the third).

The next example is of the same type as the one illustrated by Example 3.1.3. It portrays a slightly different type of problem than the coin-tossing example. The method of solution, however, involves the same type of reasoning that was used in the previous example.

Example 3.1.5 Officer Selection The board of directors of a company has selected five executives for candidacy to the positions of vice-president and president. In how many ways can these two appointments be made? (For example, if the five executives are denoted by $a, b, c, d,$ and $e,$ choosing a for president and b for vice-president is one way of choosing, and choosing d for president and a for vice-president is another way of choosing.)

There are five possible choices for president and corresponding to each choice for president there are four possible choices for vice-president (simply, five choices for president, then four choices for vice-president). Thus there are

$$4 + 4 + 4 + 4 + 4 = 5 \cdot 4 = 20$$

possibilities. Graphically, we can illustrate this result by using a tree diagram (Figure 3.1.3). For convenience we represent the five individuals by the letters $a, b, c, d,$ and $e.$

Figure 3.1.3

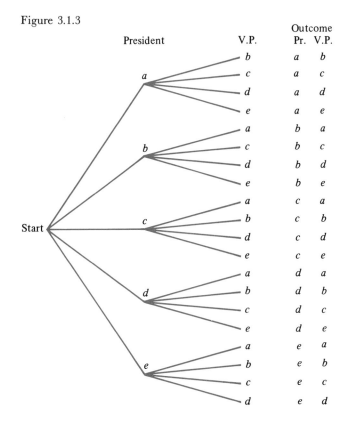

1. A coin is tossed twice and the result recorded after each toss. Let H and T represent head and tail, respectively.
   (a) List, explicitly, the possible outcomes of the experiment.
   (b) Draw a tree diagram for the experiment.

2. A man owns stock. At the end of a given day the value of the stock has either increased in value (I), remained unchanged (U), or decreased in value (D). The man observes the stock for two days and on each day records which of the three possibilities has occurred. For example, UD would represent the fact that the value of the stock remained unchanged the first day and decreased the second day.
   (a) List, explicitly, the possible outcomes.
   (b) Draw a tree diagram to illustrate the possibilities.

3. A person looking for an apartment finds himself with the following choices: a northern (N) or southern (S) exposure; upstairs (U) or downstairs (D); one (1), two (2), or three (3) bedrooms.
   (a) List the possibilities for this person. (For example, $ND2$ represents the person choosing an apartment with a northern exposure which is downstairs and has two bedrooms.)
   (b) Draw a tree diagram that illustrates the possible choices.
   (c) If all of the upstairs apartments have three bedrooms, list the possibilities.

4. The four aces from an ordinary deck of cards are placed in a stack. One ace is selected and its suit recorded. It is not replaced in the stack. Then a second ace is selected and its suit recorded. The following code is used: S, spades; H, hearts; D, diamonds; and C, clubs. Then, for example, DS represents the fact that the first ace drawn is a diamond and the second a spade.
   (a) List, explicitly, the possible outcomes of the experiment.
   (b) Draw a tree diagram that illustrates the possibilities.

5. At a political conference involving the United States (A), Russia (R), and China (C), the three delegates are to be seated.
   (a) List the possible seating arrangements (for example, CAR represents the fact that the Chinese delegate sits in the first chair, the U.S. delegate in the second, and the Russian delegate in the third).
   (b) Illustrate the possibilities via a tree diagram.
   (c) If it is required that the U.S. delegate sit next to the Chinese delegate, list the possibilities.

6. A person eating dinner has three possibilities for the dressing on his salad, two possibilities for the main course, and four choices for a beverage. How many possibilities are open to the person in the variation of his dinner involving the three components?

7. In selecting a house a person has three choices for the model, two choices for the elevation, and two choices for the location.
   (a) Taking these three items into account, how many possibilities are open to the individual?
   (b) Draw a tree diagram that illustrates the choices.

8. A person buying a particular make of car has three choices for the model: two-door, four-door, or convertible. The first two models come with a choice of three interiors; with the third there is only a choice of two.
   (a) List, explicitly, all possibilities open to the person in his selection.
   (b) Illustrate by means of a tree diagram.

Section 3.2   Sequential Counting Principle

Examples 3.1.4 and 3.1.5 illustrate an important counting technique.

Theorem 3.2.1 Sequential Counting Principle

Suppose that two or more actions are performed in a definite order. Assume that there are m possibilities for the first action and that to each of these possibilities corresponds n possibilities for the second action, and that to each of these corresponds p possibilities for the third action, and so on. Then there are $m \cdot n \cdot p \cdots$ possibilities altogether.

We now return to the solution of the first three problems of Section 3.1.

Solution to Example 3.1.1 Choosing a particular telephone number consists of selecting seven integers, the first two of which are between 2 and 9, inclusive; the third of which is between 1 and 9, inclusive; and the next four of which are between 0 and 9, inclusive. We can think of this as filling in the following seven "boxes" with numbers:

☐   ☐   ☐   ☐   ☐   ☐   ☐

The first two boxes can be "filled" with integers between 2 and 9, inclusive; the third with integers between 1 and 9, inclusive; and the other four boxes can be "filled" with integers between 0 and 9, inclusive. For example, if we put a 5 in the first box, a 7 in the second, a 5 in the third, a 2 in the fourth, an 8 in the fifth, a 0 in the sixth, and a 3 in the seventh, we would have

5   7   5   2   8   0   3

and this represents the telephone number 575-2803. If we use the sequential counting principle, we can determine the number of possible telephone numbers as follows. There are 8 possibilities for the first number (2–9), 8 possibilities for the second (2–9), 9 for the third (1–9), 10 for the fourth, 10 for the fifth, 10 for the sixth, and 10 for the seventh:

8 poss.   8 poss.   9 poss.   10 poss.   10 poss.   10 poss.   10 poss.

Hence there are

$$8 \cdot 8 \cdot 9 \cdot 10 \cdot 10 \cdot 10 \cdot 10 = 5,760,000$$

possible telephone numbers.

Notice that although it is "possible" to draw a tree diagram for this problem, it is highly impractical. Indeed, the end of the tree would have 5,760,000 branches.

Solution to Example 3.1.2 Choosing a particular license plate consists of selecting three letters and then three numbers between 0 and 9. As in the previous solution, we can think of this as filling in six boxes, the first three with letters and the last three with numbers:

☐   ☐   ☐   ☐   ☐   ☐

For example, if we put an M in the first box, an F in the second, a T in the third, a 9 in the fourth, an 8 in the fifth, and a 6 in the sixth, we would have

M   F   T   9   8   6

and this represents the license plate MFT 986. By applying the sequential counting principle, we can determine the number of different license plates that it is possible to manufacture. There are 26 possibilities for the first letter, 26 for the second, and 26 for the third; and there are 10 choices for the first number, 10 for the second, and 10 for the third:

26 poss.   26 poss.   26 poss.   10 poss.   10 poss.   10 poss.

Hence by the sequential counting principle there are

$$26 \cdot 26 \cdot 26 \cdot 10 \cdot 10 \cdot 10 = 17{,}576{,}000$$

possible license plates. Again a tree diagram or a direct listing of possibilities is prohibitively complex.

Solution to Example 3.1.3   A lock's combination is determined by three numbers between 0 and 39, inclusive. From the statement of the problem no number can appear more than once in a combination. As before, we can think of choosing a combination by filling in the three boxes

with three *different* numbers from 0 to 39. For example, if we fill in the boxes with the numbers 5, 16, and 37 in that order, we have

5   16   37

which corresponds to the lock with the combination 5–16–37.
    To count the number of possible locks we again use the sequential counting principle. There are 40 choices for the first number (0–39). Since repetitions are forbidden there are 39 choices for the second number, corresponding to each choice for the first. Finally, once the second number is chosen, there are 38 choices for the third number:

40 poss.   39 poss.   38 poss.

Thus by the sequential counting principle there are

$$40 \cdot 39 \cdot 38 = 59{,}280$$

possibilities for combinations.

    The sequential counting principle (Theorem 3.2.1) is basic to all our counting procedures. In the next sections we shall use it to study permutations and combinations.

Exercises for 3.2

1. Use the sequential counting principle to determine the number of possible outcomes for the experiment described in problem 1, Exercises 3.1.
2. Use the sequential counting principle to determine the number of possible outcomes in problem 2, Exercises 3.1.

3. Use the sequential counting principle to determine the number of alternatives open to the person in problem 3(a), Exercises 3.1.
4. Use Theorem 3.2.1 to find the number of possible outcomes for the card experiment in problem 4, Exercises 3.1.
5. Calculate the total number of possible seating arrangements in problem 5(a), Exercises 3.1.
6. Determine the total number of alternatives open to the person described in problem 6, Exercises 3.1.
7. Use the sequential counting principle to calculate the number of possibilities for the individual involved in the house-selection problem of problem 7, Exercises 3.1.
8. A person tosses a coin five times and records the result of each toss. How many possible outcomes are there for this experiment?
9. A pair of dice is rolled. The numbers appearing on the first and second dice are recorded. How many possible outcomes are there?
10. A president, vice-president, and treasurer are to be selected from a group of 10 executives. In how many ways can this be done?
11. In an office building with six vacant offices, four people desire an office. In how many ways can these four people be assigned offices? (Assume that each person requires a different office.)
12. A football team has five quarterbacks, four fullbacks, and four centers. In how many ways can the coach select a starting quarterback, fullback, and center?
13. Letters in the Morse code are obtained by a sequence of dots and dashes with repeats allowed. How many letters can be formed that use
    (a) three symbols?   (b) three or fewer symbols?
14. Assume that people are classified according to sex (male or female), marital status (single, married, divorced), and profession (34 categories). How many possible classifications are there?
15. At a film festival there are 10 films nominated for awards and 8 actors nominated for awards. There are to be first-, second-, and third-place awards for the films and first- and second-place awards for the actors. In how many ways can these awards be presented?
16. How many fraternity names consisting of three letters can be formed by using the 24 letters of the Greek alphabet?
17. Suppose that an examination is given which consists of five true–false and three multiple-choice questions, each of which has four alternatives. In how many ways is it possible to answer the examination?
18. At a bridge tournament there are 12 people, six men and six women. They are to be paired in order to form six *mixed* teams. In how many ways can this be done?
19. If a coin is tossed n times and if the outcome after each toss is recorded, how many possible outcomes are there?
20. If a die is tossed n times and if the outcome after each roll is recorded, how many possible outcomes are there?
21. Suppose that r people are to be seated in n chairs ($r \leq n$), where the chairs are in a row. In how many ways can this be done?
22. Suppose that Social Security numbers consist of nine numbers. Assume that the first two digits must be between 3 and 7, inclusive, and the last seven can be between 0 and 9, inclusive. How many possible Social Security numbers are there?

Section 3.3   Combinations and Permutations: Examples

The following problems are typical of those involving combinations and permutations.

Example 3.3.1 Committee Selection   An intercongressional committee is to consist of five members from the House and Senate combined. In how many ways can a committee be made up consisting of two senators and three representatives if there are 100 senators and 435 representatives altogether?

Example 3.3.2 Bridge A bridge hand consists of 13 cards dealt from an ordinary deck of 52. How many possible bridge hands are there? In how many ways can a person get exactly 6 spades and 5 hearts?

Example 3.3.3 Genetics Proteins are made of folded filaments called polypeptides. The blueprint for construction of these polypeptides is encoded in the long-stranded molecules of the chemical DNA. DNA is composed of two spirals of sugar-phosphate, with sets of base pairs, adenine–thymine and guanine–cytosine, linking them (Figure 3.3.1). The order of the appearance of these base pairs determines the coding, and hence their arrangement is of particular importance.

Figure 3.3.1

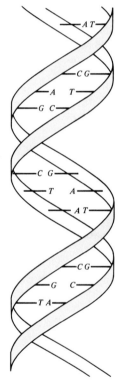

A DNA chain is known to contain 30 base pairs. Because of the pairing, no. As = no. Ts and no. Gs = no. Cs. Chemical analysis of this sample has shown that 12 pairs are A–T and 18 are G–C. In how many different ways can the 12 A–T pairs and 18 G–C pairs be arranged along the length of the DNA?

These problems seem quite complicated. However, by carefully analyzing the problems we can solve them without too much difficulty. Moreover, the method of solution is systematic and can be applied to a wide variety of problems.

In many fields of study the key to solving complicated problems is to break them up into several subproblems, all of which can be handled with relative ease. The solutions to the complicated problems are then obtained by piecing together the methods of solution of the subproblems. We apply this technique to solve the problems presented at the beginning of this section.

Example 3.3.4 Officer Selection The board of directors of a company has selected five executives, from which two will be appointed vice-presidents. Assuming that these vice-presidents have equal duties, how many possibilities are there for the selection of the two vice-presidents?

At first glance this problem may seem to be the same as the one in Example 3.1.5. So we might say that there are 20 possibilities (5 for the first, then 4 for the second). But a little closer look at the situation reveals that this is not the case. To see this, let us, for convenience, designate the executives by the letters a, b, c, d, and e. Now here is the crucial difference from Example 3.1.5. In that example ab would represent the choice of a for president and b for vice-president, and ba would represent the choice of b for president and a for vice-president; two *different* possibilities. However, in the present situation ab and ba represent the same outcome—that a and b are selected to be the two vice-presidents. In other words, in this example *order* makes no difference, whereas in Example 3.1.5 order *does* make a difference. So, instead of writing ab or ba we just write $\{a, b\}$ to represent the selection of a and b as vice-presidents.

It is, in this case, not too much trouble to list all possibilities. They are

$$
\begin{array}{ll}
\{a, b\} & \{b, d\} \\
\{a, c\} & \{b, e\} \\
\{a, d\} & \{c, d\} \\
\{a, e\} & \{c, e\} \\
\{b, c\} & \{d, e\}
\end{array}
\qquad (3.3.1)
$$

Note that, for example, $\{c, b\}$ is not listed, because it is the same as $\{b, c\}$. Both represent the fact that b and c were selected. In any case, we see that there are 10 ways (not 20) of selecting the two vice-presidents.

It should be noted that in Example 3.3.4 we cannot apply the sequential counting principle in the same way as we did to solve the problems in Sections 3.1 and 3.2. In the next few sections a systematic procedure will be developed for handling problems such as that of Example 3.3.4.

Exercises for 3.3

1. From a group of four people (call them a, b, c, d) two people are to be selected to form a subcommittee.
    (a) If the first person selected is to be the chairman and the second the vice-chairman, list the possible subcommittees. (For example, bc means that b is selected as chairman and c as vice-chairman.)
    (b) If the two people selected are to have equal duties, list the possible subcommittees (for example, $\{b, c\}$ means that b and c are selected).
2. A football team has five tackles (call them a, b, c, d, and e). The coach must select two from the five to start in the game.
    (a) If the first one selected is to be the left tackle and the second selected is to be the right tackle, list the possibilities for selection. (For example, bd means that b is selected for left tackle and d for right tackle.)
    (b) Suppose that the coach is not going to designate, at the moment, which person is going

to be left tackle and which is going to be right tackle, but is only interested in selecting two tackles from the five. List the possibilities.
3. A man is interested in five stocks. He decides that he will purchase quantities of three of the five. Denote the stocks by a, b, c, d, and e.
   (a) If he plans to buy \$100 of one stock, \$200 of a second, and \$300 of a third, list his alternatives. (For example, *abc* indicates that he will buy \$100 of stock a, \$200 of stock b, and \$300 of stock c.)
   (b) If he plans to buy \$200 worth of each of the three stocks he selects, list the possible alternatives.
4. A bridge group of six (a, b, c, d, e, f) is to select a team of four people to represent itself at a tournament. List the possible teams that can be selected.
5. A person has four suits and three pairs of shoes. List the possible ways the person can select two suits and two pairs of shoes to take along on a business trip.
6. Suppose that a committee of five is voting on a certain proposition (yes or no). List the possible ways that the outcome can be 3 yes and 2 no. (For example, YNYYN means the first, third, and fourth vote yes and that the second and fifth vote no.)

Section 3.4   Combinations and Permutations: Definitions

In this section we shall define the concepts of combinations and permutations and give some illustrative examples.

Definition
If S is a set with n elements and T is a subset of S that contains k elements, then T is called a *combination* of k elements from the set S with n elements.

A combination of k elements from a set of n elements can be thought of as a way of selecting k objects from a collection of n objects without regard to order. In statistics a combination of k elements from a set S with n elements is called a *sample, without replacement*, of size k from a population of size n.

As the previous examples indicate, what we are really interested in is the *total number* of possible combinations of k elements that can be formed from a set of n elements. The number of possible combinations of k elements from a set of n elements is denoted by

$$_nC_k$$

In Example 3.3.4 each set in Eq. (3.3.1) is a combination of two elements from the set $\{a, b, c, d, e\}$ of five elements. As we have seen, there are 10 such combinations. So $_5C_2 = 10$.

Example 3.4.1   Selecting Extras   A director of a movie needs three extras to play in a certain scene. The casting manager sends the director six actors from which to choose. In how many ways can he select the three extras from the six actors?

First, notice that the order of choice is irrelevant in this problem. Only the group (set) of actors chosen is important. For convenience, we shall denote the actors by the letters a, b, c, d, e, and f. Choosing three from these six is equivalent to forming a subset consisting of three elements from the set $S = \{a, b, c, d, e, f\}$ of six elements. Thus we can rephrase the question as follows: How many combinations of three elements can be formed from a set of six elements?

Here it is not too difficult to list the possibilities explicitly. They are

Figure 3.4.1

$\{a, b, c\}$	$\{b, c, d\}$
$\{a, b, d\}$	$\{b, c, e\}$
$\{a, b, e\}$	$\{b, c, f\}$
$\{a, b, f\}$	$\{b, d, e\}$
$\{a, c, d\}$	$\{b, d, f\}$
$\{a, c, e\}$	$\{b, e, f\}$
$\{a, c, f\}$	$\{c, d, e\}$
$\{a, d, e\}$	$\{c, d, f\}$
$\{a, d, f\}$	$\{c, e, f\}$
$\{a, e, f\}$	$\{d, e, f\}$

We see from the figure that there are 20 possible combinations of three elements from a set of six elements. So $_6C_3 = 20$. In other words, the director has 20 ways to choose the three extras.

Example 3.4.2 Population Preference   A company plans to conduct a survey to determine the population preference among several appliances. The company decides to sample by interviewing 10 people from a population of size 200. How many possibilities are there for the selection of these 10 people, assuming that no person may be selected more than once to be interviewed?

As in Example 3.4.1, the order of choice in this problem is unimportant. Only the collection (set) of people chosen is of any consequence. The question is: How many combinations of 10 elements can be formed from a set of 200 elements?

It is "possible" to proceed as in Example 3.4.1 and just list the possibilities. However, in this case it is quite unrealistic. Indeed, there are 22,451,004,309,013,280 possible combinations of 10 elements that can be formed from a set of 200. (We shall see how to compute this presently.) The point is that in this problem there are *too many possibilities to list*.

The previous example indicates the necessity to develop a formula for counting the number of possible combinations. To obtain this formula we need to introduce the notion of a *permutation*.

Definition
A *permutation* of k $(k \geq 1)$ elements from a set of n elements is any arrangement, *without repetition*, of k elements. Here *order counts*—in combinations order does *not* count.

For convenience we shall denote the number of possible permutations of k elements that can be formed from a set of n elements by

$$_nP_k$$

When we use the sequential counting principle it is not too difficult to count the number of possible permutations of k elements from a set of n elements. Before giving the formula for doing this, we present some examples.

Example 3.4.3   How many possible permutations of three elements can be formed from a set of four elements?

For convenience let the set of four elements be $\{a, b, c, d\}$. A permutation of three elements from this set is any arrangement of three of the letters without repetition (no letter can appear more than once). Some possible permutations of three elements are *abc*, *cda*, and *acb*. Note that *abc* and *acb* are different permutations (*order* matters in permutations). In this case we can use a tree diagram to list all possibilities (Figure 3.4.2). So we see by a direct count that there are 24 possible permutations of three elements that can be formed from a set of four elements. In other words, $_4P_3 = 24$.

Figure 3.4.2

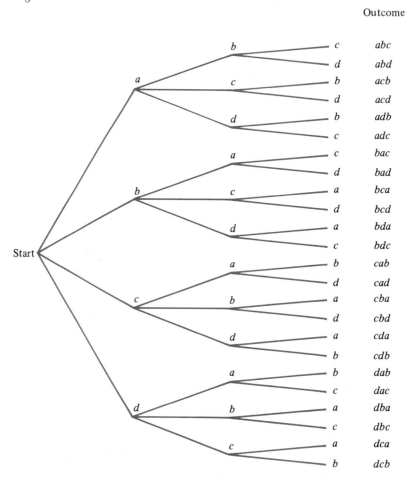

Outcome

We can get this result without resorting to a direct count by using the sequential counting principle. There are four possibilities for the first letter (a, b, c, or d). Once this has been chosen, there are three possibilities for the second letter (repetition is not allowed), and finally there are two possibilities for the third letter:

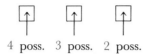

4 poss. 3 poss. 2 poss.

Hence by the sequential counting principle there are

$$4 \cdot 3 \cdot 2 = 24$$

possibilities altogether. (Simply, 4 for the first, then 3 for the second, then 2 for the third.)

Example 3.4.4   How many permutations of five elements can be formed from a set of eight elements?

It is possible, but not very desirable, to solve this problem by using a tree diagram or a direct listing. As in Example 3.4.3, the answer is easy to determine by using the sequential counting principle. There are eight choices for the first element, then seven for the second (no repetition), then six for the third, then five for the fourth, then four for the fifth.

8 poss. 7 poss. 6 poss. 5 poss. 4 poss.

Consequently, there are

$$8 \cdot 7 \cdot 6 \cdot 5 \cdot 4 = 6{,}720$$

possibilities altogether. In other words, there are 6,720 possible permutations of five elements that can be formed from a set of eight elements ($_8P_5 = 6{,}720$).

Example 3.4.5   Behavioral Patterns   A psychologist wants to determine if the behavioral pattern of white rats is affected by the order in which their diet is consumed. If the rats are fed wheat (w), fish (f), and tomatoes (t), in how many ways can the order of their diets be varied?

In mathematical terms the problem is to determine the number of possible permutations of three elements that can be formed from a set of three elements (e.g., *fwt* would represent fish first, wheat second, and tomatoes third). Now we have three possibilities for the first food (i.e., the food to be served first), two possibilities for the second, and one possibility for the third.

3 poss. 2 poss. 1 poss.

Hence, by the sequential counting principle there are

$$3 \cdot 2 \cdot 1 = 6$$

possibilities altogether. In this case it is easy to list the possible permutations explicitly (see Figure 3.4.3). In most situations this will not be the case.

Figure 3.4.3

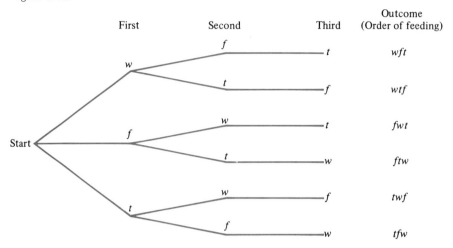

Exercises for 3.4

1. Let $S = \{a, b, c, d\}$.
   (a) List the possible combinations of S that contain
       (1) 1 element   (2) 2 elements
       (3) 3 elements   (4) 4 elements
   (b) List the possible permutations of elements of S that contain
       (1) 1 element   (2) 2 elements
       (3) 3 elements   (4) 4 elements
2. Let $S = \{a, b, c, d, e\}$.
   (a) List the possible combinations of S that contain
       (1) 1 element   (2) 2 elements
       (3) 3 elements   (4) 4 elements
       (5) 5 elements
   (b) List the possible permutations of elements of S that contain
       (1) 1 element   (2) 2 elements
3. By a direct listing of possibilities determine $_nC_k$ when
   (a) $n = 1, k = 1$ (b) $n = 2, k = 1$
   (c) $n = 2, k = 2$ (d) $n = 3, k = 1$
   (e) $n = 3, k = 2$ (f) $n = 3, k = 3$
   (g) $n = 4, k = 1$ (h) $n = 4, k = 2$
   (i) $n = 4, k = 3$ (j) $n = 4, k = 4$
4. By a direct listing of possibilities determine $_nP_k$ when
   (a) $n = 1, k = 1$ (b) $n = 2, k = 1$
   (c) $n = 2, k = 2$ (d) $n = 3, k = 1$
   (e) $n = 3, k = 2$ (f) $n = 3, k = 3$
   (g) $n = 4, k = 1$ (h) $n = 4, k = 2$
   (i) $n = 4, k = 3$ (j) $n = 4, k = 4$
   Solve problems 5–15 *without actually calculating the number* of possibilities but by writing the answers in the form $_nC_k$ or $_nP_k$, whichever is appropriate.
   5. How many possible combinations of three elements can be formed from a set of eight elements? (*Ans.* $_8C_3$)
   6. How many possible permutations of 5 elements can be formed from a set of 15 elements? (*Ans.* $_{15}P_5$)
   7. Determine the number of ways a person can choose 8 free books from a collection of 25.

8. From a collection of 25 (distinguishable) books 8 are to be arranged on a shelf. In how many ways is it possible to do this?
9. In how many ways can six people be seated in six chairs (the chairs are in a row)?
10. In how many ways can a basketball team of 5 people be selected from a group of 10 people?
11. Determine the number of possible poker hands if a poker hand consists of 5 cards from a deck of 52.
12. Find the number of possible bridge hands if a bridge hand consists of 13 cards dealt from a deck of 52.
13. In how many ways can a student select a roster of 4 courses if there are 203 courses available?
14. Suppose that 100 tickets are sold at a lottery and that three winners are to be chosen, all of whom win an equivalent prize. How many possibilities are there for the outcome of the lottery?
15. Suppose that in problem 14 there are first, second, and third prizes given. How many possibilities are there for the outcome of the lottery?

Section 3.5 Counting Permutations

With the preceding examples in mind we now develop a formula for counting permutations. Suppose that S is a set with n elements and let k be a positive integer ($k \leq n$). To count the number of possible permutations of k elements that can be formed from the set S, we can think of filling k boxes with the elements of S with no repetitions allowed.

We have n choices for the first, $n - 1$ for the second, $n - 2$ for the third, ..., $n - k + 2$ for the $(k - 1)$st, and $n - k + 1$ for the kth. Thus by the sequential counting principle there are

$$n \cdot (n - 1) \cdot (n - 2) \cdot \cdots \cdot (n - k + 2) \cdot (n - k + 1)$$

possibilities altogether. Hence the following fact has now been established.

Theorem 3.5.1
The number of possible permutations of k elements that can be formed from a set of n elements is

$$_nP_k = n \cdot (n - 1) \cdot (n - 2) \cdots (n - k + 2) \cdot (n - k + 1) \tag{3.5.1}$$

The notation $_nP_k$ is indicative of the procedure to obtain the number it represents: Start with n and consecutively multiply by the next smallest integer until there are k integers altogether in the product. For example,

$$_4P_2 = 4 \cdot 3 = 12 \qquad _6P_3 = 6 \cdot 5 \cdot 4 = 120 \qquad _8P_5 = 8 \cdot 7 \cdot 6 \cdot 5 \cdot 4 = 6,720$$

There is really no need to memorize Eq. (3.5.1), for it is simply an application of the sequential counting principle. In fact, it is much more important to remember the basic ideas and principles than to memorize formulas.

There is a very important special case of Theorem 3.5.1. It has already been illustrated in Example 3.4.5.

Example 3.5.1 Territorial Assignments A jewelry company has six salesmen covering six different states in the West: Arizona, California, Nevada, Oregon, Utah, and Washington. The company has discovered that when the territories are rotated among the salesmen, the total sales increase. In how many ways can the territories be assigned?

Mathematically, the problem is to determine how many possible permutations of six elements can be formed from a set of six elements. This is, by Theorem 3.5.1 ($n = 6$, $k = 6$),

$$_6P_6 = 6 \cdot 5 \cdot 4 \cdot 3 \cdot 2 \cdot 1 = 720$$

As was pointed out after Theorem 3.5.1, there is no need to memorize. To solve this problem we can just apply the sequential counting principle as before. There are six choices for the salesman who will cover Arizona, then five choices for the one who will cover California, and so on.

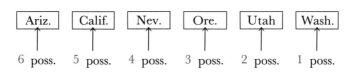

Hence by the sequential counting principle there are

$$6 \cdot 5 \cdot 4 \cdot 3 \cdot 2 \cdot 1 = 720$$

ways that the territories can be assigned.

The special case of Theorem 3.5.1 referred to above and illustrated by Example 3.5.1 is the following:

Corollary 3.5.2
The number of possible permutations of n elements (from a set of n elements) is

$$_nP_n = n \cdot (n - 1) \cdots 2 \cdot 1 \qquad (3.5.2)$$

This is just Theorem 3.5.1 with $k = n$.

It should be pointed out that $_nP_n$ is also the number of possible arrangements of n elements. For example, the three letters a, b, and c can be arranged in $_3P_3 = 3 \cdot 2 \cdot 1 = 6$ ways. They are abc, acb, bac, bca, cab, and cba.

Exercises for 3.5

1. Compute $_nP_k$ when
   (a) $n = 1$, $k = 1$ (b) $n = 2$, $k = 1$
   (c) $n = 2$, $k = 2$ (d) $n = 3$, $k = 1$
   (e) $n = 3$, $k = 2$ (f) $n = 3$, $k = 3$

(g) $n = 4$, $k = 1$ (h) $n = 4$, $k = 2$

(i) $n = 4$, $k = 3$ (j) $n = 4$, $k = 4$

2. Calculate the following numbers.

   (a) $_5P_2$ (b) $_7P_4$

   (c) $_8P_3$ (d) $_4P_4$

   (e) $_{1,000}P_2$ (f) $_6P_6$

3. In how many ways can five (distinguishable) books be arranged on a shelf?

4. An employer is going to assign seven employees to seven different jobs. In how many ways can he make the assignments?

5. A coach of a football team must choose a first-, second-, and third-string quarterback from a group of 15 applicants. How many possible selections are there?

6. An investment company is interested in 25 stocks. It plans to purchase 5 of these stocks, one each week for 5 weeks. In how many ways can these 5 stocks be purchased?

7. A movie critic must select first-, second-, and third-prize winners at a film festival in which 26 movies are entered. How many different winning selections are there?

8. A die is rolled three times. In how many ways can the faces appearing all be different?

Section 3.6   Counting Combinations

We now return to the original problem of trying to count the number of possible combinations of k elements that can be formed from a set of n elements. The formula for doing this will be obtained by applying the sequential counting principle along with our results for counting permutations. The general principle can be illustrated most easily by some simple examples.

Example 3.6.1   How many possible combinations of two elements can be formed from a set of four elements?

For convenience let the set of four elements be $\{a, b, c, d\}$. Let us first list the possible permutations of two elements from the set of four elements. We know from Theorem 3.5.1 that there are

$$_4P_2 = 4 \cdot 3 = 12$$

such permutations. They are

$$\begin{array}{cccc} ab & ba & ca & da \\ ac & bc & cb & db \\ ad & bd & cd & dc \end{array}$$

Rewrite this list as

$$\begin{array}{cccccc} ab & ac & ad & bc & bd & cd \\ ba & ca & da & cb & db & dc \end{array}$$

The possible combinations are

$$\{a, b\} \quad \{a, c\} \quad \{a, d\} \quad \{b, c\} \quad \{b, d\} \quad \{c, d\}$$

Notice that corresponding to each combination of two elements there are $_2P_2 = 2 \cdot 1 = 2$ permutations (the number of possible permutations of two elements). Thus

$$_4C_2 = \frac{_4P_2}{_2P_2} = \frac{4 \cdot 3}{2 \cdot 1} = 6$$

Example 3.6.2 How many possible combinations of three elements can be formed from a set of four elements?

Again for convenience we let the set of four elements be $\{a, b, c, d\}$. There are (Theorem 3.5.1)

$$_4P_3 = 4 \cdot 3 \cdot 2 = 24$$

possible permutations of three elements that can be formed from the set of four. They are

$$
\begin{array}{cccc}
abc & bac & cab & dab \\
abd & bad & cad & dac \\
acb & bca & cba & dba \\
acd & bcd & cbd & dbc \\
adb & bda & cda & dca \\
adc & bdc & cdb & dcb
\end{array}
$$

Let us rewrite these as

$$
\begin{array}{cccc}
abc & abd & acd & bcd \\
acb & adb & adc & bdc \\
bac & bad & cad & cbd \\
bca & bda & cda & cdb \\
cab & dab & dac & dbc \\
cba & dba & dca & dcb
\end{array}
$$

The possible combinations are

$$\{a, b, c\} \qquad \{a, b, d\} \qquad \{a, c, d\} \qquad \{b, c, d\}$$

So to each combination of three elements there corresponds $_3P_3 = 3 \cdot 2 \cdot 1 = 6$ permutations (the number of possible permutations of three elements). Hence

$$_4C_3 = \frac{_4P_3}{_3P_3} = \frac{4 \cdot 3 \cdot 2}{3 \cdot 2 \cdot 1} = 4$$

As can be seen from the last two examples, the general principle for calculating $_nC_k$ is as follows. To each combination of k elements there corresponds $_kP_k$ permutations (the number of possible permutations of k elements). Since there is a total of $_nP_k$ permutations of k elements that can be formed from a set of n elements, it must be that

$$_nP_k = {_kP_k} \cdot {_nC_k}$$

In other words,

$$_nC_k = \frac{_nP_k}{_kP_k}$$

Theorem 3.6.1
The number of possible combinations of k ($k \geq 1$) elements that can be formed from a set of n elements is

$$_nC_k = \frac{_nP_k}{_kP_k} = \frac{n(n-1) \cdots (n-k+1)}{k(k-1) \cdots 1} \tag{3.6.1}$$

In applications, $_nC_k$ is often thought of as the number of ways k objects can be chosen from n objects without regard to order. Formula (3.6.1) gives us an easy way to calculate this number.

Notice that Theorem 3.6.1 gives us a formula for $_nC_k$ only when $k \geq 1$. That is, we do not obtain a formula for $_nC_0$ from Theorem 3.6.1. This is not troublesome, however, because it is easy to figure out what $_nC_0$ equals. Recall that $_nC_0$ is defined to be the number of possible combinations of zero elements that can be formed from a set of n elements. In other words, $_nC_0$ is the number of subsets of zero elements that can be formed from a set of n elements. There is clearly exactly one such subset: $\varnothing$. Consequently, $_nC_0 = 1$.

The last equation also makes sense if $_nC_0$ is interpreted as the number of ways that zero objects can be chosen from n objects without regard to order. There is only one way to do this: do not choose any. So with this interpretation we also get $_nC_0 = 1$. In any event,

$$_nC_0 = 1 \tag{3.6.2}$$

Before proceeding let us apply Eq. (3.6.1) to Examples 3.3.4 and 3.4.1 to check our results. In Example 3.3.4 the problem is to find out how many ways two men can be selected from five. This is just another way of asking how many combinations of two elements can be formed from a set of five. By Eq. (3.6.1) this is

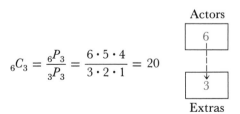

$$_5C_2 = \frac{_5P_2}{_2P_2} = \frac{5 \cdot 4}{2 \cdot 1} = 10$$

which agrees with what we obtained in Example 3.3.4 by listing directly all possible combinations.

In Example 3.4.1 the problem is to determine how many ways three extras can be chosen from six actors. Again, this is just another way of asking how many possible combinations of three elements can be formed from a set of six elements. By listing all possibilities we found the answer to be 20. Using Eq. (3.6.1) it is much easier to arrive at this result:

Actors

6
|
|
↓
3

Extras

$$_6C_3 = \frac{_6P_3}{_3P_3} = \frac{6 \cdot 5 \cdot 4}{3 \cdot 2 \cdot 1} = 20$$

Because of the large numbers involved in Example 3.4.2 we did not attempt to determine, by listing, the number of ways 10 people can be chosen from 200. We can now answer the question posed in Example 3.4.2. The number of ways that the 10 people to be interviewed can be selected from the total of 200 people is just

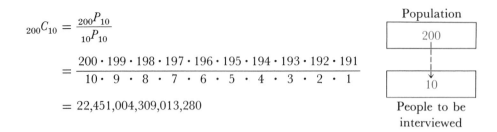

$$_{200}C_{10} = \frac{_{200}P_{10}}{_{10}P_{10}}$$

$$= \frac{200 \cdot 199 \cdot 198 \cdot 197 \cdot 196 \cdot 195 \cdot 194 \cdot 193 \cdot 192 \cdot 191}{10 \cdot 9 \cdot 8 \cdot 7 \cdot 6 \cdot 5 \cdot 4 \cdot 3 \cdot 2 \cdot 1}$$

$$= 22{,}451{,}004{,}309{,}013{,}280$$

Population

| 200 |

People to be
interviewed

Exercises for 3.6

1. Compute $_{n}C_{k}$ when
   (a) $n = 1,\ k = 1$ (b) $n = 2,\ k = 1$
   (c) $n = 2,\ k = 2$ (d) $n = 3,\ k = 1$
   (e) $n = 3,\ k = 2$ (f) $n = 3,\ k = 3$
   (g) $n = 4,\ k = 1$ (h) $n = 4,\ k = 2$
   (i) $n = 4,\ k = 3$ (j) $n = 4,\ k = 4$

2. Calculate the following numbers.
   (a) $_{5}C_{2}$ (b) $_{8}C_{3}$
   (c) $_{7}C_{7}$ (d) $_{10}C_{4}$
   (e) $_{6}C_{5}$ (f) $_{20}C_{2}$
   (g) $_{1,000}C_{1,000}$ (h) $_{100}C_{3}$

3. How many combinations of four elements can be formed from a set of six elements?

4. In how many ways can a subcommittee (all members with equal duties) of 5 people be selected from a committee of 10 people?

5. How many possible poker hands are there if a poker hand consists of 5 cards dealt from a deck of 52?

6. The Internal Revenue Service decides that it will audit the returns of 3 people from a group of 18. How many possible selections are there for the three returns to be audited?

7. An investment company is interested in 25 stocks. It decides to purchase 5 of the 25 stocks. How many possibilities are there for the selection of these 5 stocks?

8. A set consists of 15 elements. How many subsets of this set are there consisting of 4 elements?

9. Let S be a set with card $(S) = 12$. Set $A = \{ T \subset S \mid \text{card}\ (T) = 3 \}$. Find card (A).

10. At a lottery 100 tickets were sold and three prizes are to be given away.
    (a) If the prizes are equivalent, how many possible outcomes are there?
    (b) If there is a first, second, and third prize, how many possible outcomes are there?

11. In the game of keno there are 80 balls numbered 1–80. From these 80 balls, 10 are selected at random. How many possible outcomes are there? (Do not bother to simplify your answer.)

12. (a) At a horse race there are eight gates (positions for the horses). If six horses are to run in a particular race, how many ways can they be placed in the gates assuming that they do *not* all have to be next to one another?
    (b) In part (a), how many ways can the six gates be selected?

Section 3.7   Examples and Applications

We are just about in a position to solve the problems posed in the examples at the beginning of Section 3.3. Before doing so, however, it is useful to introduce the notion of partitions. The following example illustrates the situation.

Example 3.7.1 Committee Selection A group of eight scientists is composed of five psychologists and three sociologists. A committee of five is to be chosen to represent the group at a symposium. In how many ways can the committee be formed?

This is just the number of possible combinations of five elements that can be formed from a set of eight elements (i.e., the number of ways five objects can be selected from eight objects without regard to order). By Theorem 3.6.1 the number of possible committees equals

$$_8C_5 = \frac{_8P_5}{_5P_5} = \frac{8 \cdot 7 \cdot 6 \cdot 5 \cdot 4}{5 \cdot 4 \cdot 3 \cdot 2 \cdot 1} = 56$$

Scientists

8

5

Committee

Suppose that to assure adequate representation, the committee is required to consist of three psychologists and two sociologists. In how many ways can this type of committee be formed?

To solve this problem we combine our results on combinations with the sequential counting principle. The first thing to determine is: In how many ways is it possible to select the three psychologists from the five psychologists? This is just the number of possible combinations of three objects that can be formed from a set of five. Hence there are

$$_5C_3 = \frac{_5P_3}{_3P_3} = \frac{5 \cdot 4 \cdot 3}{3 \cdot 2 \cdot 1} = 10$$

Psychologists

5

3

Psychologists for committee

ways in which the psychologists can be selected.

The next thing to do is to find the number of ways in which the sociologists can be selected. In other words, in how many ways can two objects be chosen from three objects without regard to order? This is just

$$_3C_2 = \frac{_3P_2}{_2P_2} = \frac{3 \cdot 2}{2 \cdot 1} = 3$$

Sociologists

3

2

Sociologists for committee

Consequently, there are three ways in which the sociologists can be chosen.

Now, since each choice of psychologists can be paired with each choice of sociologists there are, by the sequential counting principle,

$$10 \cdot 3 = 30$$

possible committees that can be formed consisting of three psychologists and two sociologists (10 ways to choose the psychologists, 3 ways to choose the sociologists).

If, for convenience, the psychologists are denoted by p_1, p_2, p_3, p_4, p_5 and the sociologists by s_1, s_2, s_3, then, in this case, we can actually list the possible committees consisting of three psychologists and two sociologists (see Figure 3.7.1).

Figure 3.7.1

$\{p_1, p_2, p_3, s_1, s_2\}$	$\{p_1, p_4, p_5, s_1, s_2\}$
$\{p_1, p_2, p_3, s_1, s_3\}$	$\{p_1, p_4, p_5, s_1, s_3\}$
$\{p_1, p_2, p_3, s_2, s_3\}$	$\{p_1, p_4, p_5, s_2, s_3\}$
$\{p_1, p_2, p_4, s_1, s_2\}$	$\{p_2, p_3, p_4, s_1, s_2\}$
$\{p_1, p_2, p_4, s_1, s_3\}$	$\{p_2, p_3, p_4, s_1, s_3\}$
$\{p_1, p_2, p_4, s_2, s_3\}$	$\{p_2, p_3, p_4, s_2, s_3\}$
$\{p_1, p_2, p_5, s_1, s_2\}$	$\{p_2, p_3, p_5, s_1, s_2\}$
$\{p_1, p_2, p_5, s_1, s_3\}$	$\{p_2, p_3, p_5, s_1, s_3\}$
$\{p_1, p_2, p_5, s_2, s_3\}$	$\{p_2, p_3, p_5, s_2, s_3\}$
$\{p_1, p_3, p_4, s_1, s_2\}$	$\{p_2, p_4, p_5, s_1, s_2\}$
$\{p_1, p_3, p_4, s_1, s_3\}$	$\{p_2, p_4, p_5, s_1, s_3\}$
$\{p_1, p_3, p_4, s_2, s_3\}$	$\{p_2, p_4, p_5, s_2, s_3\}$
$\{p_1, p_3, p_5, s_1, s_2\}$	$\{p_3, p_4, p_5, s_1, s_2\}$
$\{p_1, p_3, p_5, s_1, s_3\}$	$\{p_3, p_4, p_5, s_1, s_3\}$
$\{p_1, p_3, p_5, s_2, s_3\}$	$\{p_3, p_4, p_5, s_2, s_3\}$

This problem is most easily handled by visualizing the group of scientists as being *partitioned* into two subgroups, the psychologists and sociologists. Figure 3.7.2 illustrates the situation precisely and enables one to solve the problem quickly and efficiently.

Figure 3.7.2

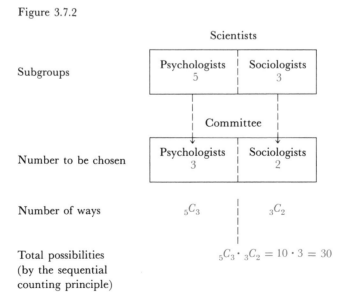

The beauty of the procedure just explained is that it works *no matter how many subgroups are involved*. This decomposes a complicated problem into several easier subproblems.

Solution to Example 3.3.1 This is the same type of problem as the one found in Example 3.7.1. We partition the Congress into two subgroups, the House and Senate (Figure 3.7.3). The two Senators can be chosen from the Senate in $_{100}C_2$ ways and

Figure 3.7.3

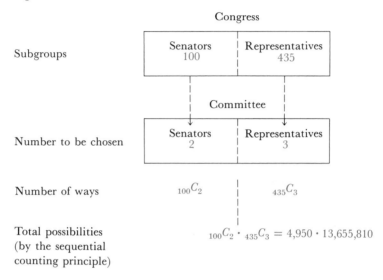

the three Representatives can be chosen from the House in $_{435}C_3$ ways. By the sequential counting principle a committee of two Senators and three Representatives can be selected in

$$_{100}C_2 \cdot {_{435}C_3} = 67,596,259,500$$

ways.

Solution to Example 3.3.2 The first question is: How many possible bridge hands are there? Since the order in which a hand is dealt is irrelevant to what the actual bridge hand is, the question really is: How many ways can 13 cards be chosen from 52 cards without regard to order? This is,

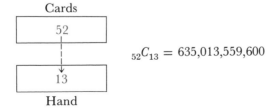

To answer the second question we must apply the technique of partitioning into subgroups. In this case we need to partition into three subgroups: spades, hearts, and others (i.e., clubs and diamonds; Figure 3.7.4). There are $_{13}C_6$ ways to choose the 6 spades from the 13 spades, $_{13}C_5$ ways to choose the 5 hearts from the 13 hearts,

Figure 3.7.4

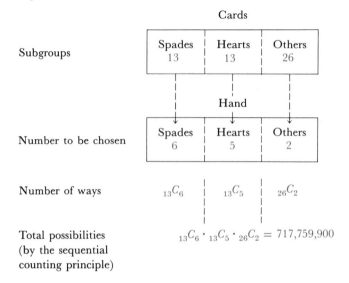

and $_{26}C_2$ ways to choose the 2 cards from the other two suits. Thus, by the sequential counting principle there are

$$_{13}C_6 \cdot _{13}C_5 \cdot _{26}C_2 = 1{,}716 \cdot 1{,}287 \cdot 325 = 717{,}759{,}900$$

possible ways to get a bridge hand with exactly 6 spades and 5 hearts.

Solution to Example 3.3.3 The solution of this problem does not involve partitioning but will be used as a platform for introducing our final type of counting problem. The problem here is to determine how many ways the pairs can be arranged along the length of the DNA. This involves finding how many possibilities there are for the selection of 12 positions for the A–T pairs from the 30 available positions. But this is just the number of ways that 12 objects can be chosen from 30 without regard to order. Thus there are

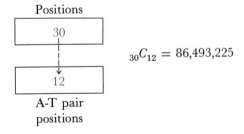

ways that the 12 A–T pairs can be arranged along the length of the DNA.

Now, once the locations of the A–T pairs are selected, this determines the locations of the G–C pairs (the locations not occupied by the A–T pairs). Consequently, there are

$$_{30}C_{12} = 86{,}493{,}225$$

possibilities for the arrangement of the pairs along the length of the DNA.

We now consider a variation of Example 3.3.3.

Example 3.7.2 On one spiral there will be 30 locations available. Because of the chemical analysis we know that the sum of the number of As and Ts on this spiral must be 12 and the sum of the number of Gs and Cs must be 18. In how many ways can the As, Ts, Gs, and Cs be arranged on this spiral if there are 4 As, 8 Ts, 11 Gs, and 7 Cs? To solve this problem we use the results on combinations and the sequential counting principle. The application of these two principles in this case is slightly different from the ones found in Examples 3.3.1 and 3.3.2. First, the positions of the 4 As can be chosen from the 30 positions in $_{30}C_4$ ways. Once this is done there are 26 locations remaining. The locations of the 8 Ts can be selected from these 26 in $_{26}C_8$ ways. Following this selection there are 18 positions remaining, and the 11 Gs positions can be selected from these in $_{18}C_{11}$ ways. Finally there are seven locations remaining. The positions of the 7 Cs can be selected from these locations in $_7C_7 = 1$ way (remember which particular Cs are in which positions is irrelevant once the positions for all are selected—the Cs are indistinguishable). Consequently, by the sequential counting principle there are

$$_{30}C_4 \cdot {}_{26}C_8 \cdot {}_{18}C_{11} \cdot {}_7C_7 = 27{,}405 \cdot 1{,}562{,}275 \cdot 31{,}824 \cdot 1$$
$$= 1{,}362{,}517{,}394{,}238{,}000$$

possible ways to arrange the 4 As, 8 Ts, 11 Gs, and 7 Cs on the spiral.

As in our other examples, a schematic representation (Figure 3.7.5) of the procedure is extremely helpful.

Figure 3.7.5

	A	T	G	C
Chemical remaining				
Positions remaining	30	26	18	7
No. positions to be selected	4	8	11	7
No. ways positions can be selected	$_{30}C_4$	$_{26}C_8$	$_{18}C_{11}$	$_7C_7$
Total possibilities	$_{30}C_4 \cdot {}_{26}C_8 \cdot {}_{18}C_{11} \cdot {}_7C_7 =$			
(by sequential counting principle)	1,362,517,394,238,000			

We give one last illustration of our final type of counting problem.

Example 3.7.3 Political Sampling In a political poll 25 people were interviewed and asked whether or not they planned to vote for the incumbent in a mayoral race. The results were that 12 people responded "yes," 8 responded "no," and 5 responded "undecided." In how many ways could this result occur?

One way the result could occur is that the first 12 people interviewed answered "yes," the second 8 answered "no," and the final 5 answered "undecided." However, there are many other possibilities.

To determine the number of possibilities we can think of the people interviewed as 25 locations and of filling these locations with ys, ns, and us in such a way that 12 of the locations contain ys, 8 contain ns, and 5 contain us. The problem is then to figure out in how many ways this can be done.

1	2	3	$\cdots$	25
y	u	y	$\cdots$	n

We argue as in Example 3.7.2. There are $_{25}C_{12}$ ways to choose the locations of the 12 ys. Once this is done, there are 13 locations remaining. Consequently, there are $_{13}C_8$ ways to choose the locations of the 8 ns from the 13 locations remaining. Finally, there are 5 locations remaining. The locations of the 5 us must then be in these locations (the locations of the 5 us can be selected from the 5 remaining locations in $_5C_5 = 1$ way). By the sequential counting principle there are

$$_{25}C_{12} \cdot {_{13}C_8} \cdot {_5C_5} = 5,200,300 \cdot 1,287 \cdot 1$$
$$= 6,692,786,100$$

ways the result could occur.

Schematically, we have Figure 3.7.6.

Figure 3.7.6

	Response		
	Yes	No	Undecided
Locations remaining	25	13	5
No. locations to be selected	12	8	5
No. ways locations can be selected	$_{25}C_{12}$	$_{13}C_8$	$_5C_5$
Total possibilities	$_{25}C_{12} \cdot {_{13}C_8} \cdot {_5C_5} =$		
(by sequential counting principle)	6,692,786,100		

Exercises for 3.7

Use the method of partitioning introduced in Example 3.7.1 to solve the following problems.

1. From a group of 10 men and 8 women a bridge team of 4 people is to be selected.
   (a) How many possible teams are there?
   (b) If the team is to consist of 2 men and 2 women, how many possible teams can be formed?
2. A company is going to purchase 5 cars and 2 trucks from a group of 7 cars and 4 trucks. How many possibilities are there for the selection?
3. A bridge hand consists of 13 cards dealt from a deck of 52. In how many ways can a person be dealt a bridge hand in which there are exactly 4 aces, 3 kings, 2 queens, and 2 jacks?
4. In a small college the number of professors in the life, social, and management sciences is 4, 5, and 7, respectively. A committee of 6 is to be chosen from this group of 16 individuals.
   (a) How many possible committees are there?
   (b) If the committee is to consist of 1, 2, and 3 people, from the life, social, and management sciences departments, respectively, in how many ways can the committee be formed?
   (c) If the only restriction is that there be three people from the management sciences department, how many different committees can be formed?
5. A shipment of 80 television sets is known to contain 10 that are defective according to some specifications. Suppose that 15 sets are selected at random from the 80. (Do not simplify.)
   (a) How many different selections are possible?
   (b) In how many ways is it possible for *none* of the sets selected to be defective?
   (c) In how many ways is it possible for the sample of 15 sets to contain all the defective ones?
   (d) How many different samples of 15 sets are possible which contain exactly 3 defective ones?

6. A legislative committee consists of 10 Democrats, 8 Republicans, and 2 independents. A subcommittee of 6 people is to be selected.
   (a) How many possible subcommittees can be formed?
   (b) How many possible subcommittees can be formed which contain no Democrats?
   (c) If the subcommittee is to consist only of Democrats, how many possibilities exist?
   (d) How many possible committees can be formed consisting of 3 Democrats, 2 Republicans, and 1 independent?
7. A poker hand consists of 5 cards dealt from a deck of 52.
   (a) How many possible poker hands are there?
   (b) A full house, "aces over fives," is a poker hand that consists of 3 aces and 2 fives. How many possible ways can a person have this hand?
   (c) In how many ways can a person get exactly 3 aces and 1 king in a poker hand?
   (d) In how many ways can a person get two pairs, that is, a hand of the form $xxyyz$, where the xs, ys, and z are distinct denominations? (This is tricky.)
   (e) In how many ways can a person get a flush (i.e., all 5 cards of the same suit)?

Use the methods introduced in Examples 3.7.2 and 3.7.3 to solve problems 8–11.

8. From a group of 50 basketball players, 5 are to be selected as centers, 10 as forwards, and 10 as guards. In how many ways can this be done?
9. From the Senate (100 members) there are 4 committees to be formed. They are to consist of 10, 7, 15, and 8 members, respectively. If no Senator is permitted to serve on more than one committee, in how many ways can these committees be formed?
10. A die is rolled 8 times. In how many ways can the die come up 4 twice, 5 thrice, 6 once, and 1 twice?
11. A company employs 10 stenographers:
    (a) If 3 are to be assigned to the executive suite, 3 to the marketing department, and 4 to a general stenographic pool, in how many different ways can they be assigned?
    (b) If the 3 in the executive suite are to be assigned to the president, executive vice-president, and financial vice-president, with the remaining 7 assigned as in part (a), in how many different ways can they now be assigned?
    (c) If the 3 in the executive suite are to be assigned as in part (b), the 3 in the marketing department are to be assigned to the general manager, manager for domestic marketing, and manager for foreign marketing, and the remaining 4 to a general stenographic pool, in how many different ways can they be assigned?
12. (a) The manager of a baseball team with 8 pitchers, 3 catchers, and 10 outfielders must select a starting pitcher and catcher and three starting outfielders. At the present time he is *not* going to designate which outfielders will play left, center, and right fields. How many possible selections are there?
    (b) Suppose that the situation is as in part (a) except that the manager is going to designate which fields the outfielders are to play. How many possible selections are there for the pitcher, catcher, and the three outfielders?
13. A teacher is going to make up an examination consisting of questions from past exams. On the old exams there are a total of 50 true–false questions and 80 multiple-choice questions. The exam to be made up is to consist of 25 questions.
    (a) How many possible exams can be constructed?
    (b) How many possible exams can be constructed consisting of exactly 13 true–false questions?
    (c) How many possible exams can be constructed consisting of all true–false questions?
14. (a) From a group of 30 football players, 8 are to be selected as quarterbacks, 7 as fullbacks, and 4 as centers. In how many ways can this be done?
    (b) Suppose that the group of 30 football players consists of 15 quarterbacks, 9 fullbacks, and 6 centers. Assume that the 8 quarterbacks to be selected must be chosen from the 15 quarterbacks, the 7 fullbacks from the 9 fullbacks, and the 4 centers from the 6 centers. How many different selections are possible?

Section 3.8 Factorial Notation and Binomial Coefficients

In the development of the counting techniques in Section 3.5 it was proved that the number of possible permutations of n elements is

$$_nP_n = n \cdot (n-1) \cdots 2 \cdot 1$$

(Corollary 3.5.2). This number arises so frequently in mathematics that it is given a special name.

Definition
If n is a positive integer, we define $n!$ (read "n factorial") by

$$n! = n \cdot (n-1) \cdots 2 \cdot 1$$

For example, $3! = 3 \cdot 2 \cdot 1 = 6$, $4! = 4 \cdot 3 \cdot 2 \cdot 1 = 24$, and $5! = 5 \cdot 4 \cdot 3 \cdot 2 \cdot 1 = 120$. It is convenient to define $0!$. Although one might think that it should be defined to be equal to zero, it will be seen that the proper convention is to define $0! = 1$.
  Now notice that, for example,

$$6! = 6 \cdot \underbrace{5 \cdot 4 \cdot 3 \cdot 2 \cdot 1} = 6 \cdot 5!$$

$$6! = 6 \cdot 5 \cdot \underbrace{4 \cdot 3 \cdot 2 \cdot 1} = 6 \cdot 5 \cdot 4!$$

$$6! = 6 \cdot 5 \cdot 4 \cdot \underbrace{3 \cdot 2 \cdot 1} = 6 \cdot 5 \cdot 4 \cdot 3!$$

and so on. This illustrates the following fact.

Proposition 3.8.1
If n is a positive integer,

$$n! = n \cdot (n-1)! \tag{3.8.1}$$

More generally, if k is a positive integer with $k \leq n$,

$$n! = n \cdot (n-1) \cdots (n-k+1) \cdot (n-k)! \tag{3.8.2}$$

PROOF

The proof follows the illustration above.

$$n! = n \cdot (n-1) \cdots (n-k+1) \cdot \underbrace{(n-k)(n-k-1) \cdots 2 \cdot 1}$$

$$= n \cdot (n-1) \cdots (n-k+1) \cdot (n-k)!$$

This proves Eq. (3.8.2). Notice that Eq. (3.8.1) is a special case of Eq. (3.8.2) with $k = 1$.

  Factorial notation and Proposition 3.8.1 will now be used to develop convenient ways to write the formulas for $_nP_k$ and $_nC_k$. First let us consider $_nP_k$. To illustrate the general idea, we work with a special case, say $_8P_5$ (i.e., $n = 8$, $k = 5$). By Theorem 3.5.1 it is known that

$$_8P_5 = 8 \cdot 7 \cdot 6 \cdot 5 \cdot 4$$

Multiplying numerator and denominator of this by 3! and using Proposition 3.8.1 gives

$$_8P_5 = 8 \cdot 7 \cdot 6 \cdot 5 \cdot 4 = \frac{8 \cdot 7 \cdot 6 \cdot 5 \cdot 4 \cdot 3!}{3!}$$

$$= \frac{8!}{3!} = \frac{8!}{(8-5)!}$$

A special case of the following proposition has now been proved.

Proposition 3.8.2

If n and k are positive integers with $k \le n$,

$$_nP_k = \frac{n!}{(n-k)!} \tag{3.8.3}$$

PROOF

By Theorem 3.5.1 and Proposition 3.8.1 we conclude that

$$_nP_k = n \cdot (n-1) \cdots (n-k+1)$$

$$= n \cdot (n-1) \cdots (n-k+1) \cdot \frac{(n-k)!}{(n-k)!}$$

$$= \frac{n \cdot (n-1) \cdots (n-k+1) \cdot (n-k)!}{(n-k)!}$$

$$= \frac{n!}{(n-k)!}$$

For example,

$$_7P_4 = \frac{7!}{3!} \qquad _{11}P_6 = \frac{11!}{5!}$$

$$_{10}P_7 = \frac{10!}{3!} \qquad _4P_3 = \frac{4!}{1!}$$

When calculating $_nP_k$ it is usually more convenient to use Eq. (3.5.1) than Eq. (3.8.3). However, for theoretical purposes and some computational purposes, Eq. (3.8.3) is often superior.

Next, consider $_nC_k$. As before, the general principle is illustrated by a specific example, say $_8C_5$. First, by Theorem 3.6.1,

$$_8C_5 = \frac{_8P_5}{_5P_5} = \frac{8 \cdot 7 \cdot 6 \cdot 5 \cdot 4}{5 \cdot 4 \cdot 3 \cdot 2 \cdot 1}$$

Multiplying numerator and denominator by 3! and using Proposition 3.8.1, we obtain

$$_8C_5 = \frac{8 \cdot 7 \cdot 6 \cdot 5 \cdot 4}{5 \cdot 4 \cdot 3 \cdot 2 \cdot 1} = \frac{8 \cdot 7 \cdot 6 \cdot 5 \cdot 4 \cdot 3!}{5 \cdot 4 \cdot 3 \cdot 2 \cdot 1 \cdot 3!}$$

$$= \frac{8!}{5!3!}$$

The general result is

Proposition 3.8.3

Let n be a positive integer and k a positive integer with $k \le n$. Then

$$_nC_k = \frac{n!}{k!(n-k)!} \qquad (3.8.4)$$

PROOF

The proof proceeds as does the special case above. By Corollary 3.5.2 and the definition of factorial we know that $_kP_k = k!$. By Proposition 3.8.2,

$$_nP_k = \frac{n!}{(n-k)!}$$

Hence, by Theorem 3.6.1,

$$_nC_k = \frac{_nP_k}{_kP_k} = \frac{n!/(n-k)!}{k!} = \frac{n!}{k!(n-k)!}$$

Some examples of Eq. (3.8.4) are

$$_5C_3 = \frac{5!}{3!2!} \qquad _8C_6 = \frac{8!}{6!2!}$$

$$_7C_4 = \frac{7!}{4!3!} \qquad _{11}C_{11} = \frac{11!}{11!0!}$$

In this case, as in Eq. (3.8.3), it is usually more convenient to use Eq. (3.6.1) instead of Eq. (3.8.4) when calculating $_nC_k$. However, formula (3.8.4) is often useful theoretically.

Now, Proposition 3.8.3 was proved for k a *positive* integer. Also, we know from Eq. (3.6.2) that $_nC_0 = 1$. The question is: Does Eq. (3.8.4) work for $k = 0$? The answer to this question is *yes*, because of the convention that $0! = 1$. Indeed,

$$\frac{n!}{0!(n-0)!} = \frac{n!}{1 \cdot n!} = 1 = {_nC_0}$$

Consequently, Eq. (3.8.4) holds for any positive integer n and for any *nonnegative* integer $k \le n$.

In mathematical literature there is a special notation for

$$\frac{n!}{k!(n-k)!}$$

It is $\binom{n}{k}$. That is, by definition,

$$\binom{n}{k} = \frac{n!}{k!(n-k)!} \qquad (3.8.5)$$

for n a positive integer and k a nonnegative integer with $k \le n$. For example,

$$\binom{4}{3} = \frac{4!}{3!1!} = 4 \qquad \binom{10}{0} = \frac{10!}{0!10!} = 1$$

$$\binom{7}{2} = \frac{7!}{2!5!} = 21 \qquad \binom{8}{8} = \frac{8!}{8!0!} = 1$$

According to Proposition 3.8.3,

$$\binom{n}{k} = {}_nC_k$$

That is, $\binom{n}{k}$ is the number of possible combinations of k elements that can be formed from a set of n elements. Thus $\binom{n}{k}$ and ${}_nC_k$ are two different notations for the same quantity. Both of these notations will be used throughout the text. The numbers $\binom{n}{k}$ are called *binomial coefficients*. A table of binomial coefficients is presented in Table 1 in Appendix B.

Exercises for 3.8

1. Evaluate the following numbers.
   (a) $1!$ (b) $2!$
   (c) $6!$ (d) $0!$
   (e) $7!$ (f) $8!$
2. Evaluate the following.
   (a) $3!3!$ (b) $8!/6!$
   (c) $4! - 5!$ (d) $4! + 5!$
   (e) $6!/(3! + 3!)$ (f) $6!/(3 + 3)!$
3. Calculate the numbers.
   (a) $5!$ (b) $5 \cdot 4!$
   (c) $5 \cdot 4 \cdot 3!$ (d) $5! \cdot 4!$
   (e) $5! \cdot 4! \cdot 3!$ (f) $5! \cdot 0!$
4. Compute the following quantities.
   (a) $6!/3!$ (b) $(6/3)!$
   (c) $100!/98!$ (d) $98!/100!$
   (e) $1,000!/998!$ (f) $10,000!/9,999!$
5. Write the quantities in terms of factorial notation.
   (a) ${}_5P_3$ (b) ${}_6P_5$
   (c) ${}_6P_6$ (d) ${}_{100}P_{20}$
   (e) ${}_{1,000}P_{50}$ (f) ${}_{10}P_4$
6. Exhibit the numbers in factorial notation.
   (a) ${}_5C_3$ (b) ${}_6C_5$
   (c) ${}_6C_6$ (d) ${}_{100}C_{20}$
   (e) ${}_{100}C_{50}$ (f) ${}_{10}C_4$
7. Evaluate the quantities.

   (a) $\binom{5}{2}$ (b) $\binom{6}{4}$

   (c) $\binom{8}{2}$ (d) $\binom{8}{6}$

   (e) $\binom{4}{2}$ (f) $\binom{4}{3}$

   (g) $\binom{1,000}{1}$ (h) $\binom{1,000}{999}$

   (i) $\binom{10,000}{0}$ (j) $\binom{100,000}{100,000}$

8. What is $\binom{n}{k} \cdot k!$?

9. In general, which is larger: $\binom{n}{k}$ or $_nP_k$?

10. Show that for any positive integer n and each nonnegative integer $k \leq n$

$$\binom{n}{k} = \binom{n}{n-k}$$

11. Write the following quantities in terms of factorials.

(a) $\binom{7}{2} \cdot \binom{5}{3} \cdot \binom{2}{2}$

(b) $\binom{10}{3} \cdot \binom{7}{2} \cdot \binom{5}{1} \cdot \binom{4}{4}$

(c) $\binom{15}{2} \cdot \binom{13}{4} \cdot \binom{9}{5} \cdot \binom{4}{1} \cdot \binom{3}{2} \cdot \binom{1}{1}$

12. Assume that n_1, n_2, n_3, and n_4 are positive integers and let $n = n_1 + n_2 + n_3 + n_4$. Show that

$$\binom{n}{n_1} \cdot \binom{n - n_1}{n_2} \cdot \binom{n - n_1 - n_2}{n_3} \cdot \binom{n - n_1 - n_2 - n_3}{n_4} = \frac{n!}{n_1! n_2! n_3! n_4!}$$

[The number

$$\frac{n!}{n_1! n_2! n_3! n_4!}$$

is called a multinomial coefficient and is frequently denoted by

$$\binom{n}{n_1, n_2, n_3, n_4}]$$

Section 3.9[1] The Binomial Theorem

One of the most important results concerning the binomial coefficients is the famous binomial theorem. The binomial theorem gives a formula for expanding algebraic expressions of the form $(a + b)^n$. Two of the formulas that arise from the binomial theorem, with which you may be familiar, are

$$(a + b)^2 = a^2 + 2ab + b^2 \tag{3.9.1}$$
$$(a + b)^3 = a^3 + 3a^2b + 3ab^2 + b^3 \tag{3.9.2}$$

Formula (3.9.2) will now be examined in detail to motivate the general formula (the binomial theorem).

First, by definition,

$$(a + b)^3 = (a + b)(a + b)(a + b)$$

The expression on the right is expanded by applying the axioms of arithmetic (i.e., associative, commutative, and distributive laws). The result is the right-hand side of Eq. (3.9.2). This can also be obtained as follows. From each of the three factors

---

[1] This section is optional.

$(a + b)(a + b)(a + b)$, choose either an a or a b. Then multiply these three letters together. For example, if b is chosen from the first factor, a from the second, and b from the third, we get

$$b \cdot a \cdot b = ab^2$$

Perform the procedure indicated above in all possible ways and then add all the terms obtained. This will also give the right-hand side of Eq. (3.9.2). The details are indicated below.

First, notice that there will be eight terms. For there are two choices for the first letter (a or b), 2 for the second, and 2 for the third. Hence by the sequential counting principle there are $2 \cdot 2 \cdot 2 = 8$ possibilities.

Notice, however, that some of the possibilities yield the same result. A tree diagram is helpful (Figure 3.9.1). Summing the products obtained in the right-hand column

Figure 3.9.1

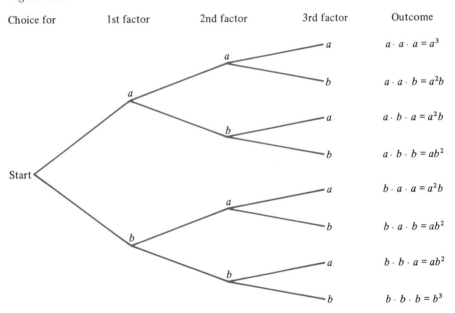

| Choice for | 1st factor | 2nd factor | 3rd factor | Outcome |

$a \cdot a \cdot a = a^3$

$a \cdot a \cdot b = a^2b$

$a \cdot b \cdot a = a^2b$

$a \cdot b \cdot b = ab^2$

$b \cdot a \cdot a = a^2b$

$b \cdot a \cdot b = ab^2$

$b \cdot b \cdot a = ab^2$

$b \cdot b \cdot b = b^3$

of the tree diagram yields

$$a^3 + a^2b + a^2b + ab^2 + a^2b + ab^2 + ab^2 + b^3$$
$$= a^3 + 3a^2b + 3ab^2 + b^3 \qquad (3.9.3)$$

which is the right-hand side of Eq. (3.9.2). This proves formula (3.9.2).

As was pointed out before, different choices for the factors may yield the same products. For example, a, a, b and a, b, a both yield the product a^2b. These like products are all combined in the final expression [see Eq. (3.9.3)]. In any event, as far as the final product is concerned, the only thing of importance is the number of times each letter is chosen—from which factors the letters are selected is of no consequence. For example, if 1 a and 2 bs are chosen, the final product will be ab^2.

An alternative derivation of Eq. (3.9.2) will now be given. This derivation can be easily extended to the general case. The terms that appear in the final expression are as follows:

No. as selected	No. bs selected	Final term
3	0	a^3
2	1	a^2b
1	2	ab^2
0	3	b^3

The problem is to "count" the number of times each of these final terms appears. As before, it is convenient to think of selecting the letters from the factors as filling in the three boxes

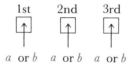

with as and bs. We shall keep track of things by the number of bs to be selected (i.e., how many boxes will be occupied by bs).

The first term on the list is a^3. This appears if the number of bs selected is zero. This can happen in as many ways as zero boxes can be chosen from the three for the locations of the bs— $\binom{3}{0} = 1$.

$$\boxed{a} \quad \boxed{a} \quad \boxed{a}$$

The second term on the list is a^2b. This appears if the number of bs selected is 1. The number of ways this can be done is just the number of ways one box can be chosen from three for the location of the b. This can be done in $\binom{3}{1} = 3$ ways.

$$\boxed{a}\ \boxed{a}\ \boxed{b} \quad \text{or} \quad \boxed{a}\ \boxed{b}\ \boxed{a} \quad \text{or} \quad \boxed{b}\ \boxed{a}\ \boxed{a}$$

The third term is ab^2. This appears if there are 2 bs selected. The number of ways this can be done is the number of ways two boxes for the locations of the bs can be selected from the three. This can be done in $\binom{3}{2} = 3$ ways:

$$\boxed{a}\ \boxed{b}\ \boxed{b} \quad \text{or} \quad \boxed{b}\ \boxed{a}\ \boxed{b} \quad \text{or} \quad \boxed{b}\ \boxed{b}\ \boxed{a}$$

Finally, b^3 appears if all three boxes are filled with bs. This can happen in as many ways as three boxes can be chosen from three without regard to order— $\binom{3}{3} = 1$.

$$\boxed{b} \quad \boxed{b} \quad \boxed{b}$$

In summary, we have the following:

Final term	No. ways it can occur
a^3	$\binom{3}{0} = 1$
$a^2 b$	$\binom{3}{1} = 3$
ab^2	$\binom{3}{2} = 3$
b^3	$\binom{3}{3} = 1$

Consequently,

$$(a + b)^3 = \binom{3}{0}a^3 + \binom{3}{1}a^2 b + \binom{3}{2}ab^2 + \binom{3}{3}b^3 \tag{3.9.4}$$
$$= a^3 + 3a^2 b + 3ab^2 + b^3$$

which is Eq. (3.9.2).

The same type of argument leading to Eq. (3.9.4) can be used to prove the binomial theorem.

Theorem 3.9.1   The Binomial Theorem

Let n be a positive integer and a, b real numbers. Then

$$(a + b)^n = \binom{n}{0}a^n + \binom{n}{1}a^{n-1}b + \binom{n}{2}a^{n-2}b^2$$
$$+ \cdots + \binom{n}{n-1}ab^{n-1} + \binom{n}{n}b^n \tag{3.9.5}$$

PROOF

We proceed as in the case $n = 3$. Let k be any nonnegative integer with $k \leq n$. It must be determined how many times the term $a^{n-k}b^k$ occurs in the expansion of $(a + b)^n$. Again, think of filling n locations with as and bs.

$$\begin{array}{cccc} 1 & 2 & n-1 & n \\ \square & \square & \cdots \quad \square & \square \end{array}$$

Now, the product of the letters chosen will be $a^{n-k}b^k$ if and only if exactly k locations are filled with bs (i.e., if b is chosen from exactly k of the n factors). This occurs in as many ways as the k locations for the bs can be chosen from the n locations. But this can be done in $\binom{n}{k}$ ways. Consequently, $a^{n-k}b^k$ appears $\binom{n}{k}$ times in the expansion of $(a + b)^n$. Thus

$$(a + b)^n = \binom{n}{0}a^n + \binom{n}{1}a^{n-1}b + \binom{n}{2}a^{n-2}b^2$$
$$+ \cdots + \binom{n}{n-1}ab^{n-1} + \binom{n}{n}b^n$$

which is Eq. (3.9.5).

Now, Eqs. (3.9.1) and (3.9.2) are special cases of Eq. (3.9.5) with $n = 2$ and $n = 3$, respectively. When, for example, we use $n = 4$ in Eq. (3.9.5) we find that

$$(a + b)^4 = \binom{4}{0}a^4 + \binom{4}{1}a^3b + \binom{4}{2}a^2b^2$$
$$+ \binom{4}{3}ab^3 + \binom{4}{4}b^4$$

or $\qquad (a + b)^4 = a^4 + 4a^3b + 6a^2b^2 + 4ab^3 + b^4$

An important special case of the binomial theorem is obtained by choosing $a = 1 - p$ and $b = p$, where $0 \le p \le 1$. Then

$$[(1 - p) + p]^n = \binom{n}{0}(1 - p)^n + \binom{n}{1}(1 - p)^{n-1}p$$
$$+ \cdots + \binom{n}{n-1}(1 - p)p^{n-1} + \binom{n}{n}p^n$$

Since $[(1 - p) + p]^n = 1^n = 1$, the following result is valid.

Corollary 3.9.2

If n is a positive integer and p is a real number with $0 \le p \le 1$, then

$$\binom{n}{0}(1 - p)^n + \binom{n}{1}p(1 - p)^{n-1} + \binom{n}{2}p^2(1 - p)^{n-2}$$

$$+ \cdots + \binom{n}{n-1}p^{n-1}(1 - p) + \binom{n}{n}p^n = 1$$

(3.9.6)

This corollary is crucial to the discussion of the binomial distribution—one of the most important distributions in probability.

Exercises for 3.9

1. Use Theorem 3.9.1 to expand the following algebraic expressions.
   (a) $(a + b)^5$ (b) $(x + y)^6$
2. Proceed as in problem 1 to find
   (a) $(1 + x)^4$ (b) $(y + 2)^5$
3. Use Theorem 3.9.1 to find
   (a) $(x - y)^3$ (*Hint:* $(x - y)^3 = [x + (-y)]^3$.)
   (b) $(1 - x)^3$
   (c) $(2 - x)^4$
   (d) $(x - 2)^4$
4. Use the binomial theorem to evaluate
   (a) $(3a + 2b)^3$
   (b) $(2x - 3y)^4$
   (c) $\left(\dfrac{u}{2} + \dfrac{v}{3}\right)^5$
5. Find the coefficient of x^2y^4 in the expansion of $(x + y)^6$.
6. Determine the coefficient of a^3b^5 in the expansion of $(a - b)^8$. (*Hint:* $(a - b)^8 = [a + (-b)]^8$.)
7. Find the coefficient of x^7 in the expansion of $(2 + x)^{10}$.

8. Determine the coefficient of u^5 in the expansion of $(u - 3)^8$.
9. Find the coefficient of u^4v^3 in the expansion of $[2u - (v/3)]^7$.
10. Show that for each positive integer n,

$$\binom{n}{0} + \binom{n}{1} + \cdots + \binom{n}{n-1} + \binom{n}{n} = 2^n$$

11. Let S be a set with n elements. How many subsets are there of the set S? (*Hint:* If $k \leq n$, the number of subsets of S that contain k elements is just the number of possible combinations of k elements that can be formed from the set S. Now apply problem 10.)
12. Show that for each positive integer n,

$$\binom{n}{0} - \binom{n}{1} + \binom{n}{2} - \cdots + (-1)^n \binom{n}{n} = 0$$

13. Prove that for each positive integer n,

$$2^n \binom{n}{0} - 2^{n-1} \binom{n}{1} + 2^{n-2} \binom{n}{2} - \cdots + (-1)^n \binom{n}{n} = 1$$

14. If n is a positive integer, show that

$$2^n \binom{n}{0} + 2^{n-1} \binom{n}{1} + 2^{n-2} \binom{n}{2} + \cdots + \binom{n}{n} = 3^n$$

Section 3.10[2] Pascal's Triangle

The binomial coefficients have an interesting property which can be illustrated as follows. We have seen that the coefficient of the term $a^{n-k}b^k$ in the expansion of $(a + b)^n$ is $\binom{n}{k}$ (the binomial theorem). Writing out the expansions from $n = 0$ to $n = 5$ gives

$$(a + b)^0 = 1$$
$$(a + b)^1 = a + b$$
$$(a + b)^2 = a^2 + 2ab + b^2$$
$$(a + b)^3 = a^3 + 3a^2b + 3ab^2 + b^3$$
$$(a + b)^4 = a^4 + 4a^3b + 6a^2b^2 + 4ab^3 + b^4$$
$$(a + b)^5 = a^5 + 5a^4b + 10a^3b^2 + 10a^2b^3 + 5ab^4 + b^5$$

An interesting pattern develops when the coefficients of these expressions are written down in the form of a triangle, called *Pascal's triangle* (Figure 3.10.1). The pattern

Figure 3.10.1

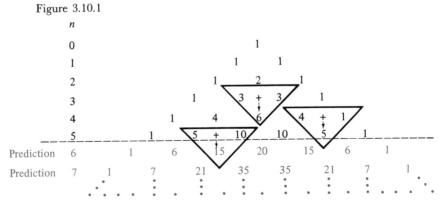

^{2}This section is optional.

is that the successive entries can be obtained by adding the two nearest entries in the row above. Hence we would predict that the sixth and seventh rows (the top row is zero) would be as depicted in the diagram. If the pattern is true in general, we should be able to state and prove it mathematically. We proceed to do this.

The kth element in the nth row of the triangle is just the coefficient of $a^{n-k+1}b^{k-1}$ in the expansion of $(a + b)^n$. By the binomial theorem this is just $\binom{n}{k-1}$. The $(k + 1)$st element in the nth row is the coefficient of $a^{n-k}b^k$ in the expansion of $(a + b)^n$, which is $\binom{n}{k}$. Referring to the diagram we are led to believe that the $(k + 1)$st element in the $(n + 1)$st row is $\binom{n}{k-1} + \binom{n}{k}$—the sum of the two nearest entries in the row above it. On the other hand, we know, in fact, that it is the coefficient of $a^{n+1-k}b^k$ in the expansion of $(a + b)^{n+1}$ which by the binomial theorem is $\binom{n+1}{k}$. So, the pattern being true in general corresponds mathematically to the truth of

$$\binom{n}{k-1} + \binom{n}{k} = \binom{n+1}{k} \tag{3.10.1}$$

This is what we want to prove is true.

The proof is accomplished by straightforward calculations using the definition of the binomial coefficients [see Eq. (3.8.5)]. Now

$$\binom{n}{k-1} = \frac{n!}{(k-1)![n-(k-1)]!} = \frac{n!}{(k-1)!(n-k+1)!} \tag{3.10.2}$$

$$\binom{n}{k} = \frac{n!}{k!(n-k)!} \tag{3.10.3}$$

$$\binom{n+1}{k} = \frac{(n+1)!}{k!(n+1-k)!} \tag{3.10.4}$$

First, Eqs. (3.10.2) and (3.10.3) must be added. This is done by putting them over a common denominator with the aid of Proposition 3.8.1. Since

$$k! = k \cdot (k-1)!$$

and $\quad (n-k+1)! = (n-k+1) \cdot (n-k)!$

the common denominator is $k!(n-k+1)!$. Multiplying numerator and denominator of Eq. (3.10.2) by k yields

$$\binom{n}{k-1} = \frac{n!}{(k-1)!(n-k+1)!} \cdot \frac{k}{k} = \frac{k \cdot n!}{k!(n-k+1)!}$$

Multiplying numerator and denominator of Eq. (3.10.3) by $n - k + 1$ gives

$$\binom{n}{k} = \frac{n!}{k!(n-k)!} \cdot \frac{n-k+1}{n-k+1} = \frac{(n-k+1) \cdot n!}{k!(n-k+1)!}$$

Adding these last two expressions yields

$$\binom{n}{k-1} + \binom{n}{k} = \frac{(n-k+1) \cdot n! + k \cdot n!}{k!(n-k+1)!}$$

However,

$$(n - k + 1) \cdot n! + k \cdot n! = n \cdot n! - k \cdot n! + n! + k \cdot n!$$
$$= n \cdot n! + n! = (n + 1) \cdot n! = (n + 1)!$$

Thus

$$\binom{n}{k - 1} + \binom{n}{k} = \frac{(n + 1)!}{k!(n + 1 - k)!} = \binom{n + 1}{k}$$

This proves Eq. (3.10.1).

Using Eq. (3.10.1) we are able to write a computer program to generate the binomial coefficients "inductively." That is, Eq. (3.10.1) and the computer can be used to generate the binomial coefficients as indicated in Pascal's triangle. Doing this, we obtain a table of binomial coefficients which is useful when solving counting problems. Such a table for $1 \leq n \leq 52$ is presented in Table 1 in Appendix B.

Exercises for 3.10

1. Verify Eq. (3.10.1) in the following cases.
   (a) $n = 2, k = 1$ (b) $n = 4, k = 3$
   (c) $n = 6, k = 4$ (d) $n = 8, k = 5$
2. Write down the first 11 rows of Pascal's triangle by using Eq. (3.10.1).
3. According to problem 10, Exercises 3.9, for each positive integer n,

$$\binom{n}{0} + \binom{n}{1} + \cdots + \binom{n}{n} = 2^n$$

Use the Pascal's triangle you wrote down in problem 2 to illustrate the validity of this equation for $1 \leq n \leq 10$.

Probability

4

The study of probability is concerned with the analysis of chance or random phenomena. Historically, probability developed partially through man's desire to analyze games of chance (gambling). Its domain now reaches out to a vast number of disciplines, including the social and management sciences. The importance and significance of the concepts and applications of probability seem to be boundless. In this chapter, the basic ideas and applications of probability will be presented.

Section 4.1 Random Experiments and the Relative Frequency Interpretation of Probability

If it is known that a specific outcome will always occur when a particular experiment is performed, there is no randomness or chance involved and such an experiment is of no interest in probability. For example, if a two-headed coin is tossed, there is only one possible outcome (heads), and so probabilistic considerations do not enter into this experiment.

On the other hand, suppose that an ordinary coin is tossed. Then, in contrast to the above example, we cannot be certain of the outcome before the experiment is performed. This is an example of a *random experiment*. The number of possible outcomes of this experiment is two (heads or tails).

Another example of a random experiment is the following. From an ordinary deck of 52 cards a hand is dealt that consists of 5 cards. In this case there are $\binom{52}{5} = 2{,}598{,}960$ possible outcomes.

In studying random experiments it is frequently important to assign probabilities to the various possible outcomes of the random experiment. Often this assignment will be clear from *context*. For example, if the random experiment consists of tossing a *fair* coin once, what assignment of probabilities should be made? The key to the answer to this question is the word "fair" in the previous sentence. This implies that head and tail are equally likely, so each outcome (head, tail) should be assigned the same probability ($\frac{1}{2}$ each).

Another way in which probabilities are often assigned is by *experimental relative frequency*. But before we discuss this method of assignment of probabilities, we make a philosophical digression and ask the question: What is meant by the statement that *an event E has probability p of occurring?* To get a feeling for this, consider the following example.

Example 4.1.1 A manufacturer of light bulbs claims that the probability that one of his light bulbs will burn out in less than 1 month is $.1 = \frac{1}{10}$. What does he mean by this statement?

The natural interpretation of this statement is that "on the average" about 1 in every 10 light bulbs he produces will burn out in less than 1 month's time. Alternatively, this means that 10 percent of the light bulbs he manufactures will burn out in less than 1 month.

Here the random experiment consists of examining a light bulb produced by this manufacturer. The event E in question is that the light bulb burns out in less than 1 month. According to the manufacturer, the probability, p, that E occurs is .1.

Returning to the question posed in the paragraph preceding Example 4.1.1, we now offer the following explanation: that an event E of a random experiment has probability p of occurring is interpreted as meaning that, if the random experiment is performed repeatedly under identical conditions, the proportion of experiments in which the event E occurs is approximately p. This is called the *relative frequency interpretation of probability.*

More precisely, in n repetitions of the random experiment, let

$$n_E = \text{no. times } E \text{ occurs}$$

Then the proportion of times E occurs in those n repetitions of the experiment is n_E/n. This fraction is called the *relative frequency of occurrence of E in n trials of the random experiment.* It is denoted by $f_E(n)$. Consequently, by definition,

$$f_E(n) = \frac{n_E}{n} = \frac{\text{no. times } E \text{ occurs}}{\text{no. trials}}$$

In this terminology the relative frequency interpretation of probability is that for a large number of trials, the relative frequency of occurrence of E is approximately equal to the probability, p, of the occurrence of the event E. That is,

$$f_E(n) \doteq p \tag{4.1.1}$$

for large n. (The symbol $\doteq$ will be used to indicate approximate equality.)
An example should help to clarify the situation.

Example 4.1.2 Consider again the light-bulb illustration of Example 4.1.1. As in Example 4.1.1, let E be the event that on a given examination of a light bulb, the light bulb burns out in less than 1 month. Suppose that a large number of light bulbs are examined and that the results are as in Table 4.1.1.

The relative frequency of the occurrence of E corresponding to each of these number of trials is

$$f_E(50) = \frac{8}{50} = .160 \qquad f_E(100) = \frac{12}{100} = .120$$

$$f_E(150) = \frac{16}{150} \doteq .107 \qquad f_E(200) = \frac{18}{200} = .090$$

$$f_E(250) = \frac{24}{250} \doteq .096 \qquad f_E(300) = \frac{31}{300} \doteq .103$$

Table 4.1.1

No. light bulbs examined (no. trials)	No. burning out in less than 1 month (no. occurrences of E)
50	8
100	12
150	16
200	18
250	24
300	31

From the data, the claim of the manufacturer that the probability is $.1 = .100$ that one of his light bulbs will burn out in less than 1 month seems to be justified according to the relative frequency interpretation of probability.

We now return to the method of assigning probabilities by means of *experimental relative frequency*. This method of assignment has its foundations in the relative frequency interpretation of probability: to assign a probability to the event E via experimental relative frequency, repeatedly perform the experiment. The relative frequency of occurrence of E after a large number of repetitions of the random experiment is then used as the probability of the occurrence of the event E when the random experiment is performed [see Eq. (4.1.1)].

Example 4.1.3 Defective Bolts To illustrate the idea of assigning probabilities via experimental relative frequency, suppose that a machine produces bolts that are considered defective if certain tolerance specifications are not met. If E is the event that a bolt produced by the machine is defective, we would like to make an assignment of probability to the event E. In other words, what number should be assigned as the probability that the machine will produce a defective bolt?

In this case the random experiment consists of examining a bolt produced by the machine and determining whether or not it is defective. The computer output shown in Table 4.1.2 could represent the continued repetition of the random experiment.

Here, the experimental relative frequency, $f_E(n)$, at the end of n trials is just the ratio of defective bolts in those n observations to the total number, n, of observations. That is,

$$f_E(n) = \frac{n_E}{n} = \frac{\text{no. defective bolts}}{\text{no. bolts examined}}$$

Table 4.1.2

Trial	No. defective bolts	Relative frequency
100	6	.060
200	19	.095
300	29	.097
400	45	.112
500	57	.114
600	70	.117
700	84	.120
800	98	.122
900	112	.124
1,000	127	.127
2,000	239	.119
3,000	367	.122
4,000	511	.128
5,000	636	.127
6,000	755	.126
7,000	876	.125
8,000	996	.125
9,000	1,121	.125
10,000	1,253	.125

For example, from Table 4.1.2 we see that

$$f_E(700) = \frac{84}{700} = .120$$

$$f_E(6,000) = \frac{755}{6,000} \doteq .126$$

$$f_E(10,000) = \frac{1,253}{10,000} \doteq .125$$

In any event, notice how the relative frequency of defective bolts is stabilizing. In this case, if experimental relative frequency were used to assign probabilities, the event E that a bolt produced by the machine is defective would be assigned probability .125 $(= \frac{1}{8})$.

Example 4.1.4 Birth Months Consider the following random experiment: a person is chosen at random from the population and the month of the person's birth is noted. In this experiment there are 12 possible outcomes—January, February, etc. We could assign probability $\frac{1}{12} \doteq .083$ to each possible outcome of the experiment. This is, in fact, the correct assignment of probabilities *assuming* that a person is as likely to be born during one month as during another. However, the data in Table 4.1.3 indicate that this may not be the most reasonable assumption. If we used the data to assign probabilities by means of experimental relative frequency, we would assign the outcome of a person being born in January probability .082, in February .077, and so on.

Although the relative frequency interpretation of probability is quite natural, it is not really used in the *theory* of probability. However, it *is* used as a *guide in developing* the theory of probability. This will be seen later in the chapter.

Table 4.1.3 Number of Births per Month in Thousands of People

	Jan.	Feb.	Mar.	Apr.	May	June	July	Aug.	Sep.	Oct.	Nov.	Dec.	Total
1958	348	317	345	327	343	345	366	367	376	372	341	357	4,204
1959	352	328	355	337	338	347	378	382	372	368	342	350	4,249
1960	338	329	347	327	335	336	370	399	385	368	351	362	4,247
1961	359	333	356	335	348	346	374	386	384	372	343	346	4,282
1962	346	318	359	328	333	329	366	373	367	363	337	346	4,165
1963	335	314	343	322	336	327	362	366	361	358	327	330	4,081
1964	336	326	337	316	331	331	359	350	356	347	328	336	4,053
1965	315	292	322	291	302	310	330	335	333	318	305	313	3,766
1966	301	281	301	291	297	291	311	319	317	317	296	307	3,629
1967	295	263	300	271	291	290	308	318	310	301	283	288	3,518
1968	284	273	286	284	294	288	315	322	317	309	295	306	3,573
1969	300	275	301	292	298	306	326	332	329	328	308	324	3,719
1970	299	284	306	290	292	285	295	306	317	305	294	287	3,560
Total	4,208	3,933	4,258	4,011	4,138	4,131	4,460	4,555	4,524	4,426	4,150	4,252	51,046
Relative frequency	.082	.077	.083	.079	.081	.081	.087	.089	.089	.087	.081	.083	

Exercises for 4.1

1. Classify each of the following experiments as random or nonrandom.
   (a) A pair of dice is rolled and the sum of the numbers appearing is noted.
   (b) The distance traveled in 1 hour by an automobile on a straight road at a given speed is observed.
   (c) A deck of cards is shuffled well and a bridge hand of 13 cards is dealt and the hand observed.
   (d) The number of people who have heart disease in a certain city is determined.
   (e) A subdivision of an automobile company produces 100 cars per day. The number of cars produced in a period of 2 weeks is noted.
2. A coin is tossed and the following data are recorded:

Toss	Total no. heads		Toss	Total no. heads
500	133		5,500	1,353
1,000	265		6,000	1,489
1,500	391		6,500	1,626
2,000	509		7,000	1,752
2,500	625		7,500	1,885
3,000	761		8,000	2,000
3,500	884		8,500	2,117
4,000	995		9,000	2,239
4,500	1,110		9,500	2,364
5,000	1,243		10,000	2,498

Let E be the event that when the coin is tossed, it comes up heads.
   (a) What is $f_E(n)$, for

   (1) $n = 500$ (2) $n = 3,000$

   (3) $n = 8,000$ (4) $n = 9,500$

   (5) $n = 10,000$

(b) Using your results in part (a), estimate via experimental relative frequency the probability that this particular coin comes up heads when it is tossed once.

3. If an automobile manufacturer claims that the probability that one of his automobiles has a serious defect is $\frac{1}{20}$, about how many cars with serious defects would you expect to find if you examined 100,000 of his cars?

4. A pair of fair dice was rolled repeatedly. The sum of the numbers on the dice was observed and the following results were tabulated:

Roll	Total no. 7s
500	81
1,000	169
1,500	267
2,000	356
2,500	424
3,000	497
3,500	598
4,000	669
4,500	765
5,000	844
5,500	918
6,000	997
6,500	1,086
7,000	1,168
7,500	1,255
8,000	1,334
8,500	1,414
9,000	1,499
9,500	1,588
10,000	1,660

(a) What is the relative frequency of occurrence of a 7 in n rolls of the dice for
(1) $n = 1,000$
(2) $n = 7,500$
(3) $n = 9,500$

(b) Estimate, by using experimental relative frequency, the probability of getting a 7 on these dice when they are rolled.

5. A washing machine manufacturer has discovered that about 1 in every 50 washing machines he produces has warranty work performed on it. If E is the event that a washing machine produced by this manufacturer has warranty work performed on it, what probability should be assigned to the event E?

6. Assume that there are 200,000 people living in a U.S. city and that 120,000 of the people own television sets. The following random experiment is performed: a person is selected "at random" from the population and it is observed whether or not this person owns a TV set. If E is the event that the person selected owns a TV set, what would be a reasonable assignment of probability to the occurrence of E?

7. (a) In a given population it is known that $100p$ percent of the individuals have a particular attribute A (e.g., it could be the attribute of a person having blue eyes). If a person is selected "at random" from the population, what probability would you assign to the event that the person selected has attribute A?

(b) You are told that the probability is p that a person selected "at random" from the population has attribute A.

(1) What percentage of the population would you estimate to have attribute A?

(2) If there are 500,000 people in the population, how many people would you estimate to have attribute A?

Section 4.2 Mathematical Models for Experiments: The Sample Space

In this section the foundations will be laid for the mathematical treatment of random experiments. If the random experiment is very simple, such as tossing a fair coin once, there is no necessity for a rigorous mathematical formulation of the experiment. However, most random experiments that occur naturally require a mathematical model in order to analyze and clarify their complex structure. Moreover, even for simple experiments it is most often useful to formulate things in a precise mathematical framework.

Before giving a formal discussion of the mathematical formulation of random experiments, the following example is presented for illustrative and reference purposes.

Example 4.2.1 Coin Tossing Consider the random experiment of tossing a *fair* coin three times. The first problem is to determine the set, Ω, of all possible outcomes of the experiment. In this case it is quite simple to list the possible outcomes:

HHH	THH
HHT	THT
HTH	TTH
HTT	TTT

Hence Ω consists of the eight elements listed above.

$$\Omega = \{\text{HHH, HHT, HTH, HTT, THH, THT, TTH, TTT}\}$$

The set Ω of possible outcomes is called the *sample space* of the random experiment. This will be the universal set (see Chapter 2) in connection with the experiment. The individual possible outcomes (i.e., the elements of the sample space Ω) are referred to as *sample points*. For example, HHH and THT are sample points.

The next thing to be done in the construction of the mathematical model for our experiment is to assign probabilities to each of the sample points. Since the coin is *fair*, it seems reasonable that each of the sample points should have the same probability. Consequently, since there are eight such sample points, probability $\frac{1}{8}$ is assigned to each one (more will be said about this later). The computer was used to simulate the experiment of tossing a fair coin three times. It repeated the experiment continually, recording the number of times HHH occurred along with its experimental relative frequency. As can be seen in Figure 4.2.1, the relative frequency interpretation justifies the assignment of probability $\frac{1}{8} = .125$ to the sample point HHH.

Using Example 4.2.1 as an illustration, we have motivated the following definitions and conventions.

Figure 4.2.1

Trial	No. occurrences of HHH	Relative frequency of HHH
10,000	1,209	.121
20,000	2,419	.121
30,000	3,670	.122
40,000	4,925	.123
50,000	6,243	.125
60,000	7,432	.124
70,000	8,641	.123
80,000	9,890	.124
90,000	11,119	.124
100,000	12,396	.124
110,000	13,683	.124
120,000	14,880	.124
130,000	16,160	.124
140,000	17,425	.124
150,000	18,695	.125
160,000	19,989	.125
170,000	21,266	.125
180,000	22,565	.125
190,000	23,778	.125
200,000	25,064	.125
210,000	26,255	.125
220,000	27,491	.125
230,000	28,799	.125
240,000	30,009	.125
250,000	31,271	.125
260,000	32,531	.125
270,000	33,734	.125
280,000	34,999	.125
290,000	36,308	.125
300,000	37,594	.125

Definition

Let Ω denote the set of all outcomes of a random experiment. Then Ω is called the *sample space* of the experiment. The individual outcomes (i.e., the members of Ω) are called the *sample points* of the experiment.

In this text we shall consider only finite sample spaces; that is, we shall only consider random experiments that have a finite number of possible outcomes.

Recall that in the previous example there are eight sample points HHH, HHT, HTH, HTT, THH, THT, TTH, TTT, and the sample space is

$$\Omega = \{HHH, HHT, HTH, HTT, THH, THT, TTH, TTT\}$$

In the study of random experiments it is assumed that with each sample point, which is denoted generically by ω, there is associated a number (the probability that ω occurs) denoted by $\Pr(\{\omega\})$. This association might have been accomplished in several ways (e.g., context, experimental relative frequency). In Example 4.2.1 each sample point was assigned probability $\frac{1}{8}$: $\Pr(\{HHH\}) = \frac{1}{8}$, $\Pr(\{HHT\}) = \frac{1}{8}$, etc.

There are two *mathematical* requirements imposed upon the assignment of probabilities. The first is that for each sample point ω (i.e., each possible outcome, ω, of the random experiment),

$$\Pr(\{\omega\}) \geq 0 \qquad (4.2.1)$$

Second, if $\Omega = \{\omega_1, \omega_2, \ldots, \omega_N\}$ (i.e., there are N sample points $\omega_1, \omega_2, \ldots, \omega_N$), it is required that

$$\Pr(\{\omega_1\}) + \Pr(\{\omega_2\}) + \cdots + \Pr(\{\omega_N\}) = 1 \qquad (4.2.2)$$

Now, Eq. (4.2.1) simply says that the probabilities must be nonnegative numbers, an obvious restriction. Requirement (4.2.2) is that the sum of the probabilities assigned to the sample points is equal to 1. This says that the sample points $\omega_1, \omega_2, \ldots, \omega_N$ form a complete list of outcomes of the random experiment.

Referring to Example 4.2.1, note that Eqs. (4.2.1) and (4.2.2) are certainly satisfied. Indeed, in this example $\Pr(\{\omega\}) = \frac{1}{8} \geq 0$ for each sample point ω, and so Eq. (4.2.1) holds. Also,

$$\begin{aligned}
\Pr(\{\omega_1\}) + \Pr(\{\omega_2\}) &+ \cdots + \Pr(\{\omega_8\}) \\
&= \Pr(\{HHH\}) + \Pr(\{HHT\}) + \cdots + \Pr(\{TTT\}) \\
&= \underbrace{\tfrac{1}{8} + \tfrac{1}{8} + \cdots + \tfrac{1}{8}}_{8 \text{ times}} = 1
\end{aligned}$$

so Eq. (4.2.2) is satisfied.

It should be emphasized that the only *mathematical* restrictions on the assignments of probabilities are Eqs. (4.2.1) and (4.2.2). However, in practice, the assignments should be made in a manner that reflects the physical situation. For example, if a coin is tossed twice, the sample space is $\Omega = \{HH, HT, TH, TT\}$. Suppose that the following assignment of probabilities is made:

$$\Pr(\{HH\}) = \tfrac{9}{16} \qquad \Pr(\{HT\}) = \Pr(\{TH\}) = \tfrac{3}{16} \qquad \Pr(\{TT\}) = \tfrac{1}{16}$$

Then conditions (4.2.1) and (4.2.2) are satisfied, so, *mathematically speaking*, this assignment of probabilities is legitimate. However, if the coin is known (or strongly suspected) to be unbiased, the above assignment, although legitimate mathematically, does not properly reflect the situation.

Exercises for 4.2

1. A coin is tossed once and the outcome observed.
   (a) How many sample points are there?
   (b) What is the sample space?
   (c) If the coin is fair, what assignment of probabilities should be made?
   (d) If experience (i.e., experimental relative frequency) indicates that about one in every five tosses yields heads, what assignment of probabilities should be made?
   (e) If experience indicates that the ratio of occurrence of heads to tails is about $3:2$, how should probabilities be assigned to the sample points?
2. A die is rolled once and the number showing is observed.
   (a) How many sample points are there?
   (b) What is the sample space for this random experiment?

(c) If the die is known to be *fair*, what assignment of probabilities should be made to the sample points?

(d) Suppose experience indicates that the percentages of occurrence of the numbers are given as follows:

Number	Percentage of occurrence
1	10
2	15
3	40
4	5
5	10
6	20

What assignment of probabilities should be made?

(e) Which of the following are legitimate (mathematically speaking) assignments of probabilities to the sample points of this random experiment?

Sample point	Assignment			
	1	2	3	4
1	.1	.2	$\frac{1}{2}$	$\frac{1}{16}$
2	.2	.2	$\frac{1}{4}$	$\frac{1}{8}$
3	.3	.2	$-\frac{1}{4}$	$\frac{1}{4}$
4	.1	.2	$\frac{1}{2}$	0
5	.2	.2	$-\frac{1}{8}$	$\frac{7}{16}$
6	.1	.2	$\frac{1}{8}$	$\frac{1}{8}$

3. Consider the experiment of tossing a coin twice and the following ways of associating numbers with the four sample points:

Sample point	Assignment				
	1	2	3	4	5
HH	$\frac{1}{4}$	1	$\frac{1}{2}$	$\frac{1}{16}$	$\frac{1}{16}$
HT	$\frac{1}{4}$	0	$\frac{1}{2}$	$\frac{3}{16}$	$\frac{1}{4}$
TH	$\frac{1}{4}$	0	$-\frac{1}{2}$	$\frac{3}{16}$	$\frac{1}{4}$
TT	$\frac{1}{4}$	0	$\frac{1}{2}$	$\frac{1}{16}$	$\frac{1}{16}$

(a) Which of the associations are legitimate assignments of probabilities to the various sample points?

(b) Which of the assignments should be used if the coin is known to be fair?

(c) Which of the assignments of probabilities should be used if the coin is known to always come up heads?

4. Suppose that a coin is tossed four times and the outcome after each toss is observed.

(a) How many sample points are there?

(b) What is the sample space?

(c) If the coin is fair, what assignment of probabilities should be made to the sample points?

(d) If the coin is known to always come up tails, what assignment of probabilities should be made to the sample points?

5. A deck of playing cards consists of 52 playing cards. A card is selected "at random" from the deck and observed.

(a) How many sample points are there for this random experiment?

(b) What assignment of probabilities should be made?

6. Suppose that the sample space, Ω, of a random experiment consists of N sample points and that it is reasonable to assign the same probability to each sample point. If $\omega \in \Omega$ (i.e., if ω is any sample point), what is $\Pr(\{\omega\})$?

7. In a certain city the following data were compiled concerning the party affiliation of the citizens:

Party	Percentage
Democrat	45
Republican	42
Other	13

Suppose that a voter is selected at random from the city and his or her party affiliation noted.

(a) Construct a sample space for this random experiment consisting of three sample points.

(b) Assign probabilities to the three sample points.

8. Statistics gathered by a government agency in a certain country indicated the following to be valid:

No. children	Percentage of families
0	5
1	25
2	35
3	15
4	10
5	7
6 (or more)	3

Suppose that a family is selected at random from the population and the number of children in the family observed.

(a) Construct a sample space for this random experiment consisting of seven sample points.

(b) Assign the appropriate probability to each of the sample points.

9. A bowl contains 10 chips, of which 5 are red, 3 are white, and 2 are blue. A chip is selected from the bowl and its color noted.

(a) Construct a sample space for this random experiment consisting of 3 sample points and make the appropriate assignment of probabilities.

(b) Construct a sample space for this random experiment consisting of 10 sample points and make the appropriate assignment of probabilities.

Section 4.3   Events and Their Probabilities

The concept of an event will now be introduced. Intuitively, an event is described in terms of the random experiment via certain restrictions. The problem at hand is to make the notion of an event precise and then determine how to compute probabilities of events. Again we begin with an example.

Example 4.3.1 Coin Tossing Consider again the experiment of tossing a fair coin three times (Example 4.2.1). What is the probability of the "event" that "exactly two of the three tosses yield heads"? To figure out the probability of this "event" it is first necessary to find the possible ways in which it can occur. They are HHT, HTH, and THH. So, if E denotes the event that exactly two of the three tosses yield heads, E occurs if and only if the experiment yields either HHT, HTH, or THH. Symbolically, then,

$$E = \{\text{HHT}, \text{HTH}, \text{THH}\}$$

and so E can be considered as a *subset of the sample space* Ω. The probability of E is denoted by $\Pr(E)$. Since E occurs if and only if the experiment results in either HHT, HTH, or THH, it is natural to set $\Pr(E)$ equal to the sum of the probabilities of the three sample points HHT, HTH, and THH. Thus we set

$$\Pr(E) = \Pr(\{\text{HHT}\}) + \Pr(\{\text{HTH}\}) + \Pr(\{\text{THH}\}) = \tfrac{1}{8} + \tfrac{1}{8} + \tfrac{1}{8} = \tfrac{3}{8}$$

With this example in mind we now make the following definitions.

Definition

Let Ω be the sample space (set of all possible outcomes) of a random experiment. An *event* E is simply a subset of the sample space Ω or equivalently a collection of sample points. In set notation, E is an event if and only if $E \subset \Omega$.

The event E is said to *occur* when the random experiment is performed, if the outcome ω is a sample point that is an element of E (i.e., $\omega \in E$). Reference to Example 4.2.1 will aid in the understanding of this idea. For example, let E be the event that the first two tosses yield heads. Then $E = \{\text{HHH}, \text{HHT}\}$. If the result of performing the experiment is HHT, the event E occurred, since HHT $\in E$. However, if the result of the experiment is HTH, E did not occur, since HTH $\notin E$.

Notice that a sample point ω can be considered an event, $\{\omega\}$. The event $\{\omega\}$ occurs if and only if the outcome of the experiment is ω. Events consisting of only one sample point are called *simple events*.

As mentioned in Example 4.3.1, it is natural to assign an event E a probability as follows:

Definition

Let Ω be the sample space of a random experiment and let E be an event; that is, $E \subset \Omega$. If $E = \{\omega_1, \omega_2, \ldots, \omega_k\}$, we define

$$\Pr(E) = \Pr(\{\omega_1\}) + \cdots + \Pr(\{\omega_k\}) \qquad (4.3.1)$$

Thus the probability of E, denoted by $\Pr(E)$, is defined to be the sum of the probabilities of the sample points making up the event E. For instance, if in Example

4.2.1, E is the event that the first two tosses are heads, then $E = \{HHH, HHT\}$ and so, by definition,

$$\begin{aligned} \Pr(E) &= \Pr(\{HHH\}) + \Pr(\{HHT\}) \\ &= \tfrac{1}{8} + \tfrac{1}{8} = \tfrac{1}{4} \end{aligned}$$

Equation (4.3.1) can be arrived at by using the relative frequency interpretation of probability. This will show that Eq. (4.3.1) is consistent with our intuition. In performing a random experiment n times, let n_E denote the numbers of times that the event E occurs. If E is an event, say

$$E = \{\omega_1, \omega_2, \ldots, \omega_k\}$$

the number of times E occurs in n repetitions of the random experiment is precisely the sum of the number of times the outcome was either $\omega_1, \omega_2, \ldots,$ or ω_k. Thus

$$n_E = n_{\{\omega_1\}} + n_{\{\omega_2\}} + \cdots + n_{\{\omega_k\}}$$

The relative frequency interpretation of probability indicates that for any event E we have, for large n, $\Pr(E) \doteq n_E/n$ ($=$ relative frequency of the occurrence of E in n repetitions of the random experiment). But then, for large n,

$$\begin{aligned} \Pr(E) &\doteq \frac{n_E}{n} = \frac{n_{\{\omega_1\}}}{n} + \frac{n_{\{\omega_2\}}}{n} + \cdots + \frac{n_{\{\omega_k\}}}{n} \\ &\doteq \Pr(\{\omega_1\}) + \Pr(\{\omega_2\}) + \cdots + \Pr(\{\omega_k\}) \end{aligned}$$

This motivates the definition in Eq. (4.3.1).

Now, Eqs. (4.2.2) and (4.3.1) imply that $\Pr(\Omega) = 1$, which is just another way of saying that something must occur. A technicality: the empty set, $\varnothing$, is a subset of Ω. It is natural (and important) to assign this event probability zero. As will be seen later, the empty set corresponds to an impossibility in terms of the random experiment. In summary,

$$\Pr(\Omega) = 1 \qquad \Pr(\varnothing) = 0 \tag{4.3.2}$$

Example 4.3.2 Personnel Records The personnel director of a large company has determined that the percentages of employees in each of the following age groups are as follows:

Sample point	Age	Percentage	$\Pr(\{\omega\})$
ω_1	Under 18	5	$\frac{1}{20}$
ω_2	18–24	20	$\frac{1}{5}$
ω_3	25–39	50	$\frac{1}{2}$
ω_4	40–55	15	$\frac{3}{20}$
ω_5	Over 55	10	$\frac{1}{10}$

If an employee is selected at random, what is the probability that he is under 25 or over 55? Let E be the event in question. Then

$$E = \{\omega_1, \omega_2, \omega_5\}$$

so that, by Eq. (4.3.1),

$$\begin{aligned} \Pr(E) &= \Pr(\{\omega_1\}) + \Pr(\{\omega_2\} + \Pr(\{\omega_5\}) \\ &= \tfrac{1}{20} + \tfrac{1}{5} + \tfrac{1}{10} = \tfrac{7}{20}(= 35\%) \end{aligned}$$

Example 4.3.3 Chips in a Bowl A bowl contains 10 chips. Three are red, 2 are white, and 5 are blue. A chip is chosen from the bowl "at random." What is the probability that a red chip is not selected?

There are two ways to solve this problem. Both will be presented, as they illustrate different approaches to the same problem.

SOLUTION 1

Consider all chips as being distinguishable and for convenience designate them as

$$r_1, r_2, r_3, w_1, w_2, b_1, b_2, b_3, b_4, b_5$$

For example, r_1 refers to red chip 1, r_2 refers to red chip 2, and so on. Then the random experiment has 10 possible outcomes. The sample space is

$$\Omega = \{r_1, r_2, r_3, w_1, w_2, b_1, b_2, b_3, b_4, b_5\}$$

Since the chip is selected "at random," we infer that each chip is equally likely to be selected, so each sample point should be assigned the same probability. Because there are 10 sample points altogether, we therefore assign probability $\tfrac{1}{10}$ to each one.

Now, let E be the event that a red chip is not selected. Then

$$E = \{w_1, w_2, b_1, b_2, b_3, b_4, b_5\}$$

Consequently,

$$\begin{aligned} \Pr(E) &= \Pr(\{w_1\}) + \Pr(\{w_2\}) + \Pr(\{b_1\}) + \Pr(\{b_2\}) \\ &\quad + \Pr(\{b_3\}) + \Pr(\{b_4\}) + \Pr(\{b_5\}) \\ &= \tfrac{1}{10} + \tfrac{1}{10} + \tfrac{1}{10} + \tfrac{1}{10} + \tfrac{1}{10} + \tfrac{1}{10} + \tfrac{1}{10} = \tfrac{7}{10} \end{aligned}$$

SOLUTION 2

For this case it is assumed that chips of the same color are indistinguishable. Then the random experiment has three possible outcomes—a red, a white, or a blue chip is selected. The sample space is

$$\Omega = \{r, w, b\}$$

where, of course, r designates the fact that a red chip was selected, and so on.

Because there are 3 red, 2 white, and 5 blue chips in the bowl and because the chip is selected at random, the probabilities are assigned to the sample points as follows:

$$\Pr(\{r\}) = \tfrac{3}{10} \quad \Pr(\{w\}) = \tfrac{2}{10} \quad \Pr(\{b\}) = \tfrac{5}{10}$$

The event E that a red chip is not selected is given by

$$E = \{w, b\}$$

and therefore

$$\Pr(E) = \Pr(\{w\}) + \Pr(\{b\}) = \tfrac{2}{10} + \tfrac{5}{10} = \tfrac{7}{10}$$

Exercises for 4.3

1. A die is rolled once and the number on the face showing is observed. Take $\Omega = \{1, 2, 3, 4, 5, 6\}$ for the sample space.
   (a) Determine the subset of Ω that corresponds to each of the following events.
      (1) The die comes up even.
      (2) The die comes up odd.
      (3) The number showing exceeds 2.
      (4) The number showing does not exceed 4.
      (5) The number showing is odd and exceeds 4.
   (b) Assume that the die is fair (so that each sample point is assigned probability $\frac{1}{6}$); calculate the probabilities of the events in (1)–(5).
   (c) Suppose that experience indicates that the appropriate assignment of probabilities is as follows:

ω	1	2	3	4	5	6
$\Pr(\{\omega\})$	.10	.15	.40	.05	.10	.20

   Calculate the probabilities of the events in (1)–(5).
2. Consider the experiment of tossing a coin twice and observing the outcome after each toss. (Take $\Omega = \{HH, HT, TH, TT\}$.)
   (a) Determine the subset of Ω corresponding to each of the following events.
      (1) The first toss is heads.
      (2) The second toss is tails.
      (3) The two tosses come up the same.
      (4) The two tosses come up with different outcomes.
      (5) The first toss is heads and the second tails.
      (6) The number of heads obtained is at least one.
      (7) The number of heads obtained is exactly one.
   (b) Assume that the coin is fair; calculate the probabilities of the above events.
   (c) Suppose it has been determined that the coin is biased and that the proper assignment of the probabilities is as follows:

ω	HH	HT	TH	TT
$\Pr(\{\omega\})$	$\frac{1}{16}$	$\frac{3}{16}$	$\frac{3}{16}$	$\frac{9}{16}$

   Calculate the probabilities of the events described in part (a).
3. A machine produces bolts that are subject to *length* and *width* specifications. It has been determined that the following assignment of probabilities is reasonably accurate.
   (1) The probability that a bolt examined is not defective in either length or width is $\frac{5}{8}$.
   (2) The probability that it is defective in both length and width is $\frac{1}{16}$.
   (3) The probability that it is defective in length but not in width is $\frac{3}{16}$.
   (4) The probability that it is defective in width but not in length is $\frac{1}{8}$.
   (a) Set up a sample space Ω for the experiment of selecting a bolt at random from the machine and determining which, if any, defects it possesses. [*Hint:* There will be four sample points, one corresponding to each of the possibilities in (1)–(4).]
   (b) What is the probability that a bolt selected will be defective in length?
   (c) What is the probability that a bolt selected will be defective in at least one of the two ways?

4. There are eight horses in a race. According to the odds, the probabilities of the various horses winning the race are given by the following table:

Horse	Probability of winning
1	$\frac{1}{4}$
2	$\frac{1}{2}$
3	$\frac{1}{8}$
4	$\frac{1}{64}$
5	$\frac{1}{32}$
6	$\frac{1}{128}$
7	$\frac{7}{128}$
8	$\frac{1}{64}$

(a) What is the probability that 1, 2, or 3 wins the race?
(b) What is the probability that neither 6 nor 7 wins the race?
(c) What is the probability that the winning horse's number is at least 5?

5. Consider the random experiment of problem 8, Exercises 4.2. Take the sample space to be $\Omega = \{0, 1, 2, 3, 4, 5, 6+\}$ and use the assignment of probabilities as indicated in the problem.
   (a) Find the subset of Ω corresponding to each of the following events.
      (1) The family selected has fewer than 3 children.
      (2) The number of children exceeds 3.
      (3) The family has between 2 and 4 children (inclusive).
      (4) The family has no more than 1 and no less than 5 children.
   (b) Calculate the probabilities of the above events.

6. Suppose that a *fair* coin is tossed four times, the result after each toss being recorded. Take $\Omega = \{\text{HHHH}, \text{HHHT}, \ldots, \text{TTTT}\}$ (i.e., Ω consists of all sequences of Hs and Ts that are four-long).
   (a) Determine the subset of Ω that corresponds to each of the following events.
      (1) The first two tosses are heads.
      (2) The last three tosses are tails.
      (3) Exactly three of the tosses come up heads.
      (4) The number of heads exceeds one but is fewer than four.
      (5) The first two tosses are heads and the second two are tails.
   (b) Calculate the probabilities of the events in part (a).

7. A pair of *fair* dice is rolled and the number appearing on each die is observed. A typical sample point is taken as an ordered pair of numbers each of which is an integer between 1 and 6. For example, [2, 4] is the sample point that represents the outcome that the first die shows 2 and the second 4. The sample space, Ω, therefore, consists of 36 sample points (6 choices for the first die and 6 choices for the second).
   (a) Determine the subset of Ω that corresponds to each of the following events.
      (1) The first die shows 4.
      (2) The second die shows 6.
      (3) The number on the first die exceeds that of the second.
      (4) The numbers on both dice are the same.
      (5) The sum of the numbers on the dice is 7.
      (6) The sum of the numbers on the dice is 11.
   (b) Calculate the probabilities of the events in part (a). (Remember that the dice are fair, so each sample point should be assigned the same probability.)

8. Suppose that Ω is the sample space of a random experiment that consists of N sample points. Assume that each of the N sample points has the same probability. If E is an event consisting of k sample points [i.e., $E \subset \Omega$ and card $(E) = k$], show that $\Pr(E) = k/N$.

9. A bowl contains 10 chips, of which 5 are red, 3 are white, and 2 are blue. A chip is selected from the bowl at random and its color is noted.
   (a) Set up a sample space for this experiment with 10 sample points.
      (1) What assignment of probabilities should be made to the various sample points?
      (2) What is the probability that the chip selected is either red or white?
   (b) Set up a sample space for this experiment which consists of three sample points.
      (1) What assignment of probabilities should be made to the various sample points?
      (2) What is the probability that the chip selected is either red or white?
10. A card is chosen at random from an ordinary deck of 52 cards. Calculate the probabilities of the following events: (*Hint:* Problem 8 is helpful here.)
   (a) A club is selected.
   (b) A red card is selected.
   (c) The 5 of diamonds is chosen.
   (d) The card selected is between 2 and 7, inclusive.
   (e) An ace or queen is chosen.
   (f) An ace and club is selected.
   (g) An ace or club is chosen.
   (h) A heart is not selected.

Section 4.4 Intersections, Unions, and Complements of Events

Now that we see how to assign probabilities to events in terms of the *given* probabilities of the sample points, we proceed to explain the method for calculating probabilities of events in terms of the probabilities of other events. Before doing this, operations with and relations among events will be discussed. This will consist of utilizing the tools of set theory to further formalize, mathematically, random experiments.

As we have seen, each event corresponds to a subset of the sample space Ω. If A and B are events, which subset of the sample space corresponds to the event that "both A and B occur"? The answer to this question is obtained as follows: that both A and B occur means that the outcome ω of the random experiment is a member of both A and B; that is, $\omega \in A$ and $\omega \in B$. But this is just another way of saying that $\omega \in A \cap B$. Hence the subset of the sample space corresponding to the event that both A and B occur is the intersection of A and B:

$$A \cap B \tag{4.4.1}$$

Example 4.4.1 Coin Tossing Again consider the random experiment of Example 4.2.1. The sample space Ω consists of eight sample points:

$$\Omega = \{HHH, HHT, HTH, HTT, THH, THT, TTH, TTT\}$$

Let A be the event that the second toss is a head, B be the event that the first toss is a head, C be the event that the first toss is a tail, and D be the event that the last two tosses yield heads. Then, in set notation,

$$
\begin{aligned}
A &= \{HHH, HHT, THH, THT\} \\
B &= \{HHH, HHT, HTH, HTT\} \\
C &= \{THH, THT, TTH, TTT\} \\
D &= \{HHH, THH\}
\end{aligned}
\tag{4.4.2}
$$

Now, in words, the event that both A and B occur means that the second toss is a head and the first toss is a head (i.e., the first two tosses are head). To explicitly determine the event that both A and B occur, we use Eqs. (4.4.1) and (4.4.2) to conclude that it is

$$A \cap B = \{\text{HHH, HHT}\}$$

As another illustration, the event that both B and C occur is given by $B \cap C$. But $B \cap C = \varnothing$, as can be seen by Eq. (4.4.2). This means that B and C contain no common sample points; in other words, they *cannot occur simultaneously*. In this respect the empty set, $\varnothing$, corresponds to an impossible event in terms of the random experiment. In the present case this is clear, because the event that both B and C occur means that the first toss is a head and the first toss is a tail, which is obviously impossible.

In general, if two events A and B cannot occur simultaneously (i.e., $A \cap B = \varnothing$), then A and B are said to be *mutually exclusive*.

To continue, we now ask which subset of the sample space corresponds to the event that "either A or B occurs"? To answer this we argue in the following manner. That either A or B occurs means that the outcome ω of the random experiment is either a member of A or a member of B (or both); that is, $\omega \in A$ or $\omega \in B$. In other words, $\omega \in A \cup B$. Consequently, the subset of the sample space corresponding to the event that either A or B occurs is just the union of the sets A and B:

$$A \cup B \tag{4.4.3}$$

Example 4.4.2 Consider again the coin-tossing experiment of Example 4.4.1. Now, in words, the event that either A or B occurs means that either the second toss is heads or the first toss is heads (i.e., at least one of the first two tosses is heads). According to Eqs. (4.4.3) and (4.4.2), this is precisely the event

$$A \cup B = \{\text{HHH, HHT, THH, THT, HTH, HTT}\}$$

Also, according to Eq. (4.4.3), the event that either B or C occurs is $B \cup C$, which by Eq. (4.4.2) is given by

$$B \cup C = \{\text{HHH, HHT, HTH, HTT, THH, THT, TTH, TTT}\}$$
$$= \Omega$$

Since the union of B and C is the entire sample space, this means that either B or C must occur. In the present case this is easily seen, since the event that either B or C occurs means that either the first toss is a head or the first toss is a tail, and this certainly must happen.

We remark that there is no problem with considering the intersection or union of more than two events. For example, the event that "A, B, and C all occur" is given by $A \cap B \cap C$, and the event that "either A, B, C, or D occurs" is given by $A \cup B \cup C \cup D$.

Finally, we shall determine which subset of the sample space corresponds to the event that "A does not occur." That A does not occur means that the outcome ω of the random experiment is not a member of A; that is, $\omega \notin A$. But this is just another way of saying that $\omega \in \bar{A}$. Hence the subset of the sample space corresponding to the nonoccurrence of A is just the complement of A:

$$\bar{A} \tag{4.4.4}$$

Example 4.4.3 Recall the random experiment and sets described in Example 4.4.1. Now, in words, the event that A does not occur is just the event that the second toss is not heads (i.e., the second toss is tails). According to Eqs. (4.4.4) and (4.4.2), this is just the event

$$\bar{A} = \{\text{HTH, HTT, TTH, TTT}\}$$

Also the event that D does not occur is just the event that the last two tosses are not both heads (i.e., at least one of the last two tosses is tails). By Eqs. (4.4.4) and (4.4.2) this is just

$$\bar{D} = \{\text{HHT, HTH, HTT, THT, TTH, TTT}\}$$

We give one final example that illustrates the above ideas.

Example 4.4.4 Dice Consider the experiment of rolling a pair of dice. There are 36 possible outcomes (6 possibilities for the first die and 6 possibilities for the second). For convenience the sample points can be represented as ordered pairs. For example, [3, 2] corresponds to the outcome of a 3 on the first die and a 2 on the second (see Figure 4.4.1).

Now, let A be the event that the sum of the faces is 7, B be the event that the number on the first die exceeds the second, C the event that the two faces show the same number, and D the event that the sum of the faces is 11.

$$\begin{aligned}
A &= \{[1, 6], [2, 5], [3, 4], [4, 3], [5, 2], [6, 1]\} \\
B &= \{[2, 1], [3, 1], [3, 2], [4, 1], [4, 2], [4, 3], \\
&\qquad [5, 1], [5, 2], [5, 3], [5, 4], [6, 1], [6, 2], \\
&\qquad [6, 3], [6, 4], [6, 5]\} \\
C &= \{[1, 1], [2, 2], [3, 3], [4, 4], [5, 5], [6, 6]\} \\
D &= \{[5, 6], [6, 5]\}
\end{aligned}$$

The event that the sum of the two dice is 7 and that the first die's numerical value exceeds the second's is just

$$A \cap B = \{[4, 3], [5, 2], [6, 1]\}$$

so this event can occur in precisely three ways.

$A \cap C$ represents the event that the sum of the faces is 7 and that both dice show the same number. This is clearly impossible and is reflected mathematically by the fact that A and C have no common sample points. That is,

$$A \cap C = \emptyset$$

Consequently, A and C are mutually exclusive.

The event that either A or D occurs is just that the sum of the faces is either 7 or 11 and is given by

$$A \cup D = \{[1, 6], [2, 5], [3, 4], [4, 3], [5, 2], [6, 1], [5, 6], [6, 5]\}$$

The event that the sum of the faces is neither 7 nor 11 is $\overline{A \cup D}$, which contains the 28 sample points not in $A \cup D$.

Figure 4.4.1

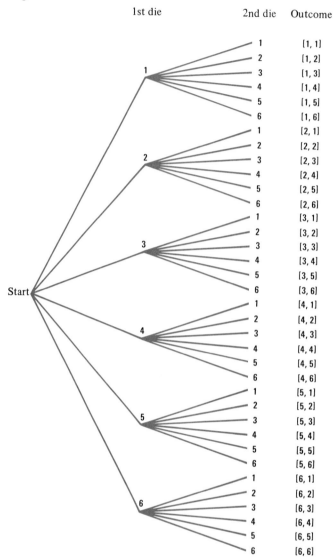

| 1st die | 2nd die | Outcome |

In summary, then, we have the following table:

Event	Subset of Ω
A and B occur	$A \cap B$
Either A or B occurs	$A \cup B$
A does not occur	$\tilde{A}$

Exercises for 4.4

1. Consider the random experiment of tossing a fair coin twice. Let Ω be the sample space that corresponds to this experiment (i.e., $\Omega = \{HH, HT, TH, TT\}$). Let A be the event

that the second toss is a head and B the event that at least one of the two tosses yields a tail.

(a) Describe in words the events corresponding to each of the following subsets of Ω:

(1) $A \cup B$ (2) $A \cap B$

(3) $\bar{A}$ (4) $\bar{B}$

(b) Determine explicitly the events (1)–(4).

(c) Are the events A and B mutually exclusive?

2. A die is rolled once and the number on the face showing is observed. Let Ω be the sample space, and let

A = event the die comes up even
B = event the die comes up odd
C = event the number showing exceeds 2
D = event the number showing does not exceed 4

(a) Indicate to which subset of Ω each of the following events corresponds (e.g., the event "the number showing is even and exceeds 2" would correspond to $A \cap C$).

(1) The number showing is odd and exceeds 2.
(2) The number showing is even and greater than 4.
(3) The number showing is even or less than 5.
(4) The number showing is odd or less than or equal to 2.
(5) The number showing is neither even nor less than 5.

(b) Are the events A and D mutually exclusive?

3. Consider the random experiment of tossing a fair coin four times. Let Ω be the sample space that corresponds to this experiment, A be the event the third toss is a head, B the event that exactly two of the four tosses yield heads, and C the event that at least two of the four tosses yield heads.

(a) Describe in words the event that corresponds to each of the following subsets of Ω.

(1) $A \cap B$ (2) $A \cap \bar{C}$

(3) $B \cap C$ (4) $A - B (= A \cap \bar{B})$

(5) $B \cup C$

(b) Determine explicitly the events (1)–(5).

(c) Of the events A, B, and C, are any two of them mutually exclusive?

4. Consider the experiment of selecting a student at random and noting the college to which the student belongs as well as the sex of the student. For simplicity the colleges are taken to be liberal arts, fine arts, business, engineering, and "others." Let

A = event the student is in the liberal arts
B = event the student is in the fine arts
C = event the student is in the business college
D = event the student is in the engineering college
E = event the student is in the "others" category
M = event the student is a male
F = event the student is a female

Indicate to which set each of the following events corresponds.

(a) in liberal arts or engineering
(b) not in business
(c) in fine arts or a female
(d) a male but not in engineering
(e) a female and in the "others" category

5. Consider the random experiment of problem 3, Exercises 4.3. Let A be the event that the bolt selected is defective in length and B the event that the bolt selected is defective

in width. Describe in words the event corresponding to each of the following subsets of Ω.

(a) $A \cap B$

(b) $A \cup B$

(c) $A - B$

(d) $B \cap \tilde{A}$

(e) $\widetilde{A \cap B}$

6. A card is drawn at random from an ordinary deck of 52 playing cards. Which of the following pairs of events are mutually exclusive?

(a) A = event card is red

B = event card is black

(b) A = event card is a diamond

B = event card is a seven

(c) A = event card is a heart or club

B = event card is a 10 or jack

(d) A = event card is a spade

B = event card is a club

(e) A = event card is a face card

B = event card is less than 10 but greater than 4

7. A dart is thrown at a circular dartboard with the numbers 1 through 6 printed on its face (see the figure). Let A be the event that an even number is obtained by a throw

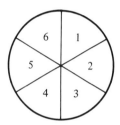

of the dart, B the event that an odd number is obtained, C the event that at least a 4 is obtained, and D the event that a 6 is obtained. Which of the following pairs of events are mutually exclusive?

(a) A and B

(b) B and C

(c) B and D

(d) A and $\tilde{C}$

(e) $\tilde{A}$ and $\tilde{B}$

8. Consider the random experiment of problem 8, Exercises 4.2. Let A be the event that the family selected has fewer than four children, B the event the number of children exceeds two, and C the event the family has either four or five children.

(a) Describe in words the event corresponding to each of the following subsets of Ω.

(1) $B \cap (A \cup C)$

(2) $(A \cap B) \cup C$

(3) $A \cup \tilde{B} \cup C$

(4) $(A - B) \cup C$

(b) Determine explicitly the events (1)–(4).

(c) Of the events A, B, and C, are any two of them mutually exclusive?

9. Let A and B be events of the sample space Ω, and suppose that A and B are mutually exclusive with $A \cup B = \Omega$. Then

(a) $\Pr(A \cap B) = ?$

(b) $\Pr(A \cup B) = ?$

10. Let A and B be events with $A \cup B = \Omega$. Prove that $\tilde{A}$ and $\tilde{B}$ are mutually exclusive events.

11. Show by example that the result of problem 10 is not valid if $A \cup B \subsetneq \Omega$.

12. Let A, B, and C be events of the sample space Ω with A and B mutually exclusive. Show that the events $A \cap C$ and $B \cap C$ are mutually exclusive.

Section 4.5 Probability of the Union of Two Events: The Addition Principle

In this section we will show how to calculate the probability of the event $E \cup F$ (i.e., the probability that E or F occurs) in terms of the probabilities of the events E and F. The formula to be developed is one of the basic principles used in the study of probability. To indicate the ideas involved, the following example is presented.

Example 4.5.1 Consider again Example 4.2.1 and the events A and B defined by

$$A = \{HHH, HHT, HTH, HTT\}$$
$$B = \{HTH, HTT, TTH, TTT\}$$

Thus A is the event that the first toss is heads and B is the event that the second toss is tails. From Eq. (4.3.1) it follows that

$$Pr(A) = Pr(\{HHH\}) + Pr(\{HHT\}) + Pr(\{HTH\}) + Pr(\{HTT\})$$
$$= \tfrac{1}{8} + \tfrac{1}{8} + \tfrac{1}{8} + \tfrac{1}{8} = \tfrac{4}{8} = \tfrac{1}{2}$$

Similarly,

$$Pr(B) = \tfrac{4}{8} = \tfrac{1}{2}$$

Now, $A \cup B$ is the event that either the first toss is heads or the second toss is tails (or both). So

$$A \cup B = \{HHH, HHT, HTH, HTT, TTH, TTT\}$$

Consequently,

$$Pr(A \cup B) = Pr(\{HHH\}) + Pr(\{HHT\}) + Pr(\{HTH\})$$
$$+ Pr(\{HTT\}) + Pr(\{TTH\}) + Pr(\{TTT\})$$
$$= \tfrac{1}{8} + \tfrac{1}{8} + \tfrac{1}{8} + \tfrac{1}{8} + \tfrac{1}{8} + \tfrac{1}{8} = \tfrac{6}{8} = \tfrac{3}{4}$$

Notice that

$$Pr(A \cup B) = \tfrac{3}{4} \qquad Pr(A) + Pr(B) = \tfrac{1}{2} + \tfrac{1}{2} = 1$$

so

$$Pr(A \cup B) \neq Pr(A) + Pr(B)$$

In words, the probability that either A or B occurs does not equal the probability that A occurs plus the probability that B occurs. The problem is that the sample points HTH and HTT belong to both A and B so that by adding $Pr(A)$ to $Pr(B)$, the sample points HTH and HTT are "counted" twice. Schematically,

$$Pr(A) + Pr(B) = \underbrace{Pr(\{HHH\}) + Pr(\{HHT\}) + Pr(\{HTH\}) + Pr(\{HTT\})}_{Pr(A)}$$

$$+ \underbrace{Pr(\{HTH\}) + Pr(\{HTT\}) + Pr(\{TTH\}) + Pr(\{TTT\})}_{Pr(B)}$$

and

$$Pr(A \cup B) = Pr(\{HHH\}) + Pr(\{HHT\}) + Pr(\{HTH\})$$
$$+ Pr(\{HTT\}) + Pr(\{TTH\}) + Pr(\{TTT\})$$

Thus to obtain $\Pr(A \cup B)$ from $\Pr(A)$ and $\Pr(B)$, add $\Pr(A)$ to $\Pr(B)$ and subtract $\Pr(\{HTH\}) + \Pr(\{HTT\})$. Hence

$$\Pr(A \cup B) = \Pr(A) + \Pr(B) - [\Pr(\{HTH\}) + \Pr(\{HTT\})]$$
$$= \tfrac{1}{2} + \tfrac{1}{2} - [\tfrac{1}{8} + \tfrac{1}{8}] = \tfrac{3}{4}$$

which was already obtained directly. Notice that $\{HTH, HTT\} = A \cap B$.

The general reasoning for calculating $\Pr(E \cup F)$ in terms of $\Pr(E)$ and $\Pr(F)$ follows the reasoning in the above example. Simply add $\Pr(E)$ to $\Pr(F)$ and subtract off the probability of the sample points common to both E and F, because they have been counted twice. In other words, it has been demonstrated that the following theorem holds.

Theorem 4.5.1

Let E and F be events. Then

$$\Pr(E \cup F) = \Pr(E) + \Pr(F) - \Pr(E \cap F) \tag{4.5.1}$$

Now, if E and F are mutually exclusive (i.e., have no common sample points), $E \cap F = \varnothing$, and so $\Pr(E \cap F) = 0$. Thus as a special case of Eq. (4.5.1), we have

---

Corollary 4.5.2

If E and F are *mutually exclusive* events (i.e., they cannot occur simultaneously),

$$\Pr(E \cup F) = \Pr(E) + \Pr(F) \tag{4.5.2}$$

This is the *addition principle* of probability: *the probability of the union of two mutually exclusive events is the sum of their probabilities.*

Three events, E, F, and G, are said to be (pairwise) *mutually exclusive* if any two of them are mutually exclusive. It is left as an exercise for the reader to show that if E, F, and G are mutually exclusive,

$$\Pr(E \cup F \cup G) = \Pr(E) + \Pr(F) + \Pr(G)$$

Of course, the same type of result holds for more than three mutually exclusive events.

It is frequently much easier to calculate the probability of an event's nonoccurrence than the probability of its occurrence. This will be seen later. Using Eq. (4.5.2) a formula relating $\Pr(E)$ and $\Pr(\tilde{E})$ can be obtained. For, since E and $\tilde{E}$ are mutually exclusive $(E \cap \tilde{E} = \varnothing)$, Eq. (4.5.2) implies that

$$\Pr(E \cup \tilde{E}) = \Pr(E) + \Pr(\tilde{E})$$

But $E \cup \tilde{E} = \Omega$, so $\Pr(E \cup \tilde{E}) = 1$ (this simply formalizes the fact that either E occurs or it does not occur). Thus

$$1 = \Pr(E) + \Pr(\tilde{E})$$

and hence the following useful fact has been proved.

Corollary 4.5.3

For any event E,

$$\Pr(E) = 1 - \Pr(\tilde{E}) \tag{4.5.3}$$

or, what is the same,

$$\Pr(\tilde{E}) = 1 - \Pr(E) \tag{4.5.4}$$

Example 4.5.2 Dice Consider the dice experiment of Example 4.4.4. There are 36 possible outcomes, and if the dice are fair, it is reasonable to assign equal probability to each sample point. Since the sum of the probabilities of all sample points must be 1 [see Eq. (4.2.2)], and there are 36 such sample points, probability $\frac{1}{36}$ is assigned to each sample point.

The events A and B (defined in Example 4.4.4) have three sample points in common: $[4, 3]$, $[5, 2]$, and $[6, 1]$. Thus $A \cap B = \{[4, 3], [5, 2], [6, 1]\}$. Now

$$\Pr(A) = \Pr(\{[1, 6]\}) + \Pr(\{[2, 5]\}) + \cdots + \Pr(\{[6, 1]\})$$
$$= \underbrace{\tfrac{1}{36} + \tfrac{1}{36} + \cdots + \tfrac{1}{36}}_{6 \text{ times}} = \tfrac{6}{36}$$

$$\Pr(B) = \Pr(\{[2, 1]\}) + \Pr(\{[3, 1]\}) + \cdots + \Pr(\{[6, 5]\})$$
$$= \underbrace{\tfrac{1}{36} + \tfrac{1}{36} + \cdots + \tfrac{1}{36}}_{15 \text{ times}} = \tfrac{15}{36}$$

$$\Pr(A \cap B) = \Pr(\{[4, 3]\}) + \Pr(\{[5, 2]\}) + \Pr(\{[6, 1]\})$$
$$= \tfrac{1}{36} + \tfrac{1}{36} + \tfrac{1}{36} = \tfrac{3}{36}$$

Consequently, by Eq. (4.5.1),

$$\Pr(A \cup B) = \Pr(A) + \Pr(B) - \Pr(A \cap B)$$
$$= \tfrac{6}{36} + \tfrac{15}{36} - \tfrac{3}{36} = \tfrac{18}{36} = \tfrac{1}{2}$$

On the other hand, A and C (defined in Example 4.4.4) are mutually exclusive, so, by the addition principle,

$$\Pr(A \cup C) = \Pr(A) + \Pr(C) = \tfrac{6}{36} + \tfrac{6}{36} = \tfrac{1}{3}$$

Finally, $A \cup D$ is the event that the sum of the faces is either 7 or 11. Since $A \cap D = \varnothing$, the addition principle implies that

$$\Pr(A \cup D) = \Pr(A) + \Pr(D) = \tfrac{1}{6} + \tfrac{2}{36} = \tfrac{2}{9}$$

Example 4.5.3 Cards Consider the experiment of selecting a card from an ordinary deck of 52 playing cards. Assuming that the cards are well shuffled, it is natural to assign equal probability to the drawing of each card. Since there are 52 cards, arguments as in Example 4.5.2 indicate that probability $\frac{1}{52}$ should be assigned to the drawing of each particular card. For example, if A is the event that a spade is selected and B is the event that a king is selected,

$$\Pr(A) = \Pr(\{\text{ace of spades}\}) + \Pr(\{2 \text{ of spades}\})$$
$$+ \cdots + \Pr(\{\text{king of spades}\})$$
$$= \underbrace{\tfrac{1}{52} + \tfrac{1}{52} + \cdots + \tfrac{1}{52}}_{13 \text{ times}} = \tfrac{13}{52} = \tfrac{1}{4}$$

$$Pr(B) = Pr(\{\text{king of spades}\}) + \cdots + Pr(\{\text{king of clubs}\})$$
$$= \underbrace{\tfrac{1}{52} + \cdots + \tfrac{1}{52}}_{4 \text{ times}} = \tfrac{4}{52} = \tfrac{1}{13}$$

Now, $A \cap B = \{\text{king of spades}\}$, so $Pr(A \cap B) = \tfrac{1}{52}$. Consequently, the probability that either a spade or a king is drawn equals

$$Pr(A \cup B) = Pr(A) + Pr(B) - Pr(A \cap B)$$
$$= \tfrac{13}{52} + \tfrac{4}{52} - \tfrac{1}{52} = \tfrac{16}{52} = \tfrac{4}{13}$$

Exercises for 4.5

1. A pair of *fair* dice is rolled. Let A be the event that the sum of the faces is 6 and B be the event that doubles are rolled. Use Theorem 4.5.1 to find $Pr(A \cup B)$.

2. Suppose that a *fair* coin is tossed three times. Let A be the event that the second toss is tails, B be the event that at least two tails are tossed, and C be the event that exactly two heads are tossed. Find the probability of each of the following events by applying Theorem 4.5.1.
   (a) $A \cup B$
   (b) $A \cup C$
   (c) $B \cup C$

3. Let A be the event that a man over 50 smokes and B the event that a man over 50 has a heart attack. Suppose recent studies indicate that $Pr(A) = \tfrac{7}{12}$, $Pr(B) = \tfrac{1}{3}$, and $Pr(A \cap B) = \tfrac{1}{8}$. What is the probability that a man over 50 has a heart attack or smokes?

4. In a recent survey it has been determined that 20 percent of the population is Catholic and 45 percent of the population votes Democratic. Moreover, it has been determined that the people who are both Catholic and Democratic voters comprise 12 percent of the population. What is the probability that a person selected at random will be either a Catholic or a person who votes Democratic?

5. Let A and B be mutually exclusive events. Why is it not possible to have the following probabilities?

$$Pr(A \cup B) = \tfrac{5}{6} \qquad Pr(A) = \tfrac{2}{3} \qquad Pr(B) = \tfrac{1}{4}$$

6. To qualify for a position in a certain firm, an applicant must pass both a written exam and a personal interview. An applicant estimates that he has probability $\tfrac{2}{5}$ of passing the written exam and probability $\tfrac{3}{5}$ of passing the personal interview. He also estimates that he has probability $\tfrac{4}{5}$ of passing either the written exam or the personal interview. What is his probability of passing both the written exam and the personal interview?

7. Let A and B be events of a sample space Ω, and let $Pr(A) = \tfrac{1}{3}$, $Pr(B) = \tfrac{1}{2}$, and $Pr(A \cap B) = \tfrac{1}{6}$. Find the probability of each of the following events.
   (a) A or B
   (b) neither A nor B
   (c) either not A or not B

8. Suppose that in a lot of bolts it is determined that 10 percent are too long, 15 percent are too wide, and 7 percent are both too long and too wide. In selecting a bolt at random, what is the probability that it will be acceptable in both length and width?

9. A pair of fair dice is rolled and the outcome on each die is recorded. What is the probability that the sum of the faces that appear will be at least 4? [*Hint:* Find the probability that the sum will be either 2 or 3 and use Eq. (4.5.3).]

10. Let A and B be events of a sample space Ω. Show that $Pr(A - B) = Pr(A) - Pr(A \cap B)$. (Recall that $A - B = A \cap \bar{B}$.)

*11. In a recent election two propositions (I and II) were voted on (Yes or No) by a voting population of 1,500 people. Some of the results on these two propositions are given below:

500 people voted in favor of I, 375 voted against II, and 125 voted against both. If a person is selected at random from the voting population, calculate the probability that the person

(a) voted for either I or II   (b) voted for both I and II
(c) voted for I but voted against II   (d) voted for II or voted against I

12. If A, B, and C are three mutually exclusive events, that is, $A \cap B = A \cap C = B \cap C = \emptyset$, show that $\Pr(A \cup B \cup C) = \Pr(A) + \Pr(B) + \Pr(C)$. (*Hint:* First look at the two events $A \cup B$ and C.)

13. Prove the following generalization of Theorem 4.5.1: Let A, B, and C be events of a sample space Ω. Then

$$\begin{aligned} \Pr(A \cup B \cup C) = {} & \Pr(A) + P(B) + \Pr(C) \\ & - \Pr(A \cap B) - \Pr(A \cap C) - \Pr(B \cap C) \\ & + \Pr(A \cap B \cap C) \end{aligned}$$

(*Hint:* Let $D = A \cup B$ and use Theorem 4.5.1.)

14. Let A and B be events of a sample space Ω such that $A \subset B$. Show that $\Pr(A) \leq \Pr(B)$. [*Hint:* Note that $B = A \cup (B \cap \bar{A})$.]

Section 4.6 Uniform Sample Spaces

Many of the elementary, but quite interesting problems in probability can be handled by the application of principles of combinatorial analysis. These problems include those which arise in such varying areas as psychology, physics, business, genetics, and many others. Before explaining the general procedure involved in attacking these types of problems, the following examples are presented.

Example 4.6.1 Coin Tossing Consider the experiment of tossing a fair coin three times. As we have seen previously, the sample space, Ω, consists of eight sample points:

$$\Omega = \{HHH, HHT, HTH, HTT, THH, THT, TTH, TTT\}$$

Because the coin is fair, we attribute probability $\frac{1}{8}$ to each sample point. Thus *each sample point has the same probability.* If E is any event (i.e., $E \subset \Omega$), the probability of E, $\Pr(E)$, is obtained by summing the probabilities of the sample points of which E consists [formula (4.3.1)]. For example, if E is the event that the second toss yields tails, then $E = \{HTH, HTT, TTH, TTT\}$, so

$$\begin{aligned} \Pr(E) &= \Pr(\{HTH\}) + \Pr(\{HTT\}) + \Pr(\{TTH\}) + \Pr(\{TTT\}) \\ &= \tfrac{1}{8} + \tfrac{1}{8} + \tfrac{1}{8} + \tfrac{1}{8} = \tfrac{4}{8} = \tfrac{1}{2} \end{aligned}$$

This result can be obtained more easily as follows: since each sample point has probability $\frac{1}{8}$, the probability of any event E can be calculated by determining the number of sample points contained in E and dividing by 8. For example, if $E = \{HTH, HTT, TTH, TTT\}$,

$$\Pr(E) = \frac{\text{no. sample points in } E}{8} = \tfrac{4}{8} = \tfrac{1}{2}$$

In other words, to calculate the probability of any event E, just determine the number of ways in which E can occur and divide by 8 (= number of possible outcomes of the random experiment). In terms of cardinality this can be written

$$\Pr(E) = \frac{\text{card } (E)}{\text{card } (\Omega)}$$

Example 4.6.2 Cards As a second example, consider the experiment of choosing a card *at random* from an ordinary deck of 52 playing cards. There are 52 possible outcomes of this experiment and since the card is chosen at random, equal probability, $\frac{1}{52}$, is assigned to each sample point.

If E is the event that a Jack is chosen,

$$E = \{\text{jack of spades, jack of hearts, jack of diamonds, jack of clubs}\}$$

and therefore

$$\Pr(E) = \Pr(\{\text{jack of spades}\}) + \Pr(\{\text{jack of hearts}\})$$
$$+ \Pr(\{\text{jack of diamonds}\}) + \Pr(\{\text{jack of clubs}\})$$
$$= \tfrac{1}{52} + \tfrac{1}{52} + \tfrac{1}{52} + \tfrac{1}{52} = \tfrac{4}{52} = \tfrac{1}{13}$$

As in Example 4.6.1, because each sample point has the same probability, the probability of E can also be calculated by

$$\Pr(E) = \frac{\text{no. sample points in } E}{\text{no. possible outcomes of random experiment}}$$
$$= \frac{\text{card } (E)}{\text{card } (\Omega)} = \tfrac{4}{52} = \tfrac{1}{13}$$

The same reasoning holds for any event in this random experiment. So, as in Example 4.6.1, for any event E,

$$\Pr(E) = \frac{\text{card } (E)}{\text{card } (\Omega)}$$

The previous two examples illustrate an alternative procedure for calculating probabilities of events in sample spaces in which all sample points have the same probability. Such sample spaces are often called *uniform sample spaces or equiprobable sample spaces*. To calculate the probability of an event in a uniform sample space, it is only necessary to calculate the number of ways the event in question can occur (i.e., the number of sample points it contains) and divide this number by the total number of possible outcomes of the random experiment. This fact was illustrated in the previous two examples and is proved in general below.

Theorem 4.6.1

Let Ω be a uniform sample space (all sample points have the same probability). Then for each event E,

$$\Pr(E) = \frac{\text{card } (E)}{\text{card } (\Omega)} \qquad\qquad (4.6.1)$$

PROOF

Let $k = \text{card } (E)$ and $N = \text{card } (\Omega)$ so that E can occur in exactly k different ways and there are N possible outcomes of the random experiment. Suppose that

$$E = \{\omega_1, \omega_2, \ldots, \omega_k\}$$

Then

$$\Pr(E) = \Pr(\{\omega_1\}) + \cdots + \Pr(\{\omega_k\})$$

Since each sample point has the same probability and there are N sample points altogether, it follows from Eq. (4.2.2) that each sample point has probability $1/N$. So

$$\Pr(E) = \underbrace{\frac{1}{N} + \cdots + \frac{1}{N}}_{k \text{ times}} = \frac{k}{N} = \frac{\text{card } (E)}{\text{card } (\Omega)}$$

By Theorem 4.6.1 the calculation of probabilities in uniform sample spaces reduces to the problem of *counting* the number of ways events can occur (i.e., the number of sample points they contain). Sometimes this problem is quite easy, as in Examples 4.6.1 and 4.6.2. However, it is quite often a very difficult problem. Before giving some examples that illustrate the use of Theorem 4.6.1, the following comment is made.

Example 4.6.3 Ages Regardless of what the random experiment is, it can be made into a uniform sample space by *assigning* equal probability to each sample point. However, this may be *unrealistic*, and so in practice not all sample spaces will be uniform. For example, suppose that a person is chosen at random from the population and his age (in years) is noted. Playing it safe, the sample space can be taken to consist of the numbers from 1 to 200, so

$$\Omega = \{x \mid x \text{ is an integer, } 1 \le x \le 200\}$$

We could assign equal probability $(\frac{1}{200})$ to each sample point and thus obtain a uniform sample space. However, this is clearly unrealistic because, for example, a person selected at random from the population is much more likely to be 25 than 105. In this case a reasonable assignment of probabilities could be made by using relative frequencies (repeated sampling) or by consulting birth and death records. In any case, it is clear that in this situation a uniform sample space is inappropriate.

Some illustrations of Theorem 4.6.1 are now presented.

Example 4.6.4 Raffles A person holds 5 tickets for a prize in a raffle in which 100 tickets were sold. What is the probability that this person wins the prize?

There are 100 possible (equally likely) outcomes of the experiment (100 different tickets) and there are five possible ways that the person wins (i.e., if any one of his 5 tickets is drawn). If E is the event that the person wins the prize, then, by Theorem 4.6.1,

$$\Pr(E) = \frac{\text{card } (E)}{\text{card } (\Omega)} = \tfrac{5}{100} = \tfrac{1}{20} = .05$$

Example 4.6.5 Raffles Consider the situation of Example 4.6.4 except assume there are six prizes given. What is the probability that the person with 5 tickets wins exactly four prizes?

Let us put this experiment in sample-space form. The number of possible outcomes of this experiment is the number of ways that 6 tickets can be chosen from 100 tickets. This is $\binom{100}{6}$. Thus card $(\Omega) = \binom{100}{6}$.

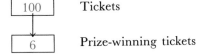

| 100 | Tickets |

| 6 | Prize-winning tickets |

Assuming that each ticket is equally likely to be chosen, we have a uniform sample space.

Now, let A be the event that the person wins exactly four prizes. To find $\Pr(A)$ it is first necessary to determine card (A) (i.e., the number of ways A can occur). As in Chapter 3, it is useful to present the situation schematically:

Tickets

	Person's	Others
Subgroups	5	95

Prize-winning tickets

	Person's	Others
Number to be chosen	4	2

| Number of ways | $\binom{5}{4}$ | $\binom{95}{2}$ |

Total possibilities
(by the sequential
counting principle) $\quad \binom{5}{4} \cdot \binom{95}{2}$

Thus card $(A) = \binom{5}{4} \cdot \binom{95}{2}$. Consequently, by Theorem 4.6.1,

$$\Pr(A) = \frac{\text{card } (A)}{\text{card } (\Omega)} = \frac{\binom{5}{4}\binom{95}{2}}{\binom{100}{6}} \doteq .00002$$

Hence it is very unlikely that the person will win exactly four prizes.

Exercises for 4.6

1. A fair die is rolled once. Let E be the event that an odd number is rolled. Use the methods of this section to determine the probability of the event E.
2. A pair of fair dice is rolled. Use the methods of this section to determine the probability that the sum of the faces showing is a 5.
3. In problem 2, what value for the sum has the highest probability of occurring? What value or values for the sum have the lowest probability of occurring?
4. Let Ω be a uniform sample space and suppose that ω is a sample point of Ω with $\Pr(\{\omega\}) = \frac{1}{5}$. What is card (Ω)?
5. A family has three children, all of different ages. Assume that it is equally likely to have male and female children and that the sexes of previous children do not affect those of the future children. Use the methods of this section to find the probability that
   (a) the oldest is a boy
   (b) the oldest two are girls
   (c) there are exactly two girls
   (d) there is at least one boy [*Hint:* Find the probability that there are no boys and use Eq. (4.5.3).]

6. Let Ω be a uniform sample space with 12 elements. What is the probability of an event that contains 8 sample points?
7. In replacing some burned-out fuses, a housewife accidently mixes four bad fuses with six good ones. If she cannot tell by looking which are the good fuses and which are the bad ones, what is the probability of picking a good fuse?
8. In problem 7, if three fuses are selected, what is the probability that all three will be good? (*Hint:* Use the methods of combinatorial analysis here.)
9. From a group of 15 boys, 5 are to be selected at random to form a basketball team. Among these 15 boys are John and Jim.
   (a) What is the probability that exactly one of them is chosen for the team?
   (b) What is the probability that they both are chosen for the team?
10. A fair die is rolled three times. What is the probability of no repeats?

Section 4.7 Applications of Combinatorial Analysis to Probability

In this section we consider several examples of uniform sample spaces in which probabilities are calculated by use of the counting principles introduced in Chapter 3.

Example 4.7.1 Light Bulbs It is known that a quantity of 100 light bulbs contains 20 defective ones. If 10 light bulbs are selected at random, what is the probability that none are defective?

There are $\binom{100}{10}$ possible outcomes of the experiment—card $(\Omega) = \binom{100}{10}$. Since the light bulbs are selected at random, each possible outcome is equally likely, and so we have a uniform sample space.

Let E be the event that none of the light bulbs are defective. To find card (E), proceed as usual:

Light bulbs

	Defective	Nondefective
Subgroups	20	80

Light bulbs selected

	Defective	Nondefective
Number to be chosen	0	10

Number of ways	$\binom{20}{0}$	$\binom{80}{10}$

Total possibilities (by the sequential counting principle)	$\binom{20}{0} \cdot \binom{80}{10}$

Thus

$$\text{card } (E) = \binom{20}{0}\binom{80}{10}$$

Consequently,

$$\Pr(E) = \frac{\text{card }(E)}{\text{card }(\Omega)} = \frac{\dbinom{20}{0}\dbinom{80}{10}}{\dbinom{100}{10}} \doteq .095$$

Example 4.7.2   Consider again the raffle experiment introduced in Example 4.6.5. What is the probability that the person with the five tickets wins at least one prize? Let E be the event that the person wins at least one prize (i.e., 1, 2, 3, 4, or 5 prizes). In this case it is easier to calculate $\Pr(\tilde{E})$. Now, $\tilde{E}$ is the event that the person wins no prizes. To determine $\Pr(\tilde{E})$ we first must find card $(\tilde{E})$ (i.e., how many sample points $\tilde{E}$ contains).

Tickets

	Person's	Others
Subgroups	5	95

Prize-winning tickets

	Person's	Others
Number to be chosen	0	6

	Person's	Others
Number of ways	$\dbinom{5}{0}$	$\dbinom{95}{6}$

Total possibilities (by the sequential counting principle)	$\dbinom{5}{0}$ ·	$\dbinom{95}{6}$

Thus card $(\tilde{E}) = \dbinom{5}{0} \cdot \dbinom{95}{6}$, so, by Theorem 4.6.1,

$$\Pr(\tilde{E}) = \frac{\text{card }(\tilde{E})}{\text{card }(\Omega)} = \frac{\dbinom{5}{0}\dbinom{95}{6}}{\dbinom{100}{6}} \doteq .729$$

Hence, by Corollary 4.5.3,

$$\Pr(E) = 1 - \Pr(\tilde{E}) \doteq 1 - .729 = .271$$

Example 4.7.3   Birthdays   In a class of 30 students, what is the probability that two or more have the same birthday?

At first glance it appears that since there are 365 possible birthdays, this probability should be relatively small, certainly less than .5. The actual results are quite surprising. Let E be the event that two or more people have the same birthday. The experiment consists of choosing 30 people at random and observing their birth dates. Each sample point can thus be represented as a sequence of 30 integers between 1 and 365. For example, if the first person chosen was born on the 11th day of the year, the second was born on the 225th day of the year, the third was born on the 2nd day of the year, . . . , the thirtieth was born on the 175th day of the year, this outcome is represented by the sample point

1st 2nd 3rd $\cdots$ 30th
[11, 225, 2, . . . , 175]

By the sequential counting principle there are

$$\underbrace{365 \cdot 365 \cdot \ldots \cdot 365}_{30 \text{ times}} = 365^{30}$$

possible outcomes of the experiment.

Table 4.7.1 Calculation of the Probability of the Event that Out of N People at Least Two Have the Same Birthday

No. people	Probability	No. people	Probability
2	.003	36	.832
3	.008	37	.849
4	.016	38	.864
5	.027	39	.873
6	.040	40	.891
7	.056	41	.903
8	.074	42	.914
9	.095	43	.924
10	.117	44	.933
11	.141	45	.941
12	.167	46	.943
13	.194	47	.955
14	.223	48	.961
15	.253	49	.966
16	.284	50	.970
17	.315	51	.974
18	.347	52	.978
19	.379	53	.981
20	.411	54	.984
21	.444	55	.986
22	.476	56	.988
23	.507	57	.990
24	.538	58	.992
25	.569	59	.993
26	.598	60	.994
27	.627	61	.995
28	.654	62	.996
29	.681	63	.997
30	.706	64	.997
31	.730	65	.998
32	.753	66	.998
33	.775	67	.998
34	.795	68	.999
35	.814	69	.999

Assuming that birth dates are equally likely, we have a uniform sample space with each sample point having probability $1/365^{30}$. Thus to calculate the probability of E, it is only necessary to count how many ways this event can occur. It is much easier to count the number of ways that $\tilde{E}$ can occur (i.e., how many sample points $\tilde{E}$ contains). Now $\tilde{E}$ occurs if and only if each person sampled has a different birthday. To determine the number of ways that $\tilde{E}$ can occur, the sequential counting principle is used: there are 365 possibilities for the birthday of the first person chosen. If $\tilde{E}$ is to occur, the second person chosen cannot have the same birthday as the first. Hence there are 364 choices for the birthday of the second person. Continuing in this manner we see that there are $_{365}P_{30}$ sample points in $\tilde{E}$. That is, $\tilde{E}$ can occur in

$$_{365}P_{30} = 365 \cdot 364 \cdots 336$$

ways. Hence, by Theorem 4.6.1,

$$\Pr(\tilde{E}) = \frac{\text{card }(\tilde{E})}{\text{card }(\Omega)} = \frac{365 \cdot 364 \cdots 336}{(365)^{30}} \doteq .294$$

So, by Corollary 4.5.3,

$$\Pr(E) = 1 - \Pr(\tilde{E}) \doteq .706$$

To most people this result is a bit surprising. They usually think that the probability will be much smaller.

The same type of argument can be used to find the probability that in a group of N people, at least two have the same birthday. The computer was used to calculate these probabilities (see Table 4.7.1). Of course, these computations could be done by hand.

Example 4.7.4 Genetics Consider a gene composed of 10 subunits and suppose that each subunit is either mutant or normal. Suppose that a cell has a gene composed of 3 mutant subunits and 7 normal subunits. The cell divides into two daughter cells, say daughter cell 1 and daughter cell 2. Before doing so the gene duplicates. The corresponding gene of daughter cell 1 is composed of 10 subunits chosen at random from the 6 mutant subunits and 14 normal subunits. Daughter cell 2 gets the remaining subunits. What is the probability that one of the daughter cells consists of all normal subunits?

The experiment consists of choosing 10 subunits at random from the 6 mutant and 14 normal subunits. The subunits selected will constitute the corresponding gene of daughter cell 1. Let Ω be the sample space. There are $\binom{20}{10}$ ways of choosing 10 things from 20 without regard to order. Hence

$$\text{card }(\Omega) = \binom{20}{10} = 184{,}756$$

Since the subunits are chosen at random, we interpret this to mean that each outcome is equally likely. That is, each sample point is assigned the same probability. Let E be the event that one of the daughter cell's gene consists of all normal subunits.

The event E occurs if either (1) the selected subunits are all normal or (2) six of the selected subunits are mutant (then the gene of daughter cell 2 will consist of all normal subunits). Let A be the former event and B the latter. Then $E = A \cup B$ and $A \cap B = \emptyset$ (i.e., A and B are mutually exclusive). Thus, by the addition principle,

$$\Pr(E) = \Pr(A \cup B) = \Pr(A) + \Pr(B)$$

To determine $\Pr(E)$ it is only necessary to find $\Pr(A)$ and $\Pr(B)$. Since the sample space is uniform, this involves calculating card (A) and card (B). Schematically,

Subunits

	Mutant	Normal
Subgroups	6	14

Subunits selected

	Mutant	Normal
Number to be chosen	0	10

Number of ways

$$\binom{6}{0} \quad \Big| \quad \binom{14}{10}$$

Total possibilities

$$\binom{6}{0} \cdot \binom{14}{10}$$

Subunits

	Mutant	Normal
Subgroups	6	14

Subunits Selected

	Mutant	Normal
Number to be chosen	6	4

Number of ways

$$\binom{6}{6} \quad \Big| \quad \binom{14}{4}$$

Total possibilities

$$\binom{6}{6} \cdot \binom{14}{4}$$

Consequently, card $(A) = \binom{6}{0} \cdot \binom{14}{10}$ and card $(B) = \binom{6}{6} \cdot \binom{14}{4}$, so

$$\Pr(A) = \frac{\text{card } (A)}{\text{card } (\Omega)} = \frac{\binom{6}{0} \cdot \binom{14}{10}}{\binom{20}{10}} \doteq .005$$

$$\Pr(B) = \frac{\text{card } (B)}{\text{card } (\Omega)} = \frac{\binom{6}{6} \cdot \binom{14}{4}}{\binom{20}{10}} \doteq .005$$

Thus, by the addition principle of probability,

$$Pr(E) = Pr(A \cup B) = Pr(A) + Pr(B) \doteq .01$$

Example 4.7.5 Poker A hand of poker consists of 5 cards dealt from an ordinary deck of 52 playing cards. What is the probability of getting a (pat) full house? (A full house is a hand consisting of 3 cards of one denomination and 2 cards of another, e.g., three kings and two 4s.)

The experiment consists of drawing 5 cards at random, without replacement, from a deck of 52 cards. This can be done in $\binom{52}{5}$ ways. Hence

$$\text{card } (\Omega) = \binom{52}{5} = 2{,}598{,}960$$

(It should be noted that a sample point is represented by 5 cards, which is a subset of 5 elements of the set of 52 cards.)

Let E be the event that a full house is obtained. We must determine how many sample points E contains, that is, how many ways a full house can be obtained. To count the ways, the methods of combinatorial analysis are used. There are 13 choices for the denomination of the three of a kind; once this has been chosen, there are 12 choices for the two of a kind. Hence there are $13 \cdot 12$ ways to choose the denominations of the cards that will appear in the hand.

Suppose that the denominations chosen are xs and ys. The number of ways it is possible to choose the 3 xs and 2 ys is $\binom{4}{3} \cdot \binom{4}{2} \cdot \binom{44}{0} = 4 \cdot 6 \cdot 1$, as indicated:

Cards

	xs	ys	Others
Subgroups	4	4	44

Hand

	xs	ys	Others
Number to be chosen	3	2	0

Number of ways	$\binom{4}{3}$	$\binom{4}{2}$	$\binom{44}{0}$
Total possibilities (by the sequential counting principle)	$\binom{4}{3}$ $\cdot$	$\binom{4}{2}$ $\cdot$	$\binom{44}{0} = 4 \cdot 6 \cdot 1$

Therefore, there are $13 \cdot 12 \cdot 4 \cdot 6 \cdot 1$ ways to get a full house. That is,

$$\text{card } (E) = 13 \cdot 12 \cdot 4 \cdot 6 \cdot 1 = 3{,}744$$

Consequently,

$$Pr(E) = \frac{3{,}744}{\binom{52}{5}} \doteq .001$$

We compiled a table of poker probabilities (Table 4.7.2). These probabilities are calculated in the same way as the above probability was calculated.

Table 4.7.2 Poker Probabilities

Hand	No. ways	Probability
1 Pair	1,098,240	.42257
2 Pair	123,552	.04754
3 of a kind	54,912	.02113
Straight*	10,200	.00392
Flush*	5,108	.00197
Full house	3,744	.00144
Four of a kind	624	.00024
Straight flush	40	.00002

*Not including straight flushes.

Exercises for 4.7

1. In a shipment of 40 bolts, 10 are defective. Twenty bolts are picked at random. Assume that all the bolts look alike and have an equal probability of being chosen; what is the probability that all 20 are nondefective?
2. A committee of 6 is selected at random from a group of faculty members consisting of 15 from the Mathematics Department, 20 from the Chemistry Department, and 10 from the English Department.
   (a) What is the probability that the committee will consist of 2 from the Mathematics Department and 4 from the Chemistry Department?
   (b) What is the probability that the committee will consist of 3 from the Mathematics Department and 3 from the English Department?
   (c) What is the probability that the committee will consist of 2 from the Mathematics Department, 2 from the Chemistry Department, and 2 from the English Department?
3. Five cards are dealt at random from a well-shuffled deck of 52 playing cards. Find the probability that
   (a) all are spades   (b) exactly two are hearts
   (c) exactly three are clubs   (d) all are red
4. An employer has three positions to fill from a group of 15 applicants, eight men and seven women. He selects at random from the applicants.
   (a) What is the probability that two will be men and one will be a woman?
   (b) What is the probability that he will select at least one woman? (*Hint:* It is easier to calculate the probability that none are women.)
5. A bridge hand consists of 13 cards dealt at random from a deck of 52. Calculate the probabilities of the following hands:
   (a) Any hand with 4 aces.
   (b) Any hand with exactly 4 aces and 2 kings.
   (c) A 6–5–2 distribution (i.e., 6 of one suit, 5 of another, and 2 of another).
   (d) A 4–3–3–3 distribution.
   (e) A 5–5–2–1 distribution.
6. Find the probability of getting exactly one pair of aces in a poker hand consisting of 5 cards dealt from a deck containing 52 cards (i.e., a hand of the form $AAxyz$, where $A = $ ace, $x \neq y \neq z \neq A$).
7. (a) Verify that the probability of getting two pairs in a poker hand of 5 cards dealt from a deck of 52 cards is approximately .04754.
   (b) Verify that the probability of getting 4 of a kind in a poker hand is about .00024.

8. In problem 9, Exercises 4.6, what is the probability that either John or Jim is chosen for the team?
9. In problem 1, what is the probability that at least three of the bolts selected are defective?
10. An elevator starts with six passengers and stops at eight floors. Assume that it is equally likely for a person to get off at any of the eight floors. What is the probability that no two passengers leave at the same floor?
11. In problem 7, Exercises 4.6, if four fuses are selected at random, what is the probability that at least three of them will be good?
12. Refer to problem 4, Exercises 3.7. If the committee of 6 is chosen at random from the 16 professors, what is the probability that it will consist of 1 life science, 2 social science, and 3 management science professors?
13. Refer to problem 6, Exercises 3.7. If the subcommittee of 6 is chosen at random from the 20 committee members, what is the probability that
    (a) none will be Democrats?
    (b) 2 will be Democrats and 4 will be Republicans?
14. If a fair die is rolled eight times, what is the probability of getting two 4s, three 5s, one 6, and two 1s. (*Hint:* See problem 10, Exercises 3.7.)

Section 4.8   Introduction to the Binomial Distribution

One of the most important applications of combinatorial analysis to probability is the development of the *binomial distribution*. This has so many applications and consequences that it will be discussed thoroughly in a later section of the chapter. At this time we shall simply illustrate the binomial distribution by considering the following example.

Example 4.8.1   Botany   A botanist is studying a delicate variety of flower. His findings show that 50 percent of all such flowers live to reach maturity. If the botanist plants 10 of these flowers, what is the probability that exactly 2 of them survive to maturity?

The random experiment consists of planting 10 flowers and noting which flowers reach maturity. An outcome (i.e., sample point) can be represented as a sequence of Ss (survived) and Ds (died). For example, the sample point

$$\omega = SDDSDDDDSS$$

represents the following outcome: the first flower survived, the second died, the third died, and so on. Since a flower is equally likely to die as survive, it is reasonable to assign equal probabilities to each possible outcome. Thus we have a uniform sample space, Ω. To figure out card (Ω) the sequential counting principal is used:

☐ ☐ ☐ ☐ ☐ ☐ ☐ ☐ ☐ ☐
S or D S or D $\cdots$

There are two possibilities for the first letter in the sequence representing a sample point, namely, S or D (the first flower either survives or dies). Corresponding to each of these possibilities, there are two possibilities for the second letter in the sequence representing a sample point (S or D), and so on. By the sequential counting principle there are

$$\underbrace{2 \cdot 2 \cdot \cdots \cdot 2}_{10 \text{ times}} = 2^{10}$$

possible outcomes. That is,

$$\text{card } (\Omega) = 2^{10} = 1{,}024$$

Let E be the event that exactly two of the flowers survive. The sample points constituting this event are just those sequences containing exactly two Ss. So the problem is to count how many of these sequences there are.

☐ ☐ $\boxed{S}$ ☐ ☐ ☐ $\boxed{S}$ ☐ ☐ ☐

This is equivalent to determining how many ways two boxes can be selected from 10. But this is just $\binom{10}{2}$. Thus

$$\text{card } (E) = \binom{10}{2} = 45$$

so

$$\Pr(E) = \frac{\text{card } (E)}{\text{card } (\Omega)} = \frac{45}{2^{10}} = \frac{45}{1{,}024} \doteq .044$$

The botanist is also interested in answering the following question. How many flowers must he plant to be at least 95 percent sure of having at least one flower survive to maturity?

This problem differs from the type previously considered, but is one that arises often. If we look back at the solution to the problem above, we see that the size of the sample space depends on the number of flowers that are planted. For example, if five flowers are planted, then the sample space consists of 2^5 sample points, and if seven flowers are planted, it consists of 2^7 sample points. If n is the number of flowers planted, the sample space consists of 2^n sample points. Let A be the event that at least one flower survives. The problem is to find n so that

$$\Pr(A) \geq .95$$

As usual, in these "at least one" situations, it is easier to calculate $\Pr(\bar{A})$. Now, $\bar{A}$ is the event that all flowers planted die before reaching maturity. It is easy to see that $\bar{A}$ consists of one sample point:

$$\omega = \underbrace{DDD \cdots D}_{n \text{ long}}$$

Thus card $(\bar{A}) = 1$. So, by Theorem 4.6.1,

$$\Pr(\bar{A}) = \frac{\text{card } (\bar{A})}{\text{card } (\Omega)} = \frac{1}{2^n}$$

This implies that

$$\Pr(A) = 1 - \frac{1}{2^n}$$

To make $\Pr(A) \geq .95$, we must choose n large enough (i.e., plant enough flowers) so that

$$1 - \frac{1}{2^n} \geq .95$$

This means that

$$\frac{1}{2^n} \le .05$$

or

$$2^n \ge 20$$

and this can be done by taking $n = 5$. In summary, then, in order to be at least 95 percent sure of getting at least one flower surviving to maturity, the botanist must plant at least five flowers.

Exercises for 4.8

1. A manufacturing company produces a product continuously throughout the year. It has been determined that under normal operating conditions, an item produced has a 50 percent chance of being defective. If on a particular day 10 items are selected at random from the assembly line, what is the probability that exactly 4 of the items are defective?
2. Assume that it is equally likely to have male and female children. If a family has five children, what is the probability that exactly three of them will be girls?
3. It has been determined that in a certain mathematics course there is a 50 percent chance that a student will drop out. In a class of 30 students, what is the probability that exactly 5 will drop out before the end of the semester?
4. If 50 percent of the population of a *large* city are Democrats, what is the probability that a random sample of 10 persons will contain exactly 6 Democrats?
5. A man is tossing a fair coin. In 10 tosses of the coin, what is the probability that the coin will come up heads exactly 3 times?
6. In problem 5, what is the minimum number of times that he must toss the coin to be at least 90 percent sure that he will get at least one head?
7. Suppose it is known that an elm tree has probability $\frac{1}{2}$ of having Dutch elm disease. If six trees are selected at random, what is the probability that
   (a) exactly five of them will have the disease?
   (b) at least one of them will have the disease?
8. A student takes a true–false exam. If the exam contains 20 questions and the student guesses at every question, what is the probability that
   (a) he gets exactly 90 percent of the questions correct?
   (b) he gets at least one answer correct?
9. It has been determined that a field-goal kicker has a 50 percent chance of making a field goal if he is kicking anywhere between the 45- and 55-yard lines.
   (a) What is the probability that he will make exactly four field goals in seven attempts from the 50-yard line?
   (b) What is the probability that he will make at least two field goals in seven attempts from the 50-yard line?
10. In problem 2:
   (a) What is the probability of the family having at least two boys?
   (b) How many children must a family have to be at least 95 percent sure of having at least one boy?
11. Fifty percent of a *large* class of stocks pays no dividends. What is the probability that out of a random sample of 15 stocks, exactly 7 will pay dividends?
12. A supposed connoisseur of wine claims that he is able to distinguish between two kinds of wines with 95 percent accuracy. He presents his claim to an agency interested in hiring a wine connoisseur. To test his claim, the following experiment is conducted: the man is to taste two types of wines and distinguish between them. This is to be done 9 times.

If the man is correct at least 7 of the 9 times, he is hired. Assume that the man is a fraud; what is the probability that he is hired? (*Hint:* If he is a fraud, he must guess at each trial.)

Section 4.9 Conditional Probability: Motivation and Definitions

Conditional probability is an important tool in the study of probability. Intuitively, the probability of an event occurring will change given additional information. Because of this, the notion of conditional probability arises naturally in countless situations.

In many instances it is quite easy to answer questions that involve conditional probability without a mathematically rigorous definition.

Example 4.9.1 Dice Suppose that a fair die is rolled. The experiment has six possible outcomes and we can set $\Omega = \{1, 2, 3, 4, 5, 6\}$. Since the die is fair, each sample point is assigned probability $\frac{1}{6}$. In particular, then, $\Pr(\{5\}) = \frac{1}{6}$.

Now, suppose that we are given the additional information that the number that appears on the die is odd. Now what is the probability that the die shows 5? It is certainly more likely now, and you may very well guess the correct answer. It is $\frac{1}{3}$.

On the other hand, suppose that we are told that the number appearing on the die is even. This certainly affects the probability that a 5 came up. Indeed, given that the number appearing is even, it is impossible that the die came up 5. So, intuitively, the "conditional" probability of a 5, given that the die shows an even number, equals zero.

The above example clearly illustrates that additional information concerning a random experiment can certainly affect the probabilities. In the example it is not too difficult to figure out what these "conditional" probabilities should be without resorting to a mathematically precise definition of conditional probability. However, it does not take long for problems that involve conditional probabilities to grow so complex that a mathematical definition of conditional probability is not only desirable but absolutely necessary.

Next we present some examples which involve conditional probabilities that will be solved following a precise definition of conditional probability. The reader is invited to try to solve these problems beforehand.

Example 4.9.2 Sexes of Children Assume that it is equally likely to have male and female children and that the sexes of previous children do not affect those of future children. Consider a family with two children. There are four possibilities and we take

$$\Omega = \{bb, bg, gb, gg\}$$

where, for example, *bg* represents "first child boy, second child girl." Because of the assumptions above, it is reasonable to assign probability $\frac{1}{4}$ to each sample point (more about this later). So

$$\Pr(\{bb\}) = \Pr(\{bg\}) = \Pr(\{gb\}) = \Pr(\{gg\}) = \tfrac{1}{4}$$

Given that a family with two children has a girl, what is the probability that both children are girls?

A slightly different type of problem is the following.

Example 4.9.3 Smoking Statistics indicate that 55 percent of the population is female and that 16.5 percent of the population consists of women who smoke. What is the probability that a woman chosen at random will be a smoker?

Before stating the formal definition of conditional probability, some simple examples will be examined to discover what a suitable definition would be. The following notation is employed. If E and F are events, the conditional probability of E given that F occurred is denoted by

$$\Pr(E\,|\,F)$$

The problem at hand is to determine how to define this quantity in terms of the original probabilities.

Example 4.9.4 Dice Consider the dice experiment of Example 4.9.1. How can we determine the probability that a 5 appears on the die *given* that the number appearing on the die is odd? We reason as follows. Given that the number appearing on the die is odd, there are three possibilities: it is 1, 3, or 5. Since each possibility is equally likely (the die is fair), it is reasonable to assign the number $\frac{1}{3}$ as the conditional probability of a 5 given that the die comes up odd. In the terminology of the previous paragraph, if $A = \{5\}$ and $B = \{1, 3, 5\}$, we would expect to have

$$\Pr(A\,|\,B) = \tfrac{1}{3} \tag{4.9.1}$$

As was pointed out in Example 4.9.1, given that the number appearing on the die is even, the probability that a 5 appears is zero. So, if C is the event that the die comes up even (i.e., $C = \{2, 4, 6\}$), we would expect to have

$$\Pr(A\,|\,C) = 0 \tag{4.9.2}$$

The idea involved in both Eqs. (4.9.1) and (4.9.2) is, given that an event F occurs, we really have a new sample space—Ω is replaced by F. The reason is that the set of all *possible* outcomes is no longer Ω but is now F.

Example 4.9.5 Coin Tossing Consider the random experiment of tossing a fair coin three times. So

$$\Omega = \{\text{HHH, HHT, HTH, HTT, THH, THT, TTH, TTT}\}$$

and each sample point has probability $\frac{1}{8}$. Let A be the event that exactly two of the three tosses yield heads and B be the event that the first toss is a head. Then

$$A = \{\text{HHT, HTH, THH}\}$$
$$B = \{\text{HHH, HHT, HTH, HTT}\}$$

What is $\Pr(A\,|\,B)$?

Given that the first toss is a head, the sample space (i.e., set of all possible outcomes) now becomes B. *Now* the only way that A can occur is if either HHT or HTH is the result of the experiment, that is, if $\{\text{HHT, HTH}\}$ occurs. But this last event is just the part of A in B—mathematically $A \cap B$. In summary, then, *given that B occurs, then A occurs if and only if $A \cap B$ occurs* (see Figure 4.9.1). Because $A \cap B$ consists of two sample points and B consists of four, it is reasonable to expect that

$$\Pr(A\,|\,B) = \tfrac{2}{4} = \tfrac{1}{2} \tag{4.9.3}$$

[We used the computer to perform the following experiment repeatedly: Toss a fair coin three times. Check and see if B occurred (i.e., the first toss was a head). If so,

Figure 4.9.1

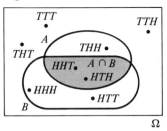

observe whether or not A occurred. Now, if Eq. (4.9.3) is correct, we expect that in the long run about two in every four times (.5) A will occur when B occurred (this is just the relative frequency interpretation again). The computer output shown in Table 4.9.1 confirms the reasonableness of Eq. (4.9.3).]

Table 4.9.1 Conditional Probability of Exactly Two Heads in Three Tosses of a Fair Coin Given that the First Toss Is a Head *

Trial	n_B	$n_{A \cap B}$	Proportion of times A occurs when B occurs
10,000	5,042	2,573	.510
20,000	10,048	5,110	.509
30,000	15,026	7,646	.509
40,000	20,045	10,162	.507
50,000	25.063	12,598	.503
60,000	30,071	15,147	.504
70,000	35,096	17,664	.503
80,000	40,133	20,207	.504
90,000	45,116	22,624	.501
100,000	50,129	25,103	.501
200,000	100,220	50,301	.502
300,000	150,079	75,231	.501
400,000	200,031	100,018	.500
500,000	250,251	125,244	.500

*A, event that exactly two heads come up; B, event that the first toss is a head; n_B = no. occurrences of B and $n_{A \cap B}$ = no. occurrences of A when B occurs.

Let us analyze Eq. (4.9.3) a little more closely. We expect Eq. (4.9.3) to be true because $A \cap B$ consists of two of the four sample points of B,

$$\frac{\text{card } (A \cap B)}{\text{card } (B)} = \tfrac{2}{4} = \tfrac{1}{2} \tag{4.9.4}$$

and because all sample points are equally likely (the coin is fair). Comparing Eqs. (4.9.3) and (4.9.4) we see that in this case (uniform sample space) it is reasonable to define

$$\Pr(A \mid B) = \frac{\text{card } (A \cap B)}{\text{card } (B)} \tag{4.9.5}$$

Using Eq. (4.9.5) it is easy to express $\Pr(A\,|\,B)$ in terms of the original probabilities. For since Ω is uniform,

$$\Pr(E) = \frac{\text{card } (E)}{\text{card } (\Omega)}$$

for any event E [Eq. (4.6.1)]. Thus

$$\frac{\text{card } (A \cap B)}{\text{card } (B)} = \frac{\text{card } (A \cap B)/\text{card } (\Omega)}{\text{card } (B)/\text{card } (\Omega)} = \frac{\Pr(A \cap B)}{\Pr(B)}$$

Comparing this with Eq. (4.9.5) gives an expression for the conditional probability in terms of the original probabilities,

$$\Pr(A\,|\,B) = \frac{\Pr(A \cap B)}{\Pr(B)}$$

Using this equation for motivation, the following definition is now made.

Definition

Let Ω be a sample space and let E and F be events. Assume that $\Pr(F) > 0$. Then the *conditional probability of E given that F occurred* is denoted by $\Pr(E\,|\,F)$ (read "the probability of E given F") and is defined to be

$$\Pr(E\,|\,F) = \frac{\Pr(E \cap F)}{\Pr(F)} \qquad\qquad (4.9.6)$$

We emphasize that we now have two means at our disposal for calculating conditional probabilities. The first is by using a *new* sample space as was done in Examples 4.9.4 and 4.9.5, and the second is by using formula (4.9.6). Notice that the probabilities involved on the right-hand side of Eq. (4.9.6) are with respect to the *original* sample space.

Exercises for 4.9

1. A fair coin is tossed twice. Find the probability of obtaining at least one head given that the first toss is a tail.
2. A pair of fair dice is rolled. If the first die turns up a 3, what is the probability that the sum showing is 6?
3. What is the probability of rolling a 7 with a pair of fair dice given that the first one shows a 4?
4. A fair coin is tossed three times. What is the probability of
   (a) exactly two tails given that the first is a head?
   (b) at least two heads if the first is a tail?
   (c) exactly three tails if the first is a head?
5. Five candidates, C_1, C_2, C_3, C_4, and C_5, are running for office each with an equal probability of being elected. Of the five, two are Democrats, two are Republicans, and one is an independent.
   (a) What is the probability that a Republican is elected given that the independent is defeated?

(b) What is the probability that a Republican is elected given that the Democrats are defeated?

6. A student is taking an exam consisting of four true–false questions. Assume that he guesses; what is the probability that
   (a) all four questions are answered correctly given that he answers the first question correctly?
   (b) all four questions are answered correctly given that he answers at least three of the four correctly?

7. Let A and B be events with $\Pr(A) = \frac{1}{3}$, $\Pr(B) = \frac{1}{2}$, and $\Pr(A \cap B) = \frac{1}{4}$. Use Eq. (4.9.6) to find
   (a) $\Pr(A \mid B)$ (b) $\Pr(B \mid A)$

8. Suppose that A and B are events with $\Pr(A \mid B) = \frac{1}{3}$ and $\Pr(B) = \frac{1}{2}$. What is $\Pr(A \cap B)$?

9. Let A and B be nonempty events. Which of the following are true and which are false?
   (a) $\Pr(A \mid A) = 1$ (b) $\Pr(B \mid \bar{B}) = 1$ (assume that $\bar{B} \neq \emptyset$)
   (c) $\Pr(\emptyset \mid B) = 0$ (d) If $\Pr(B) = 1$, $\Pr(A \mid B) = \Pr(A)$.
   (e) $\Pr(B \mid A) = \Pr(A \mid B)$

10. If $E \subset F$, what is $\Pr(F \mid E)$? (Assume that $E \neq \emptyset$.)

11. Suppose that $\Pr(E \mid F) = \Pr(E \cap F)$. Is it necessarily true that $\Pr(F) = 1$?

12. In a shipment of 1-inch finishing nails, 6 percent are crooked and 3 percent are too long and crooked. What is the probability that a nail selected at random is too long if we know that it is crooked?

13. Two digits are selected at random from the digits 1 through 9. If their sum is even, what is the probability that both numbers are even? (*Note:* A particular digit can be selected twice.)

14. A man is dealt 4 hearts from an ordinary deck of 52 playing cards. If he is given 3 more cards, what is the probability that at least one of them is also a heart?

15. Let E and F be events with $\Pr(E) = \frac{1}{3}$, $\Pr(F) = \frac{1}{2}$, and $\Pr(E \cap F) = \frac{1}{4}$. Find
    (a) $\Pr(\bar{E} \mid \bar{F})$ (b) $\Pr(\bar{F} \mid \bar{E})$

16. Let E and F be events with $\Pr(F) > 0$. Find $\Pr(E \mid F)$ if E and F are mutually exclusive.

Section 4.10   Conditional Probability: Remarks and Applications

The advantage of the use of Eq. (4.9.6) for the definition of conditional probability (i.e., of defining conditional probability in terms of the original probabilities) is that there is no need to consider F as the *new* sample space. All calculations are done within the old sample space. This, as we shall see, is advantageous when dealing with problems that concern the entire sample space which also involve conditional probabilities. Moreover, in many important applications, the conditional probabilities are given and then Eq. (4.9.6) can be used to calculate the probability of the intersection of two events (see Section 4.11). However, if the only problems to be solved are those involved with the new sample space, then it is often more desirable to discard the original sample space altogether and work exclusively with the new one as we did in Examples 4.9.4 and 4.9.5.

Example 4.10.1   Dice   Referring back to Example 4.9.4, let us check and see if by using Eq. (4.9.6), we come to the same conclusions as in Eqs. (4.9.1) and (4.9.2). Since the die is fair, for any event E,

$$\Pr(E) = \frac{\text{card } (E)}{\text{card } (\Omega)} = \frac{\text{card } (E)}{6}$$

Now $A = \{5\}$ and $B = \{1, 3, 5\}$, so $A \cap B = \{5\}$. By Eq. (4.9.6),

$$\Pr(A \mid B) = \frac{\Pr(A \cap B)}{\Pr(B)} = \frac{\text{card } (A \cap B)/6}{\text{card } (B)/6}$$

$$= \frac{\frac{1}{6}}{\frac{3}{6}} = \frac{1}{3}$$

which agrees with Eq. (4.9.1).

Next, $C = \{2, 4, 6\}$ and so $A \cap C = \emptyset$. By Eq. (4.9.6),

$$\Pr(A \mid C) = \frac{\Pr(A \cap C)}{\Pr(C)} = \frac{\text{card } (A \cap C)/6}{\text{card } (C)/6}$$

$$= \frac{\frac{0}{6}}{\frac{3}{6}} = 0$$

which agrees with Eq. (4.9.2).

Example 4.10.2 Cards Consider the experiment of choosing a card at random from an ordinary deck of 52. What is the probability that a red ace is selected given that the card chosen is a heart?

Let A be the event that a red ace is selected. Then A contains two sample points:

$$A = \{\text{ace of hearts, ace of diamonds}\}$$

Let B be the event that the card selected is a heart. Then B contains 13 sample points. Also,

$$A \cap B = \{\text{ace of hearts}\}$$

Thus

$$\Pr(A \mid B) = \frac{\Pr(A \cap B)}{\Pr(B)} = \frac{\frac{1}{52}}{\frac{13}{52}} = \frac{1}{13}$$

This certainly makes good sense. For if it is known that a heart is selected, there is only 1 chance in 13 that it is a red ace—if it is the ace of hearts.

The definition of conditional probability Eq. (4.9.6) will now be used to solve the two problems posed at the beginning of Section 4.9.

Solution to Example 4.9.2 Let A be the event that both children are girls and B be the event that the family has a girl. Then

$$A = \{gg\} \quad \text{and} \quad B = \{bg, gb, gg\}$$

We want $\Pr(A \mid B)$. Now, by definition,

$$\Pr(A \mid B) = \frac{\Pr(A \cap B)}{\Pr(B)}$$

But $A \cap B = \{gg\}$, so

$$\Pr(A \mid B) = \frac{\Pr(A \cap B)}{\Pr(B)} = \frac{\frac{1}{4}}{\frac{3}{4}} = \frac{1}{3}$$

You may have thought that the answer to this problem should be $\frac{1}{2}$. For, either the other child is a boy or the other child is a girl. This is true, but these last two events do not have the same probability. There are two ways the other child can be a boy ($\{bg\}$ or $\{gb\}$) and only one way the other child can be a girl ($\{gg\}$).

If the problem were, "What is the probability that both children are girls given that the first born is a girl?", the answer would be $\frac{1}{2}$. To see this, let C be the event that the first born is a girl. Then $C = \{gb, gg\}$, so $\Pr(C) = \frac{1}{4} + \frac{1}{4} = \frac{1}{2}$. Also, $A \cap C = \{gg\}$, so $\Pr(A \cap C) = \frac{1}{4}$. Thus

$$\Pr(A \mid C) = \frac{\Pr(A \cap C)}{\Pr(C)} = \frac{\frac{1}{4}}{\frac{1}{2}} = \frac{1}{2}$$

Solution to Example 4.9.3 To solve this problem, the data are first translated into probabilities. Let A be the event that a person chosen at random is a smoker and B be the event that a person chosen at random is a woman. That 55 percent of the population is female translates to

$$\Pr(B) = .55$$

Now, note that $A \cap B$ is the event that a person chosen at random is a smoker and a woman (i.e., a woman smoker). Hence that 16.5 percent of the population consists of women smokers means that

$$\Pr(A \cap B) = .165$$

The problem is to find the probability that a woman chosen at random will be a smoker. In other words, given that the person chosen is a woman (B), what is the (conditional) probability that the person is a smoker (A)? But this is just

$$\Pr(A \mid B) = \frac{\Pr(A \cap B)}{\Pr(B)} = \frac{.165}{.55} = .30$$

Interpreted back in percentages, this means that 30 percent of the women are smokers.

Example 4.10.3 In a city of 100,000 it has been determined that 91,000 people own a car and that 2,000 people do not own a car but own a motorcycle. What percentage of the people who *do not* own a car own a motorcycle?

To solve this problem, we first translate the data into probabilities. Let

$$C = \text{event a person selected at random owns a car}$$
$$M = \text{event a person selected at random owns a motorcycle}$$

Then according to the data,

$$\Pr(C) = .91 \qquad \Pr(\tilde{C} \cap M) = .02$$

The problem reduces to determining the conditional probability of M given $\tilde{C}$. We have $\Pr(\tilde{C}) = 1 - \Pr(C) = .09$, and so

$$\Pr(M \mid \tilde{C}) = \frac{\Pr(M \cap \tilde{C})}{\Pr(\tilde{C})} = \frac{.02}{.09} \doteq .22$$

In other words, about 22 percent of the people who do not own a car do own a motorcycle.

Exercises for 4.10

1. Suppose that a pair of fair dice is rolled. Find the following conditional probability in two ways; first by using a new sample space, and second by using Eq. (4.9.6). What is the probability that an 11 is rolled given that at least one of the dice shows a 5?

2. What is the new sample space in the first part of problem 1? If the statement "at least one of the dice shows a 5" is changed to "exactly one of the dice shows a 5" in the above conditional probability, is the new sample space changed? If it is changed, what is it?

3. Find the following conditional probability in two ways: a fair coin is tossed four times. What is the probability of obtaining exactly three heads given that the second toss resulted in a tail?

4. Compare solutions obtained to problems 2 and 3, Exercises 4.9, by using Eq. (4.9.6) and by constructing new sample spaces.

5. Assume that the birth of a boy or a girl is equally likely and that the sexes of previous offspring do not affect those of future offspring. A family is known to have four children.

   (a) What is the probability that all the children are boys given that the three oldest are boys?

   (b) Given that at least three of the children are boys, what is the probability that all are boys?

6. Suppose that a pair of fair dice is rolled.

   (a) Find the probability that a 7 is rolled given that the sum of the faces is odd.

   (b) What is the probability that a 7 is rolled given that the two dice show the same number?

7. From a group of 10 people, one president, two vice-presidents, and one treasurer are to be selected at random. Among the 10 people are Mr. Scott and Mr. Jones. What is the probability that Jones is selected as president given that Scott is selected as a vice-president?

8. From a group of 15 people, 5 are to be selected at random to represent the group at a symposium. Of the 15 people, 2 are women. What is the probability that both women are selected given that at least one of them is?

9. A poker hand consisting of 5 cards is dealt from an ordinary deck of 52 playing cards.

   (a) What is the probability that a hand will contain four aces given that it contains at least two aces?

   (b) What is the probability of getting a flush given that at least four of the cards are hearts?

10. An urn contains five red balls and three blue balls. Two balls are selected one at a time without replacement. What is the probability of

    (a) selecting two blue balls if the first ball selected was blue?

    (b) selecting a blue ball if the first ball selected was red?

    (c) selecting at least one red ball if the first ball selected was red?

11. Let A, B, and C be events of the sample space Ω with A and B mutually exclusive. If $\Pr(C) > 0$, show that

$$\Pr(A \cup B \,|\, C) = \Pr(A \,|\, C) + \Pr(B \,|\, C)$$

12. Let B, C, and D be events of the sample space Ω with $B \cup C = \Omega$ and $B \cap C = \emptyset$. Suppose that $\Pr(D) > 0$. Show that for any event A,

$$\Pr(A \,|\, D) = \Pr(A \cap B \,|\, D) + \Pr(A \cap C \,|\, D)$$

*13. Four people, called East, West, North, and South, are playing bridge. Each is dealt 13 cards from an ordinary deck of 52 playing cards.

   (a) If North has one ace, what is the probability that his partner, South, has two of the three other aces?

(b) If East and West together have seven spades, what is the probability that North and South each has three spades?

14. Let A and B be events with $\Pr(B) > 0$. Show that $\Pr(\bar{A}|B) = 1 - \Pr(A|B)$. (*Hint:* Use problem 11.)

Section 4.11 Law of Total Probability[1]

In this section we begin a deeper study into the ideas and consequences of conditional probability. We commence with two illustrative examples that will be solved following some discussion.

Example 4.11.1 Disease Testing A test for determining whether or not a person has a certain disease has been used for several years. Experience (i.e., relative frequency) indicates that if the person has the disease, the probability that the test will be positive is .9 (and so the probability that it will be negative if the person has the disease is .1). On the other hand, if the person does not have the disease, the test will be positive with probability .05 (and hence negative with probability .95). It is known that the probability of a person having this disease is .001 (i.e., about 1 in every 1,000 people has the disease).

1. If a person is selected at random and given the test, what is the probability that the test will be positive?
2. Given that the test shows positive, what is the probability that the person has the disease?
3. What is the probability that the test will yield incorrect information?

Example 4.11.2 Voting Percentages by Religion The population of the United States is 75 percent Protestant, 20 percent Catholic, and 5 percent Jewish. The voting records of these groups indicate the following:

	Democratic	Republican
Catholic	55%	45%
Jewish	60%	40%
Protestant	40%	60%

1. What percentage of the country votes Democratic (i.e., what is the probability that a person selected at random will vote Democratic)?
2. What percentage of the Democratic voters are Catholic (i.e., if a person selected at random turns out to be a Democratic voter, what is the probability that he is a Catholic)?

To solve the two problems presented at the beginning of this section, it is first necessary to discuss two results. The first is the *law of total probability* and the second is *Bayes' formula.*

The concepts involved in developing these results are most easily introduced by

[1]Those wishing a briefer treatment of probability may omit Sections 4.11 and 4.12.

an example. Before beginning, however, it should be pointed out that in many situations the conditional probability $\Pr(E \mid F)$ and the probability $\Pr(F)$ will be given or be clear from context. In these cases it is often quite important to calculate $\Pr(E \cap F)$. This can be done by rewriting Eq. (4.9.6) as

$$\Pr(E \cap F) = \Pr(E \mid F)\Pr(F) \qquad (4.11.1)$$

This is the *multiplication principle* of probability and gives us a formula for calculating the probability of the intersection of two events. It is read "the probability that E and F both occur equals the probability that E occurs given that F occurs times the probability that F occurs."

A simple example illustrating the use of the above formula is

Example 4.11.3 Cards Consider the random experiment of choosing 2 cards at random from a deck of 52. If the first card is *not* replaced before the second is drawn, what is the probability that the first card is a spade and the second a heart?
    There are actually two ways to solve this problem.

SOLUTION 1

Since order matters here, the random experiment has $52 \cdot 51$ possible outcomes (52 possibilities for the first card, then 51 possibilities for the second). Thus

$$\text{card } (\Omega) = 52 \cdot 51$$

Let A be the event that the first card is a spade and the second is a heart. Then A can occur in $13 \cdot 13$ ways (13 possibilities for the spade and 13 possibilities for the heart). So

$$\text{card } (A) = 13 \cdot 13$$

Hence, by Eq. (4.6.1),

$$\Pr(A) = \frac{\text{card } (A)}{\text{card } (\Omega)} = \frac{13 \cdot 13}{52 \cdot 51} \doteq .064$$

The second solution is actually the one we want to illustrate. It is really a more natural way to solve the problem.

SOLUTION 2

Now, let F be the event that the first card selected is a spade and E be the event that the second card is a heart. Then, in the notation of solution 1, $A = E \cap F$. To calculate $\Pr(A) = \Pr(E \cap F)$, Eq. (4.11.1) is used.
    First, it is clear that $\Pr(F) = \frac{13}{52}$ (13 spades of 52 cards). Now, given that F occurs (i.e., the first card drawn is a spade), there are 51 cards remaining and 13 of them are hearts (since a space was drawn the first time). Hence

$$\Pr(E \mid F) = \frac{13}{51}$$

Notice that we did not use Eq. (4.9.6) to calculate this. It is clear from the situation. Now, when we use Eq. (4.11.1), the following is obtained:

$$\Pr(A) = \Pr(E \cap F) = \Pr(E \mid F)\Pr(F) = \frac{13}{51} \cdot \frac{13}{52} \doteq .064$$

which agrees with solution 1. However, the reader will agree that this solution is more natural than the first.

Example 4.11.4 Chips in Bowls Two bowls are placed on a table. The first bowl contains 4 red and 2 white chips. The second contains 1 red and 3 white chips (Figure 4.11.1). A bowl is chosen at random (say, by tossing a fair coin). Following this, a chip is selected at random from the bowl chosen.

Figure 4.11.1

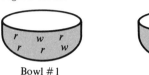

Bowl #1   Bowl #2

There are two types of questions to be answered. They are:

1. What is the probability that a white chip is selected?
2. Given that a white chip was selected, what is the probability that it was drawn from bowl 2?

To answer these questions we let

$$B_1 = \text{event bowl 1 is selected}$$
$$B_2 = \text{event bowl 2 is selected}$$
$$W = \text{event a white chip is selected}$$
$$R \ = \text{event a red chip is selected}$$

For the first question the problem is to find $\Pr(W)$. The idea is this. Once we know which bowl was selected, the probability of selecting a white chip is clear from the context of the problem. For example, *given* that bowl 1 was selected, the probability of selecting a white chip is $\frac{2}{6}$ (there are 2 white chips and 6 chips altogether in bowl 1). In other words, from the context of the problem it is known that

$$\Pr(W|B_1) = \tfrac{2}{6}$$

This is in contrast to some of the previous problems, where we calculated the conditional probabilities from the *unconditional* probabilities via Eq. (4.9.6). Here we can think of the conditional probabilities as given and from these we shall calculate *unconditional* probabilities. As above, it is clear that

$$\Pr(W|B_2) = \tfrac{3}{4}$$

Also, since each bowl is equally likely to be chosen (by assumption),

$$\Pr(B_1) = \tfrac{1}{2} \qquad \Pr(B_2) = \tfrac{1}{2}$$

Now, here is the crucial point. A white chip can be selected in either one of two mutually exclusive ways: *either bowl 1 is chosen and a white chip is selected* or *bowl 2 is chosen and a white chip is selected.*

We shall now proceed to write this statement in the terminology of sets. First, either B_1 or B_2 must occur, because either bowl 1 or bowl 2 is selected (Figure 4.11.2). Hence, in set terminology

$$B_1 \cup B_2 = \Omega \tag{4.11.2}$$

Moreover, B_1 and B_2 cannot occur simultaneously (i.e., they are mutually exclusive). (If bowl 1 is selected, bowl 2 is not.) So

$$B_1 \cap B_2 = \varnothing \tag{4.11.3}$$

Figure 4.11.2

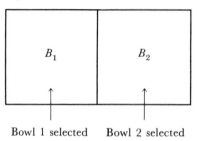

Bowl 1 selected   Bowl 2 selected

The event that bowl 1 is chosen *and* a white chip is selected is $B_1 \cap W$. The event that bowl 2 is chosen *and* a white chip is selected is $B_2 \cap W$ (Figure 4.11.3). Thus

Figure 4.11.3

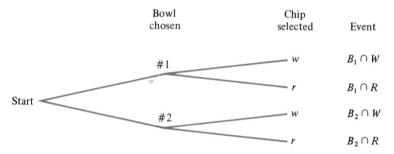

the italic statement above Eq. (4.11.2) can be written in set terminology as

$$W = (B_1 \cap W) \cup (B_2 \cap W) \tag{4.11.4}$$

Figure 4.11.4

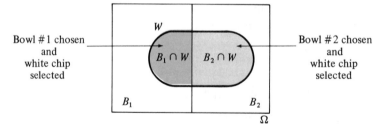

Bowl #1 chosen and white chip selected   Bowl #2 chosen and white chip selected

We can also obtain Eq. (4.11.4) directly from Eq. (4.11.2) since

$$W = \Omega \cap W = (B_1 \cup B_2) \cap W$$
$$= (B_1 \cap W) \cup (B_2 \cap W)$$

but the other derivation is more instructive.

Finally, the experiment makes it clear that $B_1 \cap W$ and $B_2 \cap W$ are mutually exclusive:

$$(B_1 \cap W) \cap (B_2 \cap W) = \emptyset \tag{4.11.5}$$

Set theoretically this follows immediately from Eq. (4.11.3), because

$$(B_1 \cap W) \cap (B_2 \cap W) = (B_1 \cap B_2) \cap W$$
$$= \emptyset \cap W = \emptyset$$

From Eqs. (4.11.4) and (4.11.5) we can now conclude by using the addition principle of probability that

$$\Pr(W) = \Pr(B_1 \cap W) + \Pr(B_2 \cap W) \qquad (4.11.6)$$

Now the problem is to calculate $\Pr(B_1 \cap W)$ and $\Pr(B_2 \cap W)$. But, by Eq. (4.11.1),

$$\Pr(B_1 \cap W) = \Pr(W \cap B_1) = \Pr(W \mid B_1)\Pr(B_1) = \tfrac{2}{6} \cdot \tfrac{1}{2} = \tfrac{1}{6}$$
$$\Pr(B_2 \cap W) = \Pr(W \cap B_2) = \Pr(W \mid B_2)\Pr(B_2) = \tfrac{3}{4} \cdot \tfrac{1}{2} = \tfrac{3}{8}$$

Consequently,

$$\Pr(W) = \tfrac{1}{6} + \tfrac{3}{8} = \tfrac{13}{24}$$

A tree diagram is quite useful for indicating the procedure used in solving this problem (Figure 4.11.5).

Figure 4.11.5

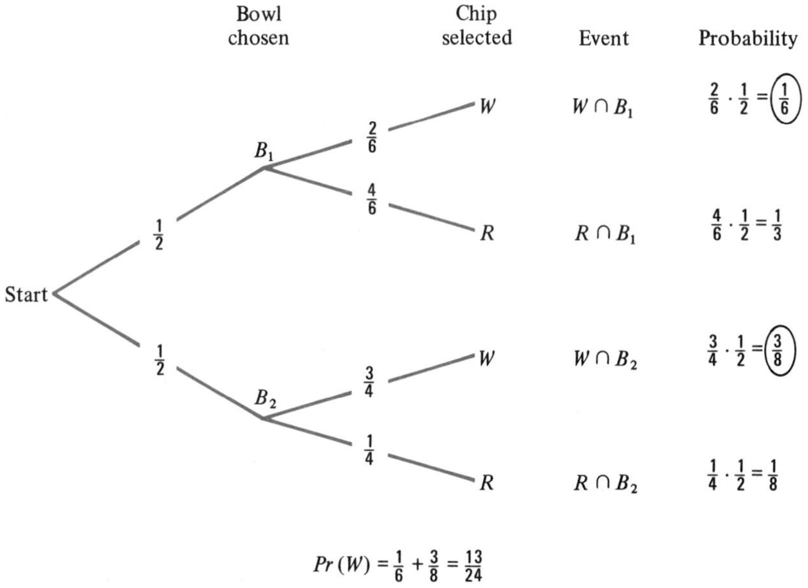

Bowl chosen	Chip selected	Event	Probability

$$Pr(W) = \tfrac{1}{6} + \tfrac{3}{8} = \tfrac{13}{24}$$

The preceding arguments are summarized in the following.

Theorem 4.11.1
Let Ω be the sample space of a random experiment and let E be an event. Suppose that F_1 and F_2 are two nonempty mutually exclusive events and that either F_1 occurs or F_2 occurs. In set terminology

$$F_1 \cap F_2 = \emptyset \qquad \text{and} \qquad F_1 \cup F_2 = \Omega \qquad (4.11.7)$$

Then

$$\Pr(E) = \Pr(E \cap F_1) + \Pr(E \cap F_2) \qquad (4.11.8)$$

so by Eq. (4.11.1),

$$Pr(E) = Pr(E \mid F_1)Pr(F_1) + Pr(E \mid F_2)Pr(F_2) \qquad (4.11.9)$$

(see Figure 4.11.6). Theorem 4.11.1 is often referred to as the *law of total probability.*

Figure 4.11.6

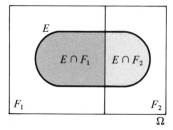

Exercises for 4.11

1. Let A, B, and C be events with $Pr(A \mid B) = .6$, $Pr(A \mid C) = .7$, $Pr(B) = .5$, and $Pr(C) = .4$. Then
   (a) $Pr(A \cap B) = ?$ (b) $Pr(A \cap C) = ?$

2. Two cards are drawn at random from an ordinary deck of 52 playing cards. If the first card is not replaced before the second is drawn, what is the probability of drawing an ace and then a queen?

3. Suppose that in a shipment of 100 light bulbs, 15 of them are defective. If 2 bulbs are picked at random without replacement, what is the probability that the first will be satisfactory and the second defective?

4. Two U.S. Senators are chosen at random to be co-chairmen of a subcommittee.
   (a) Use conditional probability to determine the probability that both Senators are from California.
   (b) What is the probability that both Senators are from the same state?

5. Let E and F be events with $Pr(E) > 0$ and $Pr(F) > 0$. Show that
   $$Pr(F) \cdot Pr(E \mid F) = Pr(E) \cdot Pr(F \mid E)$$

6. Suppose that A, B, and C are events with $Pr(A \cap B) > 0$. Show that
   (a) $Pr(A \cap B \cap C) = Pr(A)Pr(B \mid A)Pr(C \mid A \cap B)$
   (b) $Pr(B \cap C \mid A) = Pr(C \mid A \cap B)Pr(B \mid A)$

7. An urn consists of 10 chips: 3 red, 5 white, and 2 blue. Three chips are chosen at random. When a chip is selected it is *not replaced* before the next one is chosen. Use conditional probability to determine the probability that the first two chips selected are white and the third is blue. [*Hint:* Problem 6(a).]

8. Let A, B, and C be events of the sample space Ω with $B \cup C = \Omega$ and $B \cap C = \emptyset$. If $Pr(A \mid B) = \frac{4}{5}$, $Pr(A \mid C) = \frac{1}{2}$, $Pr(B) = \frac{7}{10}$, and $Pr(C) = \frac{3}{10}$, then
   (a) $Pr(A) = ?$ (b) $Pr(B \mid A) = ?$

9. Suppose that we have two boxes, I and II, containing red and blue balls. Box I contains two blue balls and three red balls, and box II contains one blue ball and two red balls. One of the boxes is selected at random and one ball drawn from it. What is the probability that it will be red?

10. The National Football League has determined that out of all college football players drafted by the NFL only 60 percent will actually be qualified to play professional football. To aid in screening the nonqualified draftees, all are put through a physical test designed so that a qualified draftee will pass the test 95 percent of the time while a nonqualified

draftee will pass the test only 15 percent of the time. What is the probability that a draftee selected at random will pass the physical test?

11. Consider a machine that produces bolts, and suppose that when the machine is working properly, 90 percent of the bolts meet the required specifications, but when the machine is not working properly, only 60 percent of the bolts meet the required specifications. It has been determined that the machine is working properly 95 percent of the time. If a bolt is selected at random as it leaves the machine, what is the probability that it meets the required specifications?

12. A questionnaire is given to a group of people consisting of 65 percent Democrats and 35 percent Republicans. Suppose that 70 percent of the Republicans and 10 percent of the Democrats vote in favor of a given policy. What is the probability that if a person is selected at random, he will vote in favor of this policy?

13. From a group of 10 executives, 2 are to be selected at random to be vice-presidents. Of the 10 executives, 7 are male and 3 are female. What is the probability that the second executive chosen to be vice-president is a female?

Section 4.12   Bayes' Formula

In this section we develop the second result that is needed to solve the types of problems introduced at the beginning of Section 4.11.

Example 4.12.1   Chips in Bowls   Here we will show how to answer the second question posed in Example 4.11.4: given that a white chip was selected, what is the probability that it was drawn from bowl 2? It seems plausible from the situation that if a white chip is selected, it is more likely to come from bowl 2 than bowl 1. Let us prove this.

The problem is to find $\Pr(B_2 \mid W)$. We know $\Pr(W \mid B_2)\ (= \frac{3}{4})$ but we do not know $\Pr(B_2 \mid W)$. The trick is to use Eqs. (4.9.6) and (4.11.1) to "switch" B_2 and W.

$$\Pr(B_2 \mid W) = \frac{\Pr(B_2 \cap W)}{\Pr(W)} = \frac{\Pr(W \cap B_2)}{\Pr(W)}$$

$$= \frac{\Pr(W \mid B_2)\Pr(B_2)}{\Pr(W)}$$

Now we know that $\Pr(W \mid B_2) = \frac{3}{4}$ and $\Pr(B_2) = \frac{1}{2}$. Also, Eq. (4.11.9) was just used to show that $\Pr(W) = \frac{13}{24}$. Thus

$$\Pr(B_2 \mid W) = \frac{(\frac{3}{4}) \cdot (\frac{1}{2})}{\frac{13}{24}} = \frac{9}{13}$$

This is greater than $\frac{1}{2}$, as expected.

The solution of question 2 of Example 4.11.4 is summarized in the next theorem. Remember that $\Pr(E \mid F_1)$, $\Pr(E \mid F_2)$, $\Pr(F_1)$, and $\Pr(F_2)$ are considered given (or easy to determine, as in Example 4.11.4).

Theorem 4.12.1   Bayes' Formula

Let the notation and assumptions be as in Theorem 4.11.1. Also, assume that $E \neq \varnothing$. Then

$$\Pr(F_1 \mid E) = \frac{\Pr(E \mid F_1)\Pr(F_1)}{\Pr(E \mid F_1)\Pr(F_1) + \Pr(E \mid F_2)\Pr(F_2)} \qquad (4.12.1)$$

and a similar expression holds for $\Pr(F_2 \,|\, E)$. This is the famous result due to Thomas Bayes.

PROOF

By Eqs. (4.9.6) and (4.11.1) (the multiplication principle of probability),

$$\Pr(F_1 \,|\, E) = \frac{\Pr(F_1 \cap E)}{\Pr(E)} = \frac{\Pr(E \cap F_1)}{\Pr(E)}$$

$$= \frac{\Pr(E \,|\, F_1)\Pr(F_1)}{\Pr(E)}$$

However, by Eq. (4.11.9),

$$\Pr(E) = \Pr(E \,|\, F_1)\Pr(F_1) + \Pr(E \,|\, F_2)\Pr(F_2)$$

Substituting this into the expression above yields Eq. (4.12.1).

As often mentioned before, it is more important to remember the concepts involved in obtaining formulas such as Eq. (4.12.1) than to memorize such formulas. Indeed, if one masters the concepts, there will be no trouble arriving at Eq. (4.12.1) from basic principles; moreover, principles and concepts will be retained much longer than formulas.

Solution to Example 4.11.1 The procedure is the same as in Example 4.11.4. Let

$$
\begin{aligned}
R &= \text{event there is a positive reaction} \\
N &= \text{event the test is negative} \\
D_1 &= \text{event the person has the disease} \\
D_2 &= \text{event the person does not have the disease}
\end{aligned}
$$

The information given is that

$$
\begin{aligned}
\Pr(R \,|\, D_1) &= .9 \quad [\text{so } \Pr(N \,|\, D_1) = .1] \\
\Pr(R \,|\, D_2) &= .05 \quad [\text{so } \Pr(N \,|\, D_2) = .95] \\
\Pr(D_1) &= .001 \quad [\text{so } \Pr(D_2) = .999]
\end{aligned}
$$

The first question is: What is $\Pr(R)$? Clearly a person either has the disease (D_1) or he does not (D_2); he cannot both have it and not have it. In other words,

$$D_1 \cup D_2 = \Omega \qquad D_1 \cap D_2 = \varnothing$$

Figure 4.12.1

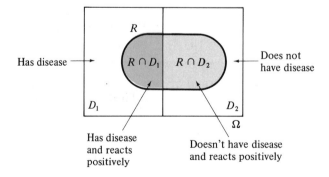

Has disease

R

$R \cap D_1$ $R \cap D_2$

Does not have disease

D_1 D_2

Ω

Has disease and reacts positively

Doesn't have disease and reacts positively

Consequently, Eq. (4.11.7) holds for D_1 and D_2. Use of Eq. (4.11.9) now yields

$$\Pr(R) = \Pr(R|D_1)\Pr(D_1) + \Pr(R|D_2)\Pr(D_2)$$
$$= (.9)(.001) + (.05)(.999)$$
$$= .0009 + .04995 = .05085 \doteq .051$$

In other words, about 5.1 percent of the people tested react positively.

As in the solution to the first part of Example 4.11.4, a tree diagram is useful for obtaining the solution (Figure 4.12.2).

Figure 4.12.2

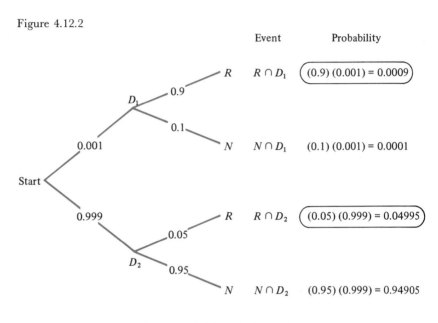

	Event	Probability
R	$R \cap D_1$	$(0.9)(0.001) = 0.0009$
N	$N \cap D_1$	$(0.1)(0.001) = 0.0001$
R	$R \cap D_2$	$(0.05)(0.999) = 0.04995$
N	$N \cap D_2$	$(0.95)(0.999) = 0.94905$

$Pr(R) = 0.0009 + 0.04995 = 0.05085$

The second question is: What is $\Pr(D_1|R)$? When we use Eq. (4.12.1), we obtain

$$\Pr(D_1|R) = \frac{\Pr(R|D_1)\Pr(D_1)}{\Pr(R|D_1)\Pr(D_1) + \Pr(R|D_2)\Pr(D_2)}$$

But $\Pr(R|D_1)\Pr(D_1) = (.9)(.001) = .0009$, and the denominator was just calculated and found to be equal to .05085. Thus

$$\Pr(D_1|R) = \frac{.0009}{.05085} \doteq .018 \qquad (4.12.2)$$

To answer the third question, let E be the event that an error occurs. Now E occurs if and only if the person does not have the disease and reacts positively $(D_2 \cap R)$ or the person has the disease and reacts negatively $(D_1 \cap N)$. So

$$E = (D_2 \cap R) \cup (D_1 \cap N)$$

The events $D_2 \cap R$ and $D_1 \cap N$ are mutually exclusive and thus, by the addition principle of probability,

$$\Pr(E) = \Pr(D_2 \cap R) + \Pr(D_1 \cap N)$$

But, by the multiplication principle of probability,

$$\Pr(D_2 \cap R) = \Pr(R \cap D_2) = \Pr(R|D_2)\Pr(D_2)$$
$$= .04995$$
$$\Pr(D_1 \cap N) = \Pr(N \cap D_1) = \Pr(N|D_1)\Pr(D_1)$$
$$= (.1)(.001) = .0001$$

Consequently,

$$\Pr(E) = .04995 + .0001 = .05005 \tag{4.12.3}$$

So the probability of error is about .05.

This last result, in conjunction with Eq. (4.12.2), is quite interesting. Although the probability of error is quite small ($\doteq .05$), the test is not that good. For, by Eq. (4.12.2), only about 1.8 percent of the people who react positively will have the disease. This is because the probability of having the disease is so small.

Theorems 4.11.1 and 4.12.1 hold if there are more than two sets F_1 and F_2 involved. This is illustrated in the following solution.

Solution to Example 4.11.2 In this example we are assuming for simplicity that people either vote Democratic or Republican and that a person is either Catholic, Jewish, or Protestant. Let

D = event person selected is a Democrat
R = event person selected is a Republican
F_1 = event person selected is a Catholic
F_2 = event person selected is Jewish
F_3 = event person selected is a Protestant

First let us translate the given information into probabilities.

$\Pr(F_1) = .20$
$\Pr(F_2) = .05$
$\Pr(F_3) = .75$

$\Pr(D|F_1) = .55 \qquad \Pr(R|F_1) = .45$
$\Pr(D|F_2) = .60 \qquad \Pr(R|F_2) = .40$
$\Pr(D|F_3) = .40 \qquad \Pr(R|F_3) = .60$

The first problem is to find $\Pr(D)$. Since a Democratic voter is either Catholic, Jewish, or Protestant, we have (see Figure 4.12.3)

$$D = (D \cap F_1) \cup (D \cap F_2) \cup (D \cap F_3)$$

Figure 4.12.3

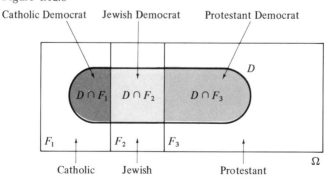

Catholic Democrat   Jewish Democrat   Protestant Democrat

The events $D \cap F_1$, $D \cap F_2$, and $D \cap F_3$ (Figure 4.12.3) are pairwise mutually exclusive (i.e., any two are mutually exclusive) and consequently, by problem 12, Exercises 4.5,

$$\Pr(D) = \Pr(D \cap F_1) + \Pr(D \cap F_2) + \Pr(D \cap F_3)$$

By the multiplication principle of probability,

$$\Pr(D \cap F_1) = \Pr(D|F_1)\Pr(F_1) = (.55)(.20) = .11$$
$$\Pr(D \cap F_2) = \Pr(D|F_2)\Pr(F_2) = (.60)(.05) = .03$$
$$\Pr(D \cap F_3) = \Pr(D|F_3)\Pr(F_3) = (.40)(.75) = .30$$

Thus

$$\Pr(D) = .11 + .03 + .30 = .44$$

Hence 44 percent of the country votes Democratic.

Note we have not referred to formulas, but in fact developed the analogue of Theorem 4.11.1, where there are 3 Fs instead of 2 Fs.

Again, a tree diagram is useful for indicating the method of solution (Figure 4.12.4).

Figure 4.12.4

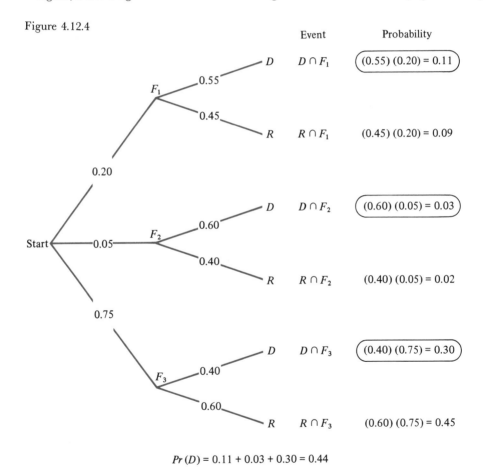

$Pr(D) = 0.11 + 0.03 + 0.30 = 0.44$

The second question is: What is $\Pr(F_1|D)$? We have

$$\Pr(F_1|D) = \frac{\Pr(F_1 \cap D)}{\Pr(D)} = \frac{\Pr(D \cap F_1)}{\Pr(D)}$$

But we have just seen that $\Pr(D \cap F_1) = .11$ and $\Pr(D) = .44$. Thus

$$\Pr(F_1 \mid D) = \frac{\Pr(D \cap F_1)}{\Pr(D)} = \frac{.11}{.44} = .25$$

In other words, 25 percent of the Democratic voters are Catholics.

Exercises for 4.12

1. In problem 9, Exercises 4.11, find the probability that the ball was drawn from the first box given that a red ball was drawn.
2. In problem 10, Exercises 4.11,
   (a) Given that the physical test is failed, what is the probability that the draftee is actually qualified to play professional football?
   (b) What is the probability that the test will yield incorrect information?
3. In problem 11, Exercises 4.11, find the probability that the machine is out of order, given that a bolt picked at random as it leaves the machine meets the necessary specifications.
4. The students of a university are examined for tuberculosis by a chest x-ray. Suppose that a student with tuberculosis has a 95 percent chance of having it detected by a chest x-ray, while a healthy student has a 6 percent chance of being told that he has tuberculosis based on the results of a chest x-ray. If .01 percent of the students have tuberculosis, what is the probability of a student not having the disease if his chest x-ray shows positive?
5. A man is going to take an automobile ride. He has a defective tire on his car. The tire has probability $\frac{3}{4}$ of blowing out. If the man replaces the tire, there is still probability $\frac{1}{8}$ that the new tire will blow out. There is probability $\frac{2}{3}$ that the man will replace the tire before leaving on the ride.
   (a) What is the probability that the tire blows out while the man is taking the ride?
   (b) Given that the tire blows out, what is the probability that the man replaced the tire?
6. A man has two coins, one with two heads and the other with one side heads and one tails. If a coin is selected at random and tossed, what is the probability that the coin is the two-headed coin, given that the outcome of the toss was heads? (Assume that the ordinary coin is fair.)
7. Assume that a recent study showed that 30 percent of people who smoke die of heart attack and that 15 percent of people who do not smoke die of heart attack. Also assume that 25 percent of people smoke.
   (a) What percentage of the population dies of a heart attack?
   (b) What percentage of the people dying of heart attacks are smokers?
8. A study of the judicial system of a given state has shown that 90 percent of those individuals brought to trial have actually committed the crime for which they are being tried. Notice that this means that 10 percent of those brought to trail have actually not committed the crime for which they are being tried. A study of court records suggests the following: The percentage of trial outcomes given that a person did (or did not) actually commit the crime is

Given	Convicted	Acquitted	Mistrial
Actually comitted crime	80%	5%	15%
Actually did not commit crime	5%	75%	20%

(a) What is the probability that a person brought to trial will be acquitted?

(b) Given that a person is acquitted, what is the probability that the person actually committed the crime?

9. Suppose that A, B, and C are nonempty events with $A \cap B = A \cap C = B \cap C = \emptyset$ and $A \cup B \cup C = \Omega$. Let E be any event. Show that

(a) $\Pr(E) = \Pr(E \cap A) + \Pr(E \cap B) + \Pr(E \cap C)$

(b) $\Pr(E) = \Pr(E \mid A)\Pr(A) + \Pr(E \mid B)\Pr(B) + \Pr(E \mid C)\Pr(C)$

10. Prove the following generalization of Bayes' formula. Let E_1, E_2, and E_3 be nonempty events of the sample space Ω such that $E_1 \cap E_2 = E_1 \cap E_3 = E_2 \cap E_3 = \emptyset$ and $E_1 \cup E_2 \cup E_3 = \Omega$. Then, for any nonempty event E,

$$\Pr(E_1 \mid E) = \frac{\Pr(E \mid E_1)\Pr(E_1)}{\Pr(E \mid E_1)\Pr(E_1) + \Pr(E \mid E_2)\Pr(E_2) + \Pr(E \mid E_3)\Pr(E_3)}$$

Similar expressions hold for $\Pr(E_2 \mid E)$ and $\Pr(E_3 \mid E)$.

11. Three urns, urn I, urn II, and urn III, contain 4 red and 3 white balls, 2 red and 2 white balls, and 5 red and 4 white balls, respectively. An urn is chosen at random and then a ball is selected at random from this urn.

(a) What is the probability that a red ball is selected?

(b) Given that a red ball was selected, what is the probability that it was drawn from urn III?

12. There are three chests, each with two drawers. In each drawer there is a coin. In chest 1 there is one gold coin and one silver coin. In chest 2 there are two silver coins and in chest 3 there are two gold coins. A chest is selected by rolling a fair die. If the die comes up even, chest 1 is selected; if it comes up 1 or 3, chest 2 is selected; and if it comes up 5, chest 3 is selected. From the chest selected a drawer is chosen at random and opened and the coin therein observed.

(a) What is the probability that the coin in the drawer opened is gold?

(b) What is the probability that chest 1 was selected given that the coin observed was gold?

13. An automobile manufacture has three production plants: I, II, and III. For every 10,000 cars manufactured, the plants produce the following quantities:

Plant	I	II	III
Quantity	4,500	2,500	3,000

Ten percent of the cars produced by plant I are station wagons, 20 percent of the cars produced by plant II are station wagons, and 5 percent of the cars produced by plant III are station wagons.

(a) What percentage of automobiles produced by this manufacturer are station wagons?

(b) What percentage of the station wagons manufactured are produced by plant I?

14. Suppose that 40 percent of the sophomores, 20 percent of the juniors, and 10 percent of the seniors of a university are taking mathematics. Of the upper-class students, 45 percent are sophomores, 30 percent are juniors, and 25 percent are seniors.

(a) If an upper-class student is selected at random, what is the probability that he is taking mathematics?

(b) What percentage of the upper-class students who are taking mathematics are juniors?

15. A grocer receives his eggs in cartons of a dozen eggs per carton. In the past, 70 percent of all such cartons have had no broken eggs, 20 percent have had one broken egg, and 10 percent have had two broken eggs. Three eggs are selected at random from a carton and one is found to be broken. What is the probability that the carton originally contained two broken eggs?

Section 4.13 Stochastic Independence and the Multiplication Principle

Everyone has some intuitive feeling for the notion of independence. For example, if a coin is tossed twice, we all believe that the event that the second toss is a head is "independent" of the event that the first toss is a head. On the other hand, it seems clear that the event that both tosses are a head "depends" on the event that the first toss is a head.

In the introduction to conditional probability it was mentioned that given additional information concerning a random experiment, the probability of an event occurring will change, in general. More precisely, if E and F are events, $\Pr(E|F)$ will, in general, differ from $\Pr(E)$. Intuitively, if E is "independent" of F, the fact that F occurs should have no influence on the probability of the occurrence of E. That is, $\Pr(E|F)$ should be the same as $\Pr(E)$.

Definition

Let Ω be the sample space of a random experiment and let E and F be events, with $\Pr(F) > 0$. Then E is said to be (stochastically) *independent* of F if

$$\Pr(E|F) = \Pr(E) \tag{4.13.1}$$

Example 4.13.1 Coin Tossing Consider the random experiment of tossing a fair coin twice. We have

$$\Omega = \{HH, HT, TH, TT\}$$

and each sample point has probability $\frac{1}{4}$. Let

A = event the second toss is head
B = event both tosses are head
C = event the first toss is head

Then $A = \{HH, TH\}$, $B = \{HH\}$, and $C = \{HH, HT\}$.

We mentioned before that it is "intuitively" clear that A is independent of C. Let us see if this statement is consistent with Eq. (4.13.1). We have

$$\Pr(A) = \tfrac{2}{4} = \tfrac{1}{2}$$

and

$$\Pr(A|C) = \frac{\Pr(A \cap C)}{\Pr(C)} = \frac{\Pr(\{HH\})}{\Pr(C)} = \frac{\frac{1}{4}}{\frac{1}{2}} = \tfrac{1}{2}$$

Thus $\Pr(A|C) = \Pr(A)$, so A is independent of C according to Eq. (4.13.1).

It was also pointed out that it seemed clear that B "depends" on C (i.e., B is not independent of C). Let us see if Eq. (4.13.1) bears this out. We have

$$\Pr(B) = \tfrac{1}{4}$$

On the other hand,

$$\Pr(B|C) = \frac{\Pr(B \cap C)}{\Pr(C)} = \frac{\Pr(\{HH\})}{\Pr(C)} = \frac{\frac{1}{4}}{\frac{1}{2}} = \tfrac{1}{2}$$

Hence $\Pr(B|C) \neq \Pr(B)$, so, by Eq. (4.13.1), B is not independent of C.

An important characterization of independence can be obtained by replacing $\Pr(E|F)$ in Eq. (4.13.1) by its definition [Eq. (4.9.6)].

Theorem 4.13.1

Let Ω be a sample space and E and F events, with $\Pr(F) > 0$. Then E is independent of F if and only if

$$\Pr(E \cap F) = \Pr(E)\Pr(F) \qquad (4.13.2)$$

PROOF

The definition of E being independent of F is

$$\Pr(E|F) = \Pr(E)$$

By Eq. (4.9.6),

$$\Pr(E|F) = \frac{\Pr(E \cap F)}{\Pr(F)}$$

so Eq. (4.13.1) is equivalent to

$$\frac{\Pr(E \cap F)}{\Pr(F)} = \Pr(E)$$

Multiplying both sides of this equation by $\Pr(F)$ yields Eq. (4.13.2).

Formula (4.13.2) is another form of the *multiplication principle* of probability [see Eq. (4.11.1)] when the events are independent. It states that *the probability of the intersection of two independent events is the product of their probabilities.*

An immediate consequence of Theorem 4.13.1 is that if E ($\neq \varnothing$) is independent of F, then F is independent of E. For if E is independent of F, then, by Eq. (4.13.2), $\Pr(E \cap F) = \Pr(E)\Pr(F)$. But this is the same as $\Pr(F \cap E) = \Pr(F)\Pr(E)$, which, by Theorem 4.13.1, means that F is independent of E. Consequently, instead of saying that E is independent of F or F is independent of E, we simply say that E *and* F *are independent.*

Example 4.13.2 Toxicity of Snakes (See Example 2.7.1.) After examining a large number of snakes, a biologist has determined the percentages in Figure 4.13.1 to be

Figure 4.13.1

Property	Percentage
Extremely toxic venom	50
White streak on head	50
Greenish-brown stripe	50
Extremely toxic venom and white streak on head	40
Extremely toxic venom and greenish-brown stripe	25

true. Let the random experiment consist of choosing a snake at random from the type of snakes the biologist is studying and let

T = event the snake has extremely toxic venom
W = event the snake has a white streak on his head
G = event the snake has a greenish-brown stripe

In terms of probabilities the data translate into

$$\Pr(T) = .5 \qquad \Pr(T \cap W) = .4$$
$$\Pr(W) = .5 \qquad \Pr(T \cap G) = .25$$
$$\Pr(G) = .5$$

From this we see that

$$\Pr(T)\Pr(G) = (.5)(.5) = .25 = \Pr(T \cap G)$$
$$\Pr(T)\Pr(W) = (.5)(.5) = .25 \neq .4 = \Pr(T \cap W)$$

and we can conclude that extreme toxicity and the appearance of a greenish-brown stripe are independent events. This means that these two characteristics are unrelated. On the other hand, the last formula implies that extreme toxicity and the appearance of a white streak on the head are not independent events. Hence these two characteristics are related in some way. Since

$$\Pr(T \mid W) = \frac{\Pr(T \cap W)}{\Pr(W)} = \frac{.4}{.5} = .8$$

while $\Pr(T) = .5$, we see that there is a "positive correlation" between high toxicity and a white streak appearing on the head of a snake.

We shall now use the concept of independence to construct probabilistic models (sample spaces) corresponding to repetitions of the same experiment. This is one of the most important and fundamental ideas in probability.

Example 4.13.3 Coin Tossing Consider the random experiment of tossing a fair coin *twice*. As we have seen before, we can take

$$\Omega = \{\text{HH, HT, TH, TT}\}$$

Since the coin is fair, we assign probability $\frac{1}{4}$ [$= 1/\text{card}(\Omega)$] to each sample point.
We can arrive at this assignment of probability by means of an alternative route. The idea is to consider the random experiment as a *two-stage* repetition of another experiment—tossing a fair coin *once* (Figure 4.13.2).

Figure 4.13.2

Experiment I (1st toss)	Experiment II (2nd toss)	Outcome
H	H	HH
	T	HT
T	H	TH
	T	TT

In discussing this experiment we have always *tacitly assumed* that the stages of the experiment are independent (i.e., the outcome of the first toss has no effect on the outcome of the second toss). This (along with the fairness of the coin) is precisely why we feel that all outcomes are equally likely and hence we assign probability $\frac{1}{4}$ to each of the four sample points. Now, let

A = event first toss is H
B = event second toss is T

Thinking of each toss as an experiment in itself, our intuition says that because the coin is fair,

$$\begin{aligned} \Pr(A) &= \tfrac{1}{2} \\ \Pr(B) &= \tfrac{1}{2} \end{aligned} \qquad (4.13.3)$$

[*Notice:* $A = \{HH, HT\}$, and so $\Pr(A) = \Pr(\{HH\}) + \Pr(\{HT\}) = \frac{1}{2}$. *But* we did not arrive at Eq. (4.13.3) in this way. We are thinking of A as the event of getting a head when a fair coin is tossed *once*. Thus since the coin is fair, we conclude immediately that $\Pr(A) = \frac{1}{2}$. These are two different ways of viewing event A. A similar remark applies to B.]

Now, because we think of the stages of the experiment (first toss, second toss) as being independent, we feel that A and B should be independent events. So, by the multiplication principle of probability for independent events, Eq. (4.13.2),

$$\Pr(A \cap B) = \Pr(A)\Pr(B) = \tfrac{1}{2} \cdot \tfrac{1}{2} = \tfrac{1}{4}$$

Now $A \cap B = \{HT\}$, so the above argument indicates that we should define $\Pr(\{HT\}) = \frac{1}{4}$. A similar argument applies to the other sample points. This is the alternative route for arriving at our assignment of probabilities to the sample points (Figure 4.13.3).

Figure 4.13.3

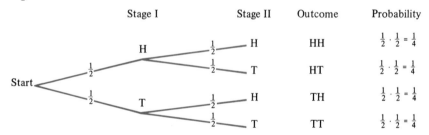

	Stage I	Stage II	Outcome	Probability
	H	H	HH	$\frac{1}{2} \cdot \frac{1}{2} = \frac{1}{4}$
		T	HT	$\frac{1}{2} \cdot \frac{1}{2} = \frac{1}{4}$
Start		H	TH	$\frac{1}{2} \cdot \frac{1}{2} = \frac{1}{4}$
	T	T	TT	$\frac{1}{2} \cdot \frac{1}{2} = \frac{1}{4}$

Exercises for 4.13

1. Let A and B be events with $\Pr(A \cap B) = \frac{1}{2}$, $\Pr(B) = \frac{3}{4}$, and $\Pr(A) = \frac{2}{3}$. Are A and B independent?
2. Two coins are tossed. Let E be the event "the coins match" and F the event "heads on the first coin."
   (a) Are the events E and F independent?
   (b) Suppose that F is the event "at least one coin is heads." Are the events E and F independent?
3. Suppose that two dice, one red and the other green, are thrown.
   (a) Let E be the event "the red die shows 3" and F the event "the green die shows a number less than 4." Are the events E and F independent?
   (b) Suppose that E is the event "the sum of the digits is 7" and F is the event "the green die shows a number different from 6." Are the events E and F independent?
4. Suppose that the 1, 2, and 5 of a die are colored red, and the 3, 4, and 6 are colored

blue. The die is rolled once. Let E be the event "the roll resulted in a number less than 3" and F be the event "the roll is blue." Are E and F independent?

5. Consider the random experiment of three tosses of a fair coin. Let E be the event "a tail turns up on the second toss" and F be the event "a head turns up on the third toss." Show that the events E and F are independent.

6. Give an example for each of the following:
   (a) two events that are independent but not mutually exclusive
   (b) two events that are mutually exclusive but not independent
   (c) two events that are neither independent nor mutually exclusive

7. (a) Show that if E and F are independent events with $\Pr(E) \neq 0$ and $\Pr(F) \neq 0$, E and F cannot be mutually exclusive.
   (b) If $E = \emptyset$ and F is any nonempty event, show that E is independent of F.

8. A machine produces nuts and bolts. As they come from the machine, the nuts and bolts are attached in a random fashion. Suppose it is known that 7 percent of the nuts and 3 percent of the bolts are defective. What is the probability that an assembled unit will be defective?

9. Two cards are drawn from an ordinary deck of 52, the first card being replaced before the second is drawn. What is the probability that
   (a) the first card selected is a heart and the second an ace?
   (b) both cards are aces?
   (c) exactly one ace is drawn?

10. A fair coin is tossed and then a pair of fair dice is rolled. What is the probability that the coin comes up heads and the sum of the dice is eleven?

11. If A, B, and C are events with A and B independent and B and C independent, is it necessarily true that A and C are independent?

12. Suppose that A, B, and C are events. Then they are said to be independent if any two of them are and if $\Pr(A \cap B \cap C) = \Pr(A)\Pr(B)\Pr(C)$.
   (a) Consider the experiment of tossing a fair coin four times. Let

   A = event first toss is heads
   B = event second toss is tails
   C = event last two tosses are heads

   Show that A, B, and C are independent.
   (b) Consider the experiment of rolling a pair of fair dice. Let

   E = event first die comes up even
   F = event second die comes up even
   G = event sum of dice is even

   Show that E, F, and G are pairwise independent (any two of them are independent) but E, F, and G are not independent.
   (c) Consider again the experiment in part (b) and let

   H = event first die comes up 1, 2, or 3
   I = event first die comes up 3, 4, or 5
   J = event sum of dice is 5

   Show that $\Pr(H \cap I \cap J) = \Pr(H)\Pr(I)\Pr(J)$ but that H, I, and J are not independent.

13. A survey over a period of a year was performed in a city to determine whether sex and/or driving while intoxicated are related to having accidents. The following data were obtained:

   Percentage of people who drive while intoxicated, 20 percent
   Percentage of people who have accidents, 30 percent
   Percentage of people who drive while intoxicated and have accidents, 15 percent

Percentage of male drivers, 60 percent
Percentage of male drivers who have accidents, 18 percent

What conclusions can be drawn from these data?

14. Show that if E and F are independent events, so are $\bar{E}$ and $\bar{F}$. (*Hint:* Use De Morgan's law.)
15. If A and B are independent and $\bar{A} \neq \emptyset$, show that $\bar{A}$ and B are also independent. (*Hint:* Use the law of total probability.)

Section 4.14 Repeated Experiments: Assignment of Probabilities

In this section we shall elaborate on the method of assigning probabilities to sample points of random experiments obtained by the independent repetition of another experiment. This procedure is illustrated by the following example and was already touched upon in Example 4.13.3.

Example 4.14.1 **Dice** Consider the random experiment of rolling a fair die three times. There are $6 \cdot 6 \cdot 6 = 216$ possible outcomes for the experiment (6 possibilities for the first roll, 6 for the second, and 6 for the third). Each sample point of Ω can be represented as a sequence of three integers from 1 to 6. For example, $[1, 5, 2]$ represents the following outcome: First roll yields "1," second yields "5," and third yields "2." Since the die is fair, it is reasonable to assume that all outcomes are equally likely and to assign probability $\frac{1}{216}$ to each sample point. Now, assume that at each roll we are only interested in whether a 5 does or does not come up. We can still use Ω as our sample space, but it is more convenient to use a different (much smaller) sample space which we shall call Ω'. We denote a "5 comes up" by S (for success) and a "5 does not come up" by F (for failure). Then, for example, FSF represents the outcome that the first roll is not a 5, the second is a 5, and the third is not a 5. With this representation of the outcomes of the experiment we get a new sample space Ω' with only 8 sample points, as opposed to the 216 sample points of Ω.

$$\Omega' = \{SSS, SSF, SFS, SFF, FSS, FSF, FFS, FFF\}$$

This sample space is sufficient to analyze the random experiment if all we are interested in is whether at each roll a 5 does or does not come up. [If, however, we need to know what number comes up at each roll in order to answer questions involving the random experiment (e.g., what is the probability of a 3 on the first toss and a 1 on the third toss), we must use the other sample space, Ω.]

The problem is to determine how to assign probabilities to the sample points of Ω'. These outcomes (sample points) are no longer equally likely, as we shall see. The reason for this is that a sample point of Ω' may correspond to many sample points of Ω and the number will vary with different sample points of Ω'. For example:

Ω'		Ω
SSS	$\longleftrightarrow$	$[5, 5, 5]$
SSF	$\longleftrightarrow$	$[5, 5, 1], [5, 5, 2], [5, 5, 3], [5, 5, 4], [5, 5, 6]$

Proceeding as in Example 4.13.3, we consider the random experiment as a *three-stage* repetition of the experiment of rolling a fair die *once* and determining whether or not a 5 comes up (Figure 4.14.1).

Figure 4.14.1

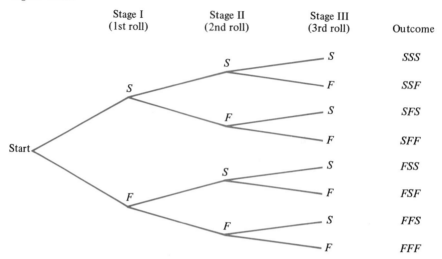

Stage I (1st roll)	Stage II (2nd roll)	Stage III (3rd roll)	Outcome

It is reasonable to assume that the stages of the experiment are independent, and so we assign probabilities as in Example 4.13.3. For example, consider the sample point SFS. Since the die is fair, the probability of a success (i.e., a 5) on a given roll of the die is $\frac{1}{6}$ and the probability of a failure on a given roll is $1 - \frac{1}{6} = \frac{5}{6}$. Also, since the rolls are independent of each other, it is reasonable to *multiply* the appropriate probabilities. Thus to the sample point SFS we assign probability

$$
\begin{array}{ccc} S & F & S \\ \frac{1}{6} \cdot & \frac{5}{6} \cdot & \frac{1}{6} = \frac{5}{216} \end{array}
$$

Figure 4.14.2

I	II	III	Sample Point	Probability
			SSS	$\frac{1}{6} \cdot \frac{1}{6} \cdot \frac{1}{6} = (\frac{1}{6})^3$
			SSF	$\frac{1}{6} \cdot \frac{1}{6} \cdot \frac{5}{6} = (\frac{1}{6})^2 \cdot \frac{5}{6}$
			SFS	$\frac{1}{6} \cdot \frac{5}{6} \cdot \frac{1}{6} = (\frac{1}{6})^2 \cdot \frac{5}{6}$
			SFF	$\frac{1}{6} \cdot \frac{5}{6} \cdot \frac{5}{6} = \frac{1}{6} \cdot (\frac{5}{6})^2$
			FSS	$\frac{5}{6} \cdot \frac{1}{6} \cdot \frac{1}{6} = (\frac{1}{6})^2 \cdot \frac{5}{6}$
			FSF	$\frac{5}{6} \cdot \frac{1}{6} \cdot \frac{5}{6} = \frac{1}{6} \cdot (\frac{5}{6})^2$
			FFS	$\frac{5}{6} \cdot \frac{5}{6} \cdot \frac{1}{6} = \frac{1}{6} \cdot (\frac{5}{6})^2$
			FFF	$\frac{5}{6} \cdot \frac{5}{6} \cdot \frac{5}{6} = (\frac{5}{6})^3$

[Alternatively, if we let

A = event first roll is a 5
B = event second roll is not a 5
C = event third roll is a 5

then $A \cap B \cap C$ represents the outcome SFS (i.e., $A \cap B \cap C = \{SFS\}$). Our intuition indicates that

$$\Pr(A) = \tfrac{1}{6} \qquad \Pr(B) = \tfrac{5}{6} \qquad \Pr(C) = \tfrac{1}{6}$$

and hence by independence (extended to three events) we get

$$\Pr(\{SFS\}) = \Pr(A \cap B \cap C) = \Pr(A) \cdot \Pr(B) \cdot \Pr(C)$$
$$= \tfrac{1}{6} \cdot \tfrac{5}{6} \cdot \tfrac{1}{6} = \tfrac{5}{216}]$$

A similar argument is used to assign probabilities to the other sample points of Ω' (Figure 4.14.2).

We used the computer to continually perform the experiment of rolling a fair die three times and to observe whether or not SFS occurred. As you can see in Table 4.14.1, the assignment of probability $\tfrac{5}{216} \doteq .023$ to the sample point SFS is consistent with the relative frequency interpretation of probability.

Table 4.14.1   Calculation of the Relative Frequency of
SFS in Rolling a Fair Die Three Times*

Trial	No. occurrences of SFS	Relative frequency
1,000	15	.016
2,000	33	.016
3,000	53	.018
4,000	83	.021
5,000	112	.022
6,000	137	.023
7,000	156	.022
8,000	190	.024
9,000	208	.023
10,000	230	.023
11,000	250	.023
12,000	271	.023
13,000	298	.023
14,000	320	.023
15,000	342	.023
16,000	367	.023
17,000	387	.023
18,000	413	.023
19,000	436	.023
20,000	458	.023

*S, a 5 comes up on a given roll; F, a 5 does not come up on a given roll.

With the above examples in mind we make the following definition.

Definition

A sequence of *independent trials* is a sequence of (independent) repetitions of the *same* experiment. If a random experiment consists of a sequence of independent trials, then the probabilities are assigned to the sample points by using the multiplicative property of independent events as illustrated in Example 4.14.1.

Example 4.14.2 Drug Effectiveness A drug company has estimated the effectiveness of an antibiotic it produces by administering it to a large number of people who have the disease it is supposed to cure. The outcomes are classified into three categories: (1) cure, (2) improvement (but not cure), (3) no change. The results are as follows:

Outcome	Percentage	Probability
Cure	70	.7
Improvement	20	.2
No change	10	.1

Now consider the random experiment consisting of selecting 4 people who have the disease, administering the antibiotic, and determining in which category the outcome belongs.

The experiment consists of a sequence of four independent trials, each of which has three possible outcomes:

C cure
I improvement
N no change

A typical sample point can be represented as a sequence, four-long, of the letters C, I, and N. For example, the sample point $CNCI$ corresponds to the following outcome of the experiment: first person, cured; second person, no change; third person, cured; fourth person, improvement.

By the sequential counting principle there are $3^4 = 81$ possible outcomes (i.e., the sample space consists of 81 sample points). When we use the multiplication principle of probability, we can assign probabilities to the sample points. Some typical assignments follow:

Sample point	Probability assigned
$CNCI$	(.7) (.1) (.7) (.2) = .0098
$CCII$	(.7) (.7) (.2) (.2) = .0196
$INNC$	(.2) (.1) (.1) (.7) = .0014
$CCNI$	(.7) (.7) (.1) (.2) = .0098
$CCCC$	(.7) (.7) (.7) (.7) = .2401
IIII	(.2) (.2) (.2) (.2) = .0016
$NNNN$	(.1) (.1) (.1) (.1) = .0001
$CNIN$	(.7) (.1) (.2) (.1) = .0014

Exercises for 4.14

1. A fair die is rolled three times, and suppose that we are only interested in whether a multiple of 3 does or does not come up. Letting S represent the outcome that a multiple of 3 was rolled and F the outcome that a multiple of 3 was not rolled, set up the sample space for this experiment and determine what probabilities should be assigned to each of the sample points.

2. A biased coin with probability $\frac{1}{3}$ of a tail coming up is tossed three times. Set up the sample space for this experiment and assign the appropriate probabilities to each of the sample points.

3. Suppose that three coins are tossed. Assume that the first two coins are fair but the third coin has probability $\frac{2}{3}$ of a head being tossed. Set up the sample space for this experiment and assign the appropriate probabilities to each of the sample points.

4. An urn contains 10 balls, 6 red balls, and 4 white balls. Three balls are selected at random, with replacement of the ball after each selection. Set up the sample space so that all possible outcomes are indicated and determine the probabilities that should be assigned to each of the sample points.

5. In problem 4, could the multiplicative property be used in assigning probabilities to the sample points if the balls were not replaced after each selection?

6. A fair coin is tossed once. If it comes up heads, it is tossed again and the experiment is over; if it comes up tails, a fair die is rolled and the experiment is over. Letting H represent the outcome a head comes up and T the outcome a tail comes up, set up the sample space for this experiment and determine the probability that should be assigned to each of the sample points.

7. A family has four children. Let B represent the outcome of having a boy and G the outcome of having a girl.
   (a) Set up the sample space that corresponds to all possible outcomes of four children.
   (b) Suppose that the probability of the first child being a boy is $\frac{1}{3}$, the probability of the second child being a boy is $\frac{3}{8}$, the probability of the third child being a boy is $\frac{5}{8}$, and the probability of the fourth child being a boy is $\frac{2}{3}$. Assign probabilities to each of the sample points assuming independence of sex among the various children.

8. Is the following sequence a sequence of independent trials? A fair coin is tossed twice, a fair die is rolled three times, two balls are chosen at random from an urn.

9. Is the following sequence a sequence of independent trials? On 10 successive days a person is selected at random from the voting population of Los Angeles and the person's party affiliation is noted. However, no person may be selected more than once in the survey.

10. (a) Indicate which of the following sequences are sequences of independent trials.
   (1) An urn contains 10 chips, of which 3 are red, 2 are white, and 5 are blue. Three chips are selected, with replacement, from the urn. At each selection the color of the chip chosen is noted.
   (2) As in part (a) except that the selecting is done without replacement.
   (b) Letting r, w, and b denote the selection of a red, white, and blue chip, respectively, construct a sample space for each experiment in part (a).
   (1) Assign probabilities to the sample points if the selection is done with replacement.
   (2) Assign probabilities to the sample points if the selection is done without replacement. [*Hint:* Use problem 6(a), Exercises 4.11.]

11. A poll taken among the employees in a plant on the question of affiliation with a union yielded the following results:

Outcome	Percentage	Probability
Favor affiliation	60	.6
Oppose affiliation	30	.3
No opinion	10	.1

Two employees are selected at random (with the possibility of the same person being selected both times) and polled on whether they favored affiliation, opposed affiliation, or had no opinion. Letting F represent "favor affiliation," O represent "oppose affiliation," and N represent "no opinion," set up the sample space of all possible outcomes of this experiment and determine the probabilities that should be assigned to each sample point.

Section 4.15   Bernoulli Trials: The Binomial Distribution

In Section 4.14 we discussed the concept of independent trials and indicated the procedure for assigning probabilities to the sample points of such an experiment. In this section we shall be concerned exclusively with the case where each trial has only two possible outcomes, which we denote by S (success) and F (failure). Such a sequence of independent trials is called a sequence of *Bernoulli trials*.

The main problem of interest in Bernoulli trials is to determine the probabilities associated with the number of successes obtained.

Example 4.15.1   Defective Bolts   Consider the random experiment of examining four bolts as they emerge from a machine and observing whether or not they are defective according to a set of tolerance specifications. Suppose it is known that the probability that the machine produces a defective bolt is $\frac{1}{8}$. What is the probability that exactly three of the four bolts are *not* defective?

To solve this problem, we consider the random experiment as a sequence of four Bernoulli trials with S (success) corresponding to a bolt being nondefective. Hence the sample space consists of $2^4 = 16$ sample points, all sequences of Ss and Fs four-long. We assign probabilities as before (Figure 4.15.1).

Let A be the event that exactly three of the four bolts are *nondefective*. First, we shall calculate card (A) (i.e., how many sample points A contains). To do this, note that a sample point belongs to A if and only if it consists of 3 Ss and 1 F. The problem is to calculate how many sample points have this property. Thinking of the experiment as filling the four boxes

with either an S or an F we see that the outcome can be 3 Ss and 1 F in as many ways as we can choose three boxes from the four boxes as locations for the Ss. But this is just

$$\binom{4}{3} = 4$$

or

Hence A contains $\binom{4}{3} = 4$ sample points. *But each sample point of A has the same probability* (see Figure 4.15.1): $(\frac{7}{8})^3 \cdot \frac{1}{8}$. Thus

Figure 4.15.1

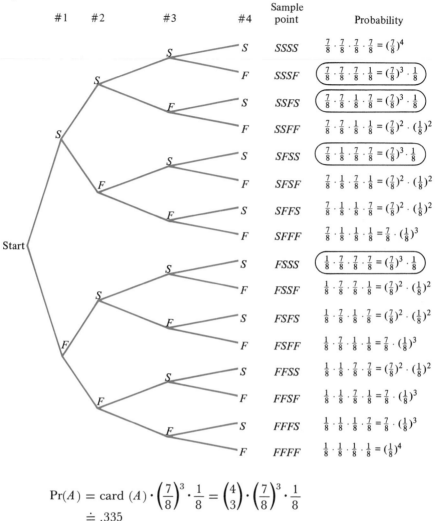

				Sample point	Probability

$$\Pr(A) = \text{card}(A) \cdot \left(\frac{7}{8}\right)^3 \cdot \frac{1}{8} = \binom{4}{3} \cdot \left(\frac{7}{8}\right)^3 \cdot \frac{1}{8}$$
$$\doteq .335$$

To exemplify the general situation, note that $\Pr(A)$ can also be written as

$$\binom{4}{3} \cdot \left(\frac{7}{8}\right)^3 \cdot \left(1 - \frac{7}{8}\right)^{4-3}$$

Using the above example as a guide, we now prove the following fundamental result concerning Bernoulli trials.

Theorem 4.15.1

In a sequence of n Bernoulli trials [i.e., n repetitions of an experiment with two possible outcomes, say success (S) or failure (F)], let p be the probability of a success on any given trial. Then the probability of exactly k successes $(0 \le k \le n)$ in n trials is

$$\binom{n}{k} p^k (1 - p)^{n-k} \tag{4.15.1}$$

The assignment of probabilities via Eq. (4.15.1) is called the *binomial distribution*.

The sample space consists of 2^n sample points, all sequences of Ss and Fs n-long. Let A be the event that there are exactly k successes out of the n trials. First we calculate card (A) (i.e., how many sample points A contains). This is the number of different sequences of Ss and Fs, n-long, with exactly k Ss (and hence $n - k$ Fs). The number of these is just the number of ways it is possible to select the k locations in the n-long sequence for the positions of the Ss (see Example 4.15.1). But this can be done in

$$\binom{n}{k}$$

ways. Thus card $(A) = \binom{n}{k}$.

Now (see Example 4.15.1), each sample point of A consists of a sequence, n-long, of Ss and Fs in which there are k Ss and $n - k$ Fs, so each sample point has probability $p^k(1 - p)^{n-k}$. Consequently,

$$\Pr(A) = \text{card } (A) \cdot p^k(1 - p)^{n-k}$$
$$= \binom{n}{k} p^k(1 - p)^{n-k}$$

We shall now apply Theorem 4.15.1 to several types of problems.

Example 4.15.2 Sales A salesman knows that 15 percent of the people he contacts will buy his product. If on a given day he contacts three people, what is the probability that *exactly one person* will buy his product? Also, what is the probability that *at least one person* will buy?

This experiment consists of three Bernoulli trials. If we take success as "a sale," $p = .15 = \frac{3}{20}$. If A is the event of exactly one sale out of three, then, by Theorem 4.15.1,

$$\Pr(A) = \binom{3}{1}\left(\frac{3}{20}\right)^1\left(1 - \frac{3}{20}\right)^{3-1}$$
$$= 3 \cdot \frac{3}{20} \cdot \left(\frac{17}{20}\right)^2 \doteq .325$$

In other words, the salesman has about a 32 percent chance of selling exactly one of his products.

The next question is: What is the probability that he sells to at least one person (i.e., either one, two, or three)? Let B be the event that at least one person buys. Then $\tilde{B}$ is the event that no one buys (i.e., zero successes). So

$$\Pr(\tilde{B}) = \binom{3}{0}\left(\frac{3}{20}\right)^0\left(1 - \frac{3}{20}\right)^{3-0}$$
$$= \left(\frac{17}{20}\right)^3 \doteq .614$$

Consequently,

$$\Pr(B) = 1 - \Pr(\tilde{B}) \doteq .386$$

The salesman has about a 39 percent chance of selling to at least one of the customers.

Example 4.15.3 Serious Defects in Automobiles A company has decided to buy a fleet of eight cars for its service representatives. It has been determined that there is a 10 percent chance of such a car having a serious defect. What is the probability that out of the eight cars there are no more than two cars with a serious defect?

The problem is to find the probability that the number of cars with serious defects is at most two (i.e., zero, one, or two). The random experiment consists of eight Bernoulli trials. If we think of a success as a car having a serious defect, then $p = .10$. The event, A, that at most two cars have a serious defect can occur in three mutually exclusive ways:

1. Zero cars have a serious defect.
2. One car has a serious defect.
3. Two cars have a serious defect.

Let A_0, A_1, and A_2 be these events. Then

$$A = A_0 \cup A_1 \cup A_2$$

and since events A_0, A_1, and A_2 are mutually exclusive, the addition principle of probability implies that

$$\Pr(A) = \Pr(A_0) + \Pr(A_1) + \Pr(A_2)$$

According to Theorem 4.15.1,

$$\Pr(A_0) = \binom{8}{0} \cdot (.10)^0 (.90)^8 \doteq .430$$

$$\Pr(A_1) = \binom{8}{1} \cdot (.10)^1 (.90)^7 \doteq .383$$

$$\Pr(A_2) = \binom{8}{2} \cdot (.10)^2 (.90)^6 \doteq .149$$

Consequently,

$$\Pr(A) \doteq .962$$

Example 4.15.4 Restaurant Reservations It has been determined that about 3 percent of all people who make reservations at a particular restaurant will not show. A maximum of how many people can make reservations at the restaurant and still have the proprietor be at least 90 percent sure that everyone who makes a reservation will show?

Here we have a "variable" number of Bernoulli trials, say n. Suppose that we consider a success as "a person who made a reservation shows up." Then $p = .97$ ($= 1 - .03$). Let A be the event that every person who makes a reservation appears. Then we want n successes in n trials, so

$$\Pr(A) = \binom{n}{n}(.97)^n (1 - .97)^{n-n}$$

$$= (.97)^n$$

That the proprietor wants to be at least 90 percent sure that everyone shows means that

$$\Pr(A) \geq .90$$

Thus we want to see how large we can make n and still have

$$(.97)^n \geq .90$$

By using trial and error or by applying logarithms to this inequality it can be shown that the biggest n that can be made is 4. In fact,

$$(.97)^4 \doteq .904$$
$$(.97)^5 \doteq .886$$

Hence, if more than four people make reservations, the proprietor can no longer be at least 90 percent sure that all these people will show.

Exercises for 4.15

1. Use Eq. (4.15.1) to find the probability of getting exactly four heads in six tosses of a fair coin.
2. Use Eq. (4.15.1) to find the probability of getting exactly two sixes in five rolls of a fair die.
3. Find the probability of getting at least four heads in six tosses of a fair coin.
4. A marksman averages 7 hits out of 10 shots at a target. What is the probability that he will hit the target in 3 out of 4 shots?
5. An urn contains 10 red chips and 20 blue chips.
   (a) What is the probability of getting exactly 5 blue chips in seven draws if each chip is replaced before the next one is drawn?
   (b) Could Eq. (4.15.1) be used if the chips were not replaced?
6. From past experience it is known that a person has probability $\frac{1}{20}$ of having a particular disease. If 10 people are selected at random, what is the probability that
   (a) at least one of them will have the disease?
   (b) exactly 5 of them will have the disease?
7. In an extrasensory perception experiment a person in one room has cards numbered 1–10. At each trial this person chooses a card at random and observes the card. Another person in another room is supposed to guess the number of the card selected. If this experiment is repeated five times, what is the probability that
   (a) the person guesses the correct number all five times?
   (b) the person guesses correctly at least three times?
8. A basketball player has a 75 percent success ratio at the free-throw line. The player has been awarded two free throws. What is the probability that he
   (a) makes both of them?
   (b) makes exactly one of them?
   (c) makes at least one of them?
9. A baseball player has a batting average of .300. What is the probability that he will get at least three hits in five times at bat?
10. A student takes a multiple-choice exam, each question of which has four possible answers. If the exam contains 10 questions and the student guesses at every question, what is the probability that he gets at least 90 percent of the questions correct?
11. In problem 10, suppose that each question is answered by drawing one card from an ordinary deck of 52 playing cards and checking answer 1, 2, 3, or 4, depending on whether the card drawn is a spade, heart, diamond, or club, respectively. What is the probability of getting at most 3 correct? (Assume that a card drawn is replaced before the next draw.)
12. The following problem is known as de Mere's paradox. Which is more likely: getting at least one 1 in four rolls of a fair die, or having the sum of two dice be 2 at least once in 24 throws?
13. An automobile manufacturer claims that, on the average, of 100 cars, 20 will have some

kind of defect. Assuming that his claim is correct, calculate the probability that if 10 cars are chosen at random, exactly 7 will have no defects.

14. Suppose that a family has five children. Assume that the probability of having a boy is $\frac{1}{3}$.
    (a) What is the probability of the family having exactly three girls?
    (b) What is the probability of the family having three or more girls?

15. Suppose that there is a 5 percent chance of a complete loss on a certain class of investments.
    (a) If eight investments are made, what is the probability that at most one will result in a complete loss?
    (b) How many investments have to be made in order that there be at least a 20 percent chance of having at least one result in a complete loss?

16. A man claims that he is able to guess an individual's weight with a 90 percent accuracy. He presents his claim to a carnival and they decide to test it by performing the following experiment. He is to guess the weights of 10 individuals, and if he is correct at least seven times, he will be hired. Assume that the man is not a fraud. What is the probability that he will be hired?

Section 4.16 Expected Value

In this section the notion of expected value is introduced. The following examples are presented to illustrate the pertinent concepts.

Example 4.16.1 Coin Tossing Consider the experiment of tossing a *fair* coin twice and suppose that we are interested only in the number of heads that come up. Then the sample space can be taken as

$$\Omega = \{0, 1, 2\}$$

and, as we know, the appropriate assignment of probabilities is

$$\Pr(\{0\}) = \tfrac{1}{4} \qquad \Pr(\{1\}) = \tfrac{1}{2} \qquad \Pr(\{2\}) = \tfrac{1}{4}$$

We now pose the following question: *On the average,* how many heads do you expect to get when the experiment is performed? To put it another way: If the experiment is repeated over and over, what do you expect to be the average number of heads per experiment?

For this particular example it seems clear that on the average one would expect to get one head. This is called the *expected value* of the experiment. We denote this number by the letter $\mathcal{E}$. So, in this case

$$\mathcal{E} = 1 \tag{4.16.1}$$

Example 4.16.2 Dice As a second example to illustrate the notion of expected value, consider the experiment of rolling a *fair* die once. Then we can take

$$\Omega = \{1, 2, 3, 4, 5, 6\}$$

and since the die is fair, each sample point is assigned probability $\frac{1}{6}$. That is,

$$\Pr(\{\omega\}) = \tfrac{1}{6}$$

for each $\omega \in \Omega$.

In this case we shall see that it is reasonable to assign the number 3.5 as the expected value of the experiment. That is,

$$\mathcal{E} = 3.5 \tag{4.16.2}$$

Note that 3.5 itself is not a possible outcome of the experiment. By saying that 3.5 is the expected value of the experiment we simply mean that in a large number of rolls of the die we would expect to get an average of about 3.5 per roll.

Although the above examples may give an intuitive explanation for the notion of expected value, we still do not have a precise definition. The appropriate definition of expected value is obtained by appealing to the relative frequency interpretation of probability.

Definition
Suppose that the possible outcomes of a random experiment are numbers, say $a_1, a_2, \ldots, a_N$. Then the *expected value* of the random experiment is defined to be the number

$$\mathcal{E} = a_1 \Pr(\{a_1\}) + a_2 \Pr(\{a_2\}) + \cdots + a_N \Pr(\{a_N\}) \tag{4.16.3}$$

To see how to obtain Eq. (4.16.3) from the relative frequency interpretation of probability, consider n repetitions of the experiment. As usual, let $n_{\{a_i\}}$ be the number of times the outcome of the experiment is a_i. Then the average value of the experiment in n repetitions is

$$\frac{n_{\{a_1\}} \cdot a_1 + n_{\{a_2\}} \cdot a_2 + \cdots + n_{\{a_N\}} \cdot a_N}{n}$$

$$= a_1 \frac{n_{\{a_1\}}}{n} + a_2 \frac{n_{\{a_2\}}}{n} + \cdots + a_N \frac{n_{\{a_N\}}}{n}$$

$$= a_1 f_{\{a_1\}}(n) + a_2 f_{\{a_2\}}(n) + \cdots + a_N f_{\{a_N\}}(n)$$

$$\doteq a_1 \Pr(\{a_1\}) + a_2 \Pr(\{a_2\}) + \cdots + a_N \Pr(\{a_N\})$$

where the last (approximate) equality is based on the relative frequency interpretation of probability and is valid for large values of n. This motivates the definition in Eq. (4.16.3).

Let us apply the definition in Eq. (4.16.3) to Examples 4.16.1 and 4.16.2.

Example 4.16.3 Coin Tossing Consider the random experiment described in Example 4.16.1. By definition, the expected value of the experiment (i.e., the expected number of heads in two tosses of a fair coin) is

$$\mathcal{E} = 0 \cdot \Pr(\{0\}) + 1 \cdot \Pr(\{1\}) + 2 \cdot \Pr(\{2\})$$
$$= 0 \cdot \tfrac{1}{4} + 1 \cdot \tfrac{1}{2} + 2 \cdot \tfrac{1}{4} = 1$$

This is the result that our intuition led us to in obtaining Eq. (4.16.1).

Example 4.16.4 Dice In Example 4.16.2 we considered the experiment of rolling a fair die once. Here $\Omega = \{1, 2, 3, 4, 5, 6\}$ and each sample point has probability $\tfrac{1}{6}$. Thus the expected value of this experiment is

$$\mathcal{E} = 1 \cdot \Pr(\{1\}) + 2 \cdot \Pr(\{2\}) + 3 \cdot \Pr(\{3\})$$
$$+ 4 \cdot \Pr(\{4\}) + 5 \cdot \Pr(\{5\}) + 6 \cdot \Pr(\{6\})$$
$$= 1 \cdot \tfrac{1}{6} + 2 \cdot \tfrac{1}{6} + 3 \cdot \tfrac{1}{6} + 4 \cdot \tfrac{1}{6} + 5 \cdot \tfrac{1}{6} + 6 \cdot \tfrac{1}{6}$$
$$= 3.5$$

as suggested in Example 4.16.2.

As our final illustration of expected value we consider a simple gambling situation.

Example 4.16.5 Roulette On a roulette wheel there are 38 numbers: 1–36, 0, and 00. Half of the numbers 1–36 are black and half are red. The 0 and 00 are both green.

If a person bets $1 on red, and red comes up (i.e., the ball lands on a red number), then he wins $1; otherwise, he loses $1.

We can consider this to be a random experiment with two possible outcomes: 1 (if the ball lands on red) and -1 (if the ball does not land on red). Thus, in this case $\Omega = \{1, -1\}$. Since there are 18 red numbers and 38 numbers altogether,

$$\Pr(\{1\}) = \tfrac{18}{38} = \tfrac{9}{19}$$

and

$$\Pr(\{-1\}) = \tfrac{20}{38} = \tfrac{10}{19}$$

The expected value of the random experiment is therefore

$$\mathcal{E} = 1 \cdot \Pr(\{1\}) + (-1)\Pr(\{-1\})$$
$$= 1 \cdot \tfrac{9}{19} - 1 \cdot \tfrac{10}{19} = -\tfrac{1}{19} \doteq -.0525$$

In the present case we can interpret this as meaning that *on the average* the player will lose a little over 5 cents per· play. For example, after 100 plays the player will, on the average, be about $5.25 behind.

Exercises for 4.16

In each of problems 1–5, determine the expected value of the given random experiment.
1. $\Omega = \{0, 1\}$; $\Pr(\{0\}) = \tfrac{1}{4}$, $\Pr(\{1\}) = \tfrac{3}{4}$.
2. $\Omega = \{0, 1, 2\}$; $\Pr(\{0\}) = \tfrac{9}{16}$, $\Pr(\{1\}) = \tfrac{6}{16}$, $\Pr(\{2\}) = \tfrac{1}{16}$.
3. $\Omega = \{0, 1, 2, 3\}$; $\Pr(\{0\}) = \tfrac{1}{125}$, $\Pr(\{1\}) = \tfrac{12}{125}$, $\Pr(\{2\}) = \tfrac{48}{125}$, $\Pr(\{3\}) = \tfrac{64}{125}$.
4. $\Omega = \{-1, 1\}$; $\Pr(\{-1\}) = \tfrac{1}{6}$, $\Pr(\{1\}) = \tfrac{5}{6}$.
5. $\Omega = \{-2, -1, 0, 1, 2\}$; $\Pr(\{-2\}) = \tfrac{2}{5}$, $\Pr(\{-1\}) = \tfrac{1}{5}$, $\Pr(\{0\}) = \tfrac{1}{5}$, $\Pr(\{1\}) = \tfrac{3}{25}$, $\Pr(\{2\}) = \tfrac{2}{25}$.
6. Consider the experiment of tossing a fair coin three times and observing the number of heads which come up. Find the expected value of the random experiment.
7. In rolling a pair of fair dice, suppose that the sum of the numbers appearing on the dice is observed. What is the expected value of this random experiment?
8. A baseball player has a batting average of .400. What is the expected number of hits by this player in five times at bat?
9. A machine that produces bolts is known to produce 12.5 percent defective ones according to certain tolerance specifications. If four bolts are examined, what is the expected number of defective ones?
10. Suppose that two cards from an ordinary deck of 52 are dealt to a player. The player wins $1 if both cards are of the same color and loses $1 otherwise. Find the expected gain of the player if
    (a) the first card is replaced before the second one is dealt
    (b) the first card is not replaced before the second one is dealt
11. A government survey has indicated that about 75 percent of all new businesses of a certain type are doomed to failure. Assume that an individual must "put up" $50,000 to start such a business. If the business fails, the $50,000 is lost. However, if the business succeeds, it should yield an eventual profit of $500,000. What is the expected gain for an individual who starts such a business?
*12. In a sequence of n Bernoulli trials with success probability p, find the expected number of successes [see Eq. (4.15.1)].

Descriptive Statistics 5

The word "statistics" means many things to many people. However, one thing is clear: statistics plays an increasingly important role in the workings of society. This is reflected partly by the fact that more and more disciplines require a knowledge of statistics for their understanding and application.

In this chapter we shall consider only one part of the subject of statistics, the part that is referred to as descriptive statistics.

Section 5.1   Introduction

In the modern sense of the word, *statistics* is the science of gathering, organizing, analyzing, and interpreting quantitative data. *Descriptive statistics* is concerned with the tabulation, organization, and pictorial representation of data, along with the use of descriptive measures as a method for summarizing the data. *Inferential statistics* or *statistical inference* involves using the results obtained from applying the methods of descriptive statistics to make certain objective inferences or generalizations. Our point of view in studying descriptive statistics will be that they are a first step toward making statistical inferences.

Example 5.1.1   Political Sampling   As a classical example involving statistics, suppose that two candidates (say I and II) are running for a particular political office in a city with a voting population of 500,000.

Assume that a polling agency interviews 1,000 qualified voters. It determines that 65 percent *of the people interviewed* will vote for candidate I. The polling agency might also choose to further describe the results of its survey by displaying them in light of such things as race, sex, religion, age, and so on. All these actions fall into the category of descriptive statistics.

However, if the polling agency makes a statement of the form "about 65 percent of the voting population of the city will choose candidate I" or one of the form "it is likely that candidate I will win the election," it is delving into the area of statistical inference. That is, the agency is making an inference concerning the candidate preference of the *entire* voting population based on the candidate preference of a *part* of the voting population.

Example 5.1.2 Dice Suppose that a gambler claims that a die is loaded (i.e., the six numbers are *not* equally likely to come up). To try to substantiate his claim, he rolls the die 300 times and obtains the results shown in Table 5.1.1. The organizing

Table 5.1.1

Number	Total number	Relative frequency
1	62	.207
2	41	.137
3	54	.180
4	60	.200
5	44	.147
6	39	.130

and displaying of these results involve descriptive statistics. A statement concerning the fairness of the die based on the data obtained involves statistical inference.

Example 5.1.3 Quality Control A manufacturer of bolts is interested in obtaining information concerning the length of a particular type of bolt which his company produces. He selects 100 bolts and measures their lengths (in millimeters). The results are displayed in Figure 5.1.1.

Figure 5.1.1

296	291	316	289	318
286	273	292	288	337
286	313	319	294	283
304	297	250	274	300
340	315	292	294	281
304	301	314	303	310
245	326	253	321	297
288	302	311	331	288
264	307	290	323	283
348	293	338	311	304
303	314	296	313	288
306	299	312	307	306
356	313	283	312	300
313	283	305	333	310
289	305	301	342	270
306	323	264	291	310
304	344	318	305	312
303	297	321	308	313
307	296	300	305	286
259	301	303	325	301

In Section 5.4 we shall indicate various ways to display data such as these in both tabular and pictorial (graphical) form. Also, in Section 5.5 we shall investigate several descriptive measures that are useful in analyzing and summarizing such data. All these things are a part of descriptive statistics.

In making inferences from the data involving such things as the average length of a bolt of this type or the variation in the lengths of the bolts manufactured, we are concerning ourselves with problems in statistical inference.

Typically, a statistical problem will involve a *population*—the set of all individuals or objects under consideration—and a *sample*—that part of the population which is observed during a statistical investigation. Thus descriptive statistics is concerned with the collecting, tabulating, organizing, and summarizing of data obtained from the sample, whereas statistical inference is concerned with drawing conclusions about the population from which the sample was chosen, based on the information obtained from the sample.

As we have already mentioned, our main concern in this text will be with the basic concepts of descriptive statistics. Before embarking on this topic, we present what is called the *summation notation*. This is a mathematical shorthand that is useful when discussing descriptive measures.

The summation notation allows us to display the addition of several quantities without actually writing out all the terms occurring in the sum. For example, consider the sum

$$1 + 2 + 3 + 4 + 5 + 6 + 7 + 8$$

In the summation notation we write the sum as

$$\sum_{i=1}^{8} i$$

which is read "the summation of i as i goes from 1 to 8." The symbol Σ is the capital Greek letter sigma, which corresponds to the English S. The "$i=1$" below the sigma indicates that the sum is to begin when $i = 1$ and the "8" above the sigma signifies that the sum is to terminate when $i = 8$. Thus i is to assume all *integer* values between 1 and 8, inclusive.

Example 5.1.4 Summation Notation Determine each of the following sums.

1. $\displaystyle\sum_{i=1}^{3} i^2 = 1^2 + 2^2 + 3^2 = 1 + 4 + 9 = 14$

2. $\displaystyle\sum_{i=2}^{5} 4i = 4 \cdot 2 + 4 \cdot 3 + 4 \cdot 4 + 4 \cdot 5$
$= 8 + 12 + 16 + 20 = 56$

3. $\displaystyle\sum_{i=3}^{8} (2i - 4) = (2 \cdot 3 - 4) + (2 \cdot 4 - 4)$
$+ (2 \cdot 5 - 4) + (2 \cdot 6 - 4)$
$+ (2 \cdot 7 - 4) + (2 \cdot 8 - 4)$
$= 2 + 4 + 6 + 8 + 10 + 12$
$= 42$

4. $\displaystyle\sum_{i=1}^{4} (2 - i)^3 = (2 - 1)^3 + (2 - 2)^3$
$$+ (2 - 3)^3 + (2 - 4)^3$$
$$= 1^3 + 0^3 + (-1)^3 + (-2)^3$$
$$= 1 + 0 - 1 - 8 = -8$$

More generally, we shall have occasion to consider summations of the form

$$x_1 + x_2 + \cdots + x_n$$

where the x_is represent certain data. In summation notation this becomes

$$\sum_{i=1}^{n} x_i$$

and is read "the summation of x_i as i goes from 1 to n." For example, if $n = 4$, $x_1 = 2$, $x_2 = 6$, $x_3 = 7$, and $x_4 = 5$,

$$\sum_{i=1}^{n} x_i = \sum_{i=1}^{4} x_i = x_1 + x_2 + x_3 + x_4$$
$$= 2 + 6 + 7 + 5 = 20$$

Frequently, the indexing system is suppressed. For instance,

$$\sum_{i=1}^{n} x_i$$

is written $\Sigma\, x_i$. In these cases we agree to sum over *all* the data. For example, if $x_1 = 3$, $x_2 = 10$, $x_3 = 17$, $x_4 = 2$, $x_5 = -4$, and $x_6 = 8$,

$$\sum x_i = \sum_{i=1}^{6} x_i = 3 + 10 + 17 + 2 - 4 + 8 = 36$$

Using the properties of real numbers (see Appendix A) we obtain the following properties of the summation notation:

S1: $\displaystyle\sum_{i=1}^{n} (x_i + y_i) = \sum_{i=1}^{n} x_i + \sum_{i=1}^{n} y_i$

S2: If c is a fixed real number,

$$\sum_{i=1}^{n} cx_i = c\sum_{i=1}^{n} x_i$$

S3: If c is a fixed real number,

$$\sum_{i=1}^{n} c = nc$$

As an illustration we prove S2. This involves using the distributive law for real numbers to obtain

$$\sum_{i=1}^{n} cx_i = cx_1 + cx_2 + \cdots + cx_n$$

$$= c(x_1 + x_2 + \cdots + x_n)$$

$$= c \sum_{i=1}^{n} x_i$$

Finally, we point out that it is *not generally* true that

$$\sum_{i=1}^{n} x_i y_i = \left(\sum_{i=1}^{n} x_i\right)\left(\sum_{i=1}^{n} y_i\right)$$

For example, suppose that $x_1 = 4$, $x_2 = 2$, $x_3 = 6$, $y_1 = 7$, $y_2 = 5$, and $y_3 = 1$. Then

$$\sum x_i y_i = \sum_{i=1}^{3} x_i y_i$$

$$= x_1 y_1 + x_2 y_2 + x_3 y_3$$

$$= 4 \cdot 7 + 2 \cdot 5 + 6 \cdot 1 = 44$$

and

$$\left(\sum x_i\right)\left(\sum y_i\right) = \left(\sum_{i=1}^{3} x_i\right)\left(\sum_{i=1}^{3} y_i\right)$$

$$= (x_1 + x_2 + x_3)(y_1 + y_2 + y_3)$$

$$= (4 + 2 + 6)(7 + 5 + 1)$$

$$= 12 \cdot 13 = 156$$

Exercises for 5.1

1. Evaluate the given sums.

(a) $\displaystyle\sum_{i=1}^{3} 2i$

(b) $\displaystyle\sum_{i=5}^{8} (3i - 2)$

(c) $\displaystyle\sum_{i=2}^{4} 6i^2$

(d) $\displaystyle\sum_{i=1}^{4} (i^3 - 7i + 3)$

(e) $\displaystyle\sum_{j=2}^{4} (3j + 7)$

(f) $\displaystyle\sum_{k=2}^{5} (4k - 10)$

2. Compute the following sums.

(a) $\displaystyle\sum_{i=1}^{5} (i - 3)$

(b) $\displaystyle\sum_{j=1}^{5} (j - 3)$

(c) $\displaystyle\sum_{i=3}^{7} 2$

(d) $\displaystyle\sum_{i=4}^{8} 2$

(e) $\displaystyle\sum_{j=1}^{4} (6j^2 - 12)$

(f) $\displaystyle\sum_{i=1}^{3} (8i^2 + 2i - 5)$

3. Evaluate the following quantities.

(a) $\frac{1}{7} \sum_{i=1}^{7} (3i - 4)$

(b) $\frac{1}{6} \sum_{j=1}^{6} (5j + 2)$

(c) $\frac{1}{10} \sum_{j=1}^{10} (2j - 5)$

(d) $\frac{1}{5} \sum_{i=1}^{5} (2i^2 - 8)$

4. Determine the values of the following quantities.

(a) $\dfrac{\sum\limits_{j=1}^{4}(3j - 1) \cdot j}{\sum\limits_{j=1}^{4} j}$

(b) $\dfrac{\sum\limits_{i=1}^{5}(2i^2 - 7) \cdot 3i}{\sum\limits_{i=1}^{5} 3i}$

(c) $\dfrac{\sum\limits_{j=1}^{3}(3j^3 - 12) \cdot 2j^2}{\sum\limits_{j=1}^{3} 2j^2}$

5. Evaluate the quantities.

(a) $\frac{1}{3} \sum_{i=1}^{4} (2i - \frac{1}{4} \sum_{j=1}^{4} 2j)^2$

(b) $\frac{1}{4} \sum_{i=1}^{5} (i^2 - \frac{1}{5} \sum_{j=1}^{5} j^2)^2$

(c) $\frac{1}{5} \sum_{j=1}^{6} \left[(3j - 4) - \frac{1}{6} \sum_{i=1}^{6} (3i - 4) \right]^2$

6. Compute the quantities.

(a) $\frac{1}{3} \left[\left(\sum_{i=1}^{4} (2i)^2 \right) - \frac{1}{4} \left(\sum_{i=1}^{4} 2i \right)^2 \right]$

(b) $\frac{1}{4} \left[\left(\sum_{i=1}^{5} (i^2)^2 \right) - \frac{1}{5} \left(\sum_{i=1}^{5} i^2 \right)^2 \right]$

(c) $\frac{1}{5} \left[\left(\sum_{i=1}^{6} (3i - 4)^2 \right) - \frac{1}{6} \left(\sum_{i=1}^{6} (3i - 4) \right)^2 \right]$

7. Let $n = 6$, $x_1 = 1$, $x_2 = 3$, $x_3 = 0$, $x_4 = -2$, $x_5 = 1$, and $x_6 = 4$. Determine

(a) $\dfrac{1}{n} \Sigma x_i$

(b) $\dfrac{1}{n-1} \Sigma (x_i - \bar{x})^2$, where $\bar{x}$ equals the quantity in part (a)

(c) $\dfrac{1}{n-1} \left[(\Sigma x_i^2) - \dfrac{1}{n}(\Sigma x_i)^2 \right]$

8. Let $n = 5$, $x_1 = 2$, $x_2 = 3$, $x_3 = -1$, $x_4 = -3$, and $x_5 = -4$. Determine

(a) $\dfrac{1}{n}\Sigma\, x_i$

(b) $\dfrac{1}{n-1}\Sigma\,(x_i - \bar{x})^2$, where $\bar{x}$ equals the quantity in part (a)

(c) $\dfrac{1}{n-1}\left[(\Sigma\, x_i^2) - \dfrac{1}{n}(\Sigma\, x_i)^2\right]$

9. Let $f_1 = 1$, $f_2 = 3$, $f_3 = 2$, $f_4 = 3$, $m_1 = 1$, $m_2 = 3$, $m_3 = 4$, and $m_4 = 6$. Determine

(a) $\dfrac{\Sigma\, f_j m_j}{\Sigma\, f_j}$

(b) $\dfrac{1}{(\Sigma\, f_j) - 1}\Sigma\, f_j \cdot (m_j - \bar{x})^2$, where $\bar{x}$ equals the quantity in part (a)

(c) $\dfrac{1}{(\Sigma\, f_j) - 1}\left[(\Sigma\, f_j m_j^2) - \dfrac{1}{\Sigma\, f_j}(\Sigma\, f_j m_j)^2\right]$

10. Let $f_1 = 2$, $f_2 = 1$, $f_3 = 4$, $f_4 = 2$, $f_5 = 1$, $m_1 = -2$, $m_2 = 0$, $m_3 = 2$, $m_4 = 4$, and $m_5 = 6$. Determine

(a) $\dfrac{\Sigma\, f_j m_j}{\Sigma\, f_j}$

(b) $\dfrac{1}{(\Sigma\, f_j) - 1}\Sigma\, f_j \cdot (m_j - \bar{x})^2$, where $\bar{x}$ equals the quantity in part (a)

(c) $\dfrac{1}{(\Sigma\, f_j) - 1}\left[(\Sigma\, f_j m_j^2) - \dfrac{1}{\Sigma\, f_j}(\Sigma\, f_j m_j)^2\right]$

11. Prove S1. That is, show that

$$\sum_{i=1}^{n}(x_i + y_i) = \sum_{i=1}^{n}x_i + \sum_{i=1}^{n}y_i$$

12. Prove S3. That is, show that if c is a fixed real number,

$$\sum_{i=1}^{n} c = nc$$

13. Suppose that a, b, and c are fixed real numbers. Use S1–S3 to prove that

$$\sum_{i=1}^{n}(ax_i + by_i + c) = a\sum_{i=1}^{n}x_i + b\sum_{i=1}^{n}y_i + nc$$

*14. Let n be a positive integer greater than 1. Show that

$$\frac{1}{n-1}\sum_{i=1}^{n}\left(x_i - \frac{1}{n}\sum_{j=1}^{n}x_j\right)^2 = \frac{1}{n-1}\left[\left(\sum_{i=1}^{n}x_i^2\right) - \frac{1}{n}\left(\sum_{i=1}^{n}x_i\right)^2\right]$$

*15. Suppose that $f_1, f_2, \ldots, f_k$ are nonnegative integers whose sum exceeds 1. Show that

$$\frac{1}{(\Sigma\, f_j) - 1}\Sigma\, f_j \cdot (m_j - \bar{x})^2 = \frac{1}{(\Sigma\, f_j) - 1}\left[(\Sigma\, f_j m_j^2) - \frac{1}{\Sigma\, f_j}(\Sigma\, f_j m_j)^2\right]$$

where $\bar{x} = (\Sigma\, f_j m_j)/\Sigma\, f_j$.

Section 5.2 Ungrouped Data: Measures of Central Tendency

In statistical procedures data will be obtained from a sample of the population under consideration. Once this is done, the data are organized and then descriptive measures that describe the sample are computed. Ideally, these values will shed some light on the characteristics of the underlying population.

When the size of the sample is relatively small (say 30 or less), the calculations of the values of the descriptive measures usually involve each piece of data (i.e., each element of the sample is considered as an entity). However, for relatively large sample sizes, the data are ordinarily grouped in some way, and then the calculations of the values of the descriptive measures involve only the grouped data.

Since the methods utilized in the small-sample-size (ungrouped-data) situation are conceptually less complicated, we shall study these methods first. This will be done here and also in Section 5.3.

One of the most common descriptive measures is a measure of *central tendency*. Any measure whose purpose is to indicate, in some sense, a center of the data is called a measure of central tendency. The most important of these measures of central tendency is called the *mean*. This is simply the numerical average of the data.

Definition

Let the data consist of the numbers $x_1, x_2, \ldots, x_n$. Then the *mean* (or average) of the sample data is defined by

$$\bar{x} = \frac{x_1 + \cdots + x_n}{n}$$

In the summation notation

$$\bar{x} = \frac{1}{n} \sum_{i=1}^{n} x_i$$

or simply,

$$\bar{x} = \frac{1}{n} \sum x_i$$

Example 5.2.1 Suppose that the data are 1, 3, 4, 6, and 3. Then the mean of the sample is

$$\bar{x} = \frac{1 + 3 + 4 + 6 + 3}{5} = \frac{17}{5} = 3.4$$

(This shows that the value of the mean of the sample data need not be equal to any of the data values.)

Example 5.2.2 Incomes In a certain suburb a sample of 10 individuals is selected. Their annual incomes are as shown in Figure 5.2.1. The mean of the data is

$$\bar{x} = \tfrac{1}{10} \sum x_i = \tfrac{1}{10}(119{,}000) = 11{,}900$$

In other words, the mean income of the individuals sampled is $11,900.

Figure 5.2.1

Individual	Income
1	$ 8,000
2	15,000
3	9,500
4	11,250
5	12,000
6	14,500
7	15,000
8	8,750
9	14,500
10	10,500
	Total $119,000

Example 5.2.3 Exam Scores On a recent exam the scores of the 15 students in the course were as given in Figure 5.2.2. The mean of the data is

Figure 5.2.2

82	87	94
70	72	75
98	54	75
77	72	54
94	82	75

$$\bar{x} = \tfrac{1}{15}\Sigma x_i = \tfrac{1}{15}(1{,}161)$$
$$= \frac{1{,}161}{15} = 77.4$$

Thus the mean score on the exam was 77.4.

The mean is the most widely used measure of central tendency. There are several good reasons for this. However, it should be pointed out that this descriptive measure, when considered alone, does have some disadvantages. One of these is that it is sensitive to extreme values.

Example 5.2.4 Incomes In a certain city a sample of 10 individuals is selected and their annual incomes are obtained. The results are shown in Figure 5.2.3. The mean of the data is

$$\bar{x} = \tfrac{1}{10}\Sigma x_i = \tfrac{1}{10}(119{,}000) = 11{,}900$$

and therefore the mean income of the 10 individuals is $11,900. Note that this is the same mean income as the one obtained in Example 5.2.2. However, it is clear that these samples are quite different (compare Figures 5.2.1 and 5.2.3). The mean income of $11,900 in Example 5.2.2 is much more indicative of the sample than the mean income of $11,900 in Example 5.2.4, where the one high-income individual ($68,100) brings the mean of the sample to a value that does not reflect the income

Figure 5.2.3

Individual	Income
1	$ 5,500
2	8,200
3	6,000
4	5,500
5	4,700
6	4,700
7	7,200
8	3,600
9	5,500
10	68,100
	Total $119,000

of *any* of the individuals in the sample. Note that if the last individual ($68,100) is not considered, the mean of the sample drops to a more representative

$$\bar{x} = \tfrac{1}{9}\Sigma\, x_i = \tfrac{1}{9}(50,900) = \$5,655.56$$

In the next section measures of dispersion are considered, and these will help us to distinguish between samples such as those found in Figures 5.2.1 and 5.2.3.

Another commonly used measure of central tendency is the median. In the case where there is an odd number of data values, this is the middle value of the data when the data are arranged in order of magnitude. However, when there is an even number of samples, there is no middle value, and the median is defined to be the average of the *two* middle values. More precisely, we have the following definition.

Definition

Let the data consist of the number $x_1, x_2, \ldots, x_n$ *arranged in order of magnitude.*

1. If n is odd, the *median* of the sample data is defined to be

$$\hat{x} = x_{(n+1)/2}$$

2. If n is even, the *median* of the sample data is defined to be

$$\hat{x} = \frac{x_{n/2} + x_{(n/2)+1}}{2}$$

Example 5.2.5   Suppose that the data are as in Example 5.2.1: 1, 3, 4, 6, and 3. To compute the median we first arrange the data in order of magnitude:

$$1, 3, 3, 4, 6 \tag{5.2.1}$$

In this case the number of data values is odd: $n = 5$. Thus since $(n + 1)/2 = (5 + 1)/2 = 3$, the median is the third value in Eq. (5.2.1), which happens to be 3 (i.e., $\hat{x} = 3$):

1, 3, 3, 4, 6
↑
median

Example 5.2.6 Suppose that the data consist of the numbers 12, 17, 14, 17, 11, 18, 20, and 12. To find the median, the data are first arranged in order of magnitude:

$$11, 12, 12, 14, 17, 17, 18, 20 \qquad (5.2.2)$$

Since the size of the sample is 8, which is even, the median is the average of the fourth ($\frac{8}{2}$) and fifth ($\frac{8}{2} + 1$) values. These values are 14 and 17, respectively. Thus the median for the data is

$$\hat{x} = \frac{14 + 17}{2} = 15.5$$

Example 5.2.7 Incomes Find the median incomes for the samples in Examples 5.2.2 and 5.2.4.

For Examples 5.2.2 and 5.2.4 the incomes arranged in order of magnitude are as follows:

Example 5.2.2	Example 5.2.4
$ 8,000	$ 3,600
8,750	4,700
9,500	4,700
10,500	5,500
11,250	5,500
12,000	5,500
14,500	6,000
14,500	7,200
15,000	8,200
15,000	68,100

In both cases $n = 10$, and so the median is the average of the fifth and sixth values. For Example 5.2.2 this is

$$\hat{x} = \frac{11,250 + 12,000}{2} = \$11,625$$

while for Example 5.2.4 we have

$$\hat{x} = \frac{5,500 + 5,500}{2} = \$5,500$$

Note that for Example 5.2.2 the mean and median are close to one another:

$$\bar{x} = \$11,900 \qquad \hat{x} = \$11,625$$

and both give a good representation for the center of the data. On the other hand, in Example 5.2.4 the mean and median differ by quite a bit:

$$\bar{x} = \$11,900 \qquad \hat{x} = \$5,500$$

and in this case the median is a better representative of the center of the data. This is because the large income ($68,100) has undesirable effects on the value of the mean but not on the median.

Example 5.2.8 Exam Scores Find the median of the exam scores of Example 5.2.3. The scores arranged in order of magnitude are

$$54, 54, 70, 72, 72, 75, 75, 75, 77, 82, 82, 87, 94, 94, 98$$

Here $n = 15$ is odd, and so the median is the eighth $[(15 + 1)/2]$ value, which is 75. Thus $\hat{x} = 75$. This is relatively close to the mean, which was found to be $\bar{x} = 1{,}161/15 = 77.4$.

As is the case for the mean, the median is subject to certain difficulties. For example, suppose that the data are 1, 1, 1, 5, and 6. Then the median is $\hat{x} = 1$. This does not describe the sample very well. The mean of the data is $\bar{x} = 2.8$ and in this case gives a better description of the center of the values in the sample.

The decision on whether to use the mean or the median in a statistical procedure will, in general, depend on the given situation. As we have seen, sometimes the mean is better as a measure of central tendency, sometimes the median is better, and sometimes they behave about the same.

However, for several mathematical reasons the mean is almost always superior to the median for purposes of statistical inference. Therefore, for all but purely descriptive purposes, we shall consider the mean to be the best choice for the measurement of central tendency.

Finally, we mention that there are still other descriptive measures of central tendency: for example, the *mode* and the *midrange*. Since these are of relatively little value when the methods of descriptive statistics are considered as a first step toward making statistical inferences, we shall delegate the consideration of these two descriptive measures to the exercises.

Exercises for 5.2

1. Find the mean of each of the following sets of sample data.
   (a) 1, 2, 5, 7
   (b) 15, 10, 13, 20, 16
   (c) 5, −3, 7, 2, 10, −8, 7
2. Determine the means of the following samples.
   (a) 3, −8, 4, 4, 3, 5, 6
   (b) 1,525, 1,326, 1,642, 1,271, 10
   (c) 5, 5, 5, 5, 5, 5
3. Find the median of each of the following sets of sample data.
   (a) 3, 8, 4, 4, 2   (b) 3, 8, 4, 4
   (c) 1, 6, 4, 1, 1, 3, 7, 2, 5   (d) 1, 6, 4, 1, 1, 3, 7, 2, 5, 10
4. Determine the medians of the following samples.
   (a) 4, −2, −7, 3, 6   (b) 1,525, 1,326, 1,642, 1,271, 10
   (c) 1,525, 1,326, 1,642, 1,271, 10, 1,427   (d) 5, 5, 5, 5, 5, 5
5. A sample of 11 students from a university was selected and their heights (in inches) recorded. The results obtained were as follows:

   68 68 71 67 72 67
   65 68 67 75 67

   (a) Find the mean height of the students.
   (b) Determine the median height of the students.
6. A sample of 16 construction workers was selected and their weights (in pounds) recorded. The results obtained were as follows:

```
186   189   177   171
182   179   155   167
180   200   187   176
177   171   182   180
```

(a) Determine the mean weight of the 16 construction workers.

(b) Find the median weight of the 16 workers.

7. In order to study the reliability of a certain vacuum tube, a sample of 14 tubes is selected. The lifetimes of the 14 tubes (in days) are as follows:

```
 78   474   337   140    41
 75    23   449   365    17
399   179   171   278
```

(a) Find the mean lifetime of these vacuum tubes.

(b) Determine the median lifetime of the tubes.

8. A book publisher is trying to obtain information concerning the number of incorrectly typeset words per 100,000 words. Results of a survey of 15 books yield the following information:

Book	1	2	3	4	5	6	7	8	9	10
N	2	5	4	3	2	2	1	5	5	1

Book	11	12	13	14	15
N	5	3	3	4	6

Here N denotes the number of incorrectly typeset words per 100,000 words.

(a) Find the mean of the sample data.

(b) Determine the median of the sample data.

9. In order to obtain some insight into the brain size of Neanderthal man, an anthropologist examines 20 skulls. He estimates that the brain sizes (in cubic centimeters) of the 20 specimens were as follows:

```
1,448   1,446   1,458   1,445   1,459
1,443   1,436   1,446   1,444   1,469
1,443   1,456   1,459   1,447   1,441
1,452   1,449   1,425   1,437   1,450
```

(a) Determine the mean of the above data.

(b) Find the median of the data.

10. Suppose that the data values of a sample are the numbers $x_1, x_2, \ldots, x_n$. Assume that all these numbers are equal, say, to b.

(a) What is the mean of the sample data?

(b) What is the median of the sample data?

11. Two samples, of sizes m and n, are taken from a certain population. If the mean of the first sample (size m) is $\bar{x}$ and the mean of the second sample (size n) is $\bar{y}$, what is the mean of the sample obtained by combining the two samples?

12. A telephone company is interested in obtaining information concerning the times (in minutes) of phone conversations. First, 20 phone calls are monitored and it is determined that the mean conversation time is 3.4 minutes. A month later 30 phone calls are monitored and the mean conversation time is found to be 4.2 minutes. Find the mean conversation time of all 50 calls in the survey. (*Hint:* Problem 11.)

13. An automobile manufacturer is interested in gathering information concerning the wages of workers at three production plants. The manufacturer receives the following data from the managers of the three production plants:

Production plant	No. workers	Mean annual salary
I	100	$ 9,600
II	230	10,100
III	175	9,800

What is the mean annual salary of the workers at all three production plants? (*Hint*: Extend the result of problem 11.)

Problems 14–17 deal with the midrange of a sample.

Definition: Let the data consist of the numbers $x_1, x_2, \ldots, x_n$ arranged in order of magnitude. Then the *midrange* of the sample data is defined to be

$$\frac{x_1 + x_n}{2}$$

In other words, the midrange of the sample data is just the average of the smallest and largest data values in the sample.

14. Find the midrange of each of the following sets of sample data.
    (a) 1, 2, 3, 7, 6, 4, 5   (b) 4, 4, 4, 4, 4, 4, 4
    (c) 1, 250, 300, 150, 200, 50, 100   (d) 1, 2, 4, 3, 300, 210
15. Find the midrange of the sample data of problem 5.
16. Determine the midrange of the sample data of problem 6.
17. Calculate the midrange of the sample data of problem 7.

Problems 18–21 deal with the mode of a sample.

Definition: The *mode* of a sample is defined as that data value which occurs most frequently. If there is no single data value that occurs most frequently, then the sample has no mode.

18. Find the mode (if it exists) of each of the following samples.
    (a) 2, 3, 6, 4, 3   (b) 2, 3, 2, 4, 3
    (c) 3, 3, 3, 3, 3   (d) 7, 5, 200, 3, 1, 200, 3, 200, 1
    (e) 150, 200, 320, 200, 400, 200, 150
19. Find the mode (if it exists) of the data in problem 5.
20. Determine the mode (if it exists) of the data in problem 6.
21. Find the mode (if it exists) of the data in problem 8.

Section 5.3 Ungrouped Data: Measures of Dispersion

As pointed out in Section 5.2, a measure of central tendency is, by itself, insufficient to give an accurate description of the sample data. For example, two samples of data can have the same mean but nevertheless can have quite different characteristics. This is illustrated in Examples 5.2.2 and 5.2.4. To distinguish between such samples it is useful to introduce descriptive *measures of dispersion*. Basically these are measures of how much the data are "spread out."

The most simple measure of dispersion of the values of the sample data is the *range*.

Definition

The *range* of the sample data $x_1, x_2, \ldots, x_n$ is the difference between the largest and smallest values of the data. That is, if M is the largest of the x_is and m is the smallest of the x_is, the range, R, of the data is defined by

$$R = M - m$$

Example 5.3.1 Suppose that the data are 1, 3, 4, 6, and 3. Here we have $M = 6$ and $m = 1$. Thus the range of the sample is

$$R = 6 - 1 = 5$$

Example 5.3.2 Incomes Consider again the samples of Examples 5.2.2 and 5.2.4 (see Figures 5.2.1 and 5.2.3).

For Example 5.2.2, $M = 15{,}000$ and $m = 8{,}000$, and so

$$R = 15{,}000 - 8{,}000 = 7{,}000 \tag{5.3.1}$$

On the other hand, for Example 5.2.4, $M = 68{,}100$ and $m = 3{,}600$. Consequently,

$$R = 68{,}100 - 3{,}600 = 64{,}500 \tag{5.3.2}$$

Recall that the means of these two samples are the same. Even this simple measure of dispersion is helpful in distinguishing between these two samples with the same mean.

Example 5.3.3 Exam Scores In Example 5.2.3 we considered a sample of 15 exam scores. The scores are given in Figure 5.2.2. Here $M = 98$ and $m = 54$, and so

$$R = 98 - 54 = 44$$

Although the range of a sample is quite easy to calculate, it is not widely used as a measure of dispersion. One reason for this is that the range ignores a large amount of pertinent data and in no way takes into account the manner in which the majority of data is dispersed within the extreme values of the sample.

A second reason for the infrequent use of the range as a measure of dispersion is that as the number of data values increases, the range tends to become larger and larger without lending additional insight into the true nature of the underlying population. An important requirement of a descriptive measure is that it give an increasingly better understanding of the properties of the underlying population as the sample size increases. As we have just seen, the range of a sample does not have this crucial characteristic.

In order to obtain a descriptive measure of dispersion that more fully takes into account all of the data, we can use the mean of the sample data as a center point and then measure the amount of *deviation* of each of the sample values from the mean. The average amount of deviation of the sample values from the mean can then be used as a measure of dispersion of the sample values.

One question that arises is: How should the deviation of a data value from the mean be computed? Probably the most natural way to compute this deviation is just to calculate the distance[1] between these numbers.

The remarks above lead us to make the following definition.

[1] By the *distance* between two real numbers a and b we mean the number of units separating a and b on the real line (see Section A.2). For example, the distance between -3 and 5 is $5 - (-3) = 8$.

Definition

Let the sample data consist of the numbers $x_1, x_2, \ldots, x_n$ and let $\bar{x}$ be the mean of the sample data. Then we define the *mean deviation* of the sample data to be the number

$$\text{m.d.} = \frac{|x_1 - \bar{x}| + |x_2 - \bar{x}| + \cdots + |x_n - \bar{x}|}{n} \tag{5.3.3}$$

Here $|x_i - \bar{x}|$ represents the distance between the numbers x_i and $\bar{x}$. This, of course, is just $x_i - \bar{x}$ if $x_i - \bar{x} \geq 0$, and is $\bar{x} - x_i$ if $x_i - \bar{x} < 0$. [To compute $|x_i - \bar{x}|$, simply calculate $x_i - \bar{x}$ and ignore the algebraic ($+$ or $-$) sign of the result.]

In summation notation the formula for mean deviation becomes

$$\frac{1}{n} \sum_{i=1}^{n} |x_i - \bar{x}| \tag{5.3.4}$$

or simply,

$$\frac{1}{n} \sum |x_i - \bar{x}| \tag{5.3.5}$$

Example 5.3.4 Consider two sets of sample data:

1. $4, 3, 5, 8, 10$
2. $1, 1, 3, 11, 14$

In both cases, the mean of the sample data equals 6:

$$\bar{x} = 6 \qquad \text{for both samples}$$

It seems clear, however, that the data of the second sample are more widely dispersed than those of the first sample. Therefore, if mean deviation is really a measure of dispersion, the mean deviation of the first sample should be smaller than that of the second. Let us show that this is actually the case.

The mean deviation of the first sample data is

$$\frac{1}{5}\sum_{i=1}^{5} |x_i - \bar{x}| = \tfrac{1}{5}(|4 - 6| + |3 - 6| + |5 - 6| + |8 - 6| + |10 - 6|)$$

$$= \tfrac{1}{5}(2 + 3 + 1 + 2 + 4)$$

$$= \tfrac{12}{5} = 2.4$$

and the mean deviation of the second sample data is

$$\frac{1}{5}\sum_{i=1}^{5} |x_i - \bar{x}| = \tfrac{1}{5}(|1 - 6| + |1 - 6| + |3 - 6| + |11 - 6| + |14 - 6|)$$

$$= \tfrac{1}{5}(5 + 5 + 3 + 5 + 8)$$

$$= \tfrac{26}{5} = 5.2$$

Therefore, as expected, the mean deviation of the second sample data exceeds that of the first sample data. *On the average*, a data value in the first sample will be ($\pm$)2.4

units from 6, and a data value in the second sample will, on the average, be $(\pm)5.2$ units from 6.

Example 5.3.5 Incomes Consider again the two sets of data obtained in Examples 5.2.2 and 5.2.4 (see Figures 5.2.1 and 5.2.3). As we have seen, $\bar{x} = 11,900$ for both samples. That is, the mean income in both cases is $11,900.

By computing the mean deviations we should obtain two numbers which indicate that there is more dispersion of incomes about the mean income of $11,900 in the second sample than in the first. From Figures 5.3.1 and 5.3.2, we see that the mean deviation for the first sample is

$$\frac{1}{10} \sum_{i=1}^{10} |x_i - \bar{x}| = \frac{1}{10} \cdot 23,000 = 2,300$$

and that for the second sample is

$$\frac{1}{10} \sum_{i=1}^{10} |x_i - \bar{x}| = \frac{1}{10} \cdot 112,400 = 11,240$$

Figure 5.3.1   First Sample

x_i	$x_i - \bar{x}$	$|x_i - \bar{x}|$
8,000	−3,900	3,900
15,000	3,100	3,100
9,500	−2,400	2,400
11,250	−650	650
12,000	100	100
14,500	2,600	2,600
15,000	3,100	3,100
8,750	−3,150	3,150
14,500	2,600	2,600
10,500	−1,400	1,400
Total 119,000	0	23,000

Figure 5.3.2   Second Sample

x_i	$x_i - \bar{x}$	$|x_i - \bar{x}|$
5,500	−6,400	6,400
8,200	−3,700	3,700
6,000	−5,900	5,900
5,500	−6,400	6,400
4,700	−7,200	7,200
4,700	−7,200	7,200
7,200	−4,700	4,700
3,600	−8,300	8,300
5,500	−6,400	6,400
68,100	56,200	56,200
Total 119,000	0	112,400

Although the mean deviation is a useful and natural measure of dispersion, it is not widely used. There are several reasons for this. First, it is relatively complicated to compute mean deviation. Second, the theoretical developments involving mean deviation are not particularly simple. For these reasons mathematicians usually prefer to use a different measure of dispersion. The most convenient measure of dispersion involves the sum of the *square deviations* of the data values from the mean.

Definition

Let the sample data consist of the numbers $x_1, x_2, \ldots, x_n$ and let $\bar{x}$ be the mean of the sample data. Then the *variance* of the sample data is defined to be

$$s^2 = \frac{(x_1 - \bar{x})^2 + (x_2 - \bar{x})^2 + \cdots + (x_n - \bar{x})^2}{n - 1} \tag{5.3.6}$$

In summation notation Eq. (5.3.6) becomes

$$s^2 = \frac{1}{n - 1} \sum_{i=1}^{n} (x_i - \bar{x})^2 \tag{5.3.7}$$

or simply,

$$s^2 = \frac{1}{n - 1} \sum (x_i - \bar{x})^2 \tag{5.3.8}$$

Notice that in contrast to the calculations of the mean and mean deviation, we divide by $n - 1$, instead of n, when computing the variance. When n is large (i.e., the sample size is large), there is little difference in dividing by n or by $n - 1$. However, when the sample size is relatively small, these differences can be significant.

Basically, the reason for dividing by $n - 1$ instead of n is that division by n tends to underestimate the true dispersion of values in the underlying population, whereas division by $n - 1$ tends to give a more accurate description.

Example 5.3.6 Consider again the two samples found in Example 5.3.4. We have $\bar{x} = 6$ for both samples. However, the variance of the first sample data is

$$s^2 = \frac{1}{n - 1} \sum_{i=1}^{n} (x_i - \bar{x})^2 = \tfrac{1}{4} \sum_{i=1}^{5} (x_i - 6)^2$$
$$= \tfrac{1}{4} [(4 - 6)^2 + (3 - 6)^2 + (5 - 6)^2 + (8 - 6)^2 + (10 - 6)^2]$$
$$= \tfrac{1}{4} (4 + 9 + 1 + 4 + 16) = \tfrac{34}{4} = 8.5$$

and the variance of the second sample data is

$$s^2 = \frac{1}{n - 1} \sum_{i=1}^{n} (x_i - \bar{x})^2 = \tfrac{1}{4} \sum_{i=1}^{5} (x_i - 6)^2$$
$$= \tfrac{1}{4} [(1 - 6)^2 + (1 - 6)^2 + (3 - 6)^2 + (11 - 6)^2 + (14 - 6)^2]$$
$$= \tfrac{1}{4} (25 + 25 + 9 + 25 + 64) = \tfrac{148}{4} = 37$$

Hence, as expected, the variance of the more widely dispersed data values of the second sample exceeds the variance of the less widely dispersed data values of the first sample.

Notice that the variance gives a measure of dispersion in units which are the square of the units of the original data. For instance, suppose that the measurements of the data in Example 5.3.6 are in feet. Then the variance will have square feet as its unit of measurement. Thus the variance of the first sample data is 8.5 square feet; that of the second is 37 square feet.

To ensure that our measure of dispersion, based on the sum of square deviations of the data values from the mean, has the same units as that of the original data we consider the *square root* of the variance.

Definition
Let the sample data consist of the numbers $x_1, x_2, \ldots, x_n$. Then the *standard deviation* of the sample data is defined to be the square root of the variance of the sample data. Thus the standard deviation is

$$s = \sqrt{s^2} = \sqrt{\frac{(x_1 - \bar{x})^2 + (x_2 - \bar{x})^2 + \cdots + (x_n - \bar{x})^2}{n - 1}} \qquad (5.3.9)$$

In summation notation Eq. (5.3.9) becomes

$$s = \sqrt{\frac{1}{n-1} \sum_{i=1}^{n} (x_i - \bar{x})^2} \qquad (5.3.10)$$

or simply,

$$s = \sqrt{\frac{1}{n-1} \sum (x_i - \bar{x})^2} \qquad (5.3.11)$$

Notice that the unit of measurement of s will be the same as that of the original data, as desired.

Example 5.3.7   Consider again the two samples found in Example 5.3.4. In Example 5.3.6 we found that the variance of the first sample data is $s^2 = 8.5$, so the standard deviation is

$$s = \sqrt{8.5} \doteq 2.92$$

On the other hand, the variance of the second sample data is $s^2 = 37$; consequently, the standard deviation is

$$s = \sqrt{37} \doteq 6.08$$

Example 5.3.8   Exam Scores   In Example 5.2.3 we considered the exam scores of 15 students (see Figure 5.2.2). We shall compute the mean deviation, variance, and standard deviation of the sample values. Recall that we determined that $\bar{x} = 77.4$. Using Figure 5.3.3, we see that the mean deviation of the sample data is

$$\tfrac{1}{15} \sum_{i=1}^{15} |x_i - \bar{x}| = \tfrac{1}{15}(145.2) = 9.68$$

The variance of the sample data is

$$s^2 = \tfrac{1}{14} \sum_{i=1}^{15} (x_i - \bar{x})^2 = \tfrac{1}{14}(2{,}335.6) \doteq 166.83$$

Figure 5.3.3

x_i	$x_i - \bar{x}$	$|x_i - \bar{x}|$	$(x_i - \bar{x})^2$
82	4.6	4.6	21.16
70	−7.4	7.4	54.76
98	20.6	20.6	424.36
77	−.4	.4	.16
94	16.6	16.6	275.56
87	9.6	9.6	92.16
72	−5.4	5.4	29.16
54	−23.4	23.4	547.56
72	−5.4	5.4	29.16
82	4.6	4.6	21.16
94	16.6	16.6	275.56
75	−2.4	2.4	5.76
75	−2.4	2.4	5.76
54	−23.4	23.4	547.56
75	−2.4	2.4	5.76
Total 1,161	0	145.2	2,335.60

and so the standard deviation of the sample data is

$$s = \sqrt{166.83} \doteq 12.92$$

Exercises for 5.3

In each of problems 1–7, determine the (1) range, (2) mean, (3) mean deviation, (4) variance, and (5) standard deviation of the given sample values.
1. 1, 2, 3
2. 1, 2, 3, 4
3. 1, 2, 3, 4, 5
4. 0, −3, 5, 2
5. 4, −1, 3, −5, 6
6. 5, −3, 1, −1, 3
7. 55, −25, 15, −5, 35
8. Suppose that the data values of a sample are the numbers $x_1, x_2, \ldots, x_n$. Assume that all these numbers are equal, say, to b.
   (a) What is the range of the sample data?
   (b) What is the mean deviation of the sample data?
   (c) What is the variance of the sample data?
   (d) What is the standard deviation of the sample data?
9. (a) Suppose that the mean deviation of the sample data $x_1, x_2, \ldots, x_n$ is equal to zero. What can be said about the x_is?
   (b) Suppose that the standard deviation of the sample data $x_1, x_2, \ldots, x_n$ is equal to zero. What can be said about the x_is?
10. Refer to problem 5, Exercises 5.2. Determine the mean deviation and standard deviation of the heights of the 11 students.
11. Find the standard deviation of the weights of the 16 construction workers given in problem 6, Exercises 5.2.
12. Determine the standard deviation of the lifetimes of the 14 vacuum tubes given in problem 7, Exercises 5.2.

13. Find the standard deviation of the data given in problem 8, Exercises 5.2.
14. Determine the standard deviation of the 20 brain sizes given in problem 9, Exercises 5.2.
15. Let the data values of a sample be $x_1, x_2, \ldots, x_n$. Show that the variance of the sample can be expressed in the form

$$s^2 = \frac{1}{n-1}\left[\sum_{i=1}^{n} x_i^2 - \frac{1}{n}\left(\sum_{i=1}^{n} x_i\right)^2\right]$$

16. Let the data values of a sample be $x_1, x_2, \ldots, x_n$ and let $\bar{x}$ denote the mean of the sample. Show that

$$\sum_{i=1}^{n}(x_i - \bar{x}) = 0$$

*17. Consider two samples of size 2. Suppose that they have the same mean and standard deviation. Prove that the samples consist of the same data values.
*18. Does the result of problem 17 hold if the samples are of size bigger than 2?

Section 5.4   Organization of Data in Large Samples

In the previous sections we considered descriptive measures for small samples (say, those with at most 30 pieces of data). In this and the following section the analysis of large samples will be considered.

Conceptually, we can use the same definitions for obtaining descriptive measures of large samples as those which were used for small samples. For example, if the data consist of 1,000 numbers $x_1, x_2, \ldots, x_{1,000}$, the mean of the sample data is

$$\bar{x} = \frac{1}{1,000}\sum_{i=1}^{1,000} x_i \tag{5.4.1}$$

and the standard deviation of the sample data is

$$s = \sqrt{\frac{1}{999}\sum_{i=1}^{1,000}(x_i - \bar{x})^2} \tag{5.4.2}$$

By examining formulas (5.4.1) and (5.4.2) we see that the calculations involved in computing these descriptive measures are extensive. Therefore, when dealing with large samples it is necessary to modify our procedures if they are to remain convenient to work with.

To begin with, we shall investigate the methods for organizing and displaying the data obtained from large samples. The following examples are presented to illustrate the pertinent concepts.

Example 5.4.1   Life Expectancy   In a certain city, death records of 105 individuals were examined and the ages at time of death were compiled. The results obtained were as given in Figure 5.4.1. The raw data displayed in the figure are a bit overwhelming and it is desirable to organize the data so that they present a clearer picture of the situation. This is accomplished by subdividing the data into classes. Once this is done we will be able to represent the data graphically (pictorially) and calculate descriptive measures of the sample data.

To accomplish the subdivision of data into classes we must first decide on how many classes to use. Typically, somewhere between 5 and 20 classes are used.

Figure 5.4.1

79	75	67	74	81
69	67	79	66	80
64	57	67	65	90
64	77	80	68	62
73	70	46	58	71
91	78	67	68	62
73	71	78	72	76
43*	84	47	81	69
65	72	76	87	65
53	75	66	83	62
95	68	90	76	73
72	78	69	78	65
74	70	77	75	74
99**	78	62	77	71
78	62	73	88	76
66	73	71	92	58
74	82	53	66	76
73	93	80	74	77
72	69	82	75	77
74	69	71	73	64
51	71	73	84	72

For this example 12 classes will be used. Now that the number of classes has been decided upon, we must specify the construction of the classes. First, note that the smallest and largest numbers appearing in Figure 5.4.1 are 43 and 99, respectively. There are 57 integers from 43 to 99, inclusive. Thus our classes must be designed to cover a range of 57 units (years). Since 12 classes are to be used, this means that each class must contain at least $\frac{57}{12} = 4.75$ years. It is convenient to have the classes contain an integral (whole) number of years, and so we specify that each class should contain 5 years.

We now select a starting point, say 40, and form the 12 classes, each of which contains 5 years:

40–44	70–74
45–49	75–79
50–54	80–84
55–59	85–89
60–64	90–94
65–69	95–99

Note that each piece of data in Figure 5.4.1 will fall into exactly one of these classes. Also note that each class is specified by the smallest and largest value that can be attained by a member of the class. These are called the *class limits*. For example, the class limits for the third class are 50 and 54.

Now that the classes have been constructed, we can sort the data into classes. The number of data values falling into a particular class is called the *class frequency*. The class frequency of the ith class is denoted by f_i. For example, Figure 5.4.2 shows that $f_1 = 1, f_5 = 8, f_8 = 22$, and $f_{11} = 5$. Note that, of course, the sum of the class frequencies must equal the total sample size (in this case 105). This fact can be used as a check to the correctness of the tallying.

Figure 5.4.2

Class	Class limits	Tallies	Frequency
1	40–44	|	1
2	45–49	| |	2
3	50–54	| | |	3
4	55–59	| | |	3
5	60–64	卌 | | |	8
6	65–69	卌 卌 卌 卌	20
7	70–74	卌 卌 卌 卌 卌 | |	27
8	75–79	卌 卌 卌 卌 | |	22
9	80–84	卌 卌	10
10	85–89	| |	2
11	90–94	卌	5
12	95–99	| |	2
			105

A table such as the one in Figure 5.4.2 is referred to as the *frequency table* or *frequency distribution* of the sample. Notice how much more information and insight into the data is obtained by viewing Figure 5.4.2 than Figure 5.4.1.

To continue with our organization of the data, we choose a number in each class that is representative of the class. The most commonly used number is simply the midpoint of the class, that is, the average value of the two class limits. This number is referred to as the *class mark*. We denote the class mark of the ith class by m_i. For example,

$$m_1 = \frac{40 + 44}{2} = 42$$

$$m_6 = \frac{65 + 69}{2} = 67$$

$$m_{11} = \frac{90 + 94}{2} = 92$$

Two additional numbers that can be displayed in a table as useful information concerning each class are the *relative class frequency* and the *percentage of observations*. The relative class frequency is the class frequency divided by the total sample size, and the percentage of observations for a class is simply 100 times the relative class frequency. For example, the relative class frequency for the eighth class is $\frac{22}{105} \doteq .210$ and the percentage of observations is about 21 percent.

The complete frequency table for the data of Figure 5.4.1 is displayed in Figure 5.4.3 (the tallies are omitted because they are of no further use).

As a final method for illustrating the data of the sample we present two graphical (pictorial) representations of the frequency table. The first of these graphical representations is called a *histogram*. To construct the histogram for the data in this example we first introduce what are called the class boundaries.

A *class boundary* is a number that lies halfway between one class's upper limit and the next class's lower limit. For example, the class boundaries arising from the first class are 39.5 and 44.5; those resulting from the second class are 44.5 and 49.5; and

Figure 5.4.3

Class	Class limits	Class frequency	Class mark	Relative frequency	Percentage of observations
1	40–44	1	42	.010	1.0
2	45–49	2	47	.019	1.9
3	50–54	3	52	.028	2.8
4	55–59	3	57	.028	2.8
5	60–64	8	62	.076	7.6
6	65–69	20	67	.191	19.1
7	70–74	27	72	.257	25.7
8	75–79	22	77	.210	21.0
9	80–84	10	82	.095	9.5
10	85–89	2	87	.019	1.9
11	90–94	5	92	.048	4.8
12	95–99	2	97	.019	1.9
		105		1.000	100.0

those arising from the third class are 49.5 and 54.5. The *width* of a class is defined to be the difference between the class's upper and lower boundaries. All the classes in this example are of width 5.

The histogram for the data of this example is now obtained as follows:

1. Along a horizontal scale we exhibit the class boundaries for the data.
2. A vertical scale is used to identify the class frequencies, as indicated in Figure 5.4.4.

Figure 5.4.4

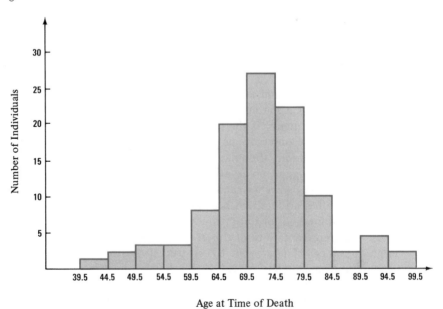

Age at Time of Death

Figure 5.4.4 gives us a vivid representation of the sample data. For example, it makes it perfectly clear that most of the individuals in the sample died between about 59 and 85 years of age.

The second of the graphical representations is called a *frequency polygon*. This is similar to the histogram except that the class marks are used on the horizontal scale. Using a vertical scale to identify frequencies, we place a dot above each class mark at the appropriate frequency level (the frequency level of the class represented by the given class mark). The dots are then connected by straight-line segments. Finally, the polygon is completed by adding a class mark with zero frequency at both ends of the scale, as illustrated in Figure 5.4.5.

Figure 5.4.5

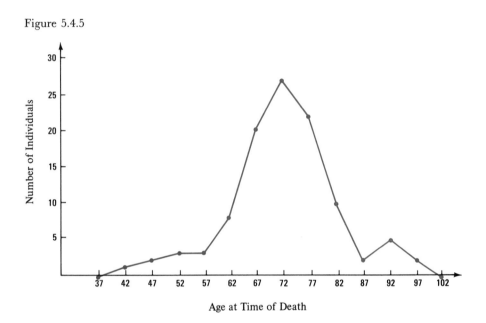

Age at Time of Death

Example 5.4.2 Telephone Switchboards   The president of a company has ordered that a study be made concerning the number of incoming calls being received at the company's telephone switchboard.

To obtain information relevant to the study, the numbers of incoming calls received per hour are tabulated for 3 weeks (120 hours). The results are given in Figure 5.4.6. The smallest and largest data values are 33 and 72, respectively. There are 40 integers from 33 to 72, inclusive. Consequently, the classes must be designed so as to cover a range of 40 units (calls per hour).

Suppose that we decide to use 10 classes so that each class will contain $\frac{40}{10} = 4$ units (calls per hour). Then proceeding as in Example 5.4.1 we obtain Figures 5.4.7 and 5.4.8.

When we use the techniques of Example 5.4.1 we get the histogram (Figure 5.4.9) and frequency polygon (Figure 5.4.10) for the data of Figure 5.4.6.

Figure 5.4.6

44	54	52	47	41
44	39	54	52	39
53	48	48	51	59
48	56	49	36	42
53	48	46	44	47
42	53	46	49	47
62	42	49	46	38
49	47	49	51	55
38	41	51	58	58
48	53	46	46	47
43	45	72**	41	48
57	48	45	51	57
35	51	43	42	37
51	51	38	45	54
51	53	50	45	53
57	46	33*	56	49
44	50	61	39	59
50	49	60	53	49
39	66	46	54	43
62	58	72	63	59
54	55	55	37	65
49	53	41	56	49
58	43	55	45	53
42	57	58	56	43

Figure 5.4.7

Class	Class limits	Tallies	Frequency
1	33–36	‖‖	3
2	37–40	⊬⊬ ‖‖‖	9
3	41–44	⊬⊬ ⊬⊬ ⊬⊬ ‖‖	18
4	45–48	⊬⊬ ⊬⊬ ⊬⊬ ⊬⊬ ‖‖‖	24
5	49–52	⊬⊬ ⊬⊬ ⊬⊬ ⊬⊬ ‖‖	23
6	53–56	⊬⊬ ⊬⊬ ⊬⊬ ⊬⊬ ‖	22
7	57–60	⊬⊬ ⊬⊬ ‖‖	13
8	61–64	‖‖‖	4
9	65–68	‖	2
10	69–72	‖	2
			120

Figure 5.4.8

Class	Class limits	Class frequency	Class mark	Relative frequency	Percentage of observations
1	33–36	3	34.5	.025	2.5
2	37–40	9	38.5	.075	7.5
3	41–44	18	42.5	.150	15.0
4	45–48	24	46.5	.200	20.0
5	49–52	23	50.5	.192	19.2
6	53–56	22	54.5	.183	18.3
7	57–60	13	58.5	.108	10.8
8	61–64	4	62.5	.033	3.3
9	65–68	2	66.5	.017	1.7
10	69–72	2	70.5	.017	1.7
		120		1.000	100.0

Figure 5.4.9

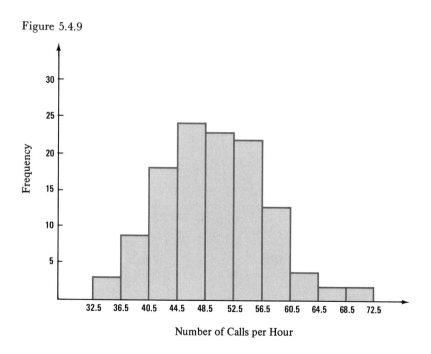

Number of Calls per Hour

Figure 5.4.10

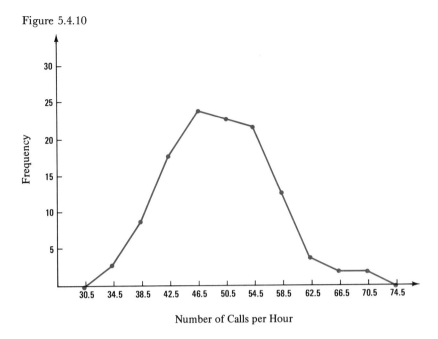

Number of Calls per Hour

Exercises for 5.4

In each of the following problems, proceed as in Example 5.4.1 to obtain the following:
(1) frequency table (as in Figure 5.4.2)
(2) complete frequency table (as in Figure 5.4.3)
(3) histogram (as in Figure 5.4.4)
(4) frequency polygon (as in Figure 5.4.5)
1. A sample of 50 high school students is given a scholastic aptitude test. The scores of the 50 students are as follows:

70	85	69	86	67
59	70	68	97	67
83	86	71	65	78
73	45	59	75	99
84	70	71	64	77
75	83	77	81	42
90	47	87	73	68
76	81	94	68	53
79	69	89	65	100
71	98	82	78	77

Determine the items in (1)–(4); use 7 classes, with 40 as the first class limit.
2. A city administrator is interested in analyzing the number of accidents per month at a certain intersection. From motor vehicle records he obtains the number of accidents per month over the past 75 months. The results are

2	5	4	3	2
2	1	5	5	1
5	3	3	4	6
3	6	4	1	2
5	3	3	2	3
2	5	3	4	3
8	2	3	3	1

```
4   3   4   4   5
1   2   4   6   6
3   5   3   3   3
2   2  12   2   3
6   3   2   4   6
0   4   2   2   1
4   4   1   2   5
4   5   4   2   5
```

Determine the items in (1)–(4); use 7 classes, with 0 as the first class limit.

3. Refer to the quality-control illustration of Example 5.1.3 (see Figure 5.1.1). Determine the items (1)–(4); use 11 classes, with 240 as the first class limit.

4. The owner of a car wash is interested in analyzing the times between customer arrivals at his car wash during the slow period of the day. On various days he measures the time (to the nearest minute) between customer arrivals. The results are as follows:

```
 1   8   6   2   1   1   0   7   6   0
 7   3   3   5  13   3  10   3   0   1
 7   3   2   1   3   1   7   2   4   3
19   1   3   2   0   4   3   3   5   8
 0   1   5  12  13   3   7   2   2   3
 1   2  42   1   3  11   3   2   5  11
 0   5   1   1   0   5   5   0   2   8
 5   6   4   2   7  11   2   0  10   3
 1   4  16   0  13   4   3  15   7   4
 0  25   2   8   1  19  12  39  20  14
 7   9   9   0  23   4   7   1   9   3
12   1   9   2   7
```

Determine the items in (1)–(4); use 12 classes, with 0 as the first class limit.

5. A meteorologist is studying the temperature patterns in Arizona during the months of March and April. The high temperatures during the 2-month period are as follows:

```
73  69  73  67  72
70  73  72  71  84
73  66  73  70  73
71  76  83  77  72
76  75  85  67  77
81  66  73  77  76
86
84  81  83  81  79
85  82  83  82  79
80  81  77  70  80
86  91  85  83  78
95  82  90  80  78
94  84  85  84  77
```

Determine the items in (1)–(4); use 10 classes, with 66 as the first class mark.

6. In an extrasensory perception experiment the test case is placed in a room. In another room a person thinks of a number between 1 and 10, inclusive. The test case then tries to "guess" the number. Each test case undergoes this experiment 200 times. The number of correct responses (out of 200) is recorded. The results from 120 test cases are as follows:

```
16  23  21  18  15
16  13  22  21  13
22  19  18  20  25
19  24  19  11  15
```

```
22  19  18  16  18
15  22  18  19  18
28  15  19  17  12
19  18  19  20  23
12  15  21  25  25
19  22  18  17  18
15  17  35  14  18
24  19  17  21  24
11  20  16  15  12
21  21  13  17  23
20  22  20  17  22
25  17  10  24  19
16  20  27  13  25
20  19  27  22  19
13  30  17  22  15
28  25  35  29  26
22  23  23  12  30
19  22  15  24  19
25  16  23  17  22
15  25  25  24  16
```

Determine the items in (1)–(4); use 8 classes, with 7 as the first class mark.

Section 5.5   Grouped Data: Descriptive Measures

As we mentioned in the previous section, descriptive measures (e.g., mean, median, variance, and standard deviation) for large samples can be defined exactly as they are for small samples. However, there are two main difficulties in doing this.

First, the large number of data values involved makes the computations quite laborious. Second, it is often the case that the data values obtained from a large sample are presented to us in grouped form (i.e., in a frequency table). Therefore, there will be no way for us to recover the original individual data values, so we have no choice but to modify our methods for obtaining descriptive measures.

To begin with, we consider the *mean* of grouped data. The following examples illustrate the general procedure.

Example 5.5.1   Life Expectancy   Consider again the life-expectancy illustration of Example 5.4.1. Using Figure 5.4.1 we could obtain the mean of the data values in the same way as was done for small samples, that is, compute

$$\frac{1}{105} \sum_{i=1}^{105} x_i \tag{5.5.1}$$

This would be quite a task, especially if the calculations were done by hand. Moreover, if instead of being given the information in Figure 5.4.1 we were given the frequency table found in Figure 5.4.3, we could not calculate the mean by means of Eq. (5.5.1) even if we wanted to. Therefore, we calculate the mean of grouped data as follows.

We proceed as if each data value in a given class were equal to the class mark of that class. For example, we operate as if each of the three data values in the fourth class of Figure 5.4.3 were equal to the class mark of 57. If this were the case, the sum of the three data values in the fourth class would be

$$57 + 57 + 57 = 3 \cdot 57 = 171$$

which is just the product of the class frequency and class mark of the fourth class. (Actually, the true sum of the data values in the fourth class is equal to $57 + 58 + 58 = 173$, as can be seen by examining Figure 5.4.1.)

More generally, if we proceeded as if each data value in the jth class were equal to the class mark m_j of the jth class, then the sum of the data values in the jth class would be $f_j \cdot m_j$, where f_j is the class frequency of the jth class. Consequently, the sum of all the data values would be

$$\sum_{j=1}^{12} f_j \cdot m_j = 1 \cdot 42 + 2 \cdot 47 + 3 \cdot 52 + 3 \cdot 57 + 8 \cdot 62$$
$$+ 20 \cdot 67 + 27 \cdot 72 + 22 \cdot 77 + 10 \cdot 82$$
$$+ 2 \cdot 87 + 5 \cdot 92 + 2 \cdot 97 = 7{,}585$$

Consequently, we take as our approximation to the true sum of the data values the number

$$\sum_{j=1}^{12} f_j \cdot m_j = 7{,}585$$

Since there are 105 data values altogether, we use the number

$$\tfrac{1}{105} \sum_{j=1}^{12} f_j \cdot m_j = \frac{7{,}585}{105} \doteq 72.24 \qquad (5.5.2)$$

as the mean for the *grouped* data. This, of course, is an approximation to the true mean of the data which can be obtained by using Eq. (5.5.1). We did the computations indicated in Eq. (5.5.1) and found that

$$\tfrac{1}{105} \sum_{i=1}^{105} x_i = \frac{7{,}596}{105} \doteq 72.34 \qquad (5.5.3)$$

Thus our approximation [given in Eq. (5.5.2)] to the mean of the data values, obtained from the grouped data, is quite close to the true mean [given in Eq. (5.5.3)] of the data values. If the reader really wants to be convinced of the value of using the grouped data method for approximating the mean [in Eq. (5.5.2)] as opposed to the exact method [in Eq. (5.5.3)], he should do both computations. The former method will be found to be considerably easier than the latter. The slight error resulting from the approximate method is completely overshadowed by the significantly easier calculations required.

Before leaving this example we make one more observation. It was pointed out earlier that the sum of the class frequencies must equal the total sample size. In the present case this means that

$$\sum_{j=1}^{12} f_j = 105 \qquad (5.5.4)$$

as noted in the third column of Figure 5.4.3. Thus the term on the left-hand side of Eq. (5.5.2) can be replaced by

$$\frac{1}{\displaystyle\sum_{j=1}^{12} f_j} \sum_{j=1}^{12} f_j \cdot m_j$$

or, what is the same,

$$\frac{\displaystyle\sum_{j=1}^{12} f_j \cdot m_j}{\displaystyle\sum_{j=1}^{12} f_j} \tag{5.5.5}$$

We now use the preceding example as motivation and define the mean of a sample of grouped data.

Definition

Consider a sample of grouped data. Let k denote the number of classes, f_j the class frequency of the jth class, and m_j the class mark of the jth class. Then the *mean of the grouped data* is defined by

$$\bar{x} = \frac{\displaystyle\sum_{j=1}^{k} f_j \cdot m_j}{\displaystyle\sum_{j=1}^{k} f_j} \tag{5.5.6}$$

or simply,

$$\bar{x} = \frac{\sum f_j \cdot m_j}{\sum f_j} \tag{5.5.7}$$

Example 5.5.2 Telephone Switchboards   Consider again the illustration of Example 5.4.2. The frequency table is given in Figure 5.4.8. The mean of the grouped data is

$$\bar{x} = \frac{\displaystyle\sum_{j=1}^{10} f_j \cdot m_j}{\displaystyle\sum_{j=1}^{10} f_j} = \frac{1}{120} \sum_{j=1}^{10} f_j \cdot m_j$$

$$= \tfrac{1}{120}(3 \cdot 34.5 + 9 \cdot 38.5 + 18 \cdot 42.5 + 24 \cdot 46.5$$
$$+ 23 \cdot 50.5 + 22 \cdot 54.5 + 13 \cdot 58.5 + 4 \cdot 62.5$$
$$+ 2 \cdot 66.5 + 2 \cdot 70.5)$$

$$= \frac{5,976}{120} = 49.8$$

Thus

$$\bar{x} = 49.8$$

We next consider the median for grouped data. Recall that if there is an odd number of sample values, the median of the sample is just the middle value of the data when the data are arranged in order of magnitude. On the other hand, if there is an even number of sample values, the median is the average of the two middle data values when the data are arranged in order of magnitude.

When considering the median for large samples we modify the above procedure for basically the same reasons as those given for the modification of the mean in such situations. To illustrate the procedure we consider again the life-expectancy illustration of Example 5.4.1.

Example 5.5.3 If we would use the data given in Figure 5.4.1, we could find the median of the sample data by the same methods as those used for small samples. Since, in this case, $n = 105$, the median of the sample data is just the fifty-third $[= (105 + 1)/2]$ data value when the data are arranged in order of magnitude. However, to arrange the 105 data values in order of magnitude would be an arduous task. Besides, if we were given only the frequency table and not the raw data, we could not calculate the true median even if we wanted to. Therefore, as in the case for the mean, an alternative procedure is developed which utilizes the frequency table of Figure 5.4.3. The procedure is based on the (not necessarily true) assumption that data values in a particular class are evenly distributed throughout the class.

Now, as mentioned above, the median is the fifty-third data value when the data values are arranged in order of magnitude. By studying the third column of Figure 5.4.3 we find that the fifty-third value lies in the *seventh* class. This is because there are 37 values in the first six classes and 64 values in the first seven.

Now, the data values in the seventh class range from 70 to 74, inclusive, so the class boundaries are 69.5 and 74.5. This means that the class width is equal to $74.5 - 69.5 = 5$. Since the class frequency for the seventh class is 27, there are a total of 27 data values in this class. Under the assumption that the data values are evenly dispersed throughout the class, each data value takes up about $\frac{5}{27}$ of a unit. The median is 16 $(= 53 - 37)$ values into the seventh class. Finally, since the lower class boundary for the seventh class is 69.5, we estimate the median to be

$$69.5 + 16 \cdot \tfrac{5}{27} \doteq 72.46 \tag{5.5.8}$$

Using Figure 5.4.1 the exact value of the median can be found. It is

$$x_{53} = 73 \tag{5.5.9}$$

Thus the approximation to the median given in Eq. (5.5.8) is an excellent estimate of the true median given in Eq. (5.5.9).

Keeping in mind the argument used to obtain Eq. (5.5.8), we define the median of a sample of grouped data.

Definition
Consider a sample of grouped data. Let l denote the lower class boundary of the class in which the (true) median is located; let w denote the width of this class (the difference between the class's upper and lower boundaries); let r denote the number

of data values in this class needed to reach the median value; and let f denote the class frequency of this class. Then the *median of the grouped data* is defined by

$$\hat{x} = l + r \cdot \frac{w}{f} \tag{5.5.10}$$

In Example 5.5.3, $l = 69.5$, $w = 5$, $r = 16$, and $f = 27$.

Next we present another illustration for calculating the median of grouped data.

Example 5.5.4 Consider the frequency table (Figure 5.4.8) for the telephone-switchboard illustration of Example 5.4.2. In this case the sample size is 120, so the true median lies *halfway* between the sixtieth and sixty-first data values when the data are arranged in order of magnitude. The total number of data values in the first four classes is 54 and that in the first five classes is 77. Therefore, the (true) median lies in the fifth class. In the notation of Eq. (5.5.10) we have

$$l = 48.5$$
$$w = 4$$
$$f = 23$$

To get to the sixtieth value we need to go 6 ($= 60 - 54$) values into the fifth class. Since the median lies halfway between the sixtieth and sixty-first values, we have

$$r = 6 + \tfrac{1}{2} = \tfrac{13}{2}$$

Therefore, the median for the grouped data is

$$\hat{x} = 48.5 + \tfrac{13}{2} \cdot \tfrac{4}{23} \doteq 48.5 + 1.13 = 49.63$$

Using Figure 5.4.5 it can be shown that the true median is 49.

We conclude this section by describing the methods for calculating the variance and standard deviation for grouped data. Recall that the variance of a sample with data values $x_1, x_2, \ldots, x_n$ is defined by

$$s^2 = \frac{1}{n-1} \sum_{i=1}^{n} (x_i - \bar{x})^2 \tag{5.5.11}$$

Clearly, for large samples (i.e., for large n) this computation will require a vast amount of labor. Of course, if we are not given the raw data but only receive the grouped data, it will not be possible to calculate the exact variance, because we will not know the values of the x_is.

Hence, just as in the cases for the mean and the median, a procedure is developed for approximating s^2. The procedure is basically the same as that for the mean. For each data value x_i in the jth class, the expression $(x_i - \bar{x})^2$ is replaced by $(m_j - \bar{x})^2$, where m_j is the class mark of the jth class and the $\bar{x}$ in the second expression is the mean for the grouped data. Now, the expression $(m_j - \bar{x})^2$ will appear as many times as there are data values in the jth class, namely, f_j times. Thus the expression on the right-hand side of Eq. (5.5.11) is approximated, in the large-sample-size case, by

$$\frac{1}{n-1} \sum_{j=1}^{k} f_j \cdot (m_j - \bar{x})^2$$

where k is the total number of classes in the grouped data. Recalling that

$$n = \sum_{j=1}^{k} f_j$$

we now make the following definition.

Definition
Consider a sample of grouped data. Let k denote the number of classes, f_j the class frequency of the jth class, and m_j the class mark for the jth class. Then the *variance and standard deviation for the grouped data* are given, respectively, by

$$s^2 = \frac{\sum_{j=1}^{k} f_j \cdot (m_j - \bar{x})^2}{\left(\sum_{j=1}^{k} f_j\right) - 1} \tag{5.5.12}$$

and

$$s = \sqrt{\frac{\sum_{j=1}^{k} f_j \cdot (m_j - \bar{x})^2}{\left(\sum_{j=1}^{k} f_j\right) - 1}} \tag{5.5.13}$$

Here $\bar{x}$ is the mean for the grouped data.

Example 5.5.5 In this example we calculate the variance and standard deviation for the grouped data of Example 5.4.1 (see Figure 5.4.3). In Example 5.5.1 the mean of the grouped data was found to be approximately

$$\bar{x} = 72.24$$

Therefore, by Eq. (5.5.12), the variance of the grouped data is

$$s^2 = \frac{\sum_{j=1}^{12} f_j \cdot (m_j - \bar{x})^2}{\left(\sum_{j=1}^{12} f_j\right) - 1} = \tfrac{1}{104} \sum_{j=1}^{12} f_j \cdot (m_j - 72.24)^2$$

$$= \tfrac{1}{104}[1 \cdot (42 - 72.24)^2 + 2 \cdot (47 - 72.24)^2 + \cdots$$
$$+ 5 \cdot (92 - 72.24)^2 + 2 \cdot (97 - 72.24)^2]$$
$$\doteq 101.62$$

By Eq. (5.5.13) the standard deviation of the grouped data is

$$s = \sqrt{s^2} \doteq \sqrt{101.62} \doteq 10.08$$

The variance and standard deviation for the grouped data are, of course, approximations to the true variance and standard deviation of the sample values. However, they are in general quite good approximations. In the present case, it can be shown (after lengthy calculations), with the aid of Figure 5.4.1, that the true variance is 98.92 and the true standard deviation is about 9.95.

Example 5.5.6 Find the variance and standard deviation for the grouped data in Figure 5.4.8.

The mean of the grouped data was found, in Example 5.5.2, to be

$$\bar{x} = 49.8$$

Thus, by Eq. (5.5.12), the variance of the grouped data is

$$s^2 = \frac{\displaystyle\sum_{j=1}^{10} f_j \cdot (m_j - \bar{x})^2}{\left(\displaystyle\sum_{j=1}^{10} f_j\right) - 1} = \frac{1}{119} \sum_{j=1}^{10} f_j \cdot (m_j - 49.8)^2$$

$$= \frac{1}{119}[3 \cdot (34.5 - 49.8)^2 + 9 \cdot (38.5 - 49.8)^2$$
$$+ \cdots + 2 \cdot (70.5 - 49.8)^2]$$
$$\doteq 55.57$$

and therefore the standard deviation of the grouped data is

$$s = \sqrt{s^2} \doteq \sqrt{55.57} \doteq 7.45$$

Exercises for 5.5

In each of problems 1–5, determine the mean, median, variance, and standard deviation of the grouped data.

1.

Class	Class limits	Class frequency
1	34–38	4
2	39–43	6
3	44–48	8
4	49–53	15
5	54–58	4

2.

Class	Class limits	Class frequency
1	54–59	16
2	60–65	18
3	66–71	9
4	72–77	6
5	78–83	12
6	84–89	4

3.

Class	Class limits	Class frequency
1	2–7	1
2	8–13	0
3	14–19	2
4	20–25	10
5	26–31	15
6	32–37	11
7	38–43	7
8	44–49	3

4.

Class	Class limits	Class frequency
1	15–21	1
2	22–28	3
3	29–35	4
4	36–42	15
5	43–49	2
6	50–56	17
7	57–63	1
8	64–70	5

5.

Class	Class limits	Class frequency
1	0–3	6
2	4–7	4
3	8–11	8
4	12–15	6
5	16–19	10
6	20–23	3
7	24–27	12
8	28–31	6
9	32–35	9
10	36–39	8

6. Consider again the data of problem 1, Exercises 5.4. When we use 7 classes with 40 as the first class limit, we obtain the following table:

Class	Class limits	Class frequency
1	40–48	3
2	49–57	1
3	58–66	5
4	67–75	17
5	76–84	13
6	85–93	6
7	94–102	5

Determine the mean, median, variance, and standard deviation of the grouped data of achievement test scores.

7. Refer to problem 2, Exercises 5.4. The number of accidents per month at the intersection for the past 75 months can be grouped as follows:

Class	Class limits	Class frequency
1	0–1	8
2	2–3	34
3	4–5	25
4	6–7	6
5	8–9	1
6	10–11	0
7	12–13	1

Determine the mean, median, variance, and standard deviation of the grouped data of number of accidents per month.

8. Refer to problem 3, Exercises 5.4. The bolt lengths can be grouped as follows:

Class	Class limits	Class frequency
1	240–250	2
2	251–261	2
3	262–272	3
4	273–283	7
5	284–294	17
6	295–305	27
7	306–316	24
8	317–327	9
9	328–338	4
10	339–349	4
11	350–360	1

Determine the mean, median, variance, and standard deviation of the grouped data.

9. Consider again the car-wash illustration of problem 4, Exercises 5.4. The times between customer arrivals (to the nearest minute) can be grouped as follows:

Class	Class limits	Class frequency
1	0–3	58
2	4–7	28
3	8–11	13
4	12–15	8
5	16–19	3
6	20–23	2
7	24–27	1
8	28–31	0
9	32–35	0
10	36–39	1
11	40–43	1
12	44–47	0

Determine the mean, median, variance, and standard deviation of the grouped data of customer interarrival times.

10. Refer to problem 5, Exercises 5.4. The daily high temperatures during March and April can be grouped as follows:

Class	Class limits	Class frequency
1	66–68	4
2	69–71	6
3	72–74	10
4	75–77	9
5	78–80	7
6	81–83	11
7	84–86	10
8	87–89	0
9	90–92	2
10	93–95	2

Determine the mean, median, variance, and standard deviation of the grouped data of high temperatures.

11. Refer to problem 6, Exercises 5.4. The number of correct responses can be grouped as follows:

Class	Class limits	Class frequency
1	7–10	1
2	11–14	12
3	15–18	36
4	19–22	40
5	23–26	22
6	27-30	7
7	31–34	0
8	35–38	2

Determine the mean, median, variance, and standard deviation of the grouped data of correct responses.

12. Show that the variance of grouped data can be written in the form

$$s^2 = \frac{1}{(\Sigma f_j) - 1}\left[\Sigma f_j m_j^2 - \frac{1}{\Sigma f_j}(\Sigma f_j m_j)^2\right]$$

Section 5.6[2] Coding

In the calculations for obtaining the values of descriptive measures, a substantial reduction in the amount of arithmetic computation can be realized by an application of the method of coding. This applies to both ungrouped and grouped data.

We present the following two examples to illustrate the basic ideas involved in coding.

[2]This section is optional.

Example 5.6.1 Suppose that the sample consists of the data values 800, 795, 802, 797, and 801. Think of these numbers plotted on the real line (Figure 5.6.1). Now

Figure 5.6.1

suppose that 800 is subtracted from each of the above data values. Then we obtain a new set of data values: 0, −5, 2, −3, and 1. Plotting these on the real line we obtain Figure 5.6.2. Studying Figures 5.6.1 and 5.6.2 we find that in terms of relative

Figure 5.6.2

position and dispersion there is no difference between the two sets of data values 800, 795, 802, 797, and 801 and 0, −5, 2, −3, and 1. Therefore, we should be able to obtain the values for the mean and variance of the first sample in terms of those of the second.

To see how to do this, let x_1, x_2, x_3, x_4, and x_5 and u_1, u_2, u_3, u_4, and u_5 denote the data values in the first and second samples, respectively. Then, for $i = 1, 2, 3, 4$, and 5,

$$u_i = x_i - 800 \qquad (5.6.1)$$

or

$$x_i = u_i + 800 \qquad (5.6.2)$$

Now, by definition,

$$\bar{u} = \tfrac{1}{5}\sum_{i=1}^{5} u_i = \tfrac{1}{5}(0 - 5 + 2 - 3 + 1) = -1 \qquad (5.6.3)$$

How can we obtain $\bar{x}$ from this? Well, note that, by Eq. (5.6.2),

$$\bar{x} = \tfrac{1}{5}\sum_{i=1}^{5} x_i = \tfrac{1}{5}\sum_{i=1}^{5} (u_i + 800)$$

$$= \tfrac{1}{5}\sum_{i=1}^{5} u_i + \tfrac{1}{5}\sum_{i=1}^{5} 800$$

$$= \bar{u} + 800$$

That is,

$$\bar{x} = \bar{u} + 800 \qquad (5.6.4)$$

Using this and Eq. (5.6.3) we find that $\bar{x} = -1 + 800 = 799$. Because of the fact that the data values of the first sample are relatively large, it turns out that it is much easier to calculate $\bar{x}$ via Eq. (5.6.4) than directly.

Next, consider the variance. Let s_x^2 and s_u^2 denote the respective variances of the first and second samples. Then, by definition,

$$s_u^2 = \tfrac{1}{4} \sum_{i=1}^{5} (u_i - \bar{u})^2$$

$$= \tfrac{1}{4} \{ [0 - (-1)]^2 + [-5 - (-1)]^2 + [2 - (-1)]^2$$
$$+ [-3 - (-1)]^2 + [1 - (-1)]^2 \}$$

$$= \tfrac{1}{4}(1 + 16 + 9 + 4 + 4) = \tfrac{34}{4}$$

Thus

$$s_u^2 = 8.5 \qquad\qquad (5.6.5)$$

To obtain s_x^2 from s_u^2, notice that, by Eqs. (5.6.2) and (5.6.4),

$$s_x^2 = \tfrac{1}{4} \sum_{i=1}^{5} (x_i - \bar{x})^2$$

$$= \tfrac{1}{4} \sum_{i=1}^{5} [(u_i + 800) - (\bar{u} + 800)]^2$$

$$= \tfrac{1}{4} \sum_{i=1}^{5} (u_i - \bar{u})^2 = s_u^2$$

In other words,

$$s_x^2 = s_u^2 \qquad\qquad (5.6.6)$$

When we use Eqs. (5.6.6) and (5.6.5) we see that $s_x^2 = 8.5$.

It should be noted that there is nothing special about the number 800, which was subtracted from each of the data values in the first sample to obtain the second. We could have used 796 or 803 or 798. The only thing to keep in mind is that the purpose is to convert the relatively large data values to relatively small data values.

There is one other technique which when used in conjunction with the aforementioned method simplifies the computations of the values of descriptive measures.

Example 5.6.2 Suppose that the data values are 71.3, 70.1, 70.4, 69.3, 68.7, and 70.8.

First, the technique of the previous example is used to reduce the size of the data values. If, for example, 70 is subtracted from each of the above data values, we obtain the following new data: 1.3, .1, .4, −.7, −1.3, and .8. Next, the decimals are dispensed with by multiplying each of the data values in the second set of sample data by 10. The resulting data are 13, 1, 4, −7, −13, and 8.

Suppose that the first, second, and third samples' data values are represented, respectively, by xs, ys, and us. For example, $x_1 = 71.3$, $y_3 = .4$, and $u_5 = -13$. The relationship between the xs and us is determined as follows. First, we have

$$y_i = x_i - 70 \qquad\qquad (5.6.7)$$

Next, note that

$$u_i = 10 y_i \qquad\qquad (5.6.8)$$

Consequently, by Eqs. (5.6.7) and (5.6.8),

$$u_i = 10 \cdot (x_i - 70) \tag{5.6.9}$$

or

$$x_i = \tfrac{1}{10}u_i + 70 \tag{5.6.10}$$

Now that Eq. (5.6.10) is established, we can obtain expressions for the mean and variance of the xs in terms of the more easily computed mean and variance of the us.

$$\bar{x} = \tfrac{1}{6}\sum_{i=1}^{6} x_i = \tfrac{1}{6}\sum_{i=1}^{6}(\tfrac{1}{10}u_i + 70)$$

$$= \tfrac{1}{10}\cdot\tfrac{1}{6}\sum_{i=1}^{6} u_i + 70 = \tfrac{1}{10}\bar{u} + 70$$

That is,

$$\bar{x} = \tfrac{1}{10}\bar{u} + 70 \tag{5.6.11}$$

Also, if s_x^2 and s_u^2 denote, respectively, the variances of the xs and us, then, by Eqs. (5.6.10) and (5.6.11),

$$s_x^2 = \tfrac{1}{5}\sum_{i=1}^{6}(x_i - \bar{x})^2$$

$$= \tfrac{1}{5}\sum_{i=1}^{6}[(\tfrac{1}{10}u_i + 70) - (\tfrac{1}{10}\bar{u} + 70)]^2$$

$$= \tfrac{1}{5}\sum_{i=1}^{6}[\tfrac{1}{10}(u_i - \bar{u})]^2$$

$$= \frac{1}{10^2}\cdot\tfrac{1}{5}\sum_{i=1}^{6}(u_i - \bar{u})^2 = \frac{1}{10^2}s_u^2$$

In other words,

$$s_x^2 = \frac{1}{10^2}s_u^2 \tag{5.6.12}$$

When we use Eqs. (5.6.11) and (5.6.12) we see that in order to calculate the mean and variance of the xs we need only determine the mean and variance of the us. But this is relatively simple:

$$\bar{u} = \tfrac{1}{6}(13 + 1 + 4 - 7 - 13 + 8)$$
$$= \tfrac{1}{6}(6) = 1$$
$$s_u^2 = \tfrac{1}{5}[(13 - 1)^2 + (1 - 1)^2 + (4 - 1)^2$$
$$+ (-7 - 1)^2 + (-13 - 1)^2 + (8 - 1)^2]$$
$$= \tfrac{1}{5}(144 + 0 + 9 + 64 + 196 + 49)$$
$$= 92.4$$

Therefore, by Eqs. (5.6.11) and (5.6.12),

$$\bar{x} = \frac{1}{10} \cdot 1 + 70 = 70.1$$

$$s_x^2 = \frac{1}{10^2} \cdot 92.4 = .924$$

Using the above examples as motivation [see, especially, Eqs. (5.6.11) and (5.6.12)], we now state the following result.

Theorem 5.6.1 Coding
Let the data values of a sample be denoted by $x_1, x_2, \ldots, x_n$. Let $a \neq 0$ and b be prescribed constants and define new data values by

$$u_i = a \cdot (x_i - b) \tag{5.6.13}$$

or, what is the same,

$$x_i = \frac{1}{a} \cdot u_i + b \tag{5.6.14}$$

Then

$$\bar{x} = \frac{1}{a}\bar{u} + b \tag{5.6.15}$$

and

$$s_x^2 = \frac{1}{a^2} s_u^2 \tag{5.6.16}$$

In Example 5.6.1, $a = 1$ and $b = 800$ [see Eq. (5.6.1)]; in Example 5.6.2, $a = 10$ and $b = 70$ [see Eq. (5.6.9)].

To fully exploit the usefulness of the coding method as a procedure for minimizing computations, we mention that the formula for the variance of data values $u_1, u_2, \ldots, u_n$,

$$s^2 = \frac{1}{n-1} \sum_{i=1}^{n} (u_i - \bar{u})^2 \tag{5.6.17}$$

can be expressed in the equivalent form

$$s^2 = \frac{1}{n-1}\left[\sum_{i=1}^{n} u_i^2 - \frac{1}{n}\left(\sum_{i=1}^{n} u_i \right)^2 \right] \tag{5.6.18}$$

Formula (5.6.18) is especially useful when the mean, $\bar{u}$, is unknown or when the expressions $u_i - \bar{u}$ involve decimals. This is usually the case when coding is applied, so, in practice, Eq. (5.6.18) will be used when the coding technique is utilized.

The coding method is simplified greatly if tables are used to carry out the process.

Example 5.6.3 Exam Scores Consider the exam-score data of Example 5.2.3 given in Figure 5.2.2. To compute the mean and standard deviation of the sample data by the coding method we can choose $a = 1$ and $b = 75$ (Figure 5.6.3). We have,

$$\bar{u} = \frac{36}{15} = 2.4$$

Figure 5.6.3

	x	$u = x - 75$	u^2
	82	7	49
	70	−5	25
	98	23	529
	77	2	4
	94	19	361
	87	12	144
	72	−3	9
	54	−21	441
	72	−3	9
	82	7	49
	94	19	361
	75	0	0
	75	0	0
	54	−21	441
	75	0	0
Total		36	2,422

and, using Eq. (5.6.18),

$$s_u^2 = \tfrac{1}{14}[2{,}422 - \tfrac{1}{15}(36)^2]$$
$$= \tfrac{1}{14}(2{,}422 - 86.4)$$
$$= \tfrac{1}{14}(2{,}335.6) \doteq 166.83$$

Therefore, by Theorem 5.6.1 (with $a = 1$, $b = 75$) we conclude that

$$\bar{x} = \bar{u} + 75 = 77.4$$

and

$$s_x^2 = s_u^2 \doteq 166.83$$

Of course, we also have

$$s_x \doteq \sqrt{166.83} \doteq 12.92$$

Finally, we remark that the coding method applies equally as well to the grouped-data case. First, one of the class marks, preferably one near the center of the frequency table, is selected to be the value b in Theorem 5.6.1. Then the *reciprocal* of the common class-width value (the difference between the upper and lower class boundaries for each class) is used for the value of a in Theorem 5.6.1.

Of course, in the grouped-data case, the mean and variance are calculated by the formulas

$$\bar{x} = \frac{\Sigma f_j m_j}{\Sigma f_j} \qquad \bar{u} = \frac{\Sigma f_j u_j}{\Sigma f_j}$$

$$s_x^2 = \frac{\Sigma f_j \cdot (m_j - \bar{x})^2}{(\Sigma f_j) - 1} \qquad s_u^2 = \frac{\Sigma f_j \cdot (u_j - \bar{u})^2}{(\Sigma f_j) - 1}$$

where $u_j = a \cdot (m_j - b)$.

As in the ungrouped-data case it is convenient to use an alternative expression for s_u^2. It is

$$s_u^2 = \frac{\Sigma f_j u_j^2 - \frac{1}{\Sigma f_j}(\Sigma f_j u_j)^2}{(\Sigma f_j) - 1} \qquad (5.6.19)$$

To illustrate the procedure we consider the following example.

Example 5.6.4 Consider the frequency table (Figure 5.4.8) for the telephone-switchboard illustration of Example 5.4.2. Suppose that we select the class mark of the fifth class for b. Then $b = 50.5$. The common class width for all classes is 4; thus $a = \frac{1}{4}$. Hence, by Theorem 5.6.1 we define

$$u_i = \tfrac{1}{4} \cdot (m_i - 50.5)$$

We then obtain the data in Figure 5.6.4. Consequently,

Figure 5.6.4

m	f	u	fu	fu^2
34.5	3	-4	-12	48
38.5	9	-3	-27	81
42.5	18	-2	-36	72
46.5	24	-1	-24	24
50.5	23	0	0	0
54.5	22	1	22	22
58.5	13	2	26	52
62.5	4	3	12	36
66.5	2	4	8	32
70.5	2	5	10	50
Total	120		-21	417

$$\bar{u} = \frac{\Sigma f_j u_j}{\Sigma f_j} = \frac{-21}{120} = -.175$$

and, by Eq. (5.6.19),

$$s_u^2 = \frac{417 - \frac{1}{120}(441)}{119} \doteq 3.473$$

Therefore, by Theorem 5.6.1,

$$\bar{x} = \frac{1}{\frac{1}{4}}\bar{u} + 50.5 = 4 \cdot (-.175) + 50.5 = 49.8$$

and

$$s_x^2 = \frac{1}{(\frac{1}{4})^2}s_u^2 = 16\, s_u^2 \doteq 55.57$$

Exercises for 5.6

In each of problems 1–7, use Theorem 5.6.1 to calculate the mean, variance, and standard deviation of the following ungrouped data.

1. 275, 274, 276, 280
2. 1,148, 1,146, 1,150, 1,144, 1,151
3. 426.5, 428.6, 426.2, 427.4, 427.5
4. 772.1, 774.3, 773.3, 773.4, 772.1
5. .03, .02, .05, .01, .02, .03
6. 570, 560, 560, 520, 510, 530, 550
7. 47,500, 48,000, 48,200, 46,800, 47,700
8. Refer to the data of problem 5, Exercises 5.2. Find the mean, variance, and standard deviation of the data by coding.
9. Use the method of coding to determine the mean, variance, and standard deviation of the data in problem 6, Exercises 5.2.
10. Apply the method of coding to obtain the mean, variance, and standard deviation of the data in problem 9, Exercises 5.2.
11. Refer to Example 5.2.2. Use the method of coding to compute the mean, variance, and standard deviation of the data in Figure 5.2.1.

In each of problems 12–16, use the method of coding for grouped data, as explained in Example 5.6.4, to determine the mean, variance, and standard deviation of the given data.

12. The grouped data of the life-expectancy illustration of Example 5.4.1 (see Figure 5.4.3).
13. The grouped data of the scholastic aptitude test scores of problem 1, Exercises 5.4 (see problem 6, Exercises 5.5 for the grouped-data table).
14. The grouped data of accidents per month of problem 2, Exercises 5.4 (see problem 7, Exercises 5.5 for the grouped-data table).
15. The grouped data of bolt lengths of problem 3, Exercises 5.4 (see problem 8, Exercises 5.5 for the grouped-data table).
16. The grouped data of high temperatures of problem 5, Exercises 5.4 (see problem 10, Exercises 5.5 for the grouped-data table).

Linear Equations, Vectors, and Matrices

6

In this chapter we first discuss the Gaussian elimination method for solving systems of linear equations. From there we are led naturally into the study of vectors and matrices. Vectors and matrices are not only useful for solving systems of linear equations but have numerous other applications. These applications will appear throughout the rest of the book. In Chapters 7 and 8 they are used in the study of linear programming, in Chapter 9 in the study of Markov chains, and in Chapter 11 they are applied in the examination of game theory.

Section 6.1 Linear Equations

In this section we begin the study of systems of linear equations. We commence by presenting examples that will be solved once the general method of solution is explained.

Example 6.1.1 The Effects of Diet on Learning A psychologist is preparing some white rats for an experiment. The experiment is to determine the effect of diet on learning, and the specific question is whether a low carbohydrate–high protein diet will produce different learning curves than a high carbohydrate–low protein diet. Two groups of test animals will be used. Each group is to receive 10 grams (g) of food per day. For the sake of simplicity, assume that the diet is composed of three foods. (There are, in fact, over 20 foods in the recommended diet for white rats, but the system of equations would be hard to handle.) The diet will be composed of wheat meal, fish meal (dehydrated), and tomatoes (partially dehydrated). Each gram of wheat meal contains $\frac{6}{10}$ g of carbohydrates and $\frac{1}{20}$ g of protein. Each gram of fish meal contains $\frac{8}{10}$ g of protein and a trace of carbohydrates (say none). Each gram of tomatoes contains $\frac{4}{10}$ g of carbohydrates and $\frac{1}{20}$ g of protein.

The animals in group I are to receive 2 g of carbohydrates and 5 g of protein per day. The animals in group II are to receive 5 g of carbohydrates and $\frac{1}{2}$ g of protein per day. What should the composition of the diets be?

229

Example 6.1.2 Advertising Expenditures A large clothing manufacturer has a budget of $7,000,000 for advertising for the coming year. The board of directors has decided that the money should be allocated in the following manner:

1. Advertising should be divided into four categories: television, radio, magazines, and direct mail.
2. Television and radio together should total $4,000,000.
3. The total spent on radio and magazines should equal the amount spent on television.
4. All the advertising should be spaced evenly throughout the year, except direct mail, which should be spaced evenly in the four months June through September.
5. The budget for the first 6 months should be $3,000,000.

Given these conditions on the allocation of advertising capital, determine how much should be spent on each category.

The first step in solving problems such as the ones illustrated in Examples 6.1.1 and 6.1.2 is to define the notion of a linear equation.

Definition

A *linear equation* in n variables is an expression of the form

$$a_1x_1 + a_2x_2 + \cdots + a_nx_n = b \tag{6.1.1}$$

where $a_1, a_2, \ldots, a_n$ and b are fixed numbers and $x_1, x_2, \ldots, x_n$ are variables.

Example 6.1.3

1. The equation

$$4x_1 = 12$$

is a linear equation in one variable (namely, x_1). In the notation of Eq. (6.1.1), $a_1 = 4$ and $b = 12$.
2. The equation

$$2x_1 + 3x_2 = 6$$

is a linear equation in two variables (namely, x_1 and x_2). In the notation of Eq. (6.1.1) we have $a_1 = 2$, $a_2 = 3$, and $b = 6$.
3. The equation

$$x_1 + 3x_2 + 2x_3 = 12$$

is a linear equation in three variables. Here $a_1 = 1$, $a_2 = 3$, $a_3 = 2$, and $b = 12$.
4. The equation

$$2x_1 - 4x_2 + x_3 - x_4 = 8$$

is a linear equation in the four variables x_1, x_2, x_3, and x_4. Here $a_1 = 2$, $a_2 = -4$, $a_3 = 1$, $a_4 = -1$, and $b = 8$.

Consider, for the moment, the second linear equation in Example 6.1.3,

$$2x_1 + 3x_2 = 6 \tag{6.1.2}$$

Let us substitute in some values for the variables x_1 and x_2 and determine whether or not Eq. (6.1.2) is true for that particular choice of values.

If, for example, we let $x_1 = 3$ and $x_2 = 4$, the left-hand side of Eq. (6.1.2) equals

$$2 \cdot 3 + 3 \cdot 4 = 18$$

and since $18 \neq 6$, Eq. (6.1.2) *is not true* for $x_1 = 3$ and $x_2 = 4$.

As another example, suppose that we let $x_1 = 9$ and $x_2 = -4$. Then the left-hand side of Eq. (6.1.2) equals

$$2 \cdot 9 + 3 \cdot (-4) = 6$$

so that the left-hand side of Eq. (6.1.2) equals the right-hand side. Hence Eq. (6.1.2) is true for $x_1 = 9$ and $x_2 = -4$.

Definition

Consider a linear equation in n variables:

$$a_1 x_1 + a_2 x_2 + \cdots + a_n x_n = b$$

Any set of values for the variables which when substituted into the left-hand side of the equation yields the value on the right-hand side of the equation is referred to as a *solution* to the equation. The set of all solutions to the linear equation is called the *solution set* of the linear equation.

Example 6.1.4 Consider again the four linear equations introduced in Example 6.1.3. By simple algebra we know that there is exactly one solution to the first equation, $x_1 = 3$. Hence the solution set for the linear equation $4x_1 = 12$ is $\{3\}$.

The next three linear equations in Example 6.1.3 have infinitely many solutions, so their solution sets are infinite sets.

To see this, consider, for example, the third equation,

$$x_1 + 3x_2 + 2x_3 = 12 \tag{6.1.3}$$

We can "solve" this equation for x_1:

$$x_1 = 12 - 3x_2 - 2x_3 \tag{6.1.4}$$

Now each choice of the values for the variables x_2 and x_3 will determine via Eq. (6.1.4) the proper choice for the value of x_1 so that Eq. (6.1.3) holds. For example, if we choose $x_2 = 1$, $x_3 = 5$, then by Eq. (6.1.4) we should choose

$$x_1 = 12 - 3 \cdot 1 - 2 \cdot 5 = 12 - 13 = -1$$

to get a solution to Eq. (6.1.3). As can be easily verified $x_1 = -1$, $x_2 = 1$, and $x_3 = 5$ is indeed a solution to Eq. (6.1.3).

Since each choice for the values of x_2 and x_3 will determine via Eq. (6.1.4) a solution to Eq. (6.1.3) and there are infinitely many different possible choices for x_2 and x_3, it follows that Eq. (6.1.3) has infinitely many solutions, so the solution set for Eq. (6.1.3) is infinite.

A similar argument applies to the second and fourth equations in Example 6.1.3.

For illustrative purposes some solutions and nonsolutions to the equations in Example 6.1.3 are presented below (LHS = left-hand side, RHS = right-hand side).

1. $4x_1 = 12$

x_1	LHS	RHS	Solution?
0	0	12	No
2	8	12	No
3	12	12	Yes
−5	−20	12	No

2. $2x_1 + 3x_2 = 6$

x_1	x_2	LHS	RHS	Solution?
3	4	18	6	No
9	−4	6	6	Yes
0	2	6	6	Yes
1	2	8	6	No
$-\frac{3}{2}$	3	6	6	Yes

3. $x_1 + 3x_2 + 2x_3 = 12$

x_1	x_2	x_3	LHS	RHS	Solution?
2	1	4	13	12	No
−1	1	5	12	12	Yes
0	0	6	12	12	Yes
14	2	−4	12	12	Yes
−2	−4	6	−2	12	No

4. $2x_1 - 4x_2 + x_3 - x_4 = 8$

x_1	x_2	x_3	x_4	LHS	RHS	Solution?
1	2	3	4	−7	8	No
$\frac{17}{2}$	2	3	4	8	8	Yes
4	0	0	0	8	8	Yes
3	1	−1	2	−1	8	No
−1	−2	5	3	8	8	Yes

Exercises for 6.1

1. Give two examples of linear equations in
   (a) two variables: x_1 and x_2
   (b) three variables: y_1, y_2, and y_3
   (c) four variables: u_1, u_2, u_3, and u_4
   (d) six variables: x_1, x_2, . . . , x_6

2. Determine the solution set of each of the following linear equations in one variable.
   (a) $2x_1 = 7$
   (b) $-3y_1 = \frac{9}{5}$
   (c) $\frac{5}{6}v_1 = \frac{15}{2}$
3. Consider the linear equation in three variables given by

$$2x_1 - x_2 - 3x_3 = 6$$

   Which of the following are solutions to this linear equation?
   (a) $x_1 = 0$, $x_2 = -6$, $x_3 = 0$ (b) $x_1 = 2$, $x_2 = 0$, $x_3 = 0$
   (c) $x_1 = 0$, $x_2 = 0$, $x_3 = 2$ (d) $x_1 = 1$, $x_2 = 5$, $x_3 = -3$
   (e) $x_1 = -2$, $x_2 = 5$, $x_3 = -5$
4. Determine which of the following are solutions to the linear equation

$$4y_1 - 2y_2 + y_3 + 3y_4 = 12$$

   (a) $y_1 = 0$, $y_2 = -6$, $y_3 = 0$, $y_4 = 0$
   (b) $y_1 = 1$, $y_2 = 3$, $y_3 = 17$, $y_4 = 5$
   (c) $y_1 = -3$, $y_2 = 4$, $y_3 = 14$, $y_4 = 6$
   (d) $y_1 = 10$, $y_2 = -3$, $y_3 = -19$, $y_4 = -5$
   (e) $y_1 = \frac{1}{2}$, $y_2 = -\frac{3}{2}$, $y_3 = \frac{25}{4}$, $y_4 = \frac{1}{4}$
5. (a) Find the value of c so that $x_1 = 1$, $x_2 = 3$, $x_3 = -6$ is a solution to the linear equation

$$2x_1 - cx_2 + 5x_3 = 11$$

   (b) Determine the value of d so that $u_1 = 3$, $u_2 = -4$, $u_3 = 6$, $u_4 = 7$ is a solution to the linear equation

$$6u_1 - 5u_2 + du_3 + u_4 = 17$$

6. Find three solutions to each of the following linear equations.
   (a) $x_1 - 4x_2 = 12$ (b) $6x_1 + x_2 - 2x_3 = 5$
   (c) $3y_1 - 4y_2 + 5y_3 = -60$ (d) $2x_1 - x_2 + 5x_4 = 10$ (be careful)
7. Determine four solutions to each of the following linear equations.
   (a) $4x_1 - 3x_2 + 7x_3 - 8x_4 + 9x_5 = 72$
   (b) $x_1 - \frac{3}{2}x_2 + \frac{7}{6}x_3 = -\frac{15}{2}$
8. Suppose that a half-gallon of milk costs $.60, a dozen eggs $.80, a pound of hamburger $.89, and a head of lettuce $.25. Assume that a person buys x_1 half-gallons of milk, x_2 dozen eggs, x_3 pounds of hamburger, and x_4 heads of lettuce. The total bill is b dollars. Write a linear equation to illustrate this.
9. A woman has $2.35 in change in her change purse. Let x_1, x_2, x_3, x_4, and x_5 denote, respectively, the number of pennies, nickels, dimes, quarters, and half-dollars in the purse.
   (a) Express the above fact as a linear equation.
   (b) Find four possibilities for the number of each denomination of coin in her purse.
10. Refer to Example 6.1.1. Let x_1, x_2, and x_3 denote the number of grams of wheat meal, fish meal, and tomatoes to be fed to the animals in group I.
    (a) Express the protein requirement as a linear equation.
    (b) List three possibilities for satisfying the requirement expressed by the linear equation in part (a).
11. Refer to Example 6.1.2. Let x_1, x_2, x_3, and x_4 denote the amount (in millions of dollars) to be spent on television, radio, magazines, and direct mail, respectively. Write the four conditions on the allocation of advertising expenditures as linear equations in x_1, x_2, x_3, and x_4.
12. Show that any linear equation in four variables x_1, x_2, x_3, and x_4 can be considered as a linear equation in six variables x_1, x_2, $\ldots$, x_6.
13. Suppose that the solution set of a linear equation in n variables has cardinality 1. What can be said about n?

Section 6.2 Systems of Linear Equations

In Section 6.1 the concept of a linear equation was introduced and we discussed the notion of a solution to such an equation. However, in most situations that arise in practice the problem will not be to find the solution(s) to a single linear equation but those to a group of linear equations.

Example 6.2.1 Consider the two linear equations

$$2x_1 + 3x_2 = 14$$
$$4x_1 - 7x_2 = 2$$
(6.2.1)

The problem is to find values of x_1 and x_2 that satisfy both equations. In other words, the problem is to determine values of x_1 and x_2 that belong to the solution sets of both linear equations.

Solutions to the individual linear equations can be obtained by using the technique of solving for one variable in terms of the other(s) as illustrated in Section 6.1. Applying this method, Table 6.2.1, which contains *some* of the solutions to each of the equations in Eq. (6.2.1), is obtained. By examining the table we see that among

Table 6.2.1

$2x_1 + 3x_2 = 14$		$4x_1 - 7x_2 = 2$	
x_1	x_2	x_1	x_2
0	$\frac{14}{3}$	0	$-\frac{2}{7}$
1	4	1	$\frac{2}{7}$
2	$\frac{10}{3}$	2	$\frac{6}{7}$
3	$\frac{8}{3}$	3	$\frac{10}{7}$
*4	2	*4	2
5	$\frac{4}{3}$	5	$\frac{18}{7}$
6	$\frac{2}{3}$	6	$\frac{22}{7}$

the seven depicted solutions to each of the linear equations there is one that is a solution to *both*: $x_1 = 4$, $x_2 = 2$. We will see later that this is, in fact, the only solution to both linear equations.

Typically, we begin with a *system* (group) of linear equations all in the same variables. The object is to determine values for the variables that will be solutions to all of the linear equations in the system. Such values for the variables are referred to as *simultaneous solutions* to the system of linear equations. For example, $x_1 = 4$, $x_2 = 2$ is a simultaneous solution to the system of two linear equations in two variables introduced in Example 6.2.1.

We remark that in the terminology of sets, the set of simultaneous solutions to a system of linear equations is the intersection of the solution sets of the individual linear equations.

In Section 6.4 an *algorithm* (method) for solving (i.e., finding the set of all simultaneous solutions to) an arbitrary system of linear equations will be presented. For now we simply illustrate this algorithm by solving the linear system introduced in Example 6.2.1.

Example 6.2.2 Consider the system of linear equations introduced in Example 6.2.1:

$$\text{(I)} \quad \begin{array}{l} 2x_1 + 3x_2 = 14 \\ 4x_1 - 7x_2 = 2 \end{array} \qquad \begin{array}{l} \text{(6.2.2)} \\ \text{(6.2.3)} \end{array}$$

Find the simultaneous solutions for this system.

To begin we make the coefficient of the first variable in the first equation (namely, 2) equal to 1 by multiplying both sides of Eq. (6.2.2) by $\frac{1}{2}$. The resulting linear equation is

$$x_1 + \tfrac{3}{2}x_2 = 7 \qquad \qquad \text{(6.2.4)}$$

As we shall see in Section 6.3, if we multiply a linear equation by a *nonzero* constant, then the resulting linear equation will have the same solution set as the original linear equation. In the present case this means that Eq. (6.2.4) has the same solution set as Eq. (6.2.2), and consequently the linear system obtained by replacing Eq. (6.2.2) by Eq. (6.2.4) has the same set of simultaneous solutions as the original system. That is, the set of simultaneous solutions to the system

$$\text{(II)} \quad \begin{array}{l} x_1 + \tfrac{3}{2}x_2 = 7 \\ 4x_1 - 7x_2 = 2 \end{array} \qquad \begin{array}{l} \text{(6.2.5)} \\ \text{(6.2.6)} \end{array}$$

is the same as that of the system in (I). Hence to solve (I) we need only solve (II).

The second step is to eliminate the first variable (x_1) in Eq. (6.2.6). To do this we *alter the second equation* in (II) by adding to it -4 times the first equation in (II):

$$\begin{array}{ll} 4x_1 - 7x_2 = 2 & \text{(second equation)} \\ \underline{-4x_1 - 6x_2 = -28} & -4 \cdot \text{(first equation)} \\ -13x_2 = -26 & \end{array}$$

Replacing Eq. (6.2.6) by this last linear equation yields the new system

$$\text{(III)} \quad \begin{array}{l} x_1 + \tfrac{3}{2}x_2 = 7 \\ -13x_2 = -26 \end{array} \qquad \begin{array}{l} \text{(6.2.7)} \\ \text{(6.2.8)} \end{array}$$

Again, it is not difficult to show that (III) has the same set of simultaneous solutions as (II) [and hence as (I)].

Next we make the coefficient of the second variable (x_2) in Eq. (6.2.8) equal to 1 by multiplying both sides of Eq. (6.2.8) by $-\frac{1}{13}$. The resulting system is

$$\text{(IV)} \quad \begin{array}{l} x_1 + \tfrac{3}{2}x_2 = 7 \\ x_2 = 2 \end{array} \qquad \begin{array}{l} \text{(6.2.9)} \\ \text{(6.2.10)} \end{array}$$

and, as before, has the same set of simultaneous solutions as (I).

The final step is to eliminate the second variable (x_2) in Eq. (6.2.9). To do this we proceed as before and alter the first equation in (IV) by adding to it $-\frac{3}{2}$ times the second equation in (IV):

$$\begin{array}{ll} x_1 + \tfrac{3}{2}x_2 = 7 & \text{(first equation)} \\ \underline{ -\tfrac{3}{2}x_2 = -3} & -\tfrac{3}{2} \cdot \text{(second equation)} \\ x_1 \phantom{+ \tfrac{3}{2}x_2} = 4 & \end{array}$$

Replacing Eq. (6.2.9) by the immediately preceding equation will give another system of linear equations:

$$(\text{V}) \quad \begin{aligned} x_1 &= 4 \\ x_2 &= 2 \end{aligned}$$

and as previously this system will have the same solution set as (I).

But it is clear that this last system has exactly one simultaneous solution, which is $x_1 = 4$ and $x_2 = 2$. Consequently, because the systems (V) and (I) have the same solution sets, it must be that the original system (I) has $x_1 = 4$ and $x_2 = 2$ as its only simultaneous solution.

The above procedure can be streamlined as follows:

$$(\text{I}) \quad \tfrac{1}{2} \rightarrow \begin{cases} 2x_1 + 3x_2 = 14 \\ 4x_1 - 7x_2 = 2 \end{cases} \qquad \begin{array}{l} \text{multiply first equation} \\ \text{by } \tfrac{1}{2} \end{array}$$

$$(\text{II}) \quad -4 \begin{cases} x_1 + \tfrac{3}{2}x_2 = 7 \\ 4x_1 - 7x_2 = 2 \end{cases} \qquad \begin{array}{l} \text{add } -4 \text{ times first} \\ \text{equation to second} \end{array}$$

$$(\text{III}) \quad -\tfrac{1}{13} \rightarrow \begin{cases} x_1 + \tfrac{3}{2}x_2 = 7 \\ -13x_2 = -26 \end{cases} \qquad \begin{array}{l} \text{multiply second equation} \\ \text{by } -\tfrac{1}{13} \end{array}$$

$$(\text{IV}) \quad -\tfrac{3}{2} \begin{cases} x_1 + \tfrac{3}{2}x_2 = 7 \\ x_2 = 2 \end{cases} \qquad \begin{array}{l} \text{add } -\tfrac{3}{2} \text{ times second} \\ \text{equation to first} \end{array}$$

$$(\text{V}) \quad \begin{cases} x_1 = 4 \\ x_2 = 2 \end{cases} \qquad \begin{array}{l} \text{simultaneous solution} \\ \text{is } x_1 = 4 \text{ and } x_2 = 2 \end{array}$$

Exercises for 6.2

1. Give three examples of systems of two linear equations in the two variables x_1 and x_2.
2. Write down two examples of systems of three linear equations in the four variables x_1, x_2, x_3, and x_4.
3. Exhibit an example of a system of five linear equations in the three variables y_1, y_2, and y_3.
4. Consider the system of two linear equations in two variables given by

$$\begin{aligned} 3x_1 + 5x_2 &= -9 \\ -5x_1 - 6x_2 &= 8 \end{aligned}$$

Which (if any) of the following are simultaneous solutions to the above system?
(a) $x_1 = 1$, $x_2 = 2$ (b) $x_1 = -3$, $x_2 = 0$
(c) $x_1 = 0$, $x_2 = -\tfrac{4}{3}$ (d) $x_1 = 2$, $x_2 = -3$
(e) $x_1 = 12$, $x_2 = -9$ (f) $x_1 = 8$, $x_2 = -8$
5. Consider the system of three linear equations in three variables given by

$$\begin{aligned} 2x_1 + 2x_2 + x_3 &= 10 \\ x_1 + 3x_2 + 2x_3 &= 10 \\ 3x_1 + x_2 - x_3 &= 8 \end{aligned}$$

Which of the following (if any) are simultaneous solutions?
(a) $x_1 = 1$, $x_2 = 2$, $x_3 = 3$ (b) $x_1 = 1$, $x_2 = 2$, $x_3 = 4$
(c) $x_1 = 4$, $x_2 = -2$, $x_3 = 6$ (d) $x_1 = 3$, $x_2 = 1$, $x_3 = 2$
(e) $x_1 = 2$, $x_2 = 4$, $x_3 = -2$
6. Consider the system of two linear equations in three variables given by

$$\begin{aligned} 3x_1 + 7x_2 - 19x_3 &= -1 \\ -4x_1 - 8x_2 + 20x_3 &= 0 \end{aligned}$$

Determine which (if any) of the following sets of values for the variables yield a simultaneous solution to the system.

(a) $x_1 = -4$, $x_2 = 7$, $x_3 = 2$ (b) $x_1 = 4$, $x_2 = 1$, $x_3 = 1$
(c) $x_1 = -1$, $x_2 = 3$, $x_3 = 1$ (d) $x_1 = -7$, $x_2 = 11$, $x_3 = 3$
(e) $x_1 = 10$, $x_2 = 1$, $x_3 = 2$

7. The system

$$2x_1 + 3x_2 = 5$$
$$x_1 + x_2 = 2$$
$$3x_1 + 4x_2 = 4$$

is one consisting of three linear equations in two variables. Determine which (if any) of the following are simultaneous solutions of the system.

(a) $x_1 = 1$, $x_2 = -2$ (b) $x_1 = -2$, $x_2 = 3$
(c) $x_1 = 1$, $x_2 = 1$ (d) $x_1 = -1$, $x_2 = \frac{7}{3}$
(e) $x_1 = \frac{5}{2}$, $x_2 = 0$

8. Refer to Example 6.1.1.
   (a) Let x_1, x_2, and x_3 denote the number of grams of wheat meal, fish meal, and tomatoes to be fed per day to the animals in group I. Write the three requirements concerning total diet, protein intake, and carbohydrate intake per day as a system of three linear equations in three variables.
   (b) Let y_1, y_2, and y_3 denote the number of grams of wheat meal, fish meal, and tomatoes, respectively, to be fed to the group II animals per day. Now proceed as in part (a).

* 9. Consider the situation of problem 9, Exercises 6.1. A woman has \$2.35 in change in her change purse. Let x_1, x_2, x_3, x_4, and x_5 denote, respectively, the number of pennies, nickels, dimes, quarters, and half-dollars in the purse. Suppose that
   (1) The number of dimes is equal to the sum of the number of quarters and half-dollars.
   (2) The number of pennies equals the number of dimes.
   (3) The sum total of the number of pennies, dimes, quarters, and half-dollars is 15 times the number of nickels.
   (4) Twice the sum of the number of nickels and quarters equals the sum of the number of pennies and dimes minus the number of half-dollars.
   Express the condition of the total amount of money in the purse, along with the restrictions given in (1)–(4), as a system of five linear equations in the five variables x_1, x_2, x_3, x_4, x_5.

10. Use the procedure indicated in Example 6.2.2 to determine the simultaneous solution to the system of equations

$$2x_1 + 6x_2 = -2$$
$$3x_1 + 4x_2 = 7$$

11. Perform the steps illustrated in Example 6.2.2 to find the solution set of the system

$$x_1 - 3x_2 = 9$$
$$2x_1 + 4x_2 = 8$$

12. Consider the system of two linear equations in two variables given by

$$4x_1 + 7x_2 = 6$$
$$4x_1 + 7x_2 = -5$$

What is the set of simultaneous solutions of this system? (No calculations are required.)

13. Find three solutions to the system of equations

$$2x_1 - 3x_2 = 1$$
$$-6x_1 + 9x_2 = -3$$
$$4x_1 - 6x_2 = 2$$

(*Hint:* Very little work is required here.)

14. Consider a system of three linear equations all in the same variables. Denote the solution sets of the individual linear equations by S_1, S_2, and S_3, respectively. Write each of the following sets in terms of some or all of the sets S_1, S_2, and S_3.
 (a) The set of simultaneous solutions to the first and third equations.
 (b) The set of simultaneous solutions to the system consisting of all three linear equations.

Section 6.3 Elementary Operations on Linear Systems

In Section 6.2 it was remarked that an algorithm (method) would be developed to determine the solution set of simultaneous solutions of a system of linear equations. The method to be developed was partially illustrated in the solution of a system of two linear equations in two variables (Example 6.2.2).

The basis for the method that will be developed is the fact that we can alter the original system of linear equations by performing certain operations on the equations and arrive at another system whose solution set of simultaneous solutions is the same as that of the original system and is easier to determine.

We begin by considering what happens to a linear equation when both sides of the equation are multiplied by a fixed *nonzero* constant. For example, consider the equation

$$3x_1 + 5x_2 = 8$$

If both sides of this equation are multiplied by 3, we get the equation

$$9x_1 + 15x_2 = 24$$

which can also be written in the form

$$3(3x_1 + 5x_2) = 3 \cdot 8$$

What is the relation between the solution set of the original equation and that of the equation resulting from multiplying both sides of the original by 3? The answer is that they have precisely the same set of solutions. There are several ways to see that this must be the case.

One way to observe this fact is to consider any set of values that satisfies one of the equations and to show that it must also satisfy the other. That is, assume first that $x_1 = a$ and $x_2 = b$ is a solution to the original equation, where a and b are two numbers. Since it is a solution to the equation, we have

$$3a + 5b = 8 \tag{6.3.1}$$

For example, we could take $a = 1$ and $b = 1$, or $a = 0$ and $b = \frac{8}{5}$, or any other solution. Since Eq. (6.3.1) holds,

$$3(3a + 5b) = 3 \cdot 8$$

or

$$9a + 15b = 24$$

That is, $x_1 = a$ and $x_2 = b$ is a solution to the equation

$$9x_1 + 15x_2 = 24$$

Hence we have shown that any solution to the first equation is also a solution to the second.

We next must show that any solution to the second equation is also a solution to the first. To see this, assume that $x_1 = c$ and $x_2 = d$ is a solution to

$$9x_1 + 15x_2 = 24$$

where c and d are two real numbers. Since it is a solution, c and d must satisfy

$$9c + 15d = 24$$

But

$$9c + 15d = 3(3c + 5d)$$

Therefore,

$$3c + 5d = \tfrac{1}{3}(9c + 15d) = \tfrac{1}{3}(24) = 8$$

So

$$3c + 5d = 8$$

and $x_1 = c$, $x_2 = d$ is a solution to

$$3x_1 + 5x_2 = 8$$

This result is true in general. That is, if an equation is multiplied by a *nonzero* constant, then the resulting linear equation has the same solution set as the original equation.

We can now apply this fact to systems of equations in the following way. Given a system of linear equations, we have said that a set of values for the variables is a simultaneous solution if it satisfies all the equations. If any equation in the system is replaced by another equation which has the same set of solutions, the simultaneous solutions to the new system are the same as those of the original. Because of this, we have the following theorem.

Theorem 6.3.1

Given a system of linear equations, and a nonzero constant c, if any equation is multiplied (on both sides) by c, the set of simultaneous solutions to the new system is the same as that of the original system.

We refer to multiplication of a linear equation by a nonzero constant as an *elementary operation* on equations. The solution method that will be devised for systems of linear equations will involve repeated application of this and two other such *elementary operations*.

The second elementary operation that we will consider is primarily a technical point at this stage. Its importance will be brought out later in the chapter. The basic idea here is that the order in which we write down the equations in a system does not affect the set of simultaneous solutions. For example, the system of equations

$$\begin{aligned} x_1 + 3x_2 &= 7 \\ 2x_1 + 4x_2 &= 5 \end{aligned}$$

clearly has the same set of simultaneous solutions as the system

$$\begin{aligned} 2x_1 + 4x_2 &= 5 \\ x_1 + 3x_2 &= 7 \end{aligned}$$

The general result is contained in the statement of the following theorem.

Theorem 6.3.2

Given a system of linear equations, if the positions of any two of the equations are interchanged, the set of simultaneous solutions to the new system is the same as that of the original system.

The interchanging of the positions of any two equations in a system of linear equations is our second elementary operation.

We are now ready to examine the third of the elementary operations on systems of equations. We begin by looking at an example. Consider the system of equations

$$x_1 + 3x_2 = 7$$
$$3x_1 + 4x_2 = 11$$

From the first of our elementary operations we know that the above system has the same solution set as the system

$$-3x_1 - 9x_2 = -21$$
$$3x_1 + 4x_2 = 11$$

Now, for any simultaneous solution to this system, since it satisfies both equations, if we add together the left-hand sides of both and set them equal to the sum of the right-hand sides of both, it must also satisfy the resulting equation. That is, for any set of values satisfying

$$-3x_1 - 9x_2 = -21$$
and
$$3x_1 + 4x_2 = 11$$

that set of values must also satisfy

$$(-3x_1 - 9x_2) + (3x_1 + 4x_2) = -21 + 11$$

Or, combining terms, it must satisfy

$$-5x_2 = -10$$

Hence, any simultaneous solution to the original system must also be a simultaneous solution to the pair of equations

$$x_1 + 3x_2 = 7$$
$$-5x_2 = -10$$

We next show that any simultaneous solution to this new system is also a simultaneous solution to the original system. To demonstrate that this is true, we observe that the system of equations

$$x_1 + 3x_2 = 7$$
$$-5x_2 = -10$$

has the same solution set as the system

$$3x_1 + 9x_2 = 21$$
$$-5x_2 = -10$$

By the same argument as above, any simultaneous solution to this new pair must, therefore, be a solution to the equation

$$(3x_1 + 9x_2) - 5x_2 = 21 - 10$$

or

$$3x_1 + 4x_2 = 11$$

Hence any simultaneous solution to the new pair must also be a simultaneous solution to the system

$$x_1 + 3x_2 = 7$$
$$3x_1 + 4x_2 = 11$$

which is the original system of equations.

To summarize, we have shown that the systems of equations

$$x_1 + 3x_2 = 7$$
$$3x_1 + 4x_2 = 11$$

and

$$x_1 + 3x_2 = 7$$
$$-5x_2 = -10$$

have precisely the same set of simultaneous solutions.

Let us consider what was done in going from one system to the other, and how a general elementary operation might be derived from it.

Beginning with the original system of equations we chose one of the equations (in this case the first equation) and added a constant multiple of it to another equation— the second equation. As a result we obtained a system of equations consisting of the original first equation and a new second equation. It was then determined that the set of simultaneous solutions was unaltered by this procedure.

Our third elementary operation on systems of linear equations and its property of leaving the solution set of the system unaltered is summarized in the theorem below:

Theorem 6.3.3

Given a system of linear equations, if a constant multiple of one of the equations is added to one of the other equations in the system, the set of simultaneous solutions to the new system is the same as that of the original system.

We now have the following three elementary operations on systems of linear equations:

1. Any equation may be multiplied by a nonzero constant.
2. The positions of any two equations in the system may be interchanged.
3. A constant multiple of any one equation may be added to any other equation in the system.

As we have shown, the result of applying any of these operations to a system of linear equations will be to leave the set of simultaneous solutions unchanged.

Exercises for 6.3

1. Consider the linear equation

$$2x_1 - 5x_2 = 7$$

and the linear equation obtained from this by multiplying both sides by 3:

$$6x_1 - 15x_2 = 21$$

According to Theorem 6.3.1, both equations have the same solution set. Illustrate this fact by "solving" for x_1 in each equation and showing that the results are the same.

2. By Theorem 6.3.1 the linear equations

and
$$3x_1 - x_2 + 4x_3 = 11$$
$$12x_1 - 4x_2 + 16x_3 = 44$$

(which is 4 times the first) have the same solution set. Illustrate this by "solving" for one variable in terms of the other two in both equations.

3. Consider the system of linear equations

$$
(*) \quad
\begin{aligned}
2x_1 - 3x_2 + 4x_3 &= 6 \\
3x_1 + 5x_2 - 6x_3 &= 7 \\
4x_1 - 2x_2 + 6x_3 &= -2 \\
5x_1 + 4x_2 - 7x_3 &= 0
\end{aligned}
$$

Perform each of the following elementary operations on this system and exhibit the resulting system.

(a) Multiply both sides of the third equation in (*) by $\frac{1}{2}$.
(b) Interchange the second and fourth equations in (*).
(c) Add -2 times the first equation in (*) to the third equation in (*).
(d) Add $\frac{3}{4}$ times the fourth equation in (*) to the first equation in (*).
(e) Multiply the second equation in (*) by $\frac{1}{3}$.
(f) Add $\frac{7}{6}$ times the third equation in (*) to the fourth equation in (*).

4. For each pair of systems of equations, indicate which one of the elementary operations justifies the statement that the systems have the same set of simultaneous solutions.

(a) $\begin{aligned} 3x_1 - 2x_2 &= 1 \\ 7x_1 + 4x_2 &= 8 \end{aligned}$ and $\begin{aligned} 7x_1 + 4x_2 &= 8 \\ 3x_1 - 2x_2 &= 1 \end{aligned}$

(b) $\begin{aligned} 2x_1 - 5x_2 &= 3 \\ 3x_1 + 6x_2 &= -3 \\ 4x_1 + 5x_2 &= 7 \end{aligned}$ and $\begin{aligned} 2x_1 - 5x_2 &= 3 \\ x_1 + 2x_2 &= -1 \\ 4x_1 + 5x_2 &= 7 \end{aligned}$

(c) $\begin{aligned} x_1 + 3x_2 - x_3 &= 5 \\ 2x_1 + 6x_2 + 7x_3 &= -2 \\ 5x_1 - 4x_2 + 2x_3 &= 1 \end{aligned}$ and $\begin{aligned} x_1 + 3x_2 - x_3 &= 5 \\ 2x_1 + 6x_2 + 7x_3 &= -2 \\ 8x_1 + 5x_2 - x_3 &= 16 \end{aligned}$

(d) $\begin{aligned} 2y_1 - 3y_2 + 4y_3 &= 2 \\ 3y_1 + 7y_2 - 8y_3 &= 4 \\ y_1 - 6y_2 + 7y_3 &= 0 \\ 6y_1 - 7y_2 + 2y_3 &= -5 \end{aligned}$ and $\begin{aligned} 2y_1 - 3y_2 + 4y_3 &= 2 \\ 3y_1 + 7y_2 - 8y_3 &= 4 \\ -11y_1 + 8y_2 + 3y_3 &= 10 \\ 6y_1 - 7y_2 + 2y_3 &= -5 \end{aligned}$

(e) $\begin{aligned} 4x_1 + 2x_2 &= -8 \\ 3x_1 - 2x_2 &= 5 \\ 2x_1 - 3x_2 &= 4 \\ x_1 + 3x_2 &= 7 \end{aligned}$ and $\begin{aligned} 4x_1 + 2x_2 &= -8 \\ x_1 + 3x_2 &= 7 \\ 2x_1 - 3x_2 &= 4 \\ 3x_1 - 2x_2 &= 5 \end{aligned}$

5. Consider the system of linear equations

$$
(*) \quad
\begin{aligned}
2x_1 - 3x_2 &= -2 \\
-4x_1 + 8x_2 &= 12
\end{aligned}
$$

Successively perform the following elementary operations and at each step exhibit the resulting system.

(a) Interchange the first and second equations in (*).
(b) Multiply the first equation of the system obtained in (a) by $-\frac{1}{4}$.

(c) Add -2 times the first equation of the system obtained in (b) to the second equation.

(d) Add 2 times the second equation of the system obtained in (c) to the first equation.

What is the simultaneous solution to the system (*)? Justify your answer.

6. Consider the system of linear equations given by

$$\begin{array}{rcl} 2x_1 + 2x_2 + x_3 &=& 10 \\ (*) \quad x_1 + 3x_2 + 2x_3 &=& 10 \\ 3x_1 + x_2 - x_3 &=& 8 \end{array}$$

Successively perform the following elementary operations and at each step exhibit the resulting system.

(a) Interchange the first and second equations in (*).

(b) For the system obtained in part (a), add -2 times the first equation to the second equation.

(c) Add -3 times the first equation of the system in part (b) to the third equation.

(d) Multiply the second equation of the system in part (c) by $-\frac{1}{4}$.

(e) Add -3 times the second equation obtained in part (d) to the first equation.

(f) Add 8 times the second equation in part (e) to the third equation.

(g) Multiply the third equation in part (f) by -1.

(h) For the system obtained in part (g), add $\frac{1}{4}$ times the third equation to the first.

(i) Add $-\frac{3}{4}$ times the third equation in part (h) to the second equation.

What is the simultaneous solution to the system (*)? Justify your answer.

7. Consider the system of three linear equations in two variables given by

$$\begin{array}{rcl} 2x_1 + 3x_2 &=& 5 \\ (*) \quad x_1 + x_2 &=& 2 \\ 3x_1 + 4x_2 &=& 4 \end{array}$$

Perform, *successively*, the following elementary operations beginning with the system (*).

(a) Interchange the first and second equations.

(b) Add -2 times the first equation in part (a) to the second equation.

(c) Add -3 times the first equation in part (b) to the third equation.

(d) Add -1 times the second equation in part (c) to the first equation.

(e) Add -1 times the second equation in part (d) to the third equation.

What is the solution set of simultaneous solutions of this last system? What is the solution set of the system (*)?

*8. Given a system of three linear equations in any number of variables, assume that the third equation can be obtained by adding a constant multiple of the first equation to the second. Show that the solution set of the original system is the same as that of the system consisting of the first two linear equations in the system.

*9. Consider a system of two linear equations in n variables ($n \geq 2$). Suppose that the second equation is a constant multiple of the first. Show that the system has infinitely many simultaneous solutions.

*10. Consider a system of m linear equations ($m \geq 2$) in n variables. Suppose that two of the equations in the system have the following property. The left-hand side of one equation is equal to c times the left-hand side of the other, but the right-hand sides do not have this property. Prove that the system has no simultaneous solutions.

Section 6.4   Gaussian Elimination

In Section 6.3 we discussed three elementary operations that may be performed on a system of linear equations without altering the set of simultaneous solutions. They are:

1. Any equation may be multiplied by a nonzero constant.
2. The positions of any two equations in the system may be interchanged.
3. A constant multiple of any equation may be added to any other equation in the system.

With these elementary operations in mind, we can now state the method for solving a system of linear equations called *Gaussian elimination*. Before doing so, we illustrate the general procedure by the following example.

Example 6.4.1 Solve the system of linear equations

$$\begin{aligned} 2x_1 + 2x_2 + x_3 &= 10 \\ x_1 + 3x_2 + 2x_3 &= 10 \\ 3x_1 + x_2 - x_3 &= 8 \end{aligned}$$

by using the elementary operations 1–3. By operation 2, we can interchange the first and second equations, to get

$$\begin{aligned} x_1 + 3x_2 + 2x_3 &= 10 \\ 2x_1 + 2x_2 + x_3 &= 10 \\ 3x_1 + x_2 - x_3 &= 8 \end{aligned}$$

By 3, we can add -2 times the first equation to the second equation, to get

$$\begin{aligned} x_1 + 3x_2 + 2x_3 &= 10 \\ -4x_2 - 3x_3 &= -10 \\ 3x_1 + x_2 - x_3 &= 8 \end{aligned}$$

Next, again by 3, we can add -3 times the first equation to the third equation. The result is:

$$\begin{aligned} x_1 + 3x_2 + 2x_3 &= 10 \\ -4x_2 - 3x_3 &= -10 \\ -8x_2 - 7x_3 &= -22 \end{aligned}$$

Applying 1, we multiply the second equation by $-\frac{1}{4}$:

$$\begin{aligned} x_1 + 3x_2 + 2x_3 &= 10 \\ x_2 + \tfrac{3}{4}x_3 &= \tfrac{5}{2} \\ -8x_2 - 7x_3 &= -22 \end{aligned}$$

We next add -3 times the second equation to the first equation, using 3:

$$\begin{aligned} x_1 \quad\quad - \tfrac{1}{4}x_3 &= \tfrac{5}{2} \\ x_2 + \tfrac{3}{4}x_3 &= \tfrac{5}{2} \\ -8x_2 - 7x_3 &= -22 \end{aligned}$$

By 3, we add 8 times the second equation to the third equation, to get

$$\begin{aligned} x_1 \quad\quad - \tfrac{1}{4}x_3 &= \tfrac{5}{2} \\ x_2 + \tfrac{3}{4}x_3 &= \tfrac{5}{2} \\ -x_3 &= -2 \end{aligned}$$

Applying 1, we multiply the third equation by -1:

$$\begin{aligned} x_1 \quad\quad - \tfrac{1}{4}x_3 &= \tfrac{5}{2} \\ x_2 + \tfrac{3}{4}x_3 &= \tfrac{5}{2} \\ x_3 &= 2 \end{aligned}$$

By 3, we add $\frac{1}{4}$ times the third equation to the first equation:

$$
\begin{aligned}
x_1 \qquad\qquad &= 3 \\
x_2 + \tfrac{3}{4}x_3 &= \tfrac{5}{2} \\
x_3 &= 2
\end{aligned}
$$

Finally, by 3, we add $-\frac{3}{4}$ times the third equation to the second equation. The result is

$$
\begin{aligned}
x_1 \qquad\qquad &= 3 \\
x_2 \qquad &= 1 \\
x_3 &= 2
\end{aligned}
$$

We have now arrived, by successive applications of our elementary operations, at a system of equations whose simultaneous solutions are the same as those of the original system. It is, of course, obvious what the solutions to this final system are. There is one simultaneous solution given by $x_1 = 3$, $x_2 = 1$, $x_3 = 2$. Since the elementary operations leave the set of simultaneous solutions unaltered, this must be a simultaneous solution to the original system, and, in fact, must be its only solution.

As a test to guarantee that no arithmetic errors were made in applying the elementary operations we can check these values in the original system. We have

$$
\begin{aligned}
2 \cdot 3 + 2 \cdot 1 + \quad 2 &= 10 \\
3 + 3 \cdot 1 + 2 \cdot 2 &= 10 \\
3 \cdot 3 + \quad 1 - \quad 2 &= 8
\end{aligned}
$$

We can now list the steps for our general method of solving systems of linear equations. This method is referred to as Gaussian elimination. The term elimination is used because the basic idea is to eliminate as many of the variables as possible in each equation, to arrive at a system such as the final one given in the example just concluded.

Keeping Example 6.4.1 in mind, the following algorithm for solving a system of linear equations is now presented.

Gaussian Elimination

To solve a system of linear equations, apply the following steps:

1. Select an equation in which x_1 appears (i.e., has nonzero coefficient). Use operation 2 to interchange this with the first equation. Then apply operation 1 to make the coefficient of x_1 in this equation equal to 1. Next use operation 3 to eliminate x_1 in all the equations other than the first.
2. Select an equation *other than the first* in which x_2 appears. Use operation 2 to interchange this with the second equation. Then apply operation 1 to make the coefficient of x_2 equal to 1. Next use operation 3 to eliminate x_2 in all equations (including the first) except the second.
3. Select an equation *other than the first or second* in which x_3 appears. Then proceed as in step 2 to make this equation the third one, to make the coefficient of x_3 in this equation 1, and to eliminate x_3 from all equations other than the third equation.
4. Continue in this manner until it is impossible to proceed further.

We remark that it may happen, for example, that at step 2, x_2 may not appear in any of the equations except possibly the first. In such a case proceed with x_3 instead of x_2. If x_3 does not appear, proceed with x_4, and so on.

Exercises for 6.4

Use the Gaussian elimination algorithm to determine the simultaneous solutions to the following systems of equations.

1. $2x_1 + 3x_2 = 8$
   $4x_1 - 8x_2 = -12$

2. $x_1 - 3x_2 = 9$
   $2x_1 + 4x_2 = 8$

3. $\frac{1}{4}x_1 + 2x_2 = 14$
   $-5x_1 + 7x_2 = 2$

4. $3x_1 - 7x_2 = 1$
   $-12x_1 + 14x_2 = -10$

5. $.4x_1 + .3x_2 = -2$
   $.5x_1 - .1x_2 = 7$

6. $3x_1 - 4x_2 + x_3 = 14$
   $2x_1 + 5x_2 - 6x_3 = -25$
   $x_1 + x_2 - 3x_3 = -11$

7. $2x_1 - x_2 - 3x_3 = 1$
   $4x_1 + x_2 - 2x_3 = 12$
   $6x_1 - 2x_3 = 16$

8. $4x_1 - 3x_2 + 5x_3 = -1$
   $2x_1 + 8x_2 - 4x_3 = 6$
   $2x_1 - 11x_2 + x_3 = 1$

9. $2x_1 - 9x_2 + 5x_3 = 8$
   $4x_1 - 12x_2 + 24x_3 = 32$
   $3x_1 - 18x_2 + 21x_3 = 24$

10. $x_1 + 3x_4 = 1$
    $2x_1 - 3x_2 + x_4 = -15$
    $3x_2 + 2x_3 + x_4 = 19$
    $x_1 + x_2 + x_3 + x_4 = 6$

11. $3x_1 + 2x_2 + 2x_3 + 3x_4 = 6$
    $x_1 + 2x_2 - x_3 + x_4 = 5$
    $x_1 - 4x_2 + 4x_3 - 6x_4 = -20$
    $3x_1 + 6x_2 - 3x_3 + 4x_4 = 17$

Section 6.5   Examples

We now present several examples illustrating the method of Gaussian elimination. In applying the method we use the streamlined procedure indicated at the end of Section 6.2.

Example 6.5.1 Solve the system of equations

$$5x_1 - 7x_2 = -1$$
$$2x_1 + 4x_2 = 20 \tag{6.5.1}$$

using Gaussian elimination.

$$\circlearrowleft \begin{cases} 5x_1 - 7x_2 = -1 \\ 2x_1 + 4x_2 = 20 \end{cases}$$

$$\tfrac{1}{2} \to \begin{cases} 2x_1 + 4x_2 = 20 \\ 5x_1 - 7x_2 = -1 \end{cases}$$

$$-5 \circlearrowleft \begin{cases} x_1 + 2x_2 = 10 \\ 5x_1 - 7x_2 = -1 \end{cases}$$

$$-\tfrac{1}{17} \to \begin{cases} x_1 + 2x_2 = 10 \\ - 17x_2 = -51 \end{cases}$$

$$-2 \ \circlearrowleft \begin{cases} x_1 + 2x_2 = 10 \\ x_2 = 3 \end{cases}$$

$$\begin{cases} x_1 = 4 \\ x_2 = 3 \end{cases}$$

The system of Eq. (6.5.1) has the unique simultaneous solution $x_1 = 4$, $x_2 = 3$.

Example 6.5.2 Solve the system of linear equations

$$-4x_1 + x_2 + x_3 = 0$$
$$3x_1 - 2x_2 + 2x_3 = 0$$
$$x_1 + x_2 - 3x_3 = 0$$
$$x_1 + x_2 + x_3 = 1 \tag{6.5.2}$$

using Gaussian elimination.

$$\circlearrowleft \begin{cases} -4x_1 + x_2 + x_3 = 0 \\ 3x_1 - 2x_2 + 2x_3 = 0 \\ x_1 + x_2 - 3x_3 = 0 \\ x_1 + x_2 + x_3 = 1 \end{cases} \begin{array}{l} \\ \\ \to \\ -1 \end{array} \qquad \begin{array}{l} \\ -3 \\ 4 \\ \to \end{array} \begin{cases} x_1 + x_2 - 3x_3 = 0 \\ 3x_1 - 2x_2 + 2x_3 = 0 \\ -4x_1 + x_2 + x_3 = 0 \\ x_1 + x_2 + x_3 = 1 \end{cases}$$

$$-\tfrac{1}{5} \to \begin{cases} x_1 + x_2 - 3x_3 = 0 \\ - 5x_2 + 11x_3 = 0 \\ 5x_2 - 11x_3 = 0 \\ 4x_3 = 1 \end{cases} \to \qquad \begin{array}{l} -1 \\ -5 \end{array} \circlearrowleft \begin{cases} x_1 + x_2 - 3x_3 = 0 \\ x_2 - \tfrac{11}{5}x_3 = 0 \\ 5x_2 - 11x_3 = 0 \\ 4x_3 = 1 \end{cases}$$

$$\circlearrowleft \begin{cases} x_1 - \tfrac{4}{5}x_3 = 0 \\ x_2 - \tfrac{11}{5}x_3 = 0 \\ 0 = 0 \\ 4x_3 = 1 \end{cases} \to \qquad \tfrac{1}{4} \to \begin{cases} x_1 - \tfrac{4}{5}x_3 = 0 \\ x_2 - \tfrac{11}{5}x_3 = 0 \\ 4x_3 = 1 \\ 0 = 0 \end{cases}$$

$$\begin{array}{l} \tfrac{4}{5} \to \\ \tfrac{11}{5} \circlearrowleft \end{array} \begin{cases} x_1 - \tfrac{4}{5}x_3 = 0 \\ x_2 - \tfrac{11}{5}x_3 = 0 \\ x_3 = \tfrac{1}{4} \\ 0 = 0 \end{cases} \to \qquad \begin{cases} x_1 = \tfrac{1}{5} \\ x_2 = \tfrac{11}{20} \\ x_3 = \tfrac{1}{4} \\ 0 = 0 \end{cases}$$

The system of Eq. (6.5.2) has exactly one simultaneous solution: $x_1 = \frac{1}{5}$, $x_2 = \frac{11}{20}$, $x_3 = \frac{1}{4}$. (*Note:* The final equation in the last system is $0 = 0$ or

$$0 \cdot x_1 + 0 \cdot x_2 + 0 \cdot x_3 = 0$$

Obviously any values for x_1, x_2, and x_3 will satisfy this equation so that we need only be concerned with the other three equations.)

Example 6.5.3 Solve the linear system

$$
\begin{aligned}
2x_1 + 3x_2 &= 5 \\
x_1 + x_2 &= 2 \\
3x_1 + 4x_2 &= 4
\end{aligned}
\tag{6.5.3}
$$

Using Gaussian elimination we get

$$
\begin{cases}
2x_1 + 3x_2 = & 5 \\
x_1 + x_2 = & 2 \\
3x_1 + 4x_2 = & 4
\end{cases}
\begin{matrix} -2 \\ -3 \end{matrix}
\longrightarrow
\begin{cases}
x_1 + x_2 = & 2 \\
2x_1 + 3x_2 = & 5 \\
3x_1 + 4x_2 = & 4
\end{cases}
$$

$$
\begin{matrix} -1 \\ \\ -1 \end{matrix}
\begin{cases}
x_1 + x_2 = & 2 \\
x_2 = & 1 \\
x_2 = & -2
\end{cases}
\longrightarrow
\begin{cases}
x_1 = & 1 \\
x_2 = & 1 \\
0 = & -3
\end{cases}
$$

Note that from the last equation in the last system it is necessary for 0 to equal -3 (i.e., $0x_1 + 0x_2 = -3$) in order that this system have a solution. Since this is impossible (regardless of the values of x_1 and x_2), the system has no solution. In set terminology the solution set of simultaneous solutions to the system in Eq. (6.5.3) is $\emptyset$.

Example 6.5.4 Using Gaussian elimination, solve the following system of linear equations:

$$
\begin{aligned}
3x_1 + 7x_2 - 19x_3 &= -1 \\
-4x_1 - 8x_2 + 20x_3 &= 0
\end{aligned}
\tag{6.5.4}
$$

We proceed as usual:

$$
\begin{cases}
3x_1 + 7x_2 - 19x_3 = -1 \\
-4x_1 - 8x_2 + 20x_3 = 0
\end{cases}
\begin{matrix} -\frac{1}{4} \to \end{matrix}
\begin{cases}
-4x_1 - 8x_2 + 20x_3 = 0 \\
3x_1 + 7x_2 - 19x_3 = -1
\end{cases}
$$

$$
\begin{matrix} -3 \end{matrix}
\begin{cases}
x_1 + 2x_2 - 5x_3 = 0 \\
3x_1 + 7x_2 - 19x_3 = -1
\end{cases}
\begin{matrix} -2 \end{matrix}
\begin{cases}
x_1 + 2x_2 - 5x_3 = 0 \\
x_2 - 4x_3 = -1
\end{cases}
$$

$$
\begin{cases}
x_1 + 3x_3 = 2 \\
x_2 - 4x_3 = -1
\end{cases}
$$

Since both equations have already been used, we can proceed no further. The two equations in the final system involve three variables. If a value for x_3 is chosen, the values for the other two variables are determined by the two equations. This is more easily seen if the last system is rewritten as follows:

$$
\begin{aligned}
x_1 &= 2 - 3x_3 \\
x_2 &= -1 + 4x_3
\end{aligned}
\tag{6.5.5}
$$

From Eq. (6.5.5) it is clear that this system [and hence the original system in Eq. (6.5.4)] has *infinitely many simultaneous solutions*: for each value of x_3, a solution to the system in Eq. (6.5.4) is determined via Eq. (6.5.5).

For example, if we set $x_3 = 2$, then by Eq. (6.5.5) we should choose

$$x_1 = \quad 2 - 3 \cdot 2 = -4$$

and

$$x_2 = -1 + 4 \cdot 2 = \quad 7$$

in order to obtain a solution of Eq. (6.5.4). Hence $x_1 = -4, x_2 = 7, x_3 = 2$ is a solution to the system in Eq. (6.5.4). *Some* other solutions to the system are given in the following table:

x_1	x_2	x_3
2	-1	0
5	-5	-1
-1	3	1
-7	11	3

We now solve the problems that were presented at the beginning of Section 6.1.

Solution to Example 6.1.1 For the test group I let

$$x_1 = \text{g of wheat meal}$$
$$x_2 = \text{g of fish meal}$$
$$x_3 = \text{g of tomatoes}$$

Since the total diet must be 10 g, we first have

$$x_1 + x_2 + x_3 = 10$$

In terms of carbohydrates, each gram of wheat meal contains $\frac{6}{10}$ g of carbohydrates, so the total supplied by the wheat will be

$$\frac{6}{10}x_1$$

Similarly, the total carbohydrates supplied by the fish meal and tomatoes are

$$0 \cdot x_2$$

and

$$\frac{4}{10}x_3$$

respectively. Hence the total carbohydrates in the diet is

$$\frac{6}{10}x_1 + \frac{4}{10}x_3$$

and this must equal 2 g. For protein, the total protein supplied by each food is $\frac{1}{20}x_1$, $\frac{8}{10}x_2$, and $\frac{1}{20}x_3$, respectively. This must equal 5. Thus we have three equations in three variables,

$$
\begin{aligned}
x_1 + \quad x_2 + \quad x_3 &= 10 \\
\tfrac{6}{10}x_1 \quad\quad\quad\ + \tfrac{4}{10}x_3 &= 2 \\
\tfrac{1}{20}x_1 + \tfrac{8}{10}x_2 + \tfrac{1}{20}x_3 &= 5
\end{aligned}
\tag{6.5.6}
$$

Applying the Gaussian elimination method we obtain

$$\left(-\frac{6}{10}\right)\left(-\frac{1}{20}\right)\begin{cases} x_1 + x_2 + x_3 = 10 \\ \frac{6}{10}x_1 + \frac{4}{10}x_3 = 2 \\ \frac{1}{20}x_1 + \frac{8}{10}x_2 + \frac{1}{20}x_3 = 5 \end{cases} \quad -\frac{10}{6} \rightarrow \begin{cases} x_1 + x_2 + x_3 = 10 \\ -\frac{6}{10}x_2 - \frac{2}{10}x_3 = -4 \\ \frac{3}{4}x_2 = \frac{9}{2} \end{cases}$$

$$-1 \begin{cases} x_1 + x_2 + x_3 = 10 \\ x_2 + \frac{1}{3}x_3 = \frac{20}{3} \\ \frac{3}{4}x_2 = \frac{9}{2} \end{cases} \quad -4 \rightarrow \begin{cases} x_1 + \frac{2}{3}x_3 = \frac{10}{3} \\ x_2 + \frac{1}{3}x_3 = \frac{20}{3} \\ -\frac{1}{4}x_3 = -\frac{1}{2} \end{cases}$$

$$-\frac{2}{3} \left(-\frac{1}{3}\right) \begin{cases} x_1 + \frac{2}{3}x_3 = \frac{10}{3} \\ x_2 + \frac{1}{3}x_3 = \frac{20}{3} \\ x_3 = 2 \end{cases} \quad \begin{cases} x_1 = 2 \\ x_2 = 6 \\ x_3 = 2 \end{cases}$$

This is the solution to the system. To interpret it we have that the diet for group I is composed of

        2 g of wheat meal
        6 g of fish meal
        2 g of tomatoes

For group II we have the same total 10 g. However, the composition will be different. Let x_1, x_2, and x_3 represent the number of grams of wheat, fish, and tomatoes in the group II diet. Then the total is 10 g, so again

$$x_1 + x_2 + x_3 = 10$$

In this diet, however, the total carbohydrates are 5 g, so

$$\tfrac{6}{10}x_1 + \tfrac{4}{10}x_3 = 5$$

The total protein is $\frac{1}{2}$ g, so

$$\tfrac{1}{20}x_1 + \tfrac{8}{10}x_2 + \tfrac{1}{20}x_3 = \tfrac{1}{2}$$

The system of linear equations, in this case, is

$$\begin{aligned} x_1 + x_2 + x_3 &= 10 \\ \tfrac{6}{10}x_1 + \tfrac{4}{10}x_3 &= 5 \\ \tfrac{1}{20}x_1 + \tfrac{8}{10}x_2 + \tfrac{1}{20}x_3 &= \tfrac{1}{2} \end{aligned} \qquad (6.5.7)$$

Again the system can be solved by using Gaussian elimination. The solution is left as an exercise for the reader.

Solution to Example 6.1.2   From the information given we can determine the amount to be spent for each medium as follows: First, let

    x_1 = amount (in millions) to be spent on television
    x_2 = amount (in millions) to be spent on magazines
    x_3 = amount (in millions) to be spent on radio
    x_4 = amount (in millions) to be spent on direct mail

The total budget is $7,000,000. Hence

$$x_1 + x_2 + x_3 + x_4 = 7$$

From item 2 (page 230),

$$x_1 \quad + x_3 \quad = 4$$

From item 3,

$$x_1 = x_2 + x_3$$

which can be rewritten as

$$x_1 \quad - x_2 \quad - x_3 \quad = 0$$

Finally, from item 4, in the first 6 months half of the amount allocated for television, magazines, and radio is to be spent, as well as one-fourth of the allocation for direct mail (the one-fourth to be spent in June). This 6-month advertising will cost $3,000,000. Hence

$$\tfrac{1}{2}x_1 + \tfrac{1}{2}x_2 + \tfrac{1}{2}x_3 + \tfrac{1}{4}x_4 = 3$$

We can now list the information in equation form:

$$\begin{aligned}
x_1 + x_2 + x_3 + x_4 &= 7 \\
x_1 \quad\;\; + x_3 \quad\;\; &= 4 \\
x_1 - x_2 - x_3 \quad\;\; &= 0 \\
\tfrac{1}{2}x_1 + \tfrac{1}{2}x_2 + \tfrac{1}{2}x_3 + \tfrac{1}{4}x_4 &= 3
\end{aligned} \qquad (6.5.8)$$

The system can be solved by Gaussian elimination and is left as an exercise for the reader. It turns out that the system in Eq. (6.5.8) has the unique solution $x_1 = \tfrac{5}{2}$, $x_2 = 1$, $x_3 = \tfrac{3}{2}$, $x_4 = 2$. In other words, the advertising expenditures should be as follows:

Television:	$2,500,000
Magazines:	$1,000,000
Radio:	$1,500,000
Direct mail:	$2,000,000

Exercises for 6.5

In problems 1–13 use Gaussian elimination to determine the solution sets of the following systems of linear equations.

1. $7x_1 - 4x_2 = 18$
   $3x_1 + 5x_2 = 1$

2. $2x_1 - 5x_2 = 8$
   $-6x_1 + 15x_2 = -24$

3. $-x_1 + 3x_2 = 5$
   $2x_1 - 6x_2 = 10$

4. $-15x_1 + 10x_2 = 0$
   $15x_1 - 10x_2 = 0$
   $x_1 + x_2 = 1$

5. $-\tfrac{1}{4}x_1 + \tfrac{5}{8}x_2 = 0$
   $x_1 + x_2 = 1$
   $2x_1 - 5x_2 = 0$

6. $\begin{aligned} x_1 + 2x_2 - 3x_3 &= -11 \\ -2x_1 - 3x_2 + 8x_3 &= 35 \\ 3x_1 + 9x_2 - 5x_3 &= -4 \end{aligned}$

7. $\begin{aligned} -3x_1 - 3x_2 + 15x_3 &= -36 \\ 4x_1 + 9x_2 - 10x_3 &= 53 \\ 2x_1 + 4x_2 - 6x_3 &= 26 \end{aligned}$

8. $\begin{aligned} x_1 + 2x_2 - 3x_3 &= -5 \\ x_1 + x_2 - 5x_3 &= 2 \\ 4x_1 + 9x_2 - 10x_3 &= 53 \end{aligned}$

9. $\begin{aligned} -3x_1 + 3x_2 - 8x_3 &= 5 \\ 2x_1 + 5x_2 + 2x_3 &= 0 \\ x_1 - x_2 + 3x_3 &= -2 \\ 6x_1 + 2x_2 - x_3 &= 7 \end{aligned}$

10. $\begin{aligned} 3x_1 + 5x_2 - 9x_3 &= 12 \\ x_1 + 6x_2 - x_3 &= 2 \\ 4x_1 - 4x_2 + 12x_3 &= -8 \\ 5x_1 + 3x_2 - 4x_3 &= 4 \end{aligned}$

11. $\begin{aligned} 2x_1 - 3x_2 + x_3 &= 1 \\ x_1 + 4x_2 + 2x_3 &= 4 \\ -5x_1 + 13x_2 - x_3 &= 1 \\ 2x_1 + 41x_2 + 13x_3 &= 29 \end{aligned}$

12. $\begin{aligned} 2x_1 - 3x_2 + 7x_3 - 4x_4 &= 2 \\ x_1 + 5x_2 - 7x_3 + 2x_4 &= 8 \end{aligned}$

13. $\begin{aligned} 3x_1 - x_2 + x_3 + 2x_4 &= 5 \\ -6x_1 + 2x_2 - 2x_3 - 4x_4 &= 7 \\ x_1 + 5x_2 - 3x_3 + 8x_4 &= 9 \end{aligned}$

14. Solve the system of linear equations given in Eq. (6.5.7), which determines the constitution of the diet for the group II test animals of Example 6.1.1.

15. Determine the simultaneous solution of the system (6.5.8), which gives the advertising expenditures for the clothing manufacturer of Example 6.1.2.

*16. Refer to problem 9, Exercises 6.2. Determine the number of each denomination of coin which the woman has in her purse by applying Gaussian elimination to the appropriate system of linear equations.

17. To test the effectiveness of a new vaccine, it is to be administered to a test group. A control group will receive a glucose substitute. The test group is to be three times as large as the control group. Each day, for 30 days, 50 persons are to be inoculated, with either the vaccine or the glucose. How many of each type must be prepared for the entire 30 days?

18. In an experiment, laboratory mice were allowed to enter one of three cages, painted either red, yellow, or blue. Of the 100 animals tested, twice as many preferred the blue cage as preferred the red cage. The total number of animals showing a preference for one of the colors was $\frac{7}{3}$ times as great as the number of animals showing no particular preference. The total number preferring yellow was 4 more than the number preferring red and blue combined. How many animals preferred red? yellow? blue? were indifferent?

*19. Consider the system of linear equations

$$\begin{aligned} a_1x_1 + b_1x_2 &= c_1 \\ a_2x_1 + b_2x_2 &= c_2 \end{aligned}$$

where a_2, b_2, and c_2 are different from zero.

(a) Show that if $a_1/a_2 = b_1/b_2 = c_1/c_2$, the system of equations has infinitely many simultaneous solutions.

(b) Show that if $a_1/a_2 = b_1/b_2 \neq c_1/c_2$, the system of equations has no simultaneous solution.

(c) Show that if $a_1/a_2 \neq b_1/b_2$, the system of equations has a unique simultaneous solution.

20. Consider the system of equations

$$2x_1 + 3x_2 = 9$$
$$4x_1 + cx_2 = d$$

(a) If $c = 6$, for what value of d will the system have more than one solution?

(b) If $d = 12$, is it possible to choose a value for c such that the system will have no solution? one solution? infinitely many solutions?

(c) If $d = 18$, is it possible to choose a value for c such that the system will have no solution? one solution? infinitely many solutions?

(*Hint:* See problem 19.)

*21. Show that the set of simultaneous solutions to a system of two linear equations in three variables can be empty or infinite but cannot be finite and nonempty.

Section 6.6   Vectors

In this section the notion of a vector will be introduced. Vectors are extremely useful objects in various branches of mathematics as well as in numerous applications. We shall use vectors many times throughout the text in applying mathematics to the management, life, and social sciences.

A *vector* is an ordered list of real numbers. There are two main types. A *row vector* of length n is simply a list of n numbers written horizontally, so

$$[2, 1, -1] \qquad [7, 8] \qquad [3, 1, 4, 7]$$

are examples of row vectors of lengths 3, 2, and 4, respectively.

A *column vector* of length n is a list of n numbers written vertically. Hence

$$\begin{bmatrix} 8 \\ 7 \\ 5 \end{bmatrix} \qquad \begin{bmatrix} 4 \\ 1 \\ 2 \\ -6 \end{bmatrix} \qquad \begin{bmatrix} 2 \\ 7 \end{bmatrix}$$

are examples of column vectors of lengths 3, 4, and 2, respectively. Depending upon the particular use being made of vectors, either row or column vectors will be used. This point will be clarified later as the various uses of vectors are examined. Here we shall be interested mainly in developing arithmetic operations for vectors. Before defining these operations we need the notion of two vectors being equal.

Two column vectors are said to be equal if they are the same size and their entries are equal term for term. For example,

$$\begin{bmatrix} 3 \\ 8 \\ 2 \\ 1 \end{bmatrix} = \begin{bmatrix} 3 \\ 8 \\ 2 \\ 1 \end{bmatrix}$$

$$\begin{bmatrix} 3 \\ 8 \end{bmatrix} \neq \begin{bmatrix} 3 \\ 8 \\ 2 \end{bmatrix}$$

$$\begin{bmatrix} 2 \\ 3 \\ 8 \\ 2 \\ 1 \end{bmatrix} \neq \begin{bmatrix} 2 \\ 8 \\ 3 \\ 2 \\ 1 \end{bmatrix}$$

A similar definition holds for row vectors. Thus

$$[1, 2, 3] = [1, 2, 3]$$
$$[1, 2, 3] \neq [2, 1, 3]$$
$$[1, 2, 3] \neq [1, 2, 3, 4]$$

The first arithmetic operation that will be defined is the *sum of two column vectors*. The sum is defined whenever two column vectors are the same size. In that case, addition is defined termwise. That is, if

$$V = \begin{bmatrix} v_1 \\ v_2 \\ \vdots \\ v_n \end{bmatrix} \quad \text{and} \quad W = \begin{bmatrix} w_1 \\ w_2 \\ \vdots \\ w_n \end{bmatrix}$$

then

$$V + W = \begin{bmatrix} v_1 + w_1 \\ v_2 + w_2 \\ \vdots \\ v_n + w_n \end{bmatrix}$$

For example,

$$\begin{bmatrix} 2 \\ 1 \\ 5 \end{bmatrix} + \begin{bmatrix} 3 \\ -1 \\ 2 \end{bmatrix} = \begin{bmatrix} 5 \\ 0 \\ 7 \end{bmatrix}$$

and

$$\begin{bmatrix} \frac{4}{3} \\ 2 \\ \frac{1}{2} \\ 7 \end{bmatrix} + \begin{bmatrix} 1 \\ 2 \\ -\frac{3}{4} \\ -\frac{1}{2} \end{bmatrix} = \begin{bmatrix} \frac{7}{3} \\ 4 \\ -\frac{1}{4} \\ \frac{13}{2} \end{bmatrix}$$

However,

$$\begin{bmatrix} 3 \\ 2 \\ -5 \end{bmatrix} + \begin{bmatrix} 6 \\ -1 \\ 4 \\ 2 \end{bmatrix}$$

is not defined, as these two column vectors are not of the same size.

Similar definitions hold for row vectors. For example,

$$[1, 3, -4] + [6, -2, 5] = [7, 1, 1]$$
$$[2, 4, 6, 8, -5] + [7, 3, -2, -6, 4] = [9, 7, 4, 2, -1]$$

Vector addition satisfies a number of properties, which will be pointed out. The first of these is that it is *commutative*. That is, if V and W are two vectors that can be added,

$$V + W = W + V$$

and so the order in which two vectors are added is immaterial.

This fact is simple to prove. We give the proof for column vectors, that for row vectors being similar. If

$$V = \begin{bmatrix} v_1 \\ v_2 \\ \vdots \\ v_n \end{bmatrix} \qquad W = \begin{bmatrix} w_1 \\ w_2 \\ \vdots \\ w_n \end{bmatrix}$$

then

$$V + W = \begin{bmatrix} v_1 + w_1 \\ v_2 + w_2 \\ \vdots \\ v_n + w_n \end{bmatrix}$$

$$W + V = \begin{bmatrix} w_1 + v_1 \\ w_2 + v_2 \\ \vdots \\ w_n + v_n \end{bmatrix}$$

For each individual entry, we have

$$v_i + w_i = w_i + v_i$$

since addition of real numbers is commutative. Hence, since $V + W$ and $W + V$ agree term for term, they are equal by the definition of equality for vectors.

A second important property of vector addition is that it is *associative*. That is, $U + (V + W) = (U + V) + W$. To prove this for column vectors, let

$$U = \begin{bmatrix} u_1 \\ u_2 \\ \vdots \\ u_n \end{bmatrix}$$

and V and W be as above. Then

$$U + (V + W) = \begin{bmatrix} u_1 + (v_1 + w_1) \\ u_2 + (v_2 + w_2) \\ \vdots \\ u_n + (v_n + w_n) \end{bmatrix} \qquad (U + V) + W = \begin{bmatrix} (u_1 + v_1) + w_1 \\ (u_2 + v_2) + w_2 \\ \vdots \\ (u_n + v_n) + w_n \end{bmatrix}$$

Again, comparing corresponding terms,

$$u_i + (v_i + w_i) = (u_i + v_i) + w_i$$

since addition of real numbers is associative. Therefore,

$$U + (V + W) = (U + V) + W$$

We next observe that there is a "zero vector." That is, there is a vector, which we shall denote by θ, with the property that for all vectors V of a given size,

$$V + \theta = V \tag{6.6.1}$$

It is easy to see that the vector θ is simply a vector all of whose entries are 0. There is a zero row and column vector of each length. For example,

$$\theta = \begin{bmatrix} 0 \\ 0 \\ 0 \end{bmatrix} \quad \text{and} \quad \theta = \begin{bmatrix} 0 \\ 0 \\ 0 \\ 0 \end{bmatrix}$$

are the zero column vectors of lengths 3 and 4, respectively, and

$$\theta = [0, 0, 0, 0] \quad \text{and} \quad \theta = [0, 0]$$

are the zero row vectors of lengths 4 and 2, respectively.

As an illustration of Eq. (6.6.1), let $V = [1, 2, -4, 5]$ and $\theta = [0, 0, 0, 0]$. Then

$$V + \theta = [1, 2, -4, 5] + [0, 0, 0, 0] = [1, 2, -4, 5] = V$$

Finally, given any vector V, we can find another vector, which we shall call $-V$, with the property that

$$V + (-V) = \theta$$

For any column vector V,

$$V = \begin{bmatrix} v_1 \\ v_2 \\ \vdots \\ v_n \end{bmatrix}$$

simply take

$$-V = \begin{bmatrix} -v_1 \\ -v_2 \\ \vdots \\ -v_n \end{bmatrix}$$

Then

$$V + (-V) = \theta \tag{6.6.2}$$

For example, to illustrate Eq. (6.6.2), if

$$V = \begin{bmatrix} 3 \\ -2 \\ 5 \end{bmatrix}$$

then

$$-V = \begin{bmatrix} -3 \\ 2 \\ -5 \end{bmatrix}$$

and we see that

$$V + (-V) = \begin{bmatrix} 3 \\ -2 \\ 5 \end{bmatrix} + \begin{bmatrix} -3 \\ 2 \\ -5 \end{bmatrix} = \begin{bmatrix} 0 \\ 0 \\ 0 \end{bmatrix} = \theta$$

Similar remarks hold for row vectors. For example, if $V = [2, -1, 6, 4]$, then $-V = [-2, 1, -6, -4]$ and

$$V + (-V) = [2, -1, 6, 4] + [-2, 1, -6, -4] = [0, 0, 0, 0] = \theta$$

We can use this notion of the negative of a vector to define subtraction for vectors. For this, we define

$$V - W = V + (-W)$$

For example, $[2, 3, -4] - [6, -5, 2] = [2, 3, -4] + [-6, 5, -2] = [-4, 8, -6]$.

Before defining the second arithmetic operation for vectors, the properties of vector addition are summarized. Let U, V, and W be vectors of length n (all column vectors or all row vectors) and define the addition of two vectors to be the vector whose entries are the sums term by term of the original two. Then vector addition satisfies the following properties:

A1: $U + V = V + U$ (commutative law)
A2: $U + (V + W) = (U + V) + W$ (associative law)
A3: There exists a unique n-vector θ, such that $U + \theta = U$, for all n-vectors U.
A4: For every n-vector V, there exists a unique n-vector $-V$, such that $V + (-V) = \theta$.

The second arithmetic operation that we shall define is *scalar multiplication*, that is, the multiplication of a vector by a real number. Let c be any real number and let

$$V = \begin{bmatrix} v_1 \\ v_2 \\ \vdots \\ v_n \end{bmatrix}$$

Then we define

$$c \cdot V = \begin{bmatrix} cv_1 \\ cv_2 \\ \vdots \\ cv_n \end{bmatrix}$$

That is, $c \cdot V$ is the vector obtained by multiplying each entry of V by the real number c. For example,

$$6 \cdot \begin{bmatrix} 4 \\ 1 \\ 8 \\ 2 \end{bmatrix} = \begin{bmatrix} 24 \\ 6 \\ 48 \\ 12 \end{bmatrix}$$

$$-4 \cdot \begin{bmatrix} 2 \\ 0 \\ \frac{1}{2} \end{bmatrix} = \begin{bmatrix} -8 \\ 0 \\ -2 \end{bmatrix}$$

A similar definition holds for row vectors. Some examples are:
$$3 \cdot [4, -6, 2] = [12, -18, 6]$$
$$-2 \cdot [1, 2, 3, -4] = [-2, -4, -6, 8]$$
$$1 \cdot [5, 7, 8, 9, 10] = [5, 7, 8, 9, 10]$$

The name *scalar* multiplication comes from the fact that real numbers, when used in this sense, are called scalars.

Again, as in the case of vector addition, we shall point out some important properties of scalar multiplication. The first two properties are what are referred to as *distributive laws*. We will not prove these, as the proofs follow easily from familiar properties of real numbers.

SM1: $c \cdot (U + V) = (c \cdot U) + (c \cdot V)$
SM2: $(c + d) \cdot U = (c \cdot U) + (d \cdot U)$
SM3: $c \cdot (d \cdot U) = (cd) \cdot U$ (associative law)

One other property that is obvious from the definition is:

SM4: $1 \cdot U = U$

Exercises for 6.6

1. (a) Give examples of row vectors of lengths 5, 6, and 7.
   (b) Give examples of column vectors of lengths 5, 6, and 7.
2. For each of the vectors V, find $-V$.

   (a) $V = [1, 7, -2, 3, -8]$ (b) $V = [0, 0, 0]$
   (c) $$V = \begin{bmatrix} -6 \\ \frac{3}{2} \\ 2 \end{bmatrix}$$ (d) $$V = \begin{bmatrix} 0 \\ 0 \\ 0 \\ 0 \end{bmatrix}$$
   (e) $V = -X$

3. For each pair of vectors, state whether the two vectors are equal or unequal.

   (a) $[1, 2, 3]$; $[1, 3, 2]$ (b) $[3, 5, -6]$; $[3, 5, -6, 1]$
   (c) $$\begin{bmatrix} 1 \\ 4 \\ -5 \end{bmatrix}; \begin{bmatrix} -1 \\ -\frac{8}{2} \\ 5 \end{bmatrix}$$ (d) $[3 - 7, 2, -1]$; $-[4, -2, 1]$
   (e) $[4, 6, 3]$; $2 \cdot [2, 3, \frac{3}{2}]$ (f) $[1, 2]$; $\begin{bmatrix} 1 \\ 2 \end{bmatrix}$

In problems 4–16, perform the indicated operation, if possible. If it is not possible to perform the operation, write "impossible."

4. $$\begin{bmatrix} 3 \\ 1 \\ 4 \end{bmatrix} + \begin{bmatrix} 2 \\ 1 \\ 8 \end{bmatrix}$$

5. $$\begin{bmatrix} -1 \\ 3 \\ 2 \\ 1 \end{bmatrix} + \begin{bmatrix} 2 \\ 1 \\ 7 \end{bmatrix}$$

6. $$\begin{bmatrix} 2 \\ 1 \\ 4 \end{bmatrix} + [-1, 3, 6]$$

7. $2 \cdot [3, 2, -4]$

8.
$$4 \cdot \begin{bmatrix} -2 \\ 1 \\ -7 \end{bmatrix}$$

9.
$$3 \cdot \begin{bmatrix} 2 \\ 7 \end{bmatrix} + 4 \cdot \begin{bmatrix} -1 \\ 3 \end{bmatrix}$$

10.
$$2 \cdot \begin{bmatrix} 2 \\ 1 \\ 8 \end{bmatrix} + 3 \cdot \begin{bmatrix} 7 \\ 2 \end{bmatrix}$$

11.
$$\begin{bmatrix} 4 \\ 1 \end{bmatrix} - \begin{bmatrix} 2 \\ 3 \end{bmatrix}$$

12.
$$[3, 1, 2] + (\tfrac{1}{2}) \cdot \begin{bmatrix} 2 \\ 4 \\ 6 \end{bmatrix}$$

13.
$$\begin{bmatrix} 2 \\ 7 \\ 9 \end{bmatrix} - (\tfrac{3}{4}) \cdot \begin{bmatrix} 3 \\ 1 \\ 6 \end{bmatrix}$$

14. $3 \cdot [3, 7, -2, 4] + 4 \cdot [8, -5, 6, 2]$
15. $([2, 1, 3] + 3 \cdot [-5, 0, 4]) - 2 \cdot [1, 6, -8]$
16. $-3 \cdot [1, -1, 0] + 5 \cdot [6, 3, -4] - 7 \cdot [0, 1, 0, 1]$

In problems 17–24, solve for the vector X.

17.
$$\begin{bmatrix} 2 \\ 1 \\ 7 \end{bmatrix} + X = \begin{bmatrix} 3 \\ 4 \\ 2 \end{bmatrix}$$

18.
$$3 \cdot X + 2 \cdot \begin{bmatrix} 1 \\ 4 \end{bmatrix} = 5 \cdot \begin{bmatrix} 1 \\ 1 \end{bmatrix}$$

19. $\tfrac{1}{2} \cdot [2, 7, 5] + \tfrac{3}{4} \cdot X = [1, 6, 6]$

20.
$$3 \cdot X = \begin{bmatrix} 0 \\ 0 \\ 0 \end{bmatrix}$$

21.
$$X - \begin{bmatrix} 1 \\ 1 \\ 2 \end{bmatrix} = \begin{bmatrix} 0 \\ 0 \\ 0 \end{bmatrix}$$

22.
$$6 \cdot X - \begin{bmatrix} 12 \\ 6 \\ 3 \end{bmatrix} = \begin{bmatrix} 5 \\ 1 \\ 2 \end{bmatrix}$$

23.
$$X + 2 \cdot \begin{bmatrix} 1 \\ 4 \end{bmatrix} = \begin{bmatrix} 2 \\ 8 \end{bmatrix}$$

24. $3 \cdot X + [7, 2, 2] = [4, 1, 5] - 2 \cdot X$
25. Prove property SM1 for column vectors.
26. Show that SM2 holds for row vectors.
27. Verify SM3 for row vectors.

28. Suppose that $c \neq 1$ is a real number and V is a vector. If $c \cdot V = V$, what can be said about V?

29. Suppose that V and W are row vectors of length n and that $V + W = 2 \cdot V$. What can you conclude about the relationship between the vectors V and W?

30. Two automobile companies (say, I and II) manufacture three types of cars: luxury, middle-priced, and compact. Let V be the row vector of length 3 whose entries are given, respectively, by the costs of the most expensive luxury, middle-priced, and compact models produced by company I. Let W be the corresponding row vector for company II. Interpret each of the following vectors:

(a) $V - W$

(b) $\frac{1}{2} \cdot (V + W)$

Answer the following questions:

(c) If company I cuts its prices by 20 percent, V should be replaced by what vector?

(d) If company II increases its prices by 25 percent, what vector should replace W?

Section 6.7 Matrices: Definitions and Examples

In the last section the concept of a vector was introduced and the basic operations and properties involving them were presented. Here, and in Section 6.8, we expand on these ideas and introduce what are called matrices. We shall find that matrices are an extremely useful tool for formulating and solving problems and we shall use them for these purposes in Section 6.9 and throughout Chapters 8–11.

In this section the basic definitions and arithmetic operations concerning matrices will be presented in an informal and concrete manner. This should give the reader an intuitive idea of the properties of matrices and their operations. Following this, we shall present a more precise and rigorous treatment in Section 6.8.

A *matrix* is simply a rectangular array of real numbers. A single line of numbers running horizontally through the matrix is referred to as a row, and a single line of numbers running vertically is called a column. The size of a matrix is specified by stating the number of rows and then the number of columns. Thus a 3 × 5 (read "3 by 5") matrix would consist of 3 rows and 5 columns. An example of a 3 × 5 matrix is

$$\begin{bmatrix} 2 & 1 & 3 & 4 & 7 \\ 0 & 1 & 2 & 5 & 1 \\ -2 & 1 & -3 & \frac{1}{2} & 0 \end{bmatrix}$$

In order to identify specific entries in a matrix, it is only necessary to specify the row and column in which the entry lies. This is done by specifying the row first and then the column. For example, in the matrix above, the 1–3 entry is 3; the 1–5 entry is 7; and the 3–4 entry is $\frac{1}{2}$.

In examining matrices we shall define matrix addition and scalar multiplication of matrices in a manner analogous to the case of vectors. This will be followed by a third operation, the multiplication of two matrices. The definitions of matrix equality, and the addition and scalar multiplication of matrices, will seem to be direct extensions of those for vectors. This is not surprising, because a vector can, in fact, be thought of as a special type of matrix in which either the number of rows or the number of columns is equal to 1. For example, a row vector of length 4 is also a 1 × 4 matrix and a column vector of length 3 is also a 3 × 1 matrix:

$$[3, 2, -5, 1] \qquad \text{is a } 1 \times 4 \text{ matrix}$$

$$\begin{bmatrix} 2 \\ -3 \\ 8 \end{bmatrix} \qquad \text{is a } 3 \times 1 \text{ matrix}$$

Two matrices are *equal* if they are the same size (in both dimensions) and if all corresponding entries are equal. For example,

$$\begin{bmatrix} 1 & 2 & 3 \\ 4 & 5 & 6 \end{bmatrix} = \begin{bmatrix} 1 & 2 & 3 \\ 4 & 5 & 6 \end{bmatrix}$$

but

$$\begin{bmatrix} 1 & 2 & 3 \\ 4 & 5 & 6 \end{bmatrix} \neq \begin{bmatrix} 1 & 2 \\ 4 & 5 \end{bmatrix}$$

and

$$\begin{bmatrix} 1 & 2 & 3 \\ 4 & 5 & 6 \end{bmatrix} \neq \begin{bmatrix} 1 & 2 & 6 \\ 4 & 5 & 3 \end{bmatrix}$$

As in the case of vectors, matrix addition is defined for matrices of the same dimensions by *termwise addition*. Some examples are:

$$\begin{bmatrix} 2 & 1 \\ 4 & 1 \end{bmatrix} + \begin{bmatrix} -1 & 2 \\ 1 & 0 \end{bmatrix} = \begin{bmatrix} 1 & 3 \\ 5 & 1 \end{bmatrix}$$

$$\begin{bmatrix} 1 & -1 & 4 & \frac{1}{8} \\ 0 & 0 & \frac{1}{2} & 2 \\ -1 & 3 & -7 & 1 \end{bmatrix} + \begin{bmatrix} 3 & -1 & \frac{1}{4} & 4 \\ \frac{1}{2} & 1 & 0 & -\frac{1}{2} \\ 2 & 1 & -1 & 0 \end{bmatrix} = \begin{bmatrix} 4 & -2 & \frac{17}{4} & \frac{33}{8} \\ \frac{1}{2} & 1 & \frac{1}{2} & \frac{3}{2} \\ 1 & 4 & -8 & 1 \end{bmatrix}$$

$$\begin{bmatrix} 1 & -6 \\ 2 & 4 \\ 3 & -8 \\ 2 & \frac{1}{2} \end{bmatrix} + \begin{bmatrix} -4 & 1 \\ 3 & 2 \\ 7 & 11 \\ 55 & 2 \end{bmatrix} = \begin{bmatrix} -3 & -5 \\ 5 & 6 \\ 10 & 3 \\ 57 & \frac{5}{2} \end{bmatrix}$$

but

$$\begin{bmatrix} 3 & 1 \\ 2 & 4 \\ 6 & 8 \end{bmatrix} + \begin{bmatrix} 4 & -3 & 6 \\ 8 & 2 & 1 \end{bmatrix}$$

is not defined, because the two matrices above are not the same size. The first is a 3×2 matrix whereas the second is a 2×3 matrix. The properties of matrix addition will be discussed in Section 6.8.

Scalar multiplication of matrices, that is, multiplication of a matrix by a real number, is also defined by analogy with that of vectors. In other words, to multiply a matrix by a real number, simply *multiply each entry of the matrix by the real number.* For example,

$$3 \cdot \begin{bmatrix} 2 & -5 \\ 6 & 1 \\ 4 & 7 \end{bmatrix} = \begin{bmatrix} 6 & -15 \\ 18 & 3 \\ 12 & 21 \end{bmatrix}$$

$$-6 \cdot \begin{bmatrix} 4 & -2 & 3 \\ \frac{1}{2} & 7 & -8 \end{bmatrix} = \begin{bmatrix} -24 & 12 & -18 \\ -3 & -42 & 48 \end{bmatrix}$$

$$\frac{1}{2} \cdot \begin{bmatrix} 5 & 6 & 8 & 12 \\ -6 & 3 & 2 & 4 \\ 10 & -5 & 6 & 7 \end{bmatrix} = \begin{bmatrix} \frac{5}{2} & 3 & 4 & 6 \\ -3 & \frac{3}{2} & 1 & 2 \\ 5 & -\frac{5}{2} & 3 & \frac{7}{2} \end{bmatrix}$$

Again, the basic properties of scalar multiplication of matrices will be examined in Section 6.8.

The next operation to be defined is the multiplication of two matrices. In view of the definition of matrix addition, it would seem natural to multiply two matrices (of the same size) by multiplying the entries termwise. For example, it would seem reasonable to define

$$\begin{bmatrix} 3 & 1 \\ 2 & 4 \end{bmatrix} \begin{bmatrix} 6 & -2 \\ 7 & 5 \end{bmatrix} = \begin{bmatrix} 18 & -2 \\ 14 & 20 \end{bmatrix}$$

However, this will *not* be the definition. The reason it will not be the definition is, as we shall see, that it would not prove useful in applications. In other words, we want to define multiplication of matrices in a way that will be appropriate for applications of matrices as a tool in problem solving.

In this section the definition of matrix multiplication will be illustrated through some examples. The precise definitions and properties concerning matrix multiplication will be presented in Section 6.8. In Section 6.9 and throughout Chapter 9 it will become evident why this definition was chosen.

As mentioned in the last paragraph, we will, at this point only illustrate the definition of matrix multiplication.

Example 6.7.1 Consider the two 2×2 matrices given by

$$A = \begin{bmatrix} 3 & 1 \\ 2 & 4 \end{bmatrix} \qquad B = \begin{bmatrix} 6 & -2 \\ 7 & 5 \end{bmatrix}$$

We perform the multiplication AB (in that order) as follows: the entry in the first row and first column of AB (i.e., the 1–1 entry of AB) is obtained by taking the first row of A and the first column of B and multiplying the first entry in the row by the first entry in the column, the second entry in the row by the second entry in the column, and then adding the terms together:

$$\begin{bmatrix} 3 & 1 \\ 2 & 4 \end{bmatrix} \begin{bmatrix} 6 & -2 \\ 7 & 5 \end{bmatrix}$$

The 1–1 entry of AB is

$$3 \cdot 6 + 1 \cdot 7 = 18 + 7 = 25$$

The 1–2 entry of AB is obtained by taking the first row of A and the second column of B and proceeding as above:

$$\begin{bmatrix} 3 & 1 \\ 2 & 4 \end{bmatrix} \begin{bmatrix} 6 & -2 \\ 7 & 5 \end{bmatrix}$$

The 1–2 entry of AB is

$$3 \cdot (-2) + 1 \cdot 5 = -6 + 5 = -1$$

Similarly, we obtain the 2–1 and 2–2 entries of AB:

$$\begin{bmatrix} 3 & 1 \\ 2 & 4 \end{bmatrix}\begin{bmatrix} 6 & -2 \\ 7 & 5 \end{bmatrix} \qquad \begin{bmatrix} 3 & 1 \\ 2 & 4 \end{bmatrix}\begin{bmatrix} 6 & -2 \\ 7 & 5 \end{bmatrix}$$

The 2–1 entry of AB is

$$2 \cdot 6 + 4 \cdot 7 = 12 + 28 = 40$$

The 2–2 entry of AB is

$$2 \cdot (-2) + 4 \cdot 5 = -4 + 20 = 16$$

Consequently,

$$\begin{bmatrix} 3 & 1 \\ 2 & 4 \end{bmatrix}\begin{bmatrix} 6 & -2 \\ 7 & 5 \end{bmatrix} = \begin{bmatrix} 25 & -1 \\ 40 & 16 \end{bmatrix}$$

As we shall see in Section 6.8, if A and B are matrices, we can perform the multiplication AB (in that order) if the number of columns of A is equal to the number of rows of B.

Example 6.7.2 Let

$$A = \begin{bmatrix} 1 & 2 & 3 \\ -1 & 4 & 0 \end{bmatrix} \qquad B = \begin{bmatrix} 4 & 1 & 0 & 6 \\ 2 & 1 & 1 & -5 \\ 0 & -1 & \frac{1}{2} & 2 \end{bmatrix}$$

Then A is 2×3 and B is 3×4, so the number of columns of A equals the number of rows of B. Hence these two matrices can be multiplied. We proceed as in Example 6.7.1:

$$\begin{bmatrix} 1 & 2 & 3 \\ -1 & 4 & 0 \end{bmatrix}\begin{bmatrix} 4 & 1 & 0 & 6 \\ 2 & 1 & 1 & -5 \\ 0 & -1 & \frac{1}{2} & 2 \end{bmatrix}$$

The 1–1 entry of AB is

$$1 \cdot 4 + 2 \cdot 2 + 3 \cdot 0 = 4 + 4 + 0 = 8$$

$$\begin{bmatrix} 1 & 2 & 3 \\ -1 & 4 & 0 \end{bmatrix}\begin{bmatrix} 4 & 1 & 0 & 6 \\ 2 & 1 & 1 & -5 \\ 0 & -1 & \frac{1}{2} & 2 \end{bmatrix}$$

The 1–2 entry of AB is

$$1 \cdot 1 + 2 \cdot 1 + 3 \cdot (-1) = 1 + 2 - 3 = 0$$

Similarly, the 1–3 entry of AB is

$$1 \cdot 0 + 2 \cdot 1 + 3 \cdot \tfrac{1}{2} = 0 + 2 + \tfrac{3}{2} = \tfrac{7}{2}$$

and the 1–4 entry is

$$1 \cdot 6 + 2 \cdot (-5) + 3 \cdot 2 = 6 - 10 + 6 = 2$$

$$\begin{bmatrix} 1 & 2 & 3 \\ -1 & 4 & 0 \end{bmatrix} \begin{bmatrix} 4 & 1 & 0 & 6 \\ 2 & 1 & 1 & -5 \\ 0 & -1 & \frac{1}{2} & 2 \end{bmatrix}$$

The 2–1 entry of AB is

$$-1 \cdot 4 + 4 \cdot 2 + 0 \cdot 0 = -4 + 8 + 0 = 4$$

and similarly, the 2–2 entry of AB is

$$-1 \cdot 1 + 4 \cdot 1 + 0 \cdot (-1) = -1 + 4 + 0 = 3$$

the 2–3 entry is

$$-1 \cdot 0 + 4 \cdot 1 + 0 \cdot \tfrac{1}{2} = 0 + 4 + 0 = 4$$

and the 2–4 entry is

$$-1 \cdot 6 + 4 \cdot (-5) + 0 \cdot 2 = -6 - 20 + 0 = -26$$

Consequently,

$$\begin{bmatrix} 1 & 2 & 3 \\ -1 & 4 & 0 \end{bmatrix} \begin{bmatrix} 4 & 1 & 0 & 6 \\ 2 & 1 & 1 & -5 \\ 0 & -1 & \frac{1}{2} & 2 \end{bmatrix} = \begin{bmatrix} 8 & 0 & \frac{7}{2} & 2 \\ 4 & 3 & 4 & -26 \end{bmatrix}$$

Note that the matrix AB is 2×4 and the matrices A and B are 2×3 and 3×4, respectively. Thus the number of rows of AB equals the number of rows of A, and the number of columns of AB equals the number of columns of B. This will be the case, in general.

Exercises for 6.7

1. Give an example of a

   (a) 2×3 matrix
   (c) 1×6 matrix
   (e) 7×7 matrix

   (b) 5×4 matrix
   (d) 3×1 matrix
   (f) 1×1 matrix

2. Consider the 5×6 matrix given by

$$\begin{bmatrix} 1 & 0 & \frac{1}{2} & 2 & -\frac{3}{4} & -4 \\ -2 & 8 & 2.5 & 1 & \frac{7}{8} & -3 \\ 4 & \pi & -6 & 0 & -7 & -\frac{1}{2} \\ 6 & 11 & 15 & \frac{1}{4} & -2 & 6 \\ 3 & 1 & 5 & \frac{7}{8} & \frac{3}{5} & 1 \end{bmatrix}$$

   Determine the following entries of this matrix.
   (a) 1–1
   (c) 5–6
   (e) 4–5

   (b) 2–3
   (d) 3–2
   (f) 5–4

   In problems 3–21, perform the indicated operation, if possible. If it is not possible to perform the operation, write "impossible."

3. $\begin{bmatrix} 2 & 1 \\ 1 & -1 \end{bmatrix} + \begin{bmatrix} -1 & 0 \\ 1 & 5 \end{bmatrix} =$

4. $\begin{bmatrix} 3 & 4 & 1 \\ 2 & 1 & 7 \end{bmatrix} - \begin{bmatrix} 2 & 1 \\ -1 & 3 \end{bmatrix} =$

5. $3 \cdot \begin{bmatrix} 1 & 1 & 0 \\ -1 & \frac{1}{2} & 5 \\ \frac{5}{3} & 3 & 1 \end{bmatrix} =$

6. $\begin{bmatrix} 1 & 2 \\ 1 & 3 \\ -1 & 4 \end{bmatrix} - \begin{bmatrix} 2 & 1 & 3 \\ 1 & 5 & \frac{1}{2} \end{bmatrix} =$

7. $3 \cdot \begin{bmatrix} 4 & 1 & 5 \\ 2 & 1 & 3 \\ 1 & 1 & -1 \end{bmatrix} - 2 \cdot \begin{bmatrix} 8 & -1 & 0 \\ \frac{1}{2} & 2 & \frac{1}{4} \\ 3 & 1 & 2 \end{bmatrix} =$

8. $\begin{bmatrix} 1 & 4 \\ 3 & 2 \end{bmatrix} \begin{bmatrix} 2 & 1 \\ 1 & 0 \end{bmatrix} =$

9. $\begin{bmatrix} 1 & 4 \\ 3 & 2 \end{bmatrix} \begin{bmatrix} -1 & 3 & 0 \\ 1 & 2 & -4 \end{bmatrix} =$

10. $\begin{bmatrix} 1 & 4 \\ 3 & 2 \end{bmatrix} \begin{bmatrix} 2 & 3 \\ -1 & 1 \\ 1 & 0 \end{bmatrix} =$

11. $\begin{bmatrix} 2 & 3 \\ -1 & 1 \\ 1 & 0 \end{bmatrix} \begin{bmatrix} 1 & 4 \\ 3 & 2 \end{bmatrix} =$

12. $\begin{bmatrix} 4 & 1 \\ 3 & 1 \end{bmatrix} \begin{bmatrix} 1 & 0 \\ 0 & 1 \end{bmatrix} =$

13. $\begin{bmatrix} \frac{1}{2} & \frac{1}{4} \\ 3 & 1 \end{bmatrix} \begin{bmatrix} 1 & 0 & 0 \\ 0 & 1 & 0 \\ 0 & 0 & 1 \end{bmatrix} =$

14. $[1, 2, 1, 4] \begin{bmatrix} 0 \\ 1 \\ 2 \\ 3 \end{bmatrix} =$

15. $\begin{bmatrix} 0 \\ 1 \\ 2 \\ 3 \end{bmatrix} [1, 2, 1, 4] =$

16. $[7][1, 4, 2, -3] =$

17. $7 \cdot [1, 4, 2, -3] =$

18. $-3 \cdot \begin{bmatrix} 1 & 2 \\ -5 & 7 \end{bmatrix} =$

19. $[-3] \begin{bmatrix} 1 & 2 \\ -5 & 7 \end{bmatrix} =$

20.
$$\begin{bmatrix} 3 & 2 & 1 & 4 \\ 5 & -1 & 6 & 1 \\ 2 & 1 & 1 & 0 \end{bmatrix} \begin{bmatrix} 1 & 3 & -8 \\ -1 & 5 & 1 \\ 2 & 6 & 2 \\ 3 & -7 & \frac{1}{2} \end{bmatrix} =$$

21.
$$\begin{bmatrix} 1 & 3 & -8 \\ -1 & 5 & 1 \\ 2 & 6 & 2 \\ 3 & -7 & \frac{1}{2} \end{bmatrix} \begin{bmatrix} 3 & 2 & 1 & 4 \\ 5 & -1 & 6 & 1 \\ 2 & 1 & 1 & 0 \end{bmatrix} =$$

22. A person goes to the supermarket and decides to buy 6 half-gallons of milk, 3 dozen eggs, 5 pounds of hamburger, 2 heads of lettuce, and nothing more. Let A be the following 1×4 matrix (or row vector of length 4): the entries of A are the quantities to be purchased of each of these four items, in the order given. Suppose that a half-gallon of milk costs 60 cents, a dozen eggs 80 cents, a pound of hamburger 89 cents, and a head of lettuce 25 cents. Arrange these prices, in this order, in a 4×1 matrix B. What does the entry of AB represent?

23. An independent building contractor can purchase his required lumber, glass, paint, and steel from either of three wholesale distributors. Designate these distributors 1, 2, and 3. Suppose that 1 charges 6, 4, 1, and 10 dollars per unit of lumber, glass, paint, and steel, respectively. Assume that 2's prices are 5, 3, 2, and 11 dollars per unit, respectively. Finally, suppose that 3 charges 7, 5, 1, and 8 dollars per unit, respectively.
   (a) Arrange the above information in a 4×3 matrix, A, whose jth column gives the prices per unit charged by distributor j for lumber, glass, paint, and steel, respectively. Suppose that a particular distributor delivers the purchased material to the job site only if the contractor buys all the required material from him. Since this is the most economical thing for the contractor to do, he has a policy of buying the material required for a specific job entirely from one of the three distributors. Additionally, the contractor will always buy from that distributor for which his total cost is smallest.
   (b) At the present time the contractor has two jobs. The first requires 20, 10, 5, and 6 units of lumber, glass, paint, and steel, respectively. The second requires 4, 1, 7, and 18 units of lumber, glass, paint, and steel, respectively. Arrange this information in a 2×4 matrix, B, whose first and second rows give the required amount of materials for the first and second jobs, respectively.
   (c) Find the matrix BA.
   (d) What do the entries of the matrix BA represent?
   (e) From which distributor should the contractor buy the material for the first job? the second job?

Section 6.8 Matrices: Basic Properties

In Section 6.7 the concept of a matrix was defined and three arithmetic operations that involve matrices were presented: *matrix addition, scalar multiplication,* and *matrix multiplication.* The presentation in Section 6.7 was informal and in this section the notions presented there are elaborated on and made precise. To begin with, it will be useful to introduce a notational scheme for writing matrices in general. The scheme applied to an arbitrary 2×3 matrix is as follows:

$$\begin{bmatrix} a_{11} & a_{12} & a_{13} \\ a_{21} & a_{22} & a_{23} \end{bmatrix}$$

For example, if the matrix is

$$\begin{bmatrix} 1 & -5 & 2 \\ -4 & 7 & 6 \end{bmatrix}$$

then $a_{11} = 1$, $a_{12} = -5$, $a_{13} = 2$, $a_{21} = -4$, $a_{22} = 7$, and $a_{23} = 6$. Notice that the i–j entry (i.e., the entry in the ith row and jth column) is given as a_{ij}.

The scheme

$$\begin{bmatrix} a_{11} & a_{12} & \cdots & a_{1n} \\ a_{21} & a_{22} & \cdots & a_{2n} \\ \vdots & \vdots & \ddots & \vdots \\ a_{m1} & a_{m2} & \cdots & a_{mn} \end{bmatrix} \qquad (6.8.1)$$

will be used as a general specification for an $m \times n$ matrix (i.e., a matrix with m rows and n columns). Again, the entry in the ith row and jth column is given as a_{ij}. We will also abbreviate this form to

$$[a_{ij}]_{mn} \qquad (6.8.2)$$

to indicate the same $m \times n$ matrix. These schemes are necessary for making precise definitions and proving general properties about matrices.

Recall that in Section 6.7 we defined two matrices to be equal if they are the same size (i.e., have the same number of rows and the same number of columns) and all corresponding entries are equal. In terms of the notation of Eq. (6.8.2), this definition can be stated more compactly and more precisely.

Definition

Let $A = [a_{ij}]_{mn}$ and $B = [b_{ij}]_{pq}$, so A is a matrix with m rows and n columns whose i–j entry is a_{ij} while B is a matrix with p rows and q columns whose i–j entry is b_{ij}. Then

$$A = B$$

if and only if $m = p$, $n = q$, and $a_{ij} = b_{ij}$ for all i and j.

The reader should refer to the examples of Section 6.7 for illustrations.

The operation of matrix addition was defined in Section 6.7 as follows. If A and B are two matrices of the same size, then $A + B$ is defined to be the matrix obtained by termwise addition of the entries of A and B. When we use the notation of Eq. (6.8.2), we can restate this definition as follows.

Definition

Let A and B be two matrices of the same size, say, $A = [a_{ij}]_{mn}$ and $B = [b_{ij}]_{mn}$. Then we define

$$A + B = [a_{ij} + b_{ij}]_{mn} \qquad (6.8.3)$$

The reader should return to Section 6.7 for some examples.

To continue, recall that scalar multiplication of a matrix by a real number was defined in Section 6.7: Multiply each entry of the matrix by the real number. Therefore, we can restate this definition in the form below.

Definition

Let c be a real number and A be a matrix, say $A = [a_{ij}]_{mn}$. Then we define

$$c \cdot A = [ca_{ij}]_{mn} \qquad (6.8.4)$$

In Section 6.6 on vectors several properties of vector addition and scalar multiplication were presented (A1–A4 and SM1–SM4). When we use similar techniques as those in Section 6.6 it is not difficult to prove that these properties also hold for *matrix addition* and *scalar multiplication*. We shall not give the proofs here but will use these properties whenever they are required in computations.

The final arithmetic operation introduced in Section 6.7 concerning matrices was matrix multiplication. Because of the relatively complicated nature of this operation we only indicated how it worked via some examples. However, now that the notational scheme of Eq. (6.8.2) is available, this definition can be made precise.

Definition

Let A and B be matrices, say $A = [a_{ij}]_{mp}$ and $B = [b_{ij}]_{qn}$. Assume that the number of columns of A equals the number of rows of B (i.e., $p = q$). Then the product AB is defined to be the $m \times n$ matrix

$$AB = [c_{ij}]_{mn} \qquad (6.8.5)$$

where $c_{ij} = a_{i1}b_{1j} + a_{i2}b_{2j} + \cdots + a_{ip}b_{pj}$.

Notice that, as was mentioned at the end of Section 6.7, if A is $m \times p$ and B is $p \times n$, then AB is $m \times n$. Some examples of matrix multiplication were presented in Section 6.7, but for emphasis we exhibit additional illustrations:

$$\begin{bmatrix} 1 & 2 & 1 \\ 0 & 1 & 3 \\ \frac{1}{2} & 1 & \frac{1}{2} \end{bmatrix} \begin{bmatrix} 0 & 1 & 1 \\ 4 & 1 & 2 \\ 2 & 1 & 0 \end{bmatrix} = \begin{bmatrix} 10 & 4 & 5 \\ 10 & 4 & 2 \\ 5 & 2 & \frac{5}{2} \end{bmatrix} \qquad (6.8.6)$$

$$\begin{bmatrix} 1 & 4 \\ 2 & 5 \\ 3 & 6 \end{bmatrix} \begin{bmatrix} 2 & 3 & 7 & 0 \\ 1 & 4 & 1 & 1 \end{bmatrix} = \begin{bmatrix} 6 & 19 & 11 & 4 \\ 9 & 26 & 19 & 5 \\ 12 & 33 & 27 & 6 \end{bmatrix} \qquad (6.8.7)$$

$$\begin{bmatrix} 1 & 3 \\ 4 & 2 \end{bmatrix} \begin{bmatrix} -\frac{1}{5} & \frac{3}{10} \\ \frac{2}{5} & -\frac{1}{10} \end{bmatrix} = \begin{bmatrix} 1 & 0 \\ 0 & 1 \end{bmatrix} \qquad (6.8.8)$$

$$\begin{bmatrix} 1 & 4 & 3 \\ 2 & 1 & 7 \\ 0 & 1 & 2 \end{bmatrix} \begin{bmatrix} 1 & 0 & 0 \\ 0 & 1 & 0 \\ 0 & 0 & 1 \end{bmatrix} = \begin{bmatrix} 1 & 4 & 3 \\ 2 & 1 & 7 \\ 0 & 1 & 2 \end{bmatrix} \qquad (6.8.9)$$

Given two matrices A and B, if the number of columns of A equals the number of rows of B, then AB is defined. This does not necessarily mean that the product BA is defined. Notice in Eq. (6.8.7), for example, that A is 3×2 and B is 2×4, so the product AB exists and is 3×4. However, BA is not defined, since the number of columns of B is 4, which does not equal the number of rows of A, which is 3.

Even if A and B can be multiplied in either order, generally $AB \neq BA$. For example, let

$$A = \begin{bmatrix} 1 & 2 & 3 \\ -1 & 4 & 0 \end{bmatrix}$$

$$B = \begin{bmatrix} 0 & 1 \\ 3 & 2 \\ 4 & \frac{1}{2} \end{bmatrix}$$

Then

$$AB = \begin{bmatrix} 1 & 2 & 3 \\ -1 & 4 & 0 \end{bmatrix} \begin{bmatrix} 0 & 1 \\ 3 & 2 \\ 4 & \frac{1}{2} \end{bmatrix} = \begin{bmatrix} 18 & \frac{13}{2} \\ 12 & 7 \end{bmatrix}$$

$$BA = \begin{bmatrix} 0 & 1 \\ 3 & 2 \\ 4 & \frac{1}{2} \end{bmatrix} \begin{bmatrix} 1 & 2 & 3 \\ -1 & 4 & 0 \end{bmatrix} = \begin{bmatrix} -1 & 4 & 0 \\ 1 & 14 & 9 \\ \frac{7}{2} & 10 & 12 \end{bmatrix}$$

Not only is $AB \neq BA$, but they are not even the same size. As another example,

$$\begin{bmatrix} 1 & 2 \\ 3 & 1 \end{bmatrix} \begin{bmatrix} 4 & 2 \\ 1 & 1 \end{bmatrix} = \begin{bmatrix} 6 & 4 \\ 13 & 7 \end{bmatrix}$$

but

$$\begin{bmatrix} 4 & 2 \\ 1 & 1 \end{bmatrix} \begin{bmatrix} 1 & 2 \\ 3 & 1 \end{bmatrix} = \begin{bmatrix} 10 & 10 \\ 4 & 3 \end{bmatrix}$$

What we have shown is that, in general, matrix multiplication is *not commutative* (i.e., the order in which matrices are multiplied is significant). There are, however, many important properties that matrix multiplication does satisfy. The first important property is the following. If

$$A = [a_{ij}]_{mp} \qquad B = [b_{ij}]_{pq} \qquad C = [c_{ij}]_{qn}$$

then these matrices are such that $(AB)C$ and $A(BC)$ are both defined. In such a case,

MM1: $(AB)C = A(BC)$

That is, matrix multiplication is associative. We also have the following properties. If a is a scalar, and A, B, and C are matrices,

MM2: $A(B + C) = AB + AC$
MM3: $a \cdot (BC) = (a \cdot B)C = B(a \cdot C)$

Exercises for 6.8

1. Consider the 4×3 matrix $A = [a_{ij}]_{43}$ given by

$$A = \begin{bmatrix} 3 & \pi & \frac{1}{2} \\ 2 & .5 & 7 \\ -1 & \frac{3}{4} & 1 \\ 0 & .3 & \frac{1}{3} \end{bmatrix}$$

Find a_{ij} for $i = 1, 2, 3, 4$ and $j = 1, 2, 3$. In other words, find $a_{11}, a_{12}, a_{13}, a_{21}, a_{22}, a_{23}, a_{31}, a_{32}$, and so on.

2. Let $B = [b_{ij}]_{36}$ be given by

$$B = \begin{bmatrix} 1 & 0 & \frac{1}{2} & 3 & 5 & 2 \\ 3 & -2 & .6 & 4 & 1 & \frac{3}{4} \\ -2 & \pi & 8 & -\frac{5}{8} & 6 & 7 \end{bmatrix}$$

Determine the following.

(a) b_{12} (b) b_{32}
(c) b_{25} (d) b_{34}
(e) b_{23} (f) b_{21}

3. Let $A = [a_{ij}]_{23}$ and assume for each i and j that $a_{ij} = (3i - 2j)/2$. Write down the matrix A.

4. Let $A = [a_{ij}]_{23}$ and $B = [b_{ij}]_{34}$ with $a_{ij} = i + 2j$ and $b_{ij} = 2ij - j^2$. Let $C = [c_{ij}]_{24}$ be defined by

$$c_{ij} = a_{i1}b_{1j} + a_{i2}b_{2j} + a_{i3}b_{3j}$$

for all i and j. Write down the matrices A, B, and C.

In problems 5–12, perform, if possible, the indicated operations. If it is not possible to perform the operation, write "impossible."

5. $2 \cdot \begin{bmatrix} 2 & 1 \\ 3 & 4 \end{bmatrix} \begin{bmatrix} 0 & 1 \\ 3 & 7 \end{bmatrix} =$

6. $3 \cdot \begin{bmatrix} 1 & 0 & 1 \\ 2 & 1 & 0 \\ 3 & -1 & 1 \end{bmatrix} + \begin{bmatrix} 2 & 1 \\ 0 & -1 \\ 1 & -3 \end{bmatrix} \begin{bmatrix} 1 & -15 \\ \frac{1}{2} & \frac{1}{20} \end{bmatrix} =$

7. $\begin{bmatrix} 5 & 1 \\ \frac{1}{2} & 2 \end{bmatrix} \begin{bmatrix} 1 & 3 & 0 \\ 2 & \frac{1}{2} & -2 \end{bmatrix} \begin{bmatrix} -1 & 1 \\ 3 & 1 \\ 4 & 0 \end{bmatrix} \begin{bmatrix} 1 & -1 & 0 \\ -2 & \frac{1}{2} & 1 \\ \frac{1}{2} & -1 & 0 \end{bmatrix} =$

8. $\begin{bmatrix} 1 & 3 & 0 \\ 2 & \frac{1}{2} & -2 \end{bmatrix} \begin{bmatrix} 1 & -1 & 0 \\ -2 & \frac{1}{2} & 1 \\ \frac{1}{2} & -1 & 0 \end{bmatrix} \begin{bmatrix} -1 & 1 \\ 3 & 1 \\ 4 & 0 \end{bmatrix} \begin{bmatrix} 5 & 1 \\ \frac{1}{2} & 2 \end{bmatrix} =$

9. $\begin{bmatrix} -1 & 1 \\ 3 & 1 \\ 4 & 0 \end{bmatrix} \begin{bmatrix} 5 & 1 \\ \frac{1}{2} & 2 \end{bmatrix} \begin{bmatrix} 1 & 3 & 0 \\ 2 & \frac{1}{2} & -2 \end{bmatrix} \begin{bmatrix} 1 & -1 & 0 \\ -2 & \frac{1}{2} & 1 \\ \frac{1}{2} & -1 & 0 \end{bmatrix} =$

10. $\begin{bmatrix} -1 & 1 \\ 3 & 1 \\ 4 & 0 \end{bmatrix} \begin{bmatrix} 5 & 1 \\ \frac{1}{2} & 2 \end{bmatrix} \begin{bmatrix} 1 & -1 & 0 \\ -2 & \frac{1}{2} & 1 \\ \frac{1}{2} & -1 & 0 \end{bmatrix} \begin{bmatrix} 1 & 3 & 0 \\ 2 & \frac{1}{2} & -2 \end{bmatrix} =$

11. $\begin{bmatrix} 1 & 4 \\ 2 & -1 \end{bmatrix} + 7 \cdot \begin{bmatrix} -3 & 0 & 4 \\ 2 & 1 & 0 \end{bmatrix} \begin{bmatrix} 2 & 1 \\ 1 & 2 \\ 0 & 3 \end{bmatrix} - 2 \cdot \begin{bmatrix} 0 & -1 \\ 2 & 1 \end{bmatrix} =$

12. $2 \cdot \begin{bmatrix} 1 & 2 \\ -1 & 3 \end{bmatrix} \begin{bmatrix} 3 & 0 & -1 \\ 1 & 2 & -3 \end{bmatrix} - 5 \cdot \begin{bmatrix} 3 & 6 \\ -2 & 1 \end{bmatrix} \begin{bmatrix} 1 & 2 \\ -1 & 5 \end{bmatrix} =$

In problems 13–16, solve for the matrix X.

13. $2 \cdot \begin{bmatrix} 2 & 1 \\ -1 & 3 \end{bmatrix} + X = \begin{bmatrix} 1 & 4 \\ 0 & -1 \end{bmatrix}$

14. $4 \cdot X - \begin{bmatrix} 1 & 2 & 1 \\ 3 & 4 & 7 \end{bmatrix} \begin{bmatrix} 1 & 0 & 1 \\ -1 & \frac{1}{2} & 1 \\ 3 & -1 & 1 \end{bmatrix} = 2 \cdot X$

15. $$3 \cdot \begin{bmatrix} 4 & 1 & 0 \\ 5 & 2 & -1 \\ \frac{1}{2} & 1 & 1 \end{bmatrix} + 2 \cdot X = \begin{bmatrix} 2 & 1 & 3 \\ 1 & 0 & 1 \\ 2 & 4 & 1 \end{bmatrix} - X$$

*16. $$\begin{bmatrix} 3 & 1 \\ -1 & 0 \end{bmatrix} X = \begin{bmatrix} 6 & 2 \\ -2 & 0 \end{bmatrix}$$

17. Let

$$A = \begin{bmatrix} 3 & 1 \\ -2 & 4 \\ 6 & 5 \end{bmatrix} \qquad X = \begin{bmatrix} x_1 \\ x_2 \end{bmatrix} \qquad B = \begin{bmatrix} -1 \\ 0 \\ 8 \end{bmatrix}$$

The matrix equation $AX = B$ represents a system of linear equations. What is this system? (*Hint:* Carry out the multiplication AX and then use the definition of equality for matrices.)

18. Consider the system of linear equations

$$(*) \quad \begin{array}{rcr} 3x_1 - 2x_2 + 5x_3 &=& 12 \\ 2x_1 + x_2 - 8x_3 &=& -2 \end{array}$$

Let

$$X = \begin{bmatrix} x_1 \\ x_2 \\ x_3 \end{bmatrix} \qquad \text{and} \qquad B = \begin{bmatrix} 12 \\ -2 \end{bmatrix}$$

Find the matrix A such that the matrix equation $AX = B$ represents the system (*) of linear equations.

19. Use the notation of this section to prove that matrix addition is commutative. That is, if A and B are matrices of the same size, $A + B = B + A$.

20. Prove that if A and B are matrices of the same size and c is a real number,

$$c \cdot (A + B) = c \cdot A + c \cdot B$$

21. Prove MM3. That is, if A and B are so that AB is defined and if c is a real number,

$$c \cdot (AB) = (c \cdot A)B = A(c \cdot B)$$

* 22. Prove MM1. That is, let $A = [a_{ij}]_{mp}$, $B = [b_{ij}]_{pq}$, and $C = [c_{ij}]_{qn}$. Show that

$$(AB)C = A(BC)$$

Problems 23–27 refer to the notion of the transpose of a matrix.

Definition: Let $A = [a_{ij}]_{mn}$ be an $m \times n$ matrix. Then the *transpose* of A is defined to be the $n \times m$ matrix $A' = [a'_{ij}]_{nm}$, where $a'_{ij} = a_{ji}$ for all i and j. In other words, the rows of A' are the columns of A. For example, if

$$A = \begin{bmatrix} 1 & 0 \\ 3 & -4 \\ 2 & 6 \end{bmatrix}$$

then

$$A' = \begin{bmatrix} 1 & 3 & 2 \\ 0 & -4 & 6 \end{bmatrix}$$

23. Find the transposes of the following matrices.

(a) $\begin{bmatrix} 3 & 1 & 6 & 5 \\ 2 & -1 & 8 & 2 \end{bmatrix}$

(b) $\begin{bmatrix} 8 & 2 & -1 \\ 5 & 6 & 1 \\ 3 & \frac{1}{2} & 4 \end{bmatrix}$

(c) $[1, 3, 5, -7]$

(d) $\begin{bmatrix} 3 & 1 & 8 \\ 1 & 0 & -5 \\ 8 & -5 & 2 \end{bmatrix}$

24. Prove that for any matrix A,

$$(A')' = A$$

25. Show that if A and B are matrices of the same size,

$$(A + B)' = A' + B'$$

26. Let

$$A = \begin{bmatrix} 1 & 2 & 3 \\ -1 & 0 & 5 \end{bmatrix} \quad \text{and} \quad B = \begin{bmatrix} 4 & -1 \\ 2 & 1 \\ 3 & 4 \end{bmatrix}$$

Find

(a) A' (b) B'

(c) $(AB)'$ (d) $A'B'$

(e) $B'A'$

27. Let $A = [a_{ij}]_{mp}$ and $B = [b_{ij}]_{pn}$. Show that

$$(AB)' = B'A'$$

and that in general $(AB)' \neq A'B'$.

Section 6.9   Systems of Equations in Matrix Form

We are now in a position to examine the first of several applications of matrices to be demonstrated in the text. We shall consider the use of matrices in solving systems of linear equations.

The basic techniques will be illustrated via some examples.

Example 6.9.1   Consider the system of linear equations given in Example 6.5.1,

$$\begin{aligned} 5x_1 - 7x_2 &= -1 \\ 2x_1 + 4x_2 &= 20 \end{aligned} \tag{6.9.1}$$

We shall write this system in *vector-matrix form* by using the definition of matrix multiplication. First, by definition of equality of matrices (or vectors) we can write Eq. (6.9.1) as

$$\begin{bmatrix} 5x_1 - 7x_2 \\ 2x_1 + 4x_2 \end{bmatrix} = \begin{bmatrix} -1 \\ 20 \end{bmatrix} \tag{6.9.2}$$

Now notice that by the definition of matrix multiplication

$$\begin{bmatrix} 5 & -7 \\ 2 & 4 \end{bmatrix} \begin{bmatrix} x_1 \\ x_2 \end{bmatrix} = \begin{bmatrix} 5x_1 - 7x_2 \\ 2x_1 + 4x_2 \end{bmatrix} \tag{6.9.3}$$

Combining Eqs. (6.9.2) and (6.9.3) we obtain the *vector-matrix form* of the system of linear equations in Eq. (6.9.1):

$$\begin{bmatrix} 5 & -7 \\ 2 & 4 \end{bmatrix} \begin{bmatrix} x_1 \\ x_2 \end{bmatrix} = \begin{bmatrix} -1 \\ 20 \end{bmatrix} \tag{6.9.4}$$

Note that the entries of the first matrix on the left-hand side of Eq. (6.9.4) are just the coefficients of the variables in the linear system Eq. (6.9.1) written down as they appear. Hence this matrix is often called the *coefficient matrix* of the linear system. Also the entries of the matrix (vector) on the right-hand side of Eq. (6.9.4) are just the numbers on the right-hand side of the system in Eq. (6.9.1) written in the proper order. We shall call this the *value vector* of the system. Finally, the entries of the second matrix (vector) on the left-hand side of Eq. (6.9.4) are just the variables written down in order, and this is called the *variable vector*.

Example 6.9.2   Write the system of linear equations (Example 6.5.2)

$$\begin{aligned}
-4x_1 + x_2 + x_3 &= 0 \\
3x_1 - 2x_2 + 2x_3 &= 0 \\
x_1 + x_2 - 3x_3 &= 0 \\
x_1 + x_2 + x_3 &= 1
\end{aligned}$$

(6.9.5)

in vector-matrix form.

First, the coefficient matrix, variable vector, and value vector of this system are given, respectively, by

$$\begin{bmatrix} -4 & 1 & 1 \\ 3 & -2 & 2 \\ 1 & 1 & -3 \\ 1 & 1 & 1 \end{bmatrix} \qquad \begin{bmatrix} x_1 \\ x_2 \\ x_3 \end{bmatrix} \qquad \begin{bmatrix} 0 \\ 0 \\ 0 \\ 1 \end{bmatrix}$$

and using the same arguments as in Example 6.9.1, we get the *vector-matrix form* of the system to be

$$\begin{bmatrix} -4 & 1 & 1 \\ 3 & -2 & 2 \\ 1 & 1 & -3 \\ 1 & 1 & 1 \end{bmatrix} \begin{bmatrix} x_1 \\ x_2 \\ x_3 \end{bmatrix} = \begin{bmatrix} 0 \\ 0 \\ 0 \\ 1 \end{bmatrix}$$

(6.9.6)

The reader should multiply the two matrices on the left-hand side of Eq. (6.9.6) and check that Eq. (6.9.6) is equivalent to Eq. (6.9.5).

Theorem 6.9.1

Consider a system of m linear equations in n variables:

$$\begin{aligned}
a_{11}x_1 + a_{12}x_2 + \cdots + a_{1n}x_n &= b_1 \\
a_{21}x_1 + a_{22}x_2 + \cdots + a_{2n}x_n &= b_2 \\
\vdots \qquad \vdots \qquad\qquad \vdots \qquad \vdots \\
a_{m1}x_1 + a_{m2}x_2 + \cdots + a_{mn}x_n &= b_m
\end{aligned}$$

(6.9.7)

Then the system can be written in *vector-matrix form* as

$$AX = B$$

(6.9.8)

where A is the *coefficient matrix*

$$A = \begin{bmatrix} a_{11} & a_{12} & \cdots & a_{1n} \\ a_{21} & a_{22} & \cdots & a_{2n} \\ \vdots & \vdots & \ddots & \vdots \\ a_{m1} & a_{m2} & \cdots & a_{mn} \end{bmatrix}$$

(6.9.9)

X is the *variable vector*

$$X = \begin{bmatrix} x_1 \\ x_2 \\ \vdots \\ x_n \end{bmatrix} \qquad\qquad (6.9.10)$$

and B is the *value vector*

$$B = \begin{bmatrix} b_1 \\ b_2 \\ \vdots \\ b_m \end{bmatrix} \qquad\qquad (6.9.11)$$

We now consider what effects the elementary operations on a linear system have on the vector-matrix form of the system.

Example 6.9.3 Consider again the system of Example 6.9.1. We carry out the steps of Gaussian elimination on the system, at the same time keeping track of the corresponding vector-matrix forms.

Linear System

$$\begin{cases} 5x_1 - 7x_2 = -1 \\ 2x_1 + 4x_2 = 20 \end{cases}$$

$\tfrac{1}{2} \rightarrow \begin{cases} 2x_1 + 4x_2 = 20 \\ 5x_1 - 7x_2 = -1 \end{cases}$

$-5 \begin{cases} x_1 + 2x_2 = 10 \\ 5x_1 - 7x_2 = -1 \end{cases}$

$-\tfrac{1}{17} \rightarrow \begin{cases} x_1 + 2x_2 = 10 \\ \quad\ -17x_2 = -51 \end{cases}$

$-2 \begin{cases} x_1 + 2x_2 = 10 \\ \quad\quad x_2 = 3 \end{cases}$

$\begin{cases} x_1 \quad\quad = 4 \\ \quad\quad x_2 = 3 \end{cases}$

Vector-Matrix Form

$$\begin{bmatrix} 5 & -7 \\ 2 & 4 \end{bmatrix}\begin{bmatrix} x_1 \\ x_2 \end{bmatrix} = \begin{bmatrix} -1 \\ 20 \end{bmatrix}$$

$$\begin{bmatrix} 2 & 4 \\ 5 & -7 \end{bmatrix}\begin{bmatrix} x_1 \\ x_2 \end{bmatrix} = \begin{bmatrix} 20 \\ -1 \end{bmatrix}$$

$$\begin{bmatrix} 1 & 2 \\ 5 & -7 \end{bmatrix}\begin{bmatrix} x_1 \\ x_2 \end{bmatrix} = \begin{bmatrix} 10 \\ -1 \end{bmatrix}$$

$$\begin{bmatrix} 1 & 2 \\ 0 & -17 \end{bmatrix}\begin{bmatrix} x_1 \\ x_2 \end{bmatrix} = \begin{bmatrix} 10 \\ -51 \end{bmatrix}$$

$$\begin{bmatrix} 1 & 2 \\ 0 & 1 \end{bmatrix}\begin{bmatrix} x_1 \\ x_2 \end{bmatrix} = \begin{bmatrix} 10 \\ 3 \end{bmatrix}$$

$$\begin{bmatrix} 1 & 0 \\ 0 & 1 \end{bmatrix}\begin{bmatrix} x_1 \\ x_2 \end{bmatrix} = \begin{bmatrix} 4 \\ 3 \end{bmatrix}$$

Notice in this example that at the first step in the Gaussian elimination the first and second equations were interchanged. If we look at the effect of this on the vector-matrix form we see that the effect was to interchange the first and second rows of the coefficient matrix and of the value vector (the variable vector remains unchanged).

The same remarks hold for the other steps in the Gaussian elimination. That is, any elementary operation performed on the linear system results in the *same* elementary operation being performed on the coefficient matrix and value vector. The variable vector remains unchanged.

Hence the Gaussian elimination method can be streamlined by *operating on the coefficient matrix and value vector* and disregarding completely the original system as well as the variable vector.

For this we form the *augmented* coefficient matrix, which has one more column than the coefficient matrix. The extra column is just the value vector. For example, the augmented matrix for the system in Example 6.9.1 is

$$\begin{bmatrix} 5 & -7 & \vdots & -1 \\ 2 & 4 & \vdots & 20 \end{bmatrix} \tag{6.9.12}$$

and that for Example 6.9.2 is

$$\begin{bmatrix} -4 & 1 & 1 & \vdots & 0 \\ 3 & -2 & 2 & \vdots & 0 \\ 1 & 1 & -3 & \vdots & 0 \\ 1 & 1 & 1 & \vdots & 1 \end{bmatrix} \tag{6.9.13}$$

The dashed line is put in to emphasize the fact that the coefficient matrix has been augmented and to indicate that only the left-hand part of the matrix is to be considered when searching for nonzero entries (coefficients). We remark that if a system has a unique solution, then following the application of the Gaussian elimination method the solution will appear in the augmented matrix to the right of the dashed line.

We now present some examples to illustrate these points.

Example 6.9.4 Use Gaussian elimination and augmented matrices to solve the system of equations in Example 6.9.1. The system is

$$5x_1 - 7x_2 = -1$$
$$2x_1 + 4x_2 = 20$$

and the augmented matrix is given by Eq. (6.9.12). We proceed as follows:

$$\circlearrowleft \begin{bmatrix} 5 & -7 & \vdots & -1 \\ 2 & 4 & \vdots & 20 \end{bmatrix} \rightarrow \quad \tfrac{1}{2} \rightarrow \begin{bmatrix} 2 & 4 & \vdots & 20 \\ 5 & -7 & \vdots & -1 \end{bmatrix}$$

$$-5 \circlearrowleft \begin{bmatrix} 1 & 2 & \vdots & 10 \\ 5 & -7 & \vdots & -1 \end{bmatrix} \rightarrow \quad -\tfrac{1}{17} \rightarrow \begin{bmatrix} 1 & 2 & \vdots & 10 \\ 0 & -17 & \vdots & -51 \end{bmatrix}$$

$$-2 \circlearrowleft \begin{bmatrix} 1 & 2 & \vdots & 10 \\ 0 & 1 & \vdots & 3 \end{bmatrix} \rightarrow \begin{bmatrix} 1 & 0 & \vdots & 4 \\ 0 & 1 & \vdots & 3 \end{bmatrix}$$

The solution is $x_1 = 4$, $x_2 = 3$.

Example 6.9.5 Solve the system of Example 6.9.2 by using augmented matrices. The augmented matrix for this system is given in Eq. (6.9.13). When we use Gaussian elimination we obtain

$$\begin{bmatrix} -4 & 1 & 1 & \vdots & 0 \\ 3 & -2 & 2 & \vdots & 0 \\ 1 & 1 & -3 & \vdots & 0 \\ 1 & 1 & 1 & \vdots & 1 \end{bmatrix} \rightarrow \begin{bmatrix} 1 & 1 & -3 & \vdots & 0 \\ 3 & -2 & 2 & \vdots & 0 \\ -4 & 1 & 1 & \vdots & 0 \\ 1 & 1 & 1 & \vdots & 1 \end{bmatrix} \rightarrow$$

$$-\tfrac{1}{5} \rightarrow \begin{bmatrix} 1 & 1 & -3 & \vdots & 0 \\ 0 & -5 & 11 & \vdots & 0 \\ 0 & 5 & -11 & \vdots & 0 \\ 0 & 0 & 4 & \vdots & 1 \end{bmatrix} \rightarrow \begin{bmatrix} 1 & 1 & -3 & \vdots & 0 \\ 0 & 1 & -\tfrac{11}{5} & \vdots & 0 \\ 0 & 5 & -11 & \vdots & 0 \\ 0 & 0 & 4 & \vdots & 1 \end{bmatrix} \rightarrow$$

$$\begin{bmatrix} 1 & 0 & -\frac{4}{5} & \vdots & 0 \\ 0 & 1 & -\frac{11}{5} & \vdots & 0 \\ 0 & 0 & 0 & \vdots & 0 \\ 0 & 0 & 4 & \vdots & 1 \end{bmatrix} \rightarrow \qquad \frac{1}{4} \rightarrow \begin{bmatrix} 1 & 0 & -\frac{4}{5} & \vdots & 0 \\ 0 & 1 & -\frac{11}{5} & \vdots & 0 \\ 0 & 0 & 4 & \vdots & 1 \\ 0 & 0 & 0 & \vdots & 0 \end{bmatrix} \rightarrow$$

$$\frac{4}{5} \left\{ \begin{array}{} \\ \end{array} \right. \frac{11}{5} \left\{ \begin{array}{} \\ \end{array} \right. \begin{bmatrix} 1 & 0 & -\frac{4}{5} & \vdots & 0 \\ 0 & 1 & -\frac{11}{5} & \vdots & 0 \\ 0 & 0 & 1 & \vdots & \frac{1}{4} \\ 0 & 0 & 0 & \vdots & 0 \end{bmatrix} \rightarrow \begin{bmatrix} 1 & 0 & 0 & \vdots & \frac{1}{5} \\ 0 & 1 & 0 & \vdots & \frac{11}{20} \\ 0 & 0 & 1 & \vdots & \frac{1}{4} \\ 0 & 0 & 0 & \vdots & 0 \end{bmatrix}$$

The solution is $x_1 = \frac{1}{5}$, $x_2 = \frac{11}{20}$, $x_3 = \frac{1}{4}$. (See the note following Example 6.5.2 for the interpretation of the zero row in the last augmented matrix.)

Example 6.9.6 Use augmented matrices to solve the system

$$\begin{aligned} -3x_1 + 4x_2 - x_3 &= 0 \\ x_1 + 2x_2 - x_3 &= 2 \end{aligned} \tag{6.9.14}$$

The augmented matrix for the system is

$$\begin{bmatrix} -3 & 4 & -1 & \vdots & 0 \\ 1 & 2 & -1 & \vdots & 2 \end{bmatrix}$$

Applying Gaussian elimination yields

$$\left. \begin{bmatrix} -3 & 4 & -1 & \vdots & 0 \\ 1 & 2 & -1 & \vdots & 2 \end{bmatrix} \right. \rightarrow \quad 3 \left. \begin{bmatrix} 1 & 2 & -1 & \vdots & 2 \\ -3 & 4 & -1 & \vdots & 0 \end{bmatrix} \right.$$

$$\frac{1}{10} \rightarrow \begin{bmatrix} 1 & 2 & -1 & \vdots & 2 \\ 0 & 10 & -4 & \vdots & 6 \end{bmatrix} \rightarrow \quad -2 \left. \begin{bmatrix} 1 & 2 & -1 & \vdots & 2 \\ 0 & 1 & -\frac{2}{5} & \vdots & \frac{3}{5} \end{bmatrix} \right.$$

$$\begin{bmatrix} 1 & 0 & -\frac{1}{5} & \vdots & \frac{4}{5} \\ 0 & 1 & -\frac{2}{5} & \vdots & \frac{3}{5} \end{bmatrix}$$

This is as far as we can proceed with Gaussian elimination. Interpreting the final augmented matrix in equation form we get

$$\begin{aligned} x_1 \quad\ - \tfrac{1}{5}x_3 &= \tfrac{4}{5} \\ x_2 - \tfrac{2}{5}x_3 &= \tfrac{3}{5} \end{aligned}$$

Consequently, the system in Eq. (6.9.14) has infinitely many solutions, namely, any values for the variables satisfying

$$\begin{aligned} x_1 &= \tfrac{1}{5}x_3 + \tfrac{4}{5} \\ x_2 &= \tfrac{2}{5}x_3 + \tfrac{3}{5} \end{aligned}$$

Example 6.9.7 Solve the system

$$\begin{aligned} 2x_1 - 4x_2 &= 8 \\ 3x_1 + x_2 &= 5 \\ 5x_1 + 4x_2 &= 5 \end{aligned} \tag{6.9.15}$$

by using augmented matrices.

Forming the augmented matrix for the system and applying Gaussian elimination we obtain

$$\tfrac{1}{2} \to \begin{bmatrix} 2 & -4 & \vdots & 8 \\ 3 & 1 & \vdots & 5 \\ 5 & 4 & \vdots & 5 \end{bmatrix} \to \begin{array}{c} \\ -3 \\ -5 \end{array} \begin{bmatrix} 1 & -2 & \vdots & 4 \\ 3 & 1 & \vdots & 5 \\ 5 & 4 & \vdots & 5 \end{bmatrix}$$

$$\tfrac{1}{7} \to \begin{bmatrix} 1 & -2 & \vdots & 4 \\ 0 & 7 & \vdots & -7 \\ 0 & 14 & \vdots & -15 \end{bmatrix} \to \begin{array}{c} 2 \\ \\ -14 \end{array} \begin{bmatrix} 1 & -2 & \vdots & 4 \\ 0 & 1 & \vdots & -1 \\ 0 & 14 & \vdots & -15 \end{bmatrix}$$

$$\begin{bmatrix} 1 & 0 & \vdots & 2 \\ 0 & 1 & \vdots & -1 \\ 0 & 0 & \vdots & -1 \end{bmatrix}$$

This is as far as we can proceed with Gaussian elimination. The last augmented matrix corresponds to the system

$$
\begin{array}{ll}
x_1 \quad\quad = \;\; 2 & \quad\quad x_1 + 0 \cdot x_2 = \quad 2 \\
\quad\; x_2 = -1 \quad \text{or} & \quad\quad 0 \cdot x_1 + \quad\; x_2 = -1 \\
\quad\; 0 \;\; = -1 & \quad\quad 0 \cdot x_1 + 0 \cdot x_2 = -1
\end{array}
$$

Obviously, the last equation in this system has no solutions and hence the system in Eq. (6.9.15) has no solutions (i.e., its solution set is $\varnothing$).

Whenever any row of an augmented matrix consists of zeros to the left of the dashed line and a *nonzero* number to the right of the dashed line, the corresponding system of equations has no solutions.

By use of the notational scheme of augmented matrices we have been able to streamline the writing of the steps of the Gaussian elimination method. This scheme is now expanded to obtain an efficient method for solving several systems of equations at one time.

The method is applicable whenever each of the systems involved has the *same coefficient matrix*. We illustrate by the following example.

Example 6.9.8 Consider the systems

$$\begin{cases} 5x_1 - 7x_2 = -1 \\ 2x_1 + 4x_2 = \;\; 20 \end{cases}$$

$$\begin{cases} 5x_1 - 7x_2 = \;\; 17 \\ 2x_1 + 4x_2 = \;\;\; 0 \end{cases}$$

Note that both systems have the same coefficient matrices. Their augmented matrices are given below in columns I and II, respectively. In column III we combine the two augmented matrices by augmenting the coefficient matrix with both value vectors. We then apply Gaussian elimination to all three augmented matrices:

$$
\begin{array}{ccc}
\text{(I)} & \text{(II)} & \text{(III)} \\[6pt]
\begin{bmatrix} 5 & -7 & \vdots & -1 \\ 2 & 4 & \vdots & 20 \end{bmatrix} &
\begin{bmatrix} 5 & -7 & \vdots & 17 \\ 2 & 4 & \vdots & 0 \end{bmatrix} &
\begin{bmatrix} 5 & -7 & \vdots & -1 & 17 \\ 2 & 4 & \vdots & 20 & 0 \end{bmatrix} \\[10pt]
\tfrac{1}{2} \to \begin{bmatrix} 2 & 4 & \vdots & 20 \\ 5 & -7 & \vdots & -1 \end{bmatrix} &
\tfrac{1}{2} \to \begin{bmatrix} 2 & 4 & \vdots & 0 \\ 5 & -7 & \vdots & 17 \end{bmatrix} &
\tfrac{1}{2} \to \begin{bmatrix} 2 & 4 & \vdots & 20 & 0 \\ 5 & -7 & \vdots & -1 & 17 \end{bmatrix}
\end{array}
$$

$$-5 \left(\begin{bmatrix} 1 & 2 & | & 10 \\ 5 & -7 & | & -1 \end{bmatrix} \right. \qquad -5 \left(\begin{bmatrix} 1 & 2 & | & 0 \\ 5 & -7 & | & 17 \end{bmatrix} \right. \qquad -5 \left(\begin{bmatrix} 1 & 2 & | & 10 & 0 \\ 5 & -7 & | & -1 & 17 \end{bmatrix} \right.$$

$$-\tfrac{1}{17} \to \begin{bmatrix} 1 & 2 & | & 10 \\ 0 & -17 & | & -51 \end{bmatrix} \qquad -\tfrac{1}{17} \to \begin{bmatrix} 1 & 2 & | & 0 \\ 0 & -17 & | & 17 \end{bmatrix} \qquad -\tfrac{1}{17} \to \begin{bmatrix} 1 & 2 & | & 10 & 0 \\ 0 & -17 & | & -51 & 17 \end{bmatrix}$$

$$-2 \left(\begin{bmatrix} 1 & 2 & | & 10 \\ 0 & 1 & | & 3 \end{bmatrix} \right. \qquad -2 \left(\begin{bmatrix} 1 & 2 & | & 0 \\ 0 & 1 & | & -1 \end{bmatrix} \right. \qquad -2 \left(\begin{bmatrix} 1 & 2 & | & 10 & 0 \\ 0 & 1 & | & 3 & -1 \end{bmatrix} \right.$$

$$\begin{bmatrix} 1 & 0 & | & 4 \\ 0 & 1 & | & 3 \end{bmatrix} \qquad \begin{bmatrix} 1 & 0 & | & 2 \\ 0 & 1 & | & -1 \end{bmatrix} \qquad \begin{bmatrix} 1 & 0 & | & 4 & 2 \\ 0 & 1 & | & 3 & -1 \end{bmatrix}$$

The solution to the first system is $x_1 = 4$, $x_2 = 3$, and the solution to the second is $x_1 = 2$, $x_2 = -1$. Note that the last augmented matrix in III contains these values in the two columns at the right of the dashed line. This is no accident. The reason is because *the steps taken to solve the systems by Gaussian elimination are determined by the portion of the augmented matrices to the left of the dashed line—the coefficient matrices.*

Consequently, if the coefficient matrices of several systems are the same, the steps taken in the Gaussian elimination will be identical and hence the augmented matrices can be combined and all systems solved at once, as was done in column III.

Example 6.9.9 Use augmented matrices to solve the three linear systems

(I) $\quad \begin{cases} 3x_1 - 12x_2 = -6 \\ 3x_1 + 7x_2 = 13 \end{cases}$

(II) $\quad \begin{cases} 3x_1 - 12x_2 = 33 \\ 3x_1 + 7x_2 = -5 \end{cases}$

(III) $\quad \begin{cases} 3x_1 - 12x_2 = -18 \\ 3x_1 + 7x_2 = 39 \end{cases}$

at the same time.

Since each of the systems has the same coefficient matrix, the above procedure is applicable. We combine the augmented matrices to get

$$\begin{bmatrix} 3 & -12 & | & -6 & 33 & -18 \\ 3 & 7 & | & 13 & -5 & 39 \end{bmatrix}$$

Then using Gaussian elimination we get

$$\tfrac{1}{3} \to \begin{bmatrix} 3 & -12 & | & -6 & 33 & -18 \\ 3 & 7 & | & 13 & -5 & 39 \end{bmatrix} \to -3 \left(\begin{bmatrix} 1 & -4 & | & -2 & 11 & -6 \\ 3 & 7 & | & 13 & -5 & 39 \end{bmatrix} \right. \to$$

$$\tfrac{1}{19} \to \begin{bmatrix} 1 & -4 & | & -2 & 11 & -6 \\ 0 & 19 & | & 19 & -38 & 57 \end{bmatrix} \to 4 \left(\begin{bmatrix} 1 & -4 & | & -2 & 11 & -6 \\ 0 & 1 & | & 1 & -2 & 3 \end{bmatrix} \right. \to$$

$$\begin{bmatrix} 1 & 0 & | & 2 & 3 & 6 \\ 0 & 1 & | & 1 & -2 & 3 \end{bmatrix}$$

Consequently, the solutions to the three systems of equations are given, respectively, by the three columns on the right of the dashed line in the last augmented matrix:

(I) $\quad x_1 = 2 \qquad x_2 = 1$
(II) $\quad x_1 = 3 \qquad x_2 = -2$
(III) $\quad x_1 = 6 \qquad x_2 = 3$

In problems 1–6, write the given system of linear equations in vector-matrix form.

1. $3x_1 + 2x_2 = 7$
   $4x_1 - 8x_2 = -3$

2. $2x_1 - 5x_2 + 7x_3 - 8x_4 = 2$

3. $3y_1 - 2y_2 + 7y_3 = 10$
   $y_1 \qquad - 6y_3 = -4$

4. $3x_1 - 2x_2 + 7x_3 = 10$
   $x_1 \qquad - 6x_3 = -4$

5. $3x_1 + 7x_2 - 4x_3 + 8x_4 = 12$
   $x_1 \qquad - x_3 + 2x_4 = 7$
   $.6x_1 + 3x_2 - .4x_3 + x_4 = \frac{1}{2}$

6. $2x_1 + 6x_2 - 3x_3 + 5x_4 - x_5 = 0$
   $\qquad 4x_2 \qquad - 3x_4 + 7x_5 = 1$
   $-x_1 - 2x_2 + 10x_3 \qquad + 11x_5 = -1$
   $x_1 + x_2 + x_3 + x_4 + x_5 = 1$
   $3x_1 - 2x_2 \qquad\qquad - 6x_5 = 15$

In problems 7–16, solve the systems of equations by using Gaussian elimination and augmented matrices.

7. $3x_1 - 4x_2 = 10$
   $2x_1 + 5x_2 = -1$

8. $-5x_1 + 7x_2 = -2$
   $x_1 + x_2 = 1$

9. $5x_1 + x_2 + 2x_3 = 10$
   $-2x_1 + 8x_2 + x_3 = -22$
   $3x_1 + 9x_2 + 7x_3 = 4$

10. $2x_1 + x_2 + x_3 = 9$
    $3x_1 - 5x_2 + \frac{1}{2}x_3 = 3$
    $x_1 \qquad - 3x_3 = -10$

11. $x_1 + x_2 - x_3 = 3$
    $2x_1 - x_2 + 5x_3 = -8$
    $-x_1 - 4x_2 + x_3 = -3$
    $5x_1 + 2x_2 \qquad = 5$

12. $2x_1 - 3x_2 = 2$
    $4x_1 - 6x_2 = -6$

13. $3x_1 - 9x_2 = -3$
    $-x_1 + 3x_2 = 1$

14. $2x_1 - 3x_2 + 7x_3 = 7$
    $4x_1 - 6x_2 + 8x_3 = 2$

15. $x_1 - 2x_2 + x_3 = 5$
    $-x_1 + x_2 + 3x_3 = 4$
    $5x_1 - 7x_2 - 7x_3 = -2$

16. $5x_1 - 4x_2 - 3x_3 = 1$
    $3x_1 + 2x_2 + x_3 = 4$
    $x_1 + 8x_2 + 5x_3 = 3$

In problems 17–20 solve all the systems given by using the same augmented matrix.

17. $-x_1 + 4x_2 = 1$ $\qquad -x_1 + 4x_2 = -13$
    $3x_1 + 5x_2 = 14$ $\qquad 3x_1 + 5x_2 = 5$

18. $3x_1 + 4x_2 = 1 \qquad 3x_1 + 4x_2 = 0$
    $2x_1 + 3x_2 = 0 \qquad 2x_1 + 3x_2 = 1$

19. $\begin{array}{rl} x_1 - x_2 - 2x_3 = & 5 \\ 2x_1 + 3x_2 - 7x_3 = & 16 \\ -2x_1 + 7x_2 + 2x_3 = & -6 \end{array} \qquad \begin{array}{rl} x_1 - x_2 - 2x_3 = & -3 \\ 2x_1 + 3x_2 - 7x_3 = & -41 \\ -2x_1 + 7x_2 + 2x_3 = & -24 \end{array}$

20. $\begin{array}{rl} 2x_1 + 5x_2 + 10x_3 = & 1 \\ -x_1 - 7x_2 + x_3 = & 0 \\ x_1 + 3x_2 + 4x_3 = & 0 \end{array} \qquad \begin{array}{rl} 2x_1 + 5x_2 + 10x_3 = & 0 \\ -x_1 - 7x_2 + x_3 = & 1 \\ x_1 + 3x_2 + 4x_3 = & 0 \end{array}$

$$\begin{array}{rl} 2x_1 + 5x_2 + 10x_3 = & 0 \\ -x_1 - 7x_2 + x_3 = & 0 \\ x_1 + 3x_2 + 4x_3 = & 1 \end{array}$$

21. Refer to Example 6.1.1. Set up the two systems of three linear equations in three variables resulting from the diet restrictions for the two test groups of animals and solve both systems at the same time [see Eqs. (6.5.6) and (6.5.7)].

22. An oil company has two refineries (I and II) in a particular city. The oil refineries produce kerosene, gasoline, and fuel oil from crude oil. Refinery I is allocated 120,000 barrels of crude oil and refinery II is allocated 140,000 barrels. We assume for simplicity that there are no losses in the conversion processes involved. For example, refinery I's total production of kerosene, gasoline, and fuel oil will be 120,000 barrels. Now, both refineries are required to produce as many barrels of gasoline as the combined production of kerosene and fuel oil. Also, refinery I is to produce the same amount of kerosene and fuel oil while refinery II is to produce 50,000 barrels more of kerosene than fuel oil.

    (a) Set up two systems of equations which represent the necessary requirements on production for both refineries.
    (b) Use augmented matrices to solve both systems at the same time.
    (c) Interpret your results in part (b).

*23. Let $A = [a_{ij}]$ be a 2×2 matrix. Assume that $a_{11} \neq 0$ and $a_{11}a_{22} - a_{12}a_{21} \neq 0$.

    (a) Use augmented matrices to solve the two systems

$$\text{(I)} \quad \begin{array}{l} a_{11}x_1 + a_{12}x_2 = 1 \\ a_{21}x_1 + a_{22}x_2 = 0 \end{array} \qquad \text{(II)} \quad \begin{array}{l} a_{11}y_1 + a_{12}y_2 = 0 \\ a_{21}y_1 + a_{22}y_2 = 1 \end{array}$$

    at the same time.

    (b) Let B be the 2×2 matrix whose first column consists of the simultaneous solution to (I) and whose second column consists of the simultaneous solution to (II). Show that

$$AB = \begin{bmatrix} 1 & 0 \\ 0 & 1 \end{bmatrix}$$

24. Let $A = [a_{ij}]_{mn}$, $Y = [y_1, y_2, \ldots, y_m]$, and $C = [c_1, c_2, \ldots, c_n]$. Show that the system of equations given by the matrix equation

$$YA = C$$

    has the vector-matrix form

$$DX = B$$

    where $D = A'$, $X = Y'$, and $B = C'$. Here, for example, A' denotes the transpose of the matrix A as defined directly preceding problem 23, Exercises 6.8.

Section 6.10 The Inverse of a Matrix

In Sections 6.7 and 6.8 the definitions and basic properties of matrices were examined. In this section we study the notion of the inverse of a matrix. There are many important theoretical and applied uses of this. We shall use the concept of the inverse of a matrix primarily in studying absorbing Markov chains (Chapter 9).

As a method of motivating the general ideas involved, consider, for the moment, the multiplication of real numbers. There are two points to be examined here. The first is the special role, in multiplication, of the number 1. This is the only number which has the property that if c is any other real number, then

$$c \cdot 1 = 1 \cdot c = c$$

The second point is that given any real number c, as long as $c \neq 0$, there exists another real number (which we write $1/c$), such that

$$c \cdot (1/c) = (1/c) \cdot c = 1$$

As a matter of notation, $1/c$ is often written c^{-1} (c inverse).

We shall now consider the question of whether there is a matrix (or matrices) that play the role of 1 in *matrix multiplication*. That is, can a matrix (or matrices) I be found, such that for any matrix A,

$$AI = IA = A?$$

The first observation we make is that the size of I will have to depend on the size of A. That is, if A is $m \times n$, then in order for AI to be defined, I must be $n \times$ "something."

But, if

$$\begin{array}{ccc} m \times n & n \times ? & = m \times n \\ \downarrow & \downarrow & \downarrow \\ A & \cdot \quad I & = \quad A \end{array}$$

AI must be $m \times n$, so I must $n \times n$. On the other hand, if

$$IA = A$$

the I must be $m \times m$.

We will say that an $m \times n$ matrix is *square* if $m = n$ (i.e., it has the same number of rows and columns). So, from the discussion above, the I in AI must be square of order n, and similarly the I in IA must be square of order m. Hence, what is really desired are matrices I_k, one for each positive integer, such that for any $m \times n$ matrix A,

$$I_m A = A I_n = A$$

When we use the definition of multiplication of matrices it is not too difficult to show that the desired matrices are

$$I_1 = [1]$$

$$I_2 = \begin{bmatrix} 1 & 0 \\ 0 & 1 \end{bmatrix}$$

$$I_3 = \begin{bmatrix} 1 & 0 & 0 \\ 0 & 1 & 0 \\ 0 & 0 & 1 \end{bmatrix}$$

$$I_4 = \begin{bmatrix} 1 & 0 & 0 & 0 \\ 0 & 1 & 0 & 0 \\ 0 & 0 & 1 & 0 \\ 0 & 0 & 0 & 1 \end{bmatrix}$$

Some examples should convince the reader that this is the case.

Example 6.10.1

1. Let

$$A = \begin{bmatrix} 2 & 1 & 1 & \frac{1}{2} \\ 4 & 2 & 0 & 1 \\ 3 & 1 & 4 & 0 \end{bmatrix}$$

Then we have

$$I_3 A = \begin{bmatrix} 1 & 0 & 0 \\ 0 & 1 & 0 \\ 0 & 0 & 1 \end{bmatrix}\begin{bmatrix} 2 & 1 & 1 & \frac{1}{2} \\ 4 & 2 & 0 & 1 \\ 3 & 1 & 4 & 0 \end{bmatrix} = \begin{bmatrix} 2 & 1 & 1 & \frac{1}{2} \\ 4 & 2 & 0 & 1 \\ 3 & 1 & 4 & 0 \end{bmatrix} = A$$

$$A I_4 = \begin{bmatrix} 2 & 1 & 1 & \frac{1}{2} \\ 4 & 2 & 0 & 1 \\ 3 & 1 & 4 & 0 \end{bmatrix}\begin{bmatrix} 1 & 0 & 0 & 0 \\ 0 & 1 & 0 & 0 \\ 0 & 0 & 1 & 0 \\ 0 & 0 & 0 & 1 \end{bmatrix} = \begin{bmatrix} 2 & 1 & 1 & \frac{1}{2} \\ 4 & 2 & 0 & 1 \\ 3 & 1 & 4 & 0 \end{bmatrix} = A$$

2. Let

$$A = \begin{bmatrix} 4 & 6 & \frac{1}{2} \\ -1 & 3 & 2 \end{bmatrix}$$

Then

$$I_2 A = \begin{bmatrix} 1 & 0 \\ 0 & 1 \end{bmatrix}\begin{bmatrix} 4 & 6 & \frac{1}{2} \\ -1 & 3 & 2 \end{bmatrix} = \begin{bmatrix} 4 & 6 & \frac{1}{2} \\ -1 & 3 & 2 \end{bmatrix} = A$$

$$A I_3 = \begin{bmatrix} 4 & 6 & \frac{1}{2} \\ -1 & 3 & 2 \end{bmatrix}\begin{bmatrix} 1 & 0 & 0 \\ 0 & 1 & 0 \\ 0 & 0 & 1 \end{bmatrix} = \begin{bmatrix} 4 & 6 & \frac{1}{2} \\ -1 & 3 & 2 \end{bmatrix} = A$$

We call the matrix I_n the *identity matrix* of order n. It has this name because it is the *multiplicative identity element* in matrix multiplication.

We can now consider the second observation made about real numbers: every real number $c \neq 0$ has a multiplicative inverse (i.e., there is a number, called c^{-1}, such that $cc^{-1} = c^{-1}c = 1$). Is this true of matrices? That is, if A is a matrix, is there another matrix (which we shall call A^{-1}) such that

$$AA^{-1} = A^{-1}A = I \tag{6.10.1}$$

for the appropriate choice of the identity matrix I? The answer is, *in general*, no. First, if A is $m \times n$, then in order for both multiplications in Eq. (6.10.1) to yield the same dimension matrix (i.e., the dimension of I) we must have $m = n$ (the proof of this fact is left as an exercise). Consequently, the problem in Eq. (6.10.1) is considered only for square matrices.

So, suppose that A is a square matrix (say, $n \times n$). If there is another matrix, A^{-1}, such that

$$AA^{-1} = A^{-1}A = I_n \qquad (6.10.2)$$

then in order for Eq. (6.10.2) to hold, it is necessary for A^{-1} to be $n \times n$.

Let us consider an example, which will help in formulating an approach to finding the inverse of a matrix, if it exists.

Example 6.10.2 Suppose that we consider the 2×2 matrix A given by

$$A = \begin{bmatrix} 3 & 2 \\ 4 & 3 \end{bmatrix}$$

The problem is to find a 2×2 matrix A^{-1} such that

$$AA^{-1} = A^{-1}A = I_2 \qquad (6.10.3)$$

First we try to find A^{-1} such that

$$AA^{-1} = I_2 \qquad (6.10.4)$$

Write

$$A^{-1} = \begin{bmatrix} x_{11} & x_{12} \\ x_{21} & x_{22} \end{bmatrix}$$

The problem is to find values for x_{11}, x_{21}, x_{12}, and x_{22} so that Eq. (6.10.4) holds. Multiplying the two matrices on the left-hand side of Eq. (6.10.4) gives

$$AA^{-1} = \begin{bmatrix} 3 & 2 \\ 4 & 3 \end{bmatrix} \begin{bmatrix} x_{11} & x_{12} \\ x_{21} & x_{22} \end{bmatrix} = \begin{bmatrix} 3x_{11} + 2x_{21} & 3x_{12} + 2x_{22} \\ 4x_{11} + 3x_{21} & 4x_{12} + 3x_{22} \end{bmatrix}$$

and setting this last matrix equal to the right-hand side of Eq. (6.10.4) yields

$$\begin{bmatrix} 3x_{11} + 2x_{21} & 3x_{12} + 2x_{22} \\ 4x_{11} + 3x_{21} & 4x_{12} + 3x_{22} \end{bmatrix} = \begin{bmatrix} 1 & 0 \\ 0 & 1 \end{bmatrix}$$

or, in other words,

$$3x_{11} + 2x_{21} = 1$$
$$4x_{11} + 3x_{21} = 0$$
$$3x_{12} + 2x_{22} = 0$$
$$4x_{12} + 3x_{22} = 1$$

Now these last four linear equations can be written as two systems of linear equations in two variables as follows:

$$\begin{cases} 3x_{11} + 2x_{21} = 1 \\ 4x_{11} + 3x_{21} = 0 \end{cases}$$
$$\begin{cases} 3x_{12} + 2x_{22} = 0 \\ 4x_{12} + 3x_{22} = 1 \end{cases} \qquad (6.10.5)$$

Notice that both systems have the same coefficient matrix, *the matrix A*, and so by the techniques of Section 6.9 both systems can be solved at once. The augmented matrix for doing this is

$$\begin{bmatrix} 3 & 2 & \vdots & 1 & 0 \\ 4 & 3 & \vdots & 0 & 1 \end{bmatrix} \qquad (6.10.6)$$

Applying Gaussian elimination we obtain

$$\tfrac{1}{3} \to \begin{bmatrix} 3 & 2 & \vdots & 1 & 0 \\ 4 & 3 & \vdots & 0 & 1 \end{bmatrix} \to \underset{-4}{\curvearrowleft} \begin{bmatrix} 1 & \tfrac{2}{3} & \vdots & \tfrac{1}{3} & 0 \\ 4 & 3 & \vdots & 0 & 1 \end{bmatrix} \to$$

$$3 \to \begin{bmatrix} 1 & \tfrac{2}{3} & \vdots & \tfrac{1}{3} & 0 \\ 0 & \tfrac{1}{3} & \vdots & -\tfrac{4}{3} & 1 \end{bmatrix} \to \underset{-\tfrac{2}{3}}{\curvearrowleft} \begin{bmatrix} 1 & \tfrac{2}{3} & \vdots & \tfrac{1}{3} & 0 \\ 0 & 1 & \vdots & -4 & 3 \end{bmatrix} \to$$

$$\begin{bmatrix} 1 & 0 & \vdots & 3 & -2 \\ 0 & 1 & \vdots & -4 & 3 \end{bmatrix} \tag{6.10.7}$$

Thus the solution to the first system in Eq. (6.10.5) is $x_{11} = 3$, $x_{21} = -4$ and that to the second is $x_{12} = -2$, $x_{22} = 3$. In other words, if we let

$$A^{-1} = \begin{bmatrix} 3 & -2 \\ -4 & 3 \end{bmatrix} \tag{6.10.8}$$

then $AA^{-1} = I_2$. To show that Eq. (6.10.3) holds, we must verify that $A^{-1}A = I_2$:

$$A^{-1}A = \begin{bmatrix} 3 & -2 \\ -4 & 3 \end{bmatrix} \begin{bmatrix} 3 & 2 \\ 4 & 3 \end{bmatrix} = \begin{bmatrix} 1 & 0 \\ 0 & 1 \end{bmatrix} = I_2$$

Hence the matrix A has the inverse given by Eq. (6.10.8).

Before leaving this example we point out that in trying to obtain the inverse of the matrix A we were led to systems of equations (6.10.5) whose augmented matrix form, given in Eq. (6.10.6), is just $[A \mid I_2]$. Moreover, in solving the systems by Gaussian elimination we arrived at the systems whose augmented matrix form [given in Eq. (6.10.7)] is just $[I_2 \mid A^{-1}]$.

The above example is typical of the general method used for finding the inverse of a matrix. We now summarize this method.

Method for Finding the Inverse of a Matrix

Suppose that A is an $n \times n$ matrix. To find A^{-1}, form the augmented matrix

$$[A \mid I_n] \tag{6.10.9}$$

and then apply Gaussian elimination to try and bring the augmented matrix into the form

$$[I_n \mid D] \tag{6.10.10}$$

If this can be done, $D = A^{-1}$. If it cannot be done, A does not have an inverse.

Example 6.10.3 Use the above method to find the inverse of the matrix

$$A = \begin{bmatrix} 2 & 1 & 4 \\ 0 & 2 & 3 \\ 3 & 2 & 4 \end{bmatrix}$$

if it exists.

The augmented matrix is

$$\begin{bmatrix} 2 & 1 & 4 & \vdots & 1 & 0 & 0 \\ 0 & 2 & 3 & \vdots & 0 & 1 & 0 \\ 3 & 2 & 4 & \vdots & 0 & 0 & 1 \end{bmatrix}$$

Applying Gaussian elimination gives

$$\tfrac{1}{2}\to \begin{bmatrix} 2 & 1 & 4 & | & 1 & 0 & 0 \\ 0 & 2 & 3 & | & 0 & 1 & 0 \\ 3 & 2 & 4 & | & 0 & 0 & 1 \end{bmatrix} \to \quad \begin{pmatrix} \begin{bmatrix} 1 & \tfrac{1}{2} & 2 & | & \tfrac{1}{2} & 0 & 0 \\ 0 & 2 & 3 & | & 0 & 1 & 0 \\ 3 & 2 & 4 & | & 0 & 0 & 1 \end{bmatrix} \end{pmatrix}$$
$$-3$$

$$\tfrac{1}{2}\to \begin{bmatrix} 1 & \tfrac{1}{2} & 2 & | & \tfrac{1}{2} & 0 & 0 \\ 0 & 2 & 3 & | & 0 & 1 & 0 \\ 0 & \tfrac{1}{2} & -2 & | & -\tfrac{3}{2} & 0 & 1 \end{bmatrix} \to \quad \begin{matrix} -\tfrac{1}{2} \\ \\ -\tfrac{1}{2} \end{matrix} \begin{bmatrix} 1 & \tfrac{1}{2} & 2 & | & \tfrac{1}{2} & 0 & 0 \\ 0 & 1 & \tfrac{3}{2} & | & 0 & \tfrac{1}{2} & 0 \\ 0 & \tfrac{1}{2} & -2 & | & -\tfrac{3}{2} & 0 & 1 \end{bmatrix}$$

$$-\tfrac{4}{11}\to \begin{bmatrix} 1 & 0 & \tfrac{5}{4} & | & \tfrac{1}{2} & -\tfrac{1}{4} & 0 \\ 0 & 1 & \tfrac{3}{2} & | & 0 & \tfrac{1}{2} & 0 \\ 0 & 0 & -\tfrac{11}{4} & | & -\tfrac{3}{2} & -\tfrac{1}{4} & 1 \end{bmatrix} \to \quad \begin{matrix} -\tfrac{5}{4} \\ -\tfrac{3}{2} \end{matrix} \begin{bmatrix} 1 & 0 & \tfrac{5}{4} & | & \tfrac{1}{2} & -\tfrac{1}{4} & 0 \\ 0 & 1 & \tfrac{3}{2} & | & 0 & \tfrac{1}{2} & 0 \\ 0 & 0 & 1 & | & \tfrac{6}{11} & \tfrac{1}{11} & -\tfrac{4}{11} \end{bmatrix}$$

$$\begin{bmatrix} 1 & 0 & 0 & | & -\tfrac{2}{11} & -\tfrac{4}{11} & \tfrac{5}{11} \\ 0 & 1 & 0 & | & -\tfrac{9}{11} & \tfrac{4}{11} & \tfrac{6}{11} \\ 0 & 0 & 1 & | & \tfrac{6}{11} & \tfrac{1}{11} & -\tfrac{4}{11} \end{bmatrix}$$

Consequently, we have

$$A^{-1} = \begin{bmatrix} -\tfrac{2}{11} & -\tfrac{4}{11} & \tfrac{5}{11} \\ -\tfrac{9}{11} & \tfrac{4}{11} & \tfrac{6}{11} \\ \tfrac{6}{11} & \tfrac{1}{11} & -\tfrac{4}{11} \end{bmatrix}$$

Example 6.10.4 Find the inverse (if it exists) of the matrix

$$A = \begin{bmatrix} 4 & 1 & 0 \\ 2 & 3 & 1 \\ 0 & -5 & -2 \end{bmatrix}$$

The augmented matrix is $[A \mid I_3]$. Applying Gaussian elimination yields

$$\tfrac{1}{4}\to \begin{bmatrix} 4 & 1 & 0 & | & 1 & 0 & 0 \\ 2 & 3 & 1 & | & 0 & 1 & 0 \\ 0 & -5 & -2 & | & 0 & 0 & 1 \end{bmatrix} \to \quad -2\begin{bmatrix} 1 & \tfrac{1}{4} & 0 & | & \tfrac{1}{4} & 0 & 0 \\ 2 & 3 & 1 & | & 0 & 1 & 0 \\ 0 & -5 & -2 & | & 0 & 0 & 1 \end{bmatrix}$$

$$\tfrac{2}{5}\to \begin{bmatrix} 1 & \tfrac{1}{4} & 0 & | & \tfrac{1}{4} & 0 & 0 \\ 0 & \tfrac{5}{2} & 1 & | & -\tfrac{1}{2} & 1 & 0 \\ 0 & -5 & -2 & | & 0 & 0 & 1 \end{bmatrix} \to \quad \begin{matrix} -\tfrac{1}{4} \\ \\ 5 \end{matrix} \begin{bmatrix} 1 & \tfrac{1}{4} & 0 & | & \tfrac{1}{4} & 0 & 0 \\ 0 & 1 & \tfrac{2}{5} & | & -\tfrac{1}{5} & \tfrac{2}{5} & 0 \\ 0 & -5 & -2 & | & 0 & 0 & 1 \end{bmatrix}$$

$$\begin{bmatrix} 1 & 0 & -\tfrac{1}{10} & | & \tfrac{3}{10} & -\tfrac{1}{10} & 0 \\ 0 & 1 & \tfrac{2}{5} & | & -\tfrac{1}{5} & \tfrac{2}{5} & 0 \\ 0 & 0 & 0 & | & -1 & 2 & 1 \end{bmatrix}$$

In this case it is impossible to proceed further with Gaussian elimination, and so the matrix A has no inverse.

Exercises for 6.10

1. Let I_n be the identity matrix of order n. Verify the equations

$$I_m A = A I_n = A$$

in case

(a) $m = 2$, $n = 3$, and

$$A = \begin{bmatrix} 2 & -1 & 5 \\ 3 & 5 & \frac{1}{2} \end{bmatrix}$$

(b) $m = 3$, $n = 3$, and

$$A = \begin{bmatrix} 1 & 5 & -7 \\ 3 & 0 & 8 \\ 2 & -2 & 4 \end{bmatrix}$$

(c) $m = 4$, $n = 2$, and

$$A = \begin{bmatrix} 2 & 0 \\ 6 & 4 \\ -3 & 2 \\ 1 & 8 \end{bmatrix}$$

(d) $m = 1$, $n = 6$, and

$$A = [3, 6, 0, -7, 4, 1]$$

In problems 2–8, find the inverse of each of the following matrices, if it exists.

2. $\begin{bmatrix} 2 & 1 \\ 3 & 1 \end{bmatrix}$

3. $\begin{bmatrix} 5 & 3 \\ 1 & 2 \end{bmatrix}$

4. $\begin{bmatrix} -3 & 2 \\ 6 & -4 \end{bmatrix}$

5. $\begin{bmatrix} 1 & 4 \\ 2 & 7 \\ 3 & -2 \end{bmatrix}$

6. $\begin{bmatrix} -3 & 2 & 1 \\ 4 & 5 & -3 \\ 10 & 1 & -5 \end{bmatrix}$

7. $\begin{bmatrix} 1 & 1 & -2 \\ 2 & 7 & 6 \\ -4 & -2 & 11 \end{bmatrix}$

8. $\begin{bmatrix} .475 & -.175 \\ -.525 & .825 \end{bmatrix}$

(*Hint:* First express the entries of this matrix in terms of fractions.)

9. Suppose that $AE = A$ for some $n \times n$ matrix A which has an inverse. Show that $E = I_n$.

*10. Suppose that $A = [a_{ij}]$ is an $n \times n$ matrix that has an inverse.
   (a) Show that the system of linear equations

$$a_{11}x_1 + a_{12}x_2 + \cdots + a_{1n}x_n = b_1$$
$$a_{21}x_1 + a_{22}x_2 + \cdots + a_{2n}x_n = b_2$$
$$\vdots \qquad \vdots \qquad \ddots \qquad \vdots \qquad \vdots$$
$$a_{n1}x_1 + a_{n2}x_2 + \cdots + a_{nn}x_n = b_n$$

has a *unique* simultaneous solution. (*Hint:* Write the system in vector-matrix form.)

(b) If $A^{-1} = [\alpha_{ij}]_{nn}$, express the unique simultaneous solution to the above system in terms of the α_{ij}s and b_is.

11. Suppose that A and B are $n \times n$ matrices each of which has an inverse. Show that AB has an inverse and determine it explicitly in terms of A^{-1} and B^{-1}.

12. Assume that A, B, and C are $n \times n$ matrices such that $AB = C$. Suppose that B has an inverse and C does not have an inverse. Show that A does not have an inverse.

Geometric Linear Programming

7

Many of the problems that arise in practice deal with maximizing or minimizing certain quantities (e.g., maximize profit, minimize cost). Various techniques have been developed for handling such problems and in this and the following chapter one such technique, *linear programming*, is presented.

Linear programming deals with problems of finding maximum or minimum values of *linear* functions. In this chapter we shall study the geometric method, which is used primarily to solve linear programs in two variables. A more general approach will be presented in Chapter 8, where we develop the simplex algorithm for linear programming.

Section 7.1   Introduction

As we have mentioned, linear programming deals with the problems involved in determining maximum or minimum values for linear functions. The concept of a linear function is closely related to the concept of a linear equation introduced in Chapter 6. Here we consider linear functions of two variables.

Definition
A *linear function, f, of two variables*, say x_1 and x_2, is a rule of the form

$$f(x_1, x_2) = a_1x_1 + a_2x_2 \tag{7.1.1}$$

where a_1 and a_2 are constants. The function f assigns to each pair of values for x_1 and x_2 a real number via the rule given in Eq. (7.1.1).

Example 7.1.1

1. $f(x_1, x_2) = 3x_1 - 4x_2$ is a linear function of two variables. In the notation of Eq. (7.1.1) we have $a_1 = 3$ and $a_2 = -4$. The number assigned to the pair of values x_1, x_2 is "three times x_1 minus four times x_2." For example,

$$f(2, 5) = 3 \cdot 2 - 4 \cdot 5 = -14$$
$$f(-7, 6) = 3 \cdot (-7) - 4 \cdot 6 = -45$$
$$f(6, -7) = 3 \cdot 6 - 4 \cdot (-7) = 46$$

2. $g(y_1, y_2) = 2y_1 + y_2$ is a linear function of the two variables y_1 and y_2. Here $a_1 = 2$ and $a_2 = 1$. We have

$$g(2, 5) = 2 \cdot 2 + 5 = 9$$
$$g(-7, 6) = 2 \cdot (-7) + 6 = -8$$
$$g(6, -7) = 2 \cdot 6 + (-7) = 5$$
$$g(0, 0) = 2 \cdot 0 + 0 = 0$$

This section is concluded by the presentation of two problems that can be solved by the geometric method of linear programming. The solutions of these problems will be given in Section 7.7.

Example 7.1.2 Fabric Manufacturing A fabric manufacturer makes two types of cloth, which we shall refer to as plain (P) and fancy (F). We shall assume for the sake of simplicity that there are only two operations necessary in the manufacturing of these cloths: machine dyeing and hand quilting. P requires 2 hours of dyeing time and 2 hours of hand quilting time per 100 yards. F requires 3 hours of dyeing time and 10 hours of hand quilting per 100 yards. The net profit (profit after all expenses) for P is \$10 per 100 yards; the net profit for F is \$25 per 100 yards.

If there are 72 hours of dyeing time and 100 hours of hand quilting time available per week, how many yards of each type of cloth should be manufactured to yield the largest (net) profit?

It should be observed that we are assuming that the manufacturer can sell as many yards of each type of cloth as he can make and that there is a sufficient supply of raw materials to allow for the manufacture of as much of each type as he wants.

Example 7.1.3 Feed Mixtures A cattle rancher must prepare a feed mixture for his herd. The mixture is to be comprised of two brands of feed, A and B. Assume that the mixture must meet two nutritional requirements: each animal must receive 24 units of a prescribed vitamin complex per day and 29 units of a prescribed mineral complex per day. Brand A contains 2 units of vitamin complex and 3 units of the mineral complex per pound. Its cost is 15 cents per pound. Brand B contains 5 units of the vitamin complex and 4 units of the mineral complex per pound. Its cost is 25 cents per pound. How many pounds of A and B should be used per animal per day to guarantee that the nutritional requirements are met at a minimum cost to the rancher?

Exercises for 7.1

1. Give two examples of linear functions in
   (a) two variables: x_1 and x_2
   (b) two variables: y_1 and y_2
2. Evaluate the linear function $f(x_1, x_2) = 4x_1 - 2x_2$ at the values indicated.
   (a) $x_1 = 3$, $x_2 = 4$
   (b) $x_1 = 4$, $x_2 = 3$
   (c) $x_1 = 0$, $x_2 = -5$

3. Evaluate the linear function $g(y_1, y_2) = 8y_1 + y_2$ at the values indicated.
   (a) $y_1 = 6, y_2 = -3$
   (b) $y_1 = 5, y_2 = 0$
   (c) $y_1 = -3, y_2 = 4$
4. Determine the values of the linear function $h(u_1, u_2) = -3u_1 - 6u_2$ when
   (a) $u_1 = 3, u_2 = 2$
   (b) $u_1 = -4, u_2 = 6$
   (c) $u_1 = -5, u_2 = -3$
5. Indicate which of the following are linear functions of two variables and which are not.
   (a) $f(x_1, x_2) = 5x_1 - 7x_2$ (b) $g(y_1, y_2) = 3y_1 + 2y_2^2$
   (c) $h(x_1, x_2) = -\frac{1}{4}x_1 + 6x_2$ (d) $f(z_1, z_2) = \sqrt{3}z_1 + 4^2z_2$
   (e) $g(x_1, x_2) = 5\sqrt{x_1} - 8x_2$
6. Which of the following are linear functions of two variables?
   (a) $f(x_1, x_2) = 6x_1 - 3x_1x_2$ (b) $g(y_1, y_2) = 8y_1 + \sqrt{5}y_2$
   (c) $h(x_1, x_2) = x_1^2 - 4x_2$ (d) $f(z_1, z_2) = 6\sqrt{z_1} - z_2$
   (e) $h(y_1, y_2) = y_1 + y_2$ (f) $g(x_1, x_2) = (3x_1 + 5x_2)^2$
7. Refer to Example 7.1.2. Let

   $x_1 = $ amount (in hundreds of yards) of the plain cloth manufactured per week
   $x_2 = $ amount (in hundreds of yards) of the fancy cloth manufactured per week

   Write the total net profit per week as a linear function of the two variables x_1 and x_2.
8. Refer to Example 7.1.3. Let

   $y_1 = $ amount (in pounds) of brand A used per animal per day
   $y_2 = $ amount (in pounds) of brand B used per animal per day

   Write the cost to the rancher per animal per day as a linear function of y_1 and y_2.

Section 7.2   Linear Equations and Their Graphs

In Chapter 6 the concept of a linear equation was introduced. Recall that a linear equation in n variables $x_1, x_2, \ldots, x_n$ is an equation of the form

$$a_1x_1 + a_2x_2 + \cdots + a_nx_n = b \tag{7.2.1}$$

where $a_1, a_2, \ldots, a_n$, b are constants. In this section we will consider linear equations in *two variables*,

$$a_1x_1 + a_2x_2 = b \tag{7.2.2}$$

and give a geometric interpretation to such equations. Basically, it will be shown that the solution set to such an equation corresponds to a (straight) line in the plane.

For our interpretation, the key notion is that of translating numerical information into geometric (pictorial) information. In order to carry out this transition from one type of information to the other, we begin with a method of specifying points in the plane. This is carried out in the following way.

We begin by specifying a particular point as "the origin." Through this point we draw two straight lines at right angles to each other. We then introduce a *scale* by specifying a unit length. Finally, we introduce an orientation by specifying a positive and a negative direction on each of the lines drawn. At this point we have Figure 7.2.1. With this picture we can now uniquely specify any point in the plane by giving two *coordinates* for the point. These coordinates represent the number of units one must go, from the origin, in the direction of each of the two lines drawn to get to the

Figure 7.2.1

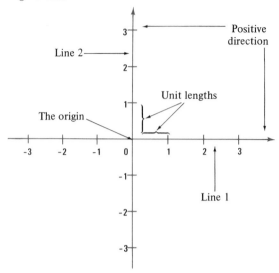

desired point. For example, the point $(2, 3)$ is 2 units in the positive direction of line 1 and 3 units in the positive direction of line 2. Our picture is then as in Figure 7.2.2. Several other points are also shown in this picture (graph).

Figure 7.2.2

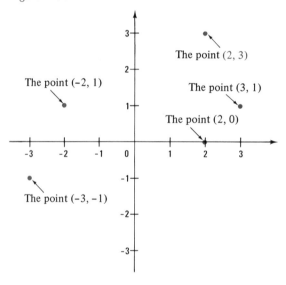

We now illustrate, by means of an example, the method of representing geometrically the solution set of a linear equation in two variables.

Example 7.2.1   Consider the linear equation in two variables given by

$$2x_1 + 3x_2 = 6 \tag{7.2.3}$$

We have seen previously that the solution set of the linear equation is infinite. That is, there are infinitely many values for x_1 and x_2 which will make Eq. (7.2.3) true.

Figure 7.2.3

x_1	x_2
0	2
3	0
-3	4
6	-2
$-\frac{3}{2}$	3
$\frac{3}{2}$	1
$\frac{9}{2}$	-1

Some solutions of Eq. (7.2.3) are listed in Figure 7.2.3. In fact, as we know from Chapter 6, we can "solve" Eq. (7.2.3) for one variable in terms of the other, say x_1 in terms of x_2:

$$x_1 = 3 - \tfrac{3}{2}x_2 \tag{7.2.4}$$

Then for each specified value of x_2, Eq. (7.2.4) can be used to determine x_1 so that Eq. (7.2.3) holds. For example, if we specify $x_2 = 4$, then by Eq. (7.2.4) we should choose

$$x_1 = 3 - \tfrac{3}{2} \cdot 4 = 3 - 6 = -3$$

in order that Eq. (7.2.3) should hold.

Now, it is natural to associate with each solution of the linear equation (7.2.3), a point in the plane. The value of the first variable represents the first coordinate of the point, and the value of the second variable represents the second coordinate of the point. For example, the solution to Eq. (7.2.3) given by $x_1 = -3$ and $x_2 = 4$ corresponds to the point $(-3, 4)$.

The points corresponding to each of the solutions listed in Figure 7.2.3 are "plotted" in Figure 7.2.4. Note that the points in Figure 7.2.4 corresponding to the solutions

Figure 7.2.4

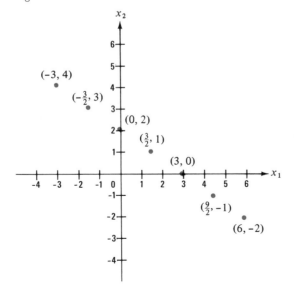

of $2x_1 + 3x_2 = 6$ listed in Figure 7.2.3 seem to be in a straight line. This is, in fact, true; by Eq. (7.2.4), every increase by 1 unit of the specified value of x_2 results in a decrease of the value of x_1 by $\frac{3}{2}$.

Finally, since any specified value for x_2 yields, via Eq. (7.2.4), a value for x_1, it follows that the set of points in the plane corresponding to the solution set of the linear equation $2x_1 + 3x_2 = 6$ is just the straight line through the points in Figure 7.2.4 (see Figure 7.2.5). For ease in notation the straight line in Figure 7.2.5 is often

Figure 7.2.5

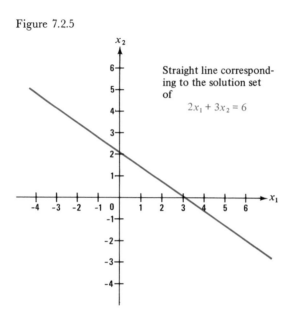

Straight line corresponding to the solution set of
$$2x_1 + 3x_2 = 6$$

referred to as the solution set of the linear equation $2x_1 + 3x_2 = 6$, although, strictly speaking, it is the set of points corresponding to the solution set.

This situation is typical of the general case. That is, consider a linear equation in two variables:

$$a_1x_1 + a_2x_2 = b \qquad (7.2.5)$$

To each solution of Eq. (7.2.5) corresponds a point in the plane, the point whose first coordinate is the value of x_1 and whose second coordinate is the value of x_2. The set of all points in the plane corresponding to the set of all solutions of Eq. (7.2.5) forms a straight line. The linear equation (7.2.5) is called the *equation of the straight line*.

When graphing the straight line corresponding to a linear equation, it is theoretically enough to find two points on the line (since two points determine a line). However, in practice it is often useful to plot several points to get a more accurate picture.

This section is concluded by the presentation of another example illustrating the above concepts.

Example 7.2.2 Graph the straight line whose equation is given by

$$2x_1 - x_2 = 1 \tag{7.2.6}$$

As before, we "solve" Eq. (7.2.6) for one variable in terms of the other. If x_2 is solved for, in terms of x_1, it follows from Eq. (7.2.6) that

$$x_2 = 2x_1 - 1 \tag{7.2.7}$$

(It would work equally well if we solved for x_1 in terms of x_2.) Using Eq. (7.2.7) it is easy to obtain solutions for Eq. (7.2.6) by specifying values of x_1 and determining x_2 via Eq. (7.2.7). *Some* solutions to Eq. (7.2.6) are given in Figure 7.2.6. The points

Figure 7.2.6

x_1	0	1	−1	2
x_2	−1	1	−3	3

in the plane corresponding to the solutions of Eq. (7.2.6) given in Figure 7.2.6 are plotted in Figure 7.2.7 together with the straight line whose equation is $2x_1 - x_2 = 1$.

Figure 7.2.7

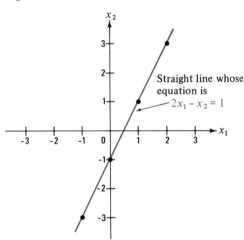

(Remember, the straight line whose equation is $2x_1 - x_2 = 1$ is just the straight line consisting of all points in the plane corresponding to all solutions of the linear equation $2x_1 - x_2 = 1$.)

Exercises for 7.2

1. Plot the following points in the plane, all on the same graph.
   (a) $(0, 0)$ (b) $(-3, 4)$
   (c) $(4, -3)$ (d) $(\frac{1}{2}, 2)$
   (e) $(-\frac{3}{2}, -\frac{5}{2})$ (f) $(0, -2)$

2. Use the same graph to plot the following points.

(a) $(4, 0)$ (b) $(-\frac{1}{2}, 6)$

(c) $(0, -3)$ (d) $(2, 2)$

(e) $(2, -2)$ (f) $(-2, 2)$

In each of problems 3–14, graph the straight line corresponding to the solution set of the given linear equation by (1) first solving for one variable in terms of the other, and then (2) determining four points on the line.

3. $2x_1 + x_2 = 1$

4. $-x_1 + 3x_2 = 2$

5. $\frac{1}{2}x_1 + 2x_2 = 3$

6. $100x_1 - 75x_2 = -200$

7. $8y_1 - 4y_2 = -16$

8. $3y_1 + 4y_2 = 12$

9. $3x_1 - 4x_2 = 12$

10. $\frac{3}{4}w_1 + w_2 = 3$

11. $x_1 = 2$ (i.e., $x_1 + 0x_2 = 2$)

12. $x_2 = -1$ (i.e., $0x_1 + x_2 = -1$)

13. $x_2 = 0$

14. $x_1 = 0$

15. The relationship between the Fahrenheit (x_1) and centigrade (x_2) temperature scales is given by the linear equation

$$(*) \quad 5x_1 - 9x_2 = 160$$

(a) What centigrade temperature corresponds to $32°$ Fahrenheit?

(b) What Fahrenheit temperature corresponds to $100°$ centigrade?

(c) Graph the linear equation (*).

16. In Example 7.1.2 the plain cloth requires 2 hours of hand quilting per 100 yards and the fancy cloth requires 10 hours of hand quilting per 100 yards. Let

$$x_1 = \text{amount (in hundreds of yards) of the plain cloth manufactured per week}$$
$$x_2 = \text{amount (in hundreds of yards) of the fancy cloth manufactured per week}$$

Assume that the manufacturer utilizes exactly 100 hours of hand quilting time per week.

(a) Write a linear equation that expresses the above facts.

(b) If the manufacturer produces 500 yards per week of the fancy cloth, how many yards per week of the plain cloth should be manufactured in order that exactly 100 hours of hand quilting time per week will be utilized?

(c) If the manufacturer produces 4,000 yards per week of the plain cloth, how many yards per week of the fancy cloth should be manufactured in order that exactly 100 hours of hand quilting time per week will be utilized?

(d) Graph the linear equation in part (a).

In each of problems 17–21, determine an equation of the straight line passing through the given points by the method illustrated in the following example.

Example: Find an equation of the straight line passing through the points $(6, -2)$ and $(-3, 4)$.

Let the equation be

$$a_1x_1 + a_2x_2 = b$$

Then we must have

$$a_1 \cdot 6 + a_2 \cdot (-2) = b$$
$$a_1 \cdot (-3) + a_2 \cdot 4 = b$$

In other words,

$$6a_1 - 2a_2 - b = 0$$
$$-3a_1 + 4a_2 - b = 0$$

To solve this system of two linear equations in the three variables a_1, a_2, and b, we apply Gaussian elimination:

$$\tfrac{1}{6} \to \begin{bmatrix} 6 & -2 & -1 & \vdots & 0 \\ -3 & 4 & -1 & \vdots & 0 \end{bmatrix} \to {}_3\!\left(\begin{bmatrix} 1 & -\tfrac{1}{3} & -\tfrac{1}{6} & \vdots & 0 \\ -3 & 4 & -1 & \vdots & 0 \end{bmatrix}\right.$$

$$\tfrac{1}{3} \to \begin{bmatrix} 1 & -\tfrac{1}{3} & -\tfrac{1}{6} & \vdots & 0 \\ 0 & 3 & -\tfrac{3}{2} & \vdots & 0 \end{bmatrix} \to {}^{\tfrac{1}{3}}\!\left(\begin{bmatrix} 1 & -\tfrac{1}{3} & -\tfrac{1}{6} & \vdots & 0 \\ 0 & 1 & -\tfrac{1}{2} & \vdots & 0 \end{bmatrix}\right.$$

$$\begin{bmatrix} 1 & 0 & -\tfrac{1}{3} & \vdots & 0 \\ 0 & 1 & -\tfrac{1}{2} & \vdots & 0 \end{bmatrix}$$

Consequently, we have $a_1 = \tfrac{1}{3}b$ and $a_2 = \tfrac{1}{2}b$. Choosing, $b = 6$, for example, shows that

$$2x_1 + 3x_2 = 6$$

is an equation of the straight line passing through $(6, -2)$ and $(-3, 4)$.

17. $(3, 2)$ and $(-2, 1)$
18. $(8, 2)$ and $(-4, 11)$
19. $(3, 6)$ and $(-6, 0)$
20. $(4, 0)$ and $(-3, 0)$
21. $(2, 4)$ and $(2, -7)$
22. A certain store deals exclusively in the sale of one item. The item yields a net profit of a dollars each. The "fixed costs" (e.g., rent, lighting) per month to the store owner total b dollars. If 100 items are sold during a month, the total net profit after "fixed costs" is $500. On the other hand, if 250 items are sold during a month, the total net profit after "fixed costs" is $2,000.
    (a) What is a?
    (b) What is b?
    (c) How many items need to be sold during a month for the store owner to "break even"?
    (d) Write a linear equation that represents the relationship between the number of items sold per month and the net profit per month after "fixed costs."

Section 7.3 Systems of Linear Equations: Geometric Interpretation

In Section 7.2 a geometric interpretation was given to the solution set of a single linear equation—there is a natural correspondence between the solution set of a linear equation in two variables and a straight line in the plane. In this section we investigate the geometric interpretation of the simultaneous solution(s) to a system of two linear equations in two variables.

The relevant ideas are best illustrated by some examples.

Example 7.3.1 Consider the system of two linear equations in two variables given by

$$3x_1 - 4x_2 = 10$$
$$6x_1 + 5x_2 = 7$$
(7.3.1)

To solve this system the method of augmented matrices and Gaussian elimination is applied. The augmented matrix for the system is

$$\begin{bmatrix} 3 & -4 & \vdots & 10 \\ 6 & 5 & \vdots & 7 \end{bmatrix}$$

Applying Gaussian elimination yields

$$\tfrac{1}{3}\to\begin{bmatrix}3 & -4 & \vdots & 10\\ 6 & 5 & \vdots & 7\end{bmatrix}\to\;-6\begin{matrix}\curvearrowleft\\ \end{matrix}\begin{bmatrix}1 & -\tfrac{4}{3} & \vdots & \tfrac{10}{3}\\ 6 & 5 & \vdots & 7\end{bmatrix}$$

$$\tfrac{1}{13}\to\begin{bmatrix}1 & -\tfrac{4}{3} & \vdots & \tfrac{10}{3}\\ 0 & 13 & \vdots & -13\end{bmatrix}\to\;\tfrac{4}{3}\begin{matrix}\curvearrowleft\\ \end{matrix}\begin{bmatrix}1 & -\tfrac{4}{3} & \vdots & \tfrac{10}{3}\\ 0 & 1 & \vdots & -1\end{bmatrix}$$

$$\begin{bmatrix}1 & 0 & \vdots & 2\\ 0 & 1 & \vdots & -1\end{bmatrix}$$

Thus the system (7.3.1) has exactly one simultaneous solution,

$$x_1 = 2 \qquad x_2 = -1 \tag{7.3.2}$$

We now investigate the geometric significance of this.

To begin, consider the first equation in the system:

$$3x_1 - 4x_2 = 10 \tag{7.3.3}$$

Recall from Section 7.2 that to each solution of Eq. (7.3.3) is associated a point in the plane whose first coordinate is the given value of x_1 and whose second coordinate is the given value of x_2. The set of all points in the plane corresponding to all solutions of Eq. (7.3.3) is a straight line whose graph is shown in Figure 7.3.1. Some solutions of $3x_1 - 4x_2 = 10$ (or $x_2 = \tfrac{3}{4}x_1 - \tfrac{5}{2}$) are also given in Figure 7.3.1.

Figure 7.3.1

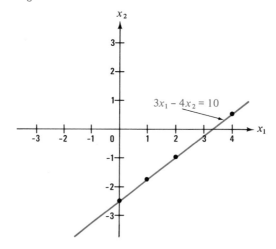

x_1	0	1	2	4
x_2	$-\tfrac{5}{2}$	$-\tfrac{7}{4}$	-1	$\tfrac{1}{2}$

The second equation in the system is given by

$$6x_1 + 5x_2 = 7 \tag{7.3.4}$$

and the straight line corresponding to its solution set is graphed in Figure 7.3.2. Some solutions of $6x_1 + 5x_2 = 7$ (or $x_2 = \tfrac{7}{5} - \tfrac{6}{5}x_1$) are also given in Figure 7.3.2.

Now, the solution set of the system of linear equations in Eq. (7.3.1) is, by definition, the intersection of the solution sets of each of the linear equations in the system. As we have seen, this intersection consists of precisely one solution, which is given in Eq. (7.3.2).

Keeping in mind the correspondence between solutions of a linear equation and points in the plane, it follows that the set of points in the plane corresponding to

Figure 7.3.2

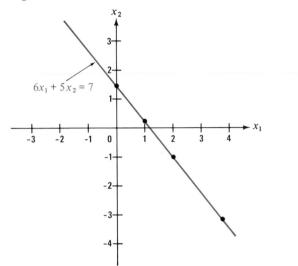

x_1	0	1	2	4
x_2	$\frac{7}{5}$	$\frac{1}{5}$	-1	$-\frac{17}{5}$

the solution set of the system of equations in Eq. (7.3.1) is just the intersection of the sets of points in the plane corresponding to each of the equations in the system. But this is just the intersection of the straight lines that correspond to each of the equations in the system.

Hence, by Eq. (7.3.2), the straight lines that correspond to each of the equations in the system (7.3.1) intersect at exactly one point, the point $(2, -1)$. This can also be seen graphically by combining Figures 7.3.1 and 7.3.2 as shown in Figure 7.3.3.

Figure 7.3.3

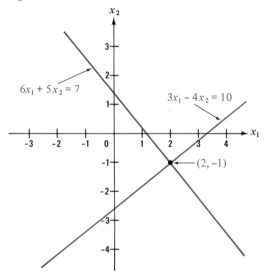

The results found in this example can be rephrased in the following way. Consider a system of two linear equations in two variables:

$$a_{11}x_1 + a_{12}x_2 = b_1$$
$$a_{21}x_1 + a_{22}x_2 = b_2$$

(7.3.5)

The set of points corresponding to the solution set of the system (7.3.5) is the intersection of the straight lines corresponding to each of the equations in the system. Putting it another way, *the points (or point) of intersection of the straight lines given by the equations in Eq. (7.3.5) are the points in the plane corresponding to the simultaneous solutions of the system of linear equations (7.3.5).*

There are basically three types of situations which can occur and they are illustrated in the following examples.

Example 7.3.2 Find the points (or point) of intersection of the straight lines whose equations are given by

$$2x_1 + 7x_2 = 6$$
$$x_1 - 3x_2 = -10 \qquad (7.3.6)$$

By the above discussion the points (or point) of intersection of the straight lines are given by the points corresponding to the simultaneous solutions of the system (7.3.6).

Applying Gaussian elimination we get

$$\begin{bmatrix} 2 & 7 & \vdots & 6 \\ 1 & -3 & \vdots & -10 \end{bmatrix} \rightarrow {}_{-2} \begin{bmatrix} 1 & -3 & \vdots & -10 \\ 2 & 7 & \vdots & 6 \end{bmatrix}$$

$${}_{\frac{1}{13}} \rightarrow \begin{bmatrix} 1 & -3 & \vdots & -10 \\ 0 & 13 & \vdots & 26 \end{bmatrix} \rightarrow {}^{3} \begin{bmatrix} 1 & -3 & \vdots & -10 \\ 0 & 1 & \vdots & 2 \end{bmatrix}$$

$$\begin{bmatrix} 1 & 0 & \vdots & -4 \\ 0 & 1 & \vdots & 2 \end{bmatrix}$$

so the system (7.3.6) has the unique solution $x_1 = -4$, $x_2 = 2$. Thus the straight lines whose equations are given by those in Eq. (7.3.6) *intersect at the point* $(-4, 2)$. (See Figure 7.3.4 for the graphs of the straight lines.)

Figure 7.3.4

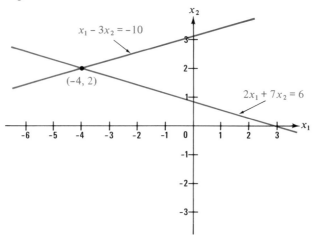

Example 7.3.3 Find the points (or point) of intersection of the straight lines whose equations are

$$2x_1 - 3x_2 = 6$$
$$-10x_1 + 15x_2 = -30 \qquad (7.3.7)$$

As before, the points (or point) of intersection are given by the points corresponding to the solutions of the system of linear equations (7.3.7). We apply Gaussian elimination to get

$$\tfrac{1}{2} \to \begin{bmatrix} 2 & -3 & \vdots & 6 \\ -10 & 15 & \vdots & -30 \end{bmatrix} \to \;10\; \Big(\begin{bmatrix} 1 & -\tfrac{3}{2} & \vdots & 3 \\ -10 & 15 & \vdots & -30 \end{bmatrix}$$

$$\begin{bmatrix} 1 & -\tfrac{3}{2} & \vdots & 3 \\ 0 & 0 & \vdots & 0 \end{bmatrix}$$

and this is as far as we can go. The last augmented matrix corresponds to the system

$$\begin{aligned} x_1 - \tfrac{3}{2}x_2 &= 3 \\ 0x_1 + 0x_2 &= 0 \qquad \text{(or } 0 = 0) \end{aligned} \qquad (7.3.8)$$

which has infinitely many solutions. This shows that the straight lines whose equations are given by those in Eq. (7.3.7) *intersect in infinitely many points and, in fact, by Eq.* (7.3.8), *they intersect in the line whose equation is* $x_1 - \tfrac{3}{2}x_2 = 3$. Of course, this means that the equations in Eq. (7.3.7) represent the same straight line as the one in Eq. (7.3.8). This can be seen quite easily by dividing the first equation in Eq. (7.3.7) by 2 and the second by -10. (See Figure 7.3.5.)

Figure 7.3.5

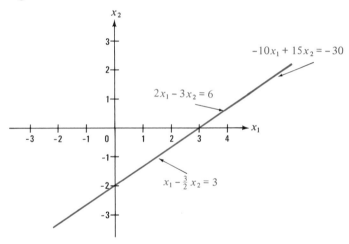

Example 7.3.4   Find the points of intersection of the two straight lines given by

$$\begin{aligned} x_1 + 2x_2 &= 4 \\ 3x_1 + 6x_2 &= -3 \end{aligned} \qquad (7.3.9)$$

Just as in the previous examples the intersection points are given by those corresponding to the solutions of the system (7.3.9). Gaussian elimination is applied to yield

$$-3 \; \Big(\begin{bmatrix} 1 & 2 & \vdots & 4 \\ 3 & 6 & \vdots & -3 \end{bmatrix} \to \begin{bmatrix} 1 & 2 & \vdots & 4 \\ 0 & 0 & \vdots & -15 \end{bmatrix}$$

and this is as far as it is possible to proceed. The last augmented matrix is that of the system

$$\begin{aligned} x_1 + 2x_2 &= 4 \\ 0x_1 + 0x_2 &= -15 \qquad \text{(or } 0 = -15) \end{aligned}$$

Obviously the second equation in this system has no solution, and hence the system has no solution. This, in turn, implies that the system (7.3.9) has no solution, which means that the straight lines corresponding to the equations in Eq. (7.3.9) *have no points of intersection*. In other words, they are parallel. (See Figure 7.3.6.)

Figure 7.3.6

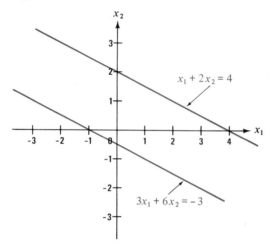

In Summary

The following three cases are possible for a system of two linear equations in two variables:

1. The system has a *unique solution*, in which case the corresponding lines intersect in exactly one point, the point corresponding to that solution.
2. The system has *infinitely many solutions*, in which case both equations represent the same line.
3. The system has *no solutions*, in which case the corresponding lines are parallel.

Exercises for 7.3

In each of problems 1–15, determine the points (point) of intersection of the straight lines whose equations are given, by solving the appropriate system of linear equations. Verify your results geometrically by graphing the two straight lines on the same graph and indicating the points (point) of intersection thereon.

1. $3x_1 + 4x_2 = 15$
   $x_1 - 2x_2 = -5$

2. $2x_1 - 3x_2 = 5$
   $6x_1 + 5x_2 = 1$

3. $-4y_1 + 3y_2 = -3$
   $8y_1 - 7y_2 = 11$

4. $x_1 - 2x_2 = 6$
   $-3x_1 + 6x_2 = -4$

5. $-2x_1 + x_2 = 3$
   $4x_1 - 2x_2 = -6$

6. $5x_1 - 3x_2 = 0$
   $6x_1 + x_2 = 0$

7. $-3x_1 + 4x_2 = 0$
   $6x_1 - 8x_2 = 0$

8. $2x_1 + 3x_2 = 75$
   $2x_1 + 10x_2 = 100$

9. $2y_1 + 5y_2 = 25$
   $3y_1 + 4y_2 = 30$

10. $x_1 \qquad = 0$
    $\qquad x_2 = 0$

11. $2x_1 + 3x_2 = 75$
    $\qquad x_2 = 0$

12. $x_1 \qquad = 0$
    $2x_1 + 10x_2 = 100$

13. $4y_1 - 7y_2 = 8$
    $-8y_1 + 14y_2 = 6$

14. $\frac{1}{3}x_1 - \frac{3}{2}x_2 = 4$
    $-2x_1 + 9x_2 = 24$

15. $1.2z_1 + 3z_2 = -1.4$
    $-6z_1 - 15z_2 = 7$

16. Use the geometric interpretation of the solution set of two linear equations in two variables to prove the following fact: the solution set of a system of two linear equations in two variables is either $\varnothing$, has cardinality 1, or is infinite.

17. Consider the following systems of equations:

    (I) $\quad 3x_1 - x_2 = 2$ $\qquad$ (II) $x_1 - x_2 = 0$
    $\quad -2x_1 - 4x_2 = -6$ $\qquad \qquad x_1 + x_2 = 2$

    (a) Use appropriate elementary operations to show that these two systems are equivalent (i.e., they have the same solution set).
    (b) Graph the equations in each system. Geometrically, what common feature do the two systems share?
    (c) From the result above, and from your understanding of the notion of the equivalence of two systems of equations, how are two equivalent systems related geometrically?

18. Consider a system of linear equations of the form

    $$a_{11}x_1 + a_{12}x_2 = 0$$
    $$a_{21}x_1 + a_{22}x_2 = 0$$

    (a) Show that the system always has at least one solution. Why is this fact evident from a geometric point of view?
    (b) If the system does not have a unique solution, indicate why it must have infinitely many (see problem 16).

Section 7.4 Linear Inequalities and Their Graphs

In our previous work we have been concerned with the study of linear equations. In this section we embark on a study of linear inequalities. The development will proceed primarily through the investigation of *linear inequalities in two variables*. In Chapter 8 linear inequalities in more than two variables will be considered. As in the case of linear equations, it will be important to obtain a geometric interpretation of linear inequalities.

Example 7.4.1 Consider the linear equation

$$2x_1 + 3x_2 = 6 \qquad\qquad (7.4.1)$$

If the equality in Eq. (7.4.1) is replaced by an inequality, there are four possibilities:

$$2x_1 + 3x_2 < 6 \qquad\qquad (7.4.2)$$

$$2x_1 + 3x_2 > 6 \qquad\qquad (7.4.3)$$

$$2x_1 + 3x_2 \leq 6 \qquad\qquad (7.4.4)$$

$$2x_1 + 3x_2 \geq 6 \qquad\qquad (7.4.5)$$

Each of these expressions is referred to as a *linear inequality*.

As in the case of linear equations, values for x_1 and x_2 which satisfy a particular linear inequality are called solutions to the linear inequality. For example, $x_1 = 5$, $x_2 = -4$ is a solution to the linear inequality (7.4.2), because

$$2 \cdot 5 + 3 \cdot (-4) = -2 < 6$$

On the other hand, $x_1 = -2$, $x_2 = 7$ is *not* a solution to Eq. (7.4.2), because

$$2 \cdot (-2) + 3 \cdot 7 = 17 \not< 6$$

But, of course, $x_1 = -2$, $x_2 = 7$ is a solution to Eq. (7.4.3), because

$$2 \cdot (-2) + 3 \cdot 7 = 17 > 6$$

Finally, note that $x_1 = -3$, $x_2 = 4$ is a solution to Eq. (7.4.4), because

$$2 \cdot (-3) + 3 \cdot 4 = 6 \leq 6$$

and similarly it is a solution to Eq. (7.4.5). However, it is *not* a solution to either Eq. (7.4.2) or (7.4.3).

Using Example 7.4.1 as motivation, the following definition is now presented.

Definition

A *linear inequality* in two variables x_1 and x_2 is an expression of one of the following four types:

$$a_1 x_1 + a_2 x_2 < b$$
$$a_1 x_1 + a_2 x_2 > b$$
$$a_1 x_1 + a_2 x_2 \leq b$$
$$a_1 x_1 + a_2 x_2 \geq b$$

Here a_1, a_2, and b are constants. Values for x_1 and x_2 which satisfy a linear inequality are called *solutions* to the linear inequality. The set of all solutions to a linear inequality is called its *solution set*.

To each solution of a linear inequality in two variables corresponds a point in the plane; namely, the point whose first coordinate is the given value of x_1 and whose second coordinate is the given value of x_2. In this way we see that the solution set of a linear inequality corresponds to a subset of the plane.

In Section 7.2 it was shown that the subset of the plane corresponding to the solution set of a linear equation (in two variables) is a straight line. We now proceed to determine the form of the subset of the plane which corresponds to the solution set of a linear inequality. An example will illustrate the general situation quite well.

Example 7.4.2 Consider again the linear inequalities introduced in Example 7.4.1. First we graph the solution set of the linear equation

$$2x_1 + 3x_2 = 6$$

Figure 7.4.1

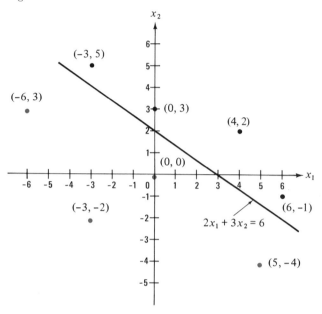

Next we shall list in Table 7.4.1 some solutions of the inequalities (7.4.2) and (7.4.3) and plot the corresponding points in the plane in Figure 7.4.1. Those corresponding

Table 7.4.1

Some Solutions of $2x_1 + 3x_2 < 6$		Some Solutions of $2x_1 + 3x_2 > 6$	
x_1	x_2	x_1	x_2
5	-4	4	2
-3	-2	0	3
0	0	-3	5
-6	3	6	-1

to Eq. (7.4.2) are plotted in color and those corresponding to Eq. (7.4.3) in black. Now note that all the points plotted which correspond to solutions of $2x_1 + 3x_2 < 6$ lie on one side of the line and all those plotted which correspond to solutions of $2x_1 + 3x_2 > 6$ lie on the other side of the line. As a matter of fact, it can be proved that the subset of the plane corresponding to the solution set of $2x_1 + 3x_2 < 6$ consists of all points on one side of the straight line in Figure 7.4.1 and the subset of the plane corresponding to the solution set of $2x_1 + 3x_2 > 6$ consists of all points on the other side of the straight line. This fact is indicated graphically in Figure 7.4.2.

Figure 7.4.2

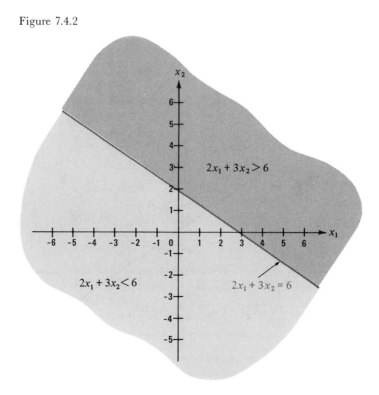

The result suggested by this example is stated formally in the next theorem.

Theorem 7.4.1

Consider the two linear inequalities given by

$$a_1x_1 + a_2x_2 < b \tag{7.4.6}$$

$$a_1x_1 + a_2x_2 > b \tag{7.4.7}$$

Then the subset of the plane corresponding to the solution set of the linear inequality (7.4.6) consists of all points in the plane on one side of the straight line whose equation is $a_1x_1 + a_2x_2 = b$ and the subset of the plane corresponding to the solution set of the linear inequality (7.4.7) consists of all points in the plane on the other side of the straight line.

Because of Theorem 7.4.1 it is quite simple to graph the solution sets of linear inequalities of the form (7.4.6) and (7.4.7). First graph the straight line whose equation is $a_1x_1 + a_2x_2 = b$. Then choose any point not on the line and determine which of the linear inequalities it satisfies (i.e., which inequality its coordinates satisfy). The graph of the solution set to that linear inequality will consist of all points in the plane on the same side of the line as the point chosen and the graph of the solution set to the other linear inequality will consist of all points in the plane on the other side of the line. The graph of the solution set of a linear inequality of the form (7.4.6) or (7.4.7) is called an *open half-plane.* The adjective "open" is used to emphasize the fact that the points on the line are *not* included.

Example 7.4.3 Graph the solution set of the linear inequality

$$5x_1 - 2x_2 > 10 \tag{7.4.8}$$

First, we graph the straight line whose equation is $5x_1 - 2x_2 = 10$. Next, we select any point not on the line, say $(-1, 3)$. (See Figure 7.4.3.) Now we have

Figure 7.4.3

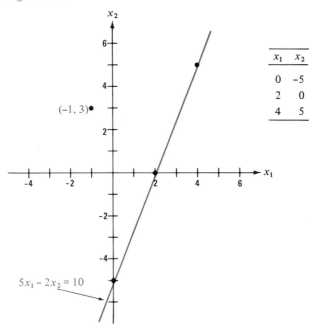

x_1	x_2
0	-5
2	0
4	5

$$5 \cdot (-1) - 2 \cdot 3 = -5 - 6 = -11$$

so this point corresponds to a solution of the linear inequality

$$5x_1 - 2x_2 < 10 \tag{7.4.9}$$

By Theorem 7.4.1 the graph of the solution set of Eq. (7.4.9) consists of all points on the same side of the line as $(-1, 3)$, and the graph of the solution set of Eq. (7.4.8) consists of all points on the other side of the straight line.

Consequently, the graph of the solution set of the linear inequality

$$5x_1 - 2x_2 > 10$$

is given by the shaded portion of Figure 7.4.4.

In most problems that involve linear programming, we shall be graphing the solution sets of linear inequalities of the form (7.4.4) or (7.4.5), in other words, ones involving $\leq$ or $\geq$ as opposed to those involving $<$ or $>$. This will cause no additional problem, because, for example, the graph of the solution set of a linear inequality of the form $a_1x_1 + a_2x_2 \leq b$ consists of the graph of the solution set of $a_1x_1 + a_2x_2 < b$ along with that of $a_1x_1 + a_2x_2 = b$. In other words, the graph of $a_1x_1 + a_2x_2 \leq b$ will be the *open* half-plane corresponding to $a_1x_1 + a_2x_2 < b$ along with the straight line

Figure 7.4.4

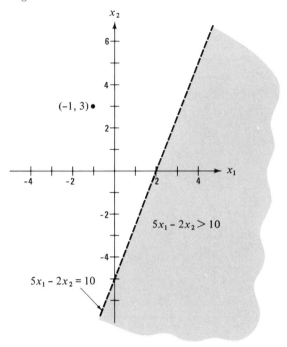

corresponding to $a_1x_1 + a_2x_2 = b$.

The graphs of linear inequalities of the form

$$a_1x_1 + a_2x_2 \leq b$$

or

$$a_1x_1 + a_2x_2 \geq b$$

are called *closed half-planes* because they contain the straight line $a_1x_1 + a_2x_2 = b$.

Example 7.4.4 Graph the solution set of the linear inequality

$$3x_1 + 4x_2 \leq 12 \tag{7.4.10}$$

As before, we first graph the straight line whose equation is $3x_1 + 4x_2 = 12$ (Figure 7.4.5). Then we choose any point not on the line, say $(-4, 2)$. Now

Figure 7.4.5

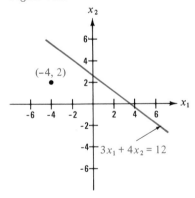

$$3 \cdot (-4) + 4 \cdot 2 = -4 < 12$$

and so the graph of the solution set of $3x_1 + 4x_2 < 12$ consists of all points in the plane on the same side of the straight line as $(-4, 2)$. Consequently, the graph of the solution set of Eq. (7.4.10) consists of all points in the plane on the same side of the straight line as $(-4, 2)$, *along with* the points on the straight line. (See Figure 7.4.6.)

Figure 7.4.6

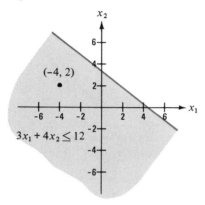

Finally, we remark that, as in the case of straight lines, we shall refer to the half-plane corresponding to the solution set of a linear inequality as the solution set of the linear inequality, although strictly speaking it is the set of points in the plane corresponding to the set of solutions of the linear inequality.

Exercises for 7.4

1. Indicate to which of the following linear inequalities $x_1 = 3$, $x_2 = -4$ is a solution.
   (a) $5x_1 + 2x_2 \leq 7$
   (b) $-3x_1 + 4x_2 \leq -8$
   (c) $8x_1 + 2x_2 < 16$
   (d) $3x_1 - \frac{1}{2}x_2 \geq 11$
   (e) $\frac{2}{3}x_1 + 5x_2 > -10$
   (f) $x_1 \leq -5$
   (g) $x_2 > 0$
   (h) $x_1 > 0$

In each of problems 2 and 3, which (if any) of the points
   (1) $(3, -5)$
   (2) $(0, 4)$
   (3) $(-2, 6)$
   (4) $(-3, 0)$
   (5) $(\frac{1}{2}, 8)$
   (6) $(-\frac{2}{5}, -\frac{3}{4})$
correspond to solutions of each of the following linear inequalities?

2. (a) $2x_1 - 7x_2 < 5$
   (b) $-3x_1 + x_2 > 4$
   (c) $4x_1 + 5x_2 \leq -12$

3. (a) $-8x_1 - 3x_2 \geq -2$
   (b) $x_1 > 0$
   (c) $x_2 \leq 0$
   (d) $5x_1 - 4x_2 < 1$

In each of problems 4–19, graph the solution set of the given linear inequality by using the methods of this section.

4. $x_1 - 2x_2 < 2$
5. $4x_1 - 2x_2 > 10$
6. $3y_1 + 4y_2 < -12$

7. $-6x_1 + 7x_2 \geq -14$
8. $2x_1 - x_2 \geq 4$
9. $-5y_1 + 3y_2 \leq 15$
10. $\frac{2}{3}x_1 - 4x_2 \geq -8$
11. $-100x_1 - 75x_2 \leq 250$
12. $x_1 > -2$
13. $x_2 < 5$
14. $y_1 \geq 0$
15. $y_2 \geq 0$
16. $x_1 \geq x_2$
17. $y_1 \leq 2y_2 + 4$
18. $x_2 < -3x_1 + 1$
19. $-y_2 > \frac{3}{2}y_1$
20. Suppose that milk costs $.60 per half-gallon, eggs cost $.90 per dozen, lettuce costs $.25 per head, and hamburger costs $.95 per pound. For a particular family assume that

$$x_1 = \text{no. of half-gallons of milk purchased per week}$$
$$x_2 = \text{no. of dozens of eggs purchased per week}$$
$$y_1 = \text{no. of heads of lettuce purchased per week}$$
$$y_2 = \text{no. of pounds of hamburger purchased per week}$$

(a) Assume that the family allows itself *at most* $7 per week for milk and eggs. Write this restriction as a linear inequality in x_1 and x_2.
(b) Graph the linear inequality in part (a).
(c) Suppose that the family allocates *at least* $6 per week for lettuce and hamburger. Express this fact as a linear inequality in y_1 and y_2.
(d) Graph the linear inequality in part (c).

21. A small accounting firm handles income tax returns of two types, which it classifies as "simple" and "complex." The "simple" returns take (an average of) 2 hours to complete, while the "complex" returns require (an average of) 10 hours to complete. Let

$$x_1 = \text{no. of "simple" returns processed per week}$$
$$x_2 = \text{no. of "complex" returns processed per week}$$

If the firm has 120 hours per week of working time available,
(a) express the restriction on the number of each type of return which can be processed as a linear inequality in x_1 and x_2. (*Hint:* First find an expression for the total number of hours required to complete x_1 "simple" forms and x_2 "complex" forms.)
(b) Graph the linear inequality in part (a).
Suppose company policy dictates (for public relations purposes) that the firm process at least as many "simple" forms as "complex" ones.
(c) Express this condition as a linear inequality in x_1 and x_2.
(d) Graph the linear inequality in part (c).

22. A certain company supplies two sizes of cartons which are referred to as sizes A and B. Its contract obligations call for *at least* 2,800 and 1,400 cartons of sizes A and B, respectively, per week. The company has two factories, I and II. The first factory produces 500 and 200 cartons of sizes A and B, respectively, per day; the second factory produces 400 and 300 cartons of sizes A and B, respectively, per day. Let

$$y_1 = \text{no. of days per week that factory I operates}$$
$$y_2 = \text{no. of days per week that factory II operates}$$

(a) Write the production requirement on size A cartons as a linear inequality in y_1 and y_2. (*Hint:* First find an expression for the number of size A cartons produced per week by the two factories.)
(b) Graph the linear inequality in part (a).

(c) Express the production requirement on size B cartons as a linear inequality in y_1 and y_2.

(d) Graph the linear inequality in part (c).

23. Refer to Example 7.1.2. Let

x_1 = amount (in hundreds of yards) of the plain cloth manufactured per week
x_2 = amount (in hundreds of yards) of the fancy cloth manufactured per week

(a) Write the restriction on dyeing time as a linear inequality in x_1 and x_2.

(b) Graph the linear inequality in part (a).

(c) Write the restriction on hand-quilting time as a linear inequality in x_1 and x_2.

(d) Graph the linear inequality in part (c).

24. Refer to Example 7.1.3. Let

y_1 = amount (in pounds) of brand A used per animal per day
y_2 = amount (in pounds) of brand B used per animal per day

(a) Write the vitamin constraint as a linear inequality in y_1 and y_2.

(b) Graph the linear inequality in part (a).

(c) Write the mineral complex requirement as a linear inequality in y_1 and y_2.

(d) Graph the linear inequality in part (c).

Section 7.5 Systems of Linear Inequalities and Polyhedral Convex Sets

In Section 7.4 we examined the notion of a linear inequality and the related geometry. We shall now consider the set of simultaneous solutions of several linear inequalities. As we have already seen, the solution set for a single linear inequality is a half-plane. Given a number of linear inequalities, the solution set to each is a half-plane. In order for a point to be a simultaneous solution (satisfy all of the inequalities), it must lie in all the corresponding half-planes. Therefore, *the set of simultaneous solutions for a system of linear inequalities is the intersection of the half-planes that represent the solutions to each of the individual inequalities.* The intersection of a finite number of *closed* half-planes is called a *polyhedral convex set.*

Example 7.5.1 Graph the set of simultaneous solutions to the system of linear inequalities in two variables x_1 and x_2 given by

$$
\begin{aligned}
2x_1 + 3x_2 &\leq 72 \\
2x_1 + 10x_2 &\leq 100 \\
x_1 &\geq 0 \\
x_2 &\geq 0
\end{aligned}
\qquad (7.5.1)
$$

Note, for example, that the linear inequality $x_1 \geq 0$ can be considered as one in two variables, $x_1 + 0x_2 \geq 0$.

To graph the simultaneous solutions we shall first find the appropriate half-plane for each individual inequality and then take the intersection. The general method is to find the straight line bounding the half-plane in question and then to determine on which side of that line the desired points lie (see Section 7.4). Notice that in all the linear inequalities above, the graphs will include the straight line (i.e., they are *closed* half-planes).

For the inequality $2x_1 + 3x_2 \leq 72$, the bounding straight line is given by $2x_1 + 3x_2 = 72$. After plotting this line, we observe that

$$2 \cdot 0 + 3 \cdot 0 = 0 < 72$$

Hence the half-plane that represents $2x_1 + 3x_2 \leq 72$ is the half-plane bounded by the straight line and including the point $(0, 0)$. This is shown in Figure 7.5.1.

Figure 7.5.1

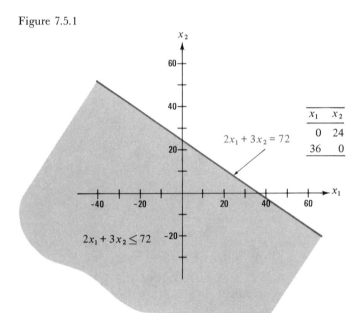

x_1	x_2
0	24
36	0

Next consider the linear inequality $2x_1 + 10x_2 \leq 100$. The straight line bounding the closed half-plane is $2x_1 + 10x_2 = 100$. Testing the point $(0, 0)$ we get

$$2 \cdot 0 + 10 \cdot 0 = 0 < 100$$

and so the half-plane that represents $2x_1 + 10x_2 \leq 100$ consists of all points in the plane on the same side of the line as $(0, 0)$, along with the straight line itself. This is shown in Figure 7.5.2.

To continue, we next consider the linear inequality $x_1 \geq 0$ (or, equivalently, $x_1 + 0x_2 \geq 0$). The straight line bounding the appropriate half-plane is

$$x_1 = 0 \qquad \text{(or } 1x_1 + 0x_2 = 0)$$

Testing, for example, the point $(-20, 30)$ we see that

$$1 \cdot (-20) + 0 \cdot 30 = -20 < 0$$

Consequently, the graph of the linear inequality $x_1 \geq 0$ consists of all points in the plane on the opposite side of the straight line $x_1 = 0$ as the point $(-20, 30)$ (including the straight line). This is depicted in Figure 7.5.3.

Finally, the linear inequality $x_2 \geq 0$ (or $0x_1 + 1x_2 \geq 0$) is considered. The bounding straight line of the half-plane that corresponds to the solution set of this linear inequality is

$$x_2 = 0 \qquad \text{(or } 0x_1 + 1x_2 = 0)$$

Figure 7.5.2

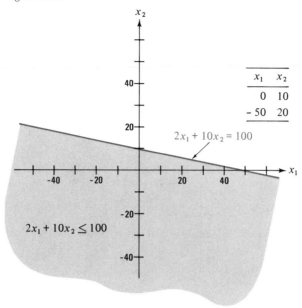

	x_1	x_2
	0	10
	-50	20

$2x_1 + 10x_2 = 100$

$2x_1 + 10x_2 \leq 100$

Its graph is shown in Figure 7.5.4. Using, for example, the point $(30, 10)$ as a test point gives

$$0 \cdot 30 + 1 \cdot 10 = 10 > 0$$

and hence the graph of the linear inequality $x_2 \geq 0$ consists of the straight line $x_2 = 0$ along with all points on the same side of this straight line as $(30, 10)$. Figure 7.5.4 illustrates these results.

As mentioned in the beginning of this section, the graph of the solution set of the

Figure 7.5.3

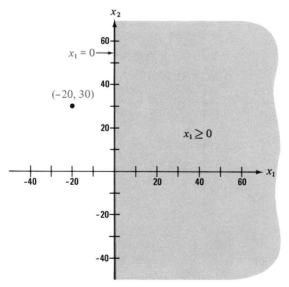

$x_1 = 0$

$(-20, 30)$

$x_1 \geq 0$

Figure 7.5.4

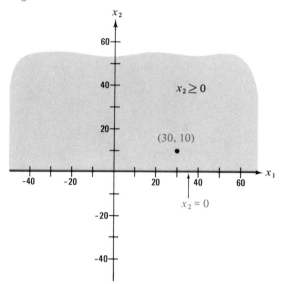

system of linear inequalities in Eq. (7.5.1) is just the intersection of the closed half-planes that represent the solution sets of each of the individual linear inequalities. The graphs of the solution sets, shown in Figures 7.5.1–7.5.4, of the four linear inequalities are combined in Figure 7.5.5. The intersection of these four half-planes is shaded in the figure. This is the graph of the solution set of the system of linear inequalities (7.5.1).

Figure 7.5.5

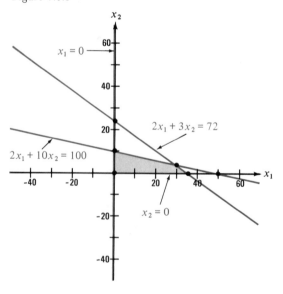

In solving linear programming problems it will be crucial to determine the "corner" points of polyhedral convex sets such as the one shown in Figure 7.5.5. In mathematical terminology these are called the *extreme points* of the polyhedral convex set.

Definition
Let S be a polyhedral convex set (in the plane). A point is called an *extreme point* of S if it belongs to S and is the intersection of (at least) two of the distinct straight lines bounding the half planes.

Example 7.5.1 (continued)
The polyhedral convex set in Figure 7.5.5 has four extreme points, which are shown in Figure 7.5.6.

Figure 7.5.6

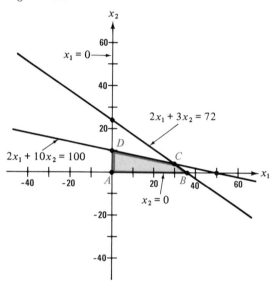

Since each extreme point occurs at the intersection of two of the four bounding straight lines, each can be determined explicitly by solving a system of two linear equations in two variables. This is because the point of intersection of two straight lines is given by the simultaneous solution to the two linear equations representing the straight lines (see Section 7.3).

We now proceed to determine the extreme points of the polyhedral convex set in Figure 7.5.6.

1. A: The point A is the intersection of the two straight lines whose equations are $x_1 = 0$ and $x_2 = 0$. In system form we have

$$\begin{aligned} x_1 &= 0 \\ x_2 &= 0 \end{aligned}$$

This system obviously has exactly one solution, $x_1 = 0$, $x_2 = 0$. Hence, by the above remarks, $\boxed{A = (0, 0)}$.

2. B: The point B is the intersection of the two straight lines whose equations are $2x_1 + 3x_2 = 72$ and $x_2 = 0$. In system form this becomes

$$\begin{aligned} 2x_1 + 3x_2 &= 72 \\ x_2 &= 0 \end{aligned}$$

The system is solved when we apply Gaussian elimination and augmented matrices:

$$\tfrac{1}{2}\rightarrow \begin{bmatrix} 2 & 3 & \vdots & 72 \\ 0 & 1 & \vdots & 0 \end{bmatrix} \xrightarrow{-\tfrac{3}{2}\big\langle} \begin{bmatrix} 1 & \tfrac{3}{2} & \vdots & 36 \\ 0 & 1 & \vdots & 0 \end{bmatrix} \rightarrow \begin{bmatrix} 1 & 0 & \vdots & 36 \\ 0 & 1 & \vdots & 0 \end{bmatrix}$$

and consequently the system has the unique solution $x_1 = 36$, $x_2 = 0$. In other words, $\boxed{B = (36, 0)}$.

3. C: The point C is the intersection of the straight lines whose equations are given by

$$\begin{aligned} 2x_1 + 3x_2 &= 72 \\ 2x_1 + 10x_2 &= 100 \end{aligned}$$

We solve the system as before:

$$\big\langle \begin{bmatrix} 2 & 3 & \vdots & 72 \\ 2 & 10 & \vdots & 100 \end{bmatrix} \rightarrow \tfrac{1}{2}\rightarrow \begin{bmatrix} 2 & 10 & \vdots & 100 \\ 2 & 3 & \vdots & 72 \end{bmatrix}$$

$$-2\big\langle \begin{bmatrix} 1 & 5 & \vdots & 50 \\ 2 & 3 & \vdots & 72 \end{bmatrix} \rightarrow -\tfrac{1}{7}\rightarrow \begin{bmatrix} 1 & 5 & \vdots & 50 \\ 0 & -7 & \vdots & -28 \end{bmatrix}$$

$$-5\big\langle \begin{bmatrix} 1 & 5 & \vdots & 50 \\ 0 & 1 & \vdots & 4 \end{bmatrix} \rightarrow \begin{bmatrix} 1 & 0 & \vdots & 30 \\ 0 & 1 & \vdots & 4 \end{bmatrix}$$

Thus $C = \boxed{(30, 4)}$.

4. D: Finally, the point D is the intersection of the straight lines whose equations are given by the system

$$\begin{aligned} x_1 &= 0 \\ 2x_1 + 10x_2 &= 100 \end{aligned}$$

The solution of the system is obtained in the usual way:

$$-2\big\langle \begin{bmatrix} 1 & 0 & \vdots & 0 \\ 2 & 10 & \vdots & 100 \end{bmatrix} \rightarrow \tfrac{1}{10}\rightarrow \begin{bmatrix} 1 & 0 & \vdots & 0 \\ 0 & 10 & \vdots & 100 \end{bmatrix} \rightarrow \begin{bmatrix} 1 & 0 & \vdots & 0 \\ 0 & 1 & \vdots & 10 \end{bmatrix}$$

Consequently, $\boxed{D = (0, 10)}$.

In summary, then, the extreme points of the polyhedral convex set corresponding to the solution set of the system of linear inequalities (7.5.1) are

$$(0, 0), \ (36, 0), \ (30, 4), \ (0, 10)$$

The polyhedral convex set illustrated in Figure 7.5.6 is one of the two types that will be considered. The other type is represented by the following example.

Example 7.5.2 Graph the set of simultaneous solutions to the system of linear inequalities

$$\begin{aligned} 2y_1 + y_2 &\geq 25 \\ 3y_1 + 6y_2 &\geq 60 \\ y_1 &\geq 0 \\ y_2 &\geq 0 \end{aligned} \tag{7.5.2}$$

and find the extreme points of the resulting polyhedral convex set.

The straight lines bounding the half-planes corresponding to the linear inequalities in the system (7.5.2) are graphed in Figure 7.5.7.

Figure 7.5.7

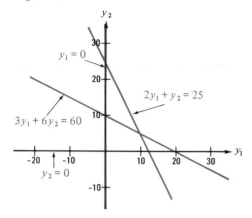

By using test points as in Example 7.5.1, it can be seen that the half-planes that correspond to each of the linear inequalities in Eq. (7.5.2) are as depicted in Figure 7.5.8. The intersection of these half-planes is the polyhedral convex set shown in Figure

Figure 7.5.8

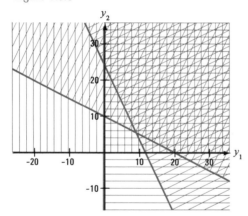

7.5.9. This, of course, is the graph of the set of simultaneous solutions to the system of linear inequalities (7.5.2). This polyhedral convex set has three extreme points, labeled A, B, and C in Figure 7.5.9. To find these points explicitly, it is necessary to solve the following systems of equations (see Example 7.5.1):

$$
\begin{array}{ccc}
A & B & C \\
\begin{aligned} y_1 &= 0 \\ 2y_1 + y_2 &= 25 \end{aligned} &
\begin{aligned} 2y_1 + y_2 &= 25 \\ 3y_1 + 6y_2 &= 60 \end{aligned} &
\begin{aligned} 3y_1 + 6y_2 &= 60 \\ y_2 &= 0 \end{aligned}
\end{array}
$$

Using Gaussian elimination, these three systems can be solved. The results are:

$$
\begin{aligned}
A\colon\ y_1 &= 0 & y_2 &= 25 \\
B\colon\ y_1 &= 10 & y_2 &= 5 \\
C\colon\ y_1 &= 20 & y_2 &= 0
\end{aligned}
$$

Figure 7.5.9

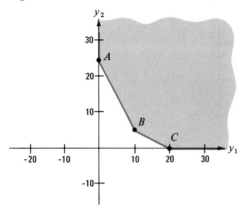

In other words, the extreme points of the polyhedral convex set that corresponds to the solution set of the system of linear inequalities (7.5.2) are

$$(0, 25), (10, 5), (20, 0)$$

Exercises for 7.5

In each of problems 1–12, graph the set of simultaneous solutions to the given system of linear inequalities and find the extreme points of the resulting polyhedral convex set.

1. $3x_1 + 4x_2 \le 15$
   $x_1 - 2x_2 \le -5$

2. $-4y_1 + 3y_2 \ge -3$
   $2y_1 - 7y_2 \ge 11$

3. $2x_1 + x_2 \le 6$
   $-3x_1 + 4x_2 \le 2$
   $2x_1 + 3x_2 \ge -6$

4. $x_1 - 2x_2 \le 8$
   $-3x_1 + 6x_2 \le 12$

5. $2y_1 + 3y_2 \ge 6$
   $6y_1 + 9y_2 \ge 0$

6. $x_1 \ge 0$
   $x_2 \ge 0$
   $x_1 \le 2$
   $x_2 \le 3$

7. $x_1 + x_2 \le 1$
   $-x_1 + x_2 \le 1$
   $x_1 \le 1$
   $x_1 \ge -1$
   $x_2 \ge -1$

8. $x_1 + 2x_2 \le 8$
   $3x_1 + x_2 \le 9$
   $x_1 \ge 0$
   $x_2 \ge 0$

9. $x_1 + x_2 \leq 1$
   $2x_1 + x_2 \leq 2$
   $x_1 \geq 0$
   $x_2 \geq 0$

10. $3y_1 + y_2 \geq 5$
    $y_1 + y_2 \geq 3$
    $y_1 \geq 0$
    $y_2 \geq 0$

11. $4y_1 + 3y_2 \geq 12$
    $3y_1 + y_2 \geq 3$
    $y_1 \geq 0$
    $y_2 \geq 0$

12. $2x_1 + 3x_2 \geq 6$
    $4x_1 + x_2 \geq 4$
    $x_1 + 2x_2 \leq 12$
    $x_1 \geq 0$
    $x_2 \geq 0$

13. Refer to problem 21, Exercises 7.4. The linear inequality which represents the restriction on the number of each type of return that can be processed is $2x_1 + 10x_2 \leq 120$. The fact that the firm must process at least as many "simple" forms as "complex" forms is represented by the linear inequality $x_1 \geq x_2$ (or $-x_1 + x_2 \leq 0$). Clearly, the quantity of each form processed per week must be nonnegative. Thus $x_1 \geq 0$ and $x_2 \geq 0$. Therefore, this problem gives rise to the system of linear inequalities

$$2x_1 + 10x_2 \leq 120$$
$$-x_1 + x_2 \leq 0$$
$$x_1 \geq 0$$
$$x_2 \geq 0$$

Graph the polyhedral convex set that corresponds to the solution set of this system and determine the extreme points.

14. Refer to problem 22, Exercises 7.4. The production requirements on sizes A and B cartons are represented by the linear inequalities $500y_1 + 400y_2 \geq 2,800$ and $200y_1 + 300y_2 \geq 1,400$, respectively. Since y_1 and y_2 correspond to the number of days per week which factories I and II operate, respectively, it must be that $y_1 \geq 0$ and $y_2 \geq 0$. Thus we obtain the system of linear inequalities

$$500y_1 + 400y_2 \geq 2,800$$
$$200y_1 + 300y_2 \geq 1,400$$
$$y_1 \geq 0$$
$$y_2 \geq 0$$

Graph the solution set of this system and determine the extreme points of the resulting polyhedral convex set.

Problems 15–18 deal with the notion of a convex set.

Definition: A set C in the plane is said to be *convex* if whenever P and Q are points in C, the straight-line segment joining P and Q also lies in C.

15. Indicate which of the sets are convex.

(a)

(b)

(c)

(d)

(e)

(f)

16. Indicate which of the sets are convex.

(a)

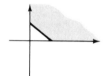

(b)

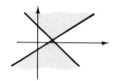

(c)

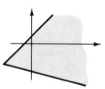

(d)

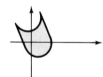

(e)

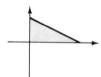

(f)

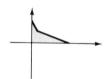

17. Let C_1 and C_2 be convex sets.
    (a) Is $C_1 \cap C_2$ necessarily convex?
    (b) Is $C_1 \cup C_2$ necessarily convex?
    (c) Is $\tilde{C}_1$ necessarily convex?
18. Assuming that a half-plane is a convex set, prove that the subset of the plane that corresponds to the solution set of a system of linear inequalities is a convex set. This shows that a polyhedral convex set is, in fact, convex.

Section 7.6 Linear Functions Evaluated on Polyhedral Convex Sets

We are now ready to consider the last theoretical point necessary for solving linear programming problems by the geometric method. Recall from Section 7.1 that a linear function of two variables, say x_1 and x_2, is of the form

$$f(x_1, x_2) = a_1 x_1 + a_2 x_2 \qquad (7.6.1)$$

where a_1 and a_2 are constants. Also recall that a polyhedral convex set is a set in the plane which corresponds to the solution set of some system of linear inequalities.

The question we will need to answer to solve our linear programming problems is as follows. If S is a polyhedral convex set and f is a linear function defined on S, is there some simple method for finding a point in S at which the value of f is a maximum (or minimum) among all the values which f assumes for all the points in S? Symbolically, can we find a point $(p_1, p_2) \in S$ such that $f(p_1, p_2) \geq f(x_1, x_2)$ for all points $(x_1, x_2) \in S$?

Before answering this question, we should point out that f need not have a maximum (or minimum) value among all the points in S. To see this, consider the following example.

Example 7.6.1 Let $f(x_1, x_2) = 2x_1 + x_2$ and S be the polyhedral convex set that corresponds to the solution set of the system of linear inequalities

$$x_1 + x_2 \geq 1$$
$$x_1 \geq 0$$
$$x_2 \geq 0$$

Using the usual techniques we find that S is the set depicted in Figure 7.6.1.

Figure 7.6.1

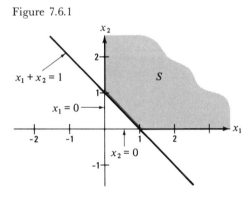

Notice that the value of f increases as x_1 and x_2 increase. But, according to the conditions on the points in S, x_1 and x_2 can get arbitrarily large and still remain in the set. We describe this situation by saying that f goes to infinity on S. That is, its value can get arbitrarily large, and consequently it has no maximum value in the set S.

In view of Example 7.6.1, our original question should be rephrased as follows. If f is a linear function defined on a polyhedral convex set S and if f has a maximum value on S, how can we find a point $(p_1, p_2) \in S$ so that $f(p_1, p_2)$ is equal to this maximum value? The situation for minimum values is analogous to that of maximum values, and the same techniques developed for maximum values will apply to minimum values.

The answer to the above question will be illustrated in the following example.

Example 7.6.2   Let f be defined by

$$f(x_1, x_2) = 10x_1 + 25x_2 \qquad (7.6.2)$$

and let S be the polyhedral convex set that corresponds to the solution set of the system of linear inequalities

$$\begin{aligned} 2x_1 + 3x_2 &\le 72 \\ 2x_1 + 10x_2 &\le 100 \\ x_1 &\ge 0 \\ x_2 &\ge 0 \end{aligned} \qquad (7.6.3)$$

The graph of the polyhedral convex set corresponding to Eq. (7.6.3) was determined in Example 7.5.1 and is shown in Figure 7.6.2. The extreme points of S were also found in Example 7.5.1 and are indicated in the figure.

Figure 7.6.2

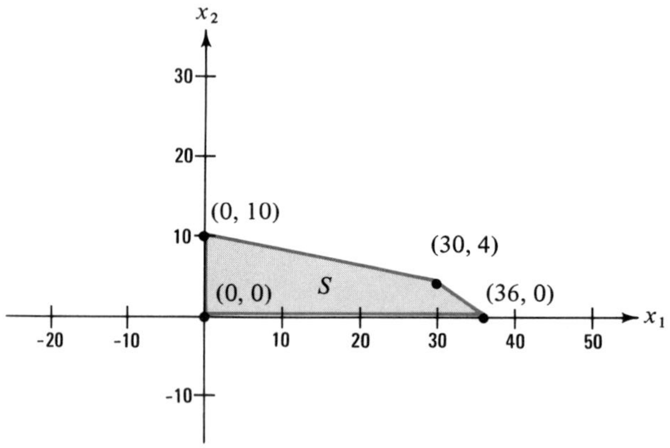

We first evaluate the function f at the extreme points of S.

$$\begin{aligned} f(0, 0) &= 10 \cdot 0 + 25 \cdot 0 = 0 \\ f(36, 0) &= 10 \cdot 36 + 25 \cdot 0 = 360 \\ f(30, 4) &= 10 \cdot 30 + 25 \cdot 4 = 400 \\ f(0, 10) &= 10 \cdot 0 + 25 \cdot 10 = 250 \end{aligned}$$

In Figure 7.6.3 several other values of the function f are given for various points *in* S.

If we examine the tables in Figure 7.6.3 we see that of all the points in S listed, the minimum value (first row on the left) and the maximum value (third row on the left) attained by the function f occur at points of S which are extreme points. This is, in fact, typical of the general situation, as indicated in the following theorem.

Figure 7.6.3

	(x_1, x_2)	$f(x_1, x_2)$	(x_1, x_2)	$f(x_1, x_2)$
extreme	$(0, 0)$	0	$(1, 0)$	10
points	$(36, 0)$	360	$(15, 5)$	225
	$(30, 4)$	400	$(0, 2)$	50
	$(0, 10)$	250	$(35, 1)$	375
	$(10, 2)$	150	$(1, 1)$	35
	$(30, 0)$	300	$(1, 6)$	160
	$(0, 5)$	125	$(11, 4)$	210
	$(0, 9)$	225	$(\frac{1}{2}, 0)$	5

Theorem 7.6.1

Let S be a polyhedral convex set with at least one extreme point and suppose that f is a linear function defined on S. If f has a maximum value on S, then there is an extreme point of S where f takes on this maximum value. The same is true for a minimum value.

We must make a point before we demonstrate the applicability of this theorem. In the statement of the theorem we have asserted that a maximum (or minimum) value will occur at an extreme point if the linear function takes on such a value, at all, on S. As we demonstrated at the beginning of this section (Example 7.6.1), the function may go to infinity on S and hence have no maximum value on S. The only way in which this can happen is if the set S extends out infinitely in some direction. That is, if the set does not extend out infinitely in any direction, a linear function will always have a maximum *and* minimum value on the set, and the theorem will be applicable.

For the case in which the set extends out infinitely, the theorem will apply as long as the function does not go to infinity (or minus infinity when checking for minimum values). Because of this, for such sets it is necessary to examine what happens to the function in question on the portion of the set that extends out infinitely.

Some additional examples concerning Theorem 7.6.1 are now presented.

Example 7.6.3   Let

$$f(x_1, x_2) = 25x_1 + 60x_2$$

and let S be the polyhedral convex set given by the system of linear inequalities

$$2x_1 + 3x_2 \leq 1$$
$$x_1 + 6x_2 \leq 3$$
$$x_1 \geq 0$$
$$x_2 \geq 0$$

Find the maximum and minimum values taken on by f on S (if they exist).

First, the graph of the set S can be obtained by the methods of Section 7.5. Applying these methods we get Figure 7.6.4. From the right-hand diagram it is clear that S

Figure 7.6.4

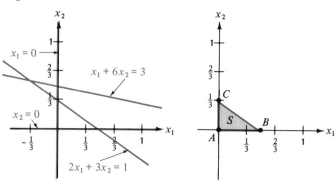

has three extreme points. When we solve the appropriate systems of equations, we find that

$$A = (0, 0) \qquad B = (\tfrac{1}{2}, 0) \qquad C = (0, \tfrac{1}{3})$$

Since the set S does not extend out infinitely in any direction, the function f has a maximum and minimum value on S. According to Theorem 7.6.1, these maximum and minimum values are taken on at certain of the extreme points. But

$$f(0, 0) = 25 \cdot 0 + 60 \cdot 0 = 0$$
$$f(\tfrac{1}{2}, 0) = 25 \cdot \tfrac{1}{2} + 60 \cdot 0 = \tfrac{25}{2}$$
$$f(0, \tfrac{1}{3}) = 25 \cdot 0 + 60 \cdot \tfrac{1}{3} = 20$$

Consequently, the maximum and minimum values of f on S are 20 and 0, respectively.

Example 7.6.4 Let

$$f(x_1, x_2) = x_1 + 3x_2$$

and let S be the polyhedral convex set that corresponds to the solution set of the system of linear inequalities

$$
\begin{aligned}
2x_1 + x_2 &\geq 25 \\
3x_1 + 6x_2 &\geq 60 \\
x_1 &\geq 0 \\
x_2 &\geq 0
\end{aligned}
$$

The graph of the set S is obtained in the usual way and is shown in Figure 7.6.5. The extreme points of S are also shown in Figure 7.6.5. When we use the methods explained in Section 7.5 we get

$$A = (0, 25) \qquad B = (10, 5) \qquad C = (20, 0)$$

If the function f has a maximum (or minimum) value on S, then, by Theorem 7.6.1, this value must be attained at one of the extreme points of S. Note, however, that the set S extends out infinitely as indicated in the above graph. As x_1 and x_2 become very large, so does $f(x_1, x_2)$. Consequently, f does not have a maximum value on S. However, it does have a minimum value. Now

$$f(0, 25) = 0 + 3 \cdot 25 = 75$$
$$f(10, 5) = 10 + 3 \cdot 5 = 25$$
$$f(20, 0) = 20 + 3 \cdot 0 = 20$$

Figure 7.6.5

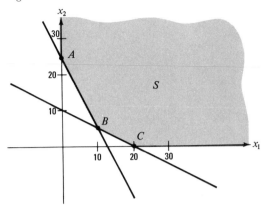

Since, by Theorem 7.6.1, the minimum value of f must be assumed at an extreme point, we see that the minimum value of f on S is equal to 20.

Examples 7.6.3 and 7.6.4 both illustrate the geometric method for solving linear programming problems.

Exercises for 7.6

In each of problems 1–7, determine the maximum and minimum of the linear function on the polyhedral convex set described by the given system of linear inequalities.

1. $f(x_1, x_2) = 3x_1 - 5x_2$ on

$$x_1 + x_2 \leq 1$$
$$x_1 \geq 0$$
$$x_2 \geq 0$$

2. $f(x_1, x_2) = 6x_1 - 2x_2$ on

$$3x_1 + 4x_2 \leq 15$$
$$-x_1 + 2x_2 \leq 5$$
$$x_1 \geq 0$$
$$x_2 \geq 0$$

3. $f(x_1, x_2) = -x_1 + 4x_2$ on

$$3x_1 + 4x_2 \leq 15$$
$$-x_1 + 2x_2 \leq 5$$
$$x_1 \geq 0$$
$$x_2 \geq 0$$

4. $g(y_1, y_2) = 2y_1 + 4y_2$ on

$$y_1 + 2y_2 \leq 8$$
$$3y_1 + y_2 \leq 9$$
$$y_1 \geq 0$$
$$y_2 \geq 0$$

5. $h(x_1, x_2) = -6x_1 - 2x_2$ on

$$x_1 + 2x_2 \leq 8$$
$$3x_1 + x_2 \leq 9$$
$$x_1 \geq 0$$
$$x_2 \geq 0$$

6. $f(x_1, x_2) = 4x_1 + 7x_2$ on

$$\begin{aligned} x_1 + x_2 &\leq 1 \\ 8x_1 + 2x_2 &\leq 4 \\ x_1 &\geq 0 \\ x_2 &\geq 0 \end{aligned}$$

7. $f(x_1, x_2) = -3x_1 + x_2$ on

$$\begin{aligned} x_1 + x_2 &\leq 1 \\ 8x_1 + 2x_2 &\leq 4 \\ x_1 &\geq 0 \\ x_2 &\geq 0 \end{aligned}$$

In each of problems 8–15, determine whether the given linear function has a maximum and/or minimum value on the polyhedral convex set S determined by the indicated system of linear inequalities. If the linear function has a maximum and/or minimum on S, give the extreme points at which these values are attained, as well as the values themselves.

8. $f(x_1, x_2) = 8x_1 + 7x_2$ on

$$\begin{aligned} 2x_1 + x_2 &\leq 10 \\ x_1 + 4x_2 &\leq 12 \\ x_1 &\geq 0 \\ x_2 &\geq 0 \end{aligned}$$

9. $g(y_1, y_2) = 2y_1 - 5y_2$ on

$$\begin{aligned} 2y_1 + y_2 &\leq 10 \\ y_1 + 4y_2 &\leq 12 \\ y_1 &\geq 0 \\ y_2 &\geq 0 \end{aligned}$$

10. $g(y_1, y_2) = 3y_1 + 2y_2$ on

$$\begin{aligned} 2y_1 + y_2 &\geq 10 \\ y_1 + 4y_2 &\geq 12 \\ y_1 &\geq 0 \\ y_2 &\geq 0 \end{aligned}$$

11. $f(x_1, x_2) = 3x_1 + x_2$ on

$$\begin{aligned} 2x_1 + x_2 &\geq 10 \\ x_1 + 4x_2 &\geq 12 \\ x_1 &\geq 0 \\ x_2 &\geq 0 \end{aligned}$$

12. $h(y_1, y_2) = 3y_1 - 2y_2$ on

$$\begin{aligned} 2y_1 + y_2 &\geq 10 \\ y_1 + 4y_2 &\geq 12 \\ y_1 &\geq 0 \\ y_2 &\geq 0 \end{aligned}$$

13. $f(x_1, x_2) = 7x_1 + 2x_2$ on

$$\begin{aligned} 2x_1 + 3x_2 &\geq 6 \\ 4x_1 + 3x_2 &\geq 12 \\ x_1 &\geq 0 \\ x_2 &\geq 0 \end{aligned}$$

14. $g(y_1, y_2) = -2y_1 - y_2$ on

$$2y_1 + 3y_2 \geq 6$$
$$4y_1 + 3y_2 \geq 12$$
$$y_1 \geq 0$$
$$y_2 \geq 0$$

15. $h(x_1, x_2) = 2x_1 - 8x_2$ on

$$2x_1 + 3x_2 \geq 6$$
$$4x_1 + x_2 \geq 4$$
$$x_1 \geq 0$$
$$x_2 \geq 0$$

16. Let S be the polyhedral convex set shown in the diagram. Find a linear function $g(y_1, y_2)$ so that

(a) g has a minimum on S but no maximum

(b) g has a maximum on S but no minimum

(c) g has neither a maximum nor a minimum on S

(d) g has both a maximum and minimum on S

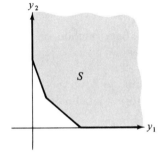

17. Let S be the polyhedral convex set shown.

(a) Is it possible to find a linear function f on S which does not attain a maximum value on S? a minimum value on S?

(b) If f is a linear function on S, at how many points must f be evaluated in order to determine its maximum and minimum values on S?

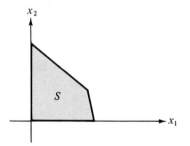

*18. Let S be the polyhedral convex set shown. Suppose that g is a linear function with the property that g has both a maximum and a minimum value on S. Prove that

$$g(y_1, y_2) = 0 \, (= 0 \cdot y_1 + 0 \cdot y_2)$$

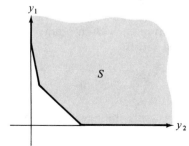

Section 7.7 Linear Programming: Geometric Method

In Section 7.6 the basis for the geometric method for solving linear programs was established (Theorem 7.6.1):

To find the maximum or minimum value of a linear function f on a polyhedral convex set S, proceed as follows:

1. Determine the extreme points of the polyhedral convex set by the methods of Section 7.5.
2. Evaluate the linear function at the extreme points.
3. The maximum and minimum values of f on S (if they exist) are given by the maximum and minimum values of f at the extreme points.

The above method is illustrated in the solutions to Examples 7.1.2 and 7.1.3. The reader should now return to Section 7.1 and reread these examples.

Solution to Example 7.1.2 The problem is to determine the quantities of each type of fabric that should be produced to yield the largest profit. Let

x_1 = number of yards (in hundreds) of plain cloth manufactured per week
x_2 = number of yards (in hundreds) of fancy cloth manufactured per week

Since the profit for the plain cloth (P) is \$10 per hundred yards and that for the fancy cloth (F) is \$25 per hundred yards, it follows that the profit per week will be

$$10x_1 + 25x_2 \tag{7.7.1}$$

This is the quantity that is to be maximized. The conditions of production are as follows:

1. P and F require 2 and 3 hours, respectively, of dyeing time per hundred yards. Hence the total dyeing time per week will be $2x_1 + 3x_2$. Since the total dyeing time available is 72 hours, we must have

$$2x_1 + 3x_2 \leq 72 \tag{7.7.2}$$

2. P and F require 2 and 10 hours, respectively, of hand quilting per hundred yards. Hence the total hand-quilting time required per week will be $2x_1 + 10x_2$. Since the total amount of hand-quilting time available per week is 100 hours, x_1 and x_2 must satisfy the linear inequality

$$2x_1 + 10x_2 \leq 100 \tag{7.7.3}$$

3. Finally, it is clear that the amount of each cloth produced must be nonnegative. Consequently, the variables must satisfy

$$\begin{aligned} x_1 &\geq 0 \\ x_2 &\geq 0 \end{aligned} \tag{7.7.4}$$

In summary, the problem is to *maximize* the linear function

$$f(x_1, x_2) = 10x_1 + 25x_2 \tag{7.7.5}$$

subject to the conditions that

$$2x_1 + 3x_2 \le 72$$
$$2x_1 + 10x_2 \le 100 \qquad\qquad (7.7.6)$$
$$x_1 \ge 0$$
$$x_2 \ge 0$$

In the terminology of Section 7.6, this means that we wish to determine the maximum value of the linear function f on the polyhedral convex set S corresponding to the solution set of the system of linear inequalities (7.7.6).

To accomplish this we use the method described in steps 1–3. The graph of the polyhedral convex set S and its extreme points were determined in Example 7.5.1. The results obtained there are summarized in Figure 7.7.1. The values of f at the

Figure 7.7.1

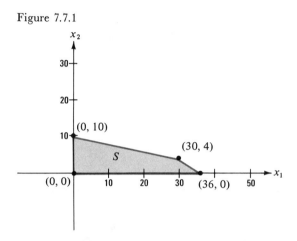

extreme points are

$$f(0, 0) = 10 \cdot 0 + 25 \cdot 0 = 0$$
$$f(36, 0) = 10 \cdot 36 + 25 \cdot 0 = 360$$
$$f(30, 4) = 10 \cdot 30 + 25 \cdot 4 = 400$$
$$f(0, 10) = 10 \cdot 0 + 25 \cdot 10 = 250$$

Thus the maximum value of f on S is 400, and this value is assumed at the point $(30, 4)$. Consequently, we should take

$$x_1 = 30 \qquad \text{and} \qquad x_2 = 4$$

Thus the maximum profit is obtained by manufacturing

$$30 \cdot 100 = 3{,}000 \quad \text{yards of } P \text{ per week}$$
$$\text{and} \qquad 4 \cdot 100 = 400 \qquad \text{yards of } F \text{ per week}$$

The total profit is \$400 per week.

Solution to Example 7.1.3   The problem here is to determine how much of each feed mixture the cattle rancher should buy to guarantee that the nutritional requirements for the animals are met at a minimum cost. Let

$$y_1 = \text{amount (in pounds) of brand } A \text{ used per animal per day}$$
$$y_2 = \text{amount (in pounds) of brand } B \text{ used per animal per day}$$

Now, the cost for brand A is 15 cents per pound and that for B is 25 cents per pound. Hence the cost to the rancher per animal per day is

$$15y_1 + 25y_2 \qquad (7.7.7)$$

cents. This is the quantity that the rancher would like to minimize.

The constraints on his purchasing are determined by the following factors:

1. Each animal must receive at least 24 units of the prescribed vitamin per day. Since brand A contains 2 units and brand B 5 units of the vitamin per pound, the total vitamin content received by an animal per day is $2y_1 + 5y_2$. Consequently, we must have

$$2y_1 + 5y_2 \geq 24 \qquad (7.7.8)$$

2. Now, each animal requires 29 units of the prescribed mineral complex per day. Brands A and B contain 3 and 4 units of the mineral complex, respectively, per pound. This means that the total mineral content received by an animal per day is $3y_1 + 4y_2$. Hence it is required that

$$3y_1 + 4y_2 \geq 29 \qquad (7.7.9)$$

3. Since the amount of each brand purchased per animal per day must be nonnegative, we also have that

$$\begin{aligned} y_1 &\geq 0 \\ y_2 &\geq 0 \end{aligned} \qquad (7.7.10)$$

Taking Eqs. (7.7.7)–(7.7.10) into account, the problem can be phrased in the following way. Determine the minimum value of the linear function

$$g(y_1, y_2) = 15y_1 + 25y_2 \qquad (7.7.11)$$

on the polyhedral convex set S corresponding to the system of linear inequalities

$$\begin{aligned} 2y_1 + 5y_2 &\geq 24 \\ 3y_1 + 4y_2 &\geq 29 \\ y_1 &\geq 0 \\ y_2 &\geq 0 \end{aligned} \qquad (7.7.12)$$

We again apply steps 1–3. First we use the methods of Section 7.5 to graph the set S corresponding to Eq. (7.7.12). The set S has three extreme points, which are indicated in Figure 7.7.2. Solving the appropriate systems of linear equations, these extreme points can be determined explicitly (see Section 7.5). They are

$$A = (0, \tfrac{29}{4}) \qquad B = (7, 2) \qquad C = (12, 0)$$

Since S extends out infinitely we must check to see that the linear function g does, in fact, have a minimum value on S. This actually is the case because g gets large (and not small) as y_1 and y_2 get large; hence g has a minimum value on S. To find this minimum value we need only evaluate the function at the extreme points of S since, by Theorem 7.6.1, the minimum value of g on S will occur at some extreme point. Now

$$\begin{aligned} g(0, \tfrac{29}{4}) &= 15 \cdot 0 + 25 \cdot \tfrac{29}{4} = \tfrac{725}{4} = 181.25 \\ g(7, 2) &= 15 \cdot 7 + 25 \cdot 2 = 155 \\ g(12, 0) &= 15 \cdot 12 + 25 \cdot 0 = 180 \end{aligned}$$

Hence the minimum value of g on S is 155, which occurs when $y_1 = 7$ and $y_2 = 2$.

Figure 7.7.2

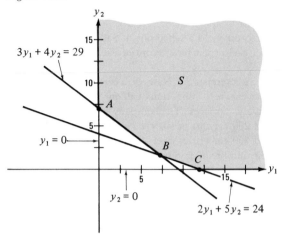

In terms of the original problem, this means that for the cattle rancher to minimize his cost and still satisfy the nutritional requirements of the animals, he should purchase

       7 pounds of brand A per animal per day

and

       2 pounds of brand B per animal per day

This will cost him 155 cents (i.e., $1.55) per animal per day.

In the context of a linear programming problem the polyhedral convex set on which the linear function is to be maximized or minimized is called the *feasible region.*

Exercises for 7.7

1. A restaurant has been reserved for a special banquet. A total of 150 people will attend the banquet. There will be two main courses, steak dinners and lobster dinners. The manager of the restaurant is told that there should be at least 30 more steak dinners available than lobster dinners and that there should be at least 40 lobster dinners available.
   (a) If the restaurant pays $3.00 for its steak dinners and $2.00 for its lobster dinners, how many of each should it prepare to minimize its cost while still satisfying all requirements?
   (b) What if steak dinners cost the restaurant $3.00 and lobster dinners cost $4.00?

2. A manufacturer of stereo consoles makes two models, "standard" and "deluxe." The standard model requires 2 hours of assembly time and 24 square feet of lumber per unit; the deluxe model requires 2 hours of assembly time and 32 square feet of lumber per unit. The manufacturer has available 600 hours of assembly time and 8,000 square feet of lumber per month.
   (a) If the manufacturer makes a profit of $100 on the standard model and $150 on the deluxe model, how many of each should he manufacture per month to maximize his profit?
   (b) What if the profits on the standard and deluxe models are $100 and $125, respectively?

3. Refer to problem 21, Exercises 7.4. A small accounting firm handles income tax returns of two types, "simple" and "complex." The simple forms take 2 hours to complete; the complex returns require 10 hours. The firm has 120 hours per week of working time available. Now, company policy dictates that the firm process at least as many simple forms as complex forms.

(a) If the simple forms yield a net profit of $30 each and the complex forms yield a net profit of $200 each, then how many of each type of return should be processed to maximize profit?

(b) If the simple forms yield a net profit of $30 each and the complex forms yield a net profit of $130 each, then how many of each type should be processed to maximize profit?

4. Refer to problem 22, Exercises 7.4. Namely, a certain company supplies two sizes of cartons, sizes A and B. Its contract obligations call for at least 2,800 and 1,400 cartons of sizes A and B, respectively, per week. The company has two factories, I and II. The first factory produces 500 and 200 cartons of sizes A and B, respectively, per day; the second factory produces 400 and 300 cartons of sizes A and B, respectively, per day.

(a) Determine the number of days per week each factory should be operational to minimize costs if

(1) Both factories cost $200 per day to run.

(2) Factory I costs $260 per day to run and factory II costs $200 per day to run.

(3) Factory I costs $200 per day to run and factory II costs $260 per day to run.

(b) If factory I costs $200 per day to operate, how much must factory II cost to operate per day in order that it be less expensive to operate only factory I and still satisfy all requirements?

5. A farm supply firm decides to sell a line of vitamin and mineral supplements in liquid form. Addition of these supplements to the animals' drinking water eliminates the need for a feed mixture in their diets. Assume that each animal requires 24 units of the vitamin and 29 units of the mineral supplement per day. At the present time the ranchers are using feed mixtures to satisfy these requirements. Brand A feed mixture contains 2 units of the vitamin complex and 3 units of the mineral complex per pound and costs 15 cents per pound. Brand B feed mixture contains 5 units of the vitamin complex and 4 units of the mineral complex per pound and costs 25 cents per pound.

Although the use of these liquid supplements is easier than mixing and using the feeds, the farm supplier realizes that the cost of using these supplements must be no greater than that of the feeds, or the ranchers will simply continue to use that mixture. That is, the cost of 2 units of the vitamin complex plus 3 units of the mineral complex (the contents of 1 pound of brand A) must be less than or equal to 15 cents (the cost of 1 pound of brand A); and the price of 5 units of vitamins plus 4 units of minerals (the contents of 1 pound of brand B) must be less than or equal to 25 cents (the cost of 1 pound of brand B). At what price should each of the supplements be sold in order that the supplier have the largest income while remaining competitive with the feed mixtures?

6. A building contractor builds two types of houses, single level and multilevel. A single-level home requires 3 units of glass, 40 units of wood, and 90 units of block. A multilevel home requires 4 units of glass, 80 units of wood, and 70 units of block. The contractor has available to him a total of 90 units of glass, 1,600 units of wood, and 2,250 units of block.

(a) If the profit on a single-level house is $4,000 and the profit on a multilevel house is $6,000, how many of each type should the contractor build to maximize his profit?

(b) What if the profit on both a single-level and a multilevel house is $5,000?

7. An oil company receives oil products from two refineries in a certain county. The company needs a total of at least 6,000 barrels of gasoline, 3,000 barrels of kerosene, and 2,000 barrels of fuel oil per week. Refinery I will supply 1,000 barrels of gasoline, 1,500 barrels of kerosene, and 500 barrels of fuel oil per day. Refinery II will supply 3,000 barrels of gasoline, 500 barrels of kerosene, and 500 barrels of fuel oil per day.

(a) If refineries I and II charge, respectively, $30,000 and $35,000 per day, how many days per week should the company buy from each refinery in order to minimize costs?

(b) What if the refineries charge $30,000 and $40,000 per day, respectively?

The Simplex Method for Linear Programming

8

As indicated in Chapter 7, linear programming deals with problems of finding maximum or minimum values of linear functions. In that chapter we dealt exclusively with linear functions of two variables and developed a geometric method for solving linear programming problems that involve two variables.

For problems involving more than two variables it is in general not possible to draw pictures to find a solution. For this reason it is necessary to develop a more general approach to linear programming problems. This problem of finding a more general solution method will be considered in this chapter.

We begin by defining linear functions and inequalities in an arbitrary (finite) number of variables. These definitions are direct extensions of those given in Chapter 7 for linear functions and inequalities in two variables.

Section 8.1 Linear Functions and Inequalities in n Variables

Definition
A *linear function*, f, of the n variables $x_1, x_2, \ldots, x_n$ is a rule of the form

$$f(x_1, x_2, \ldots, x_n) = a_1 x_1 + a_2 x_2 + \cdots + a_n x_n \tag{8.1.1}$$

where $a_1, a_2, \ldots, a_n$ are prescribed constants. To each n-tuple of values for $x_1, x_2, \ldots, x_n$, the function f assigns a real number according to the rule (8.1.1).

Example 8.1.1

1. The function f defined by

$$f(x_1, x_2, x_3) = 3x_1 - 4x_2 + 5x_3$$

is a linear function of the three variables x_1, x_2, x_3. In the notation of Eq. (8.1.1),

$a_1 = 3$, $a_2 = -4$, $a_3 = 5$. We have, for example, that

$$f(1, -2, -3) = 3 \cdot 1 - 4 \cdot (-2) + 5 \cdot (-3) = -4$$
$$f(0, 0, 0) = 3 \cdot 0 - 4 \cdot 0 + 5 \cdot 0 = 0$$
$$f(-2, -3, 1) = 3 \cdot (-2) - 4 \cdot (-3) + 5 \cdot 1 = 11$$

2. The function g defined by

$$g(x_1, x_2, x_3, x_4) = 2x_1 + 3x_2 - 4x_3 + x_4$$

is a linear function of the four variables x_1, x_2, x_3, x_4. Here $a_1 = 2$, $a_2 = 3$, $a_3 = -4$, and $a_4 = 1$. For example, we have

$$g(1, 2, 3, 4) = 2 \cdot 1 + 3 \cdot 2 - 4 \cdot 3 + 4 = 0$$
$$g(0, 0, 0, 0) = 2 \cdot 0 + 3 \cdot 0 - 4 \cdot 0 + 0 = 0$$
$$g(-4, 6, 2, 3) = 2 \cdot (-4) + 3 \cdot 6 - 4 \cdot 2 + 3 = 5$$

3. The function h defined by

$$h(y_1, y_2, y_3, y_4, y_5) = y_1 - y_2 + 3y_3 - 5y_4 + 2y_5$$

is a linear function of the five variables y_1, y_2, y_3, y_4, y_5. Here $a_1 = 1$, $a_2 = -1$, $a_3 = 3$, $a_4 = -5$, $a_5 = 2$. Note, for example, that

$$h(5, 4, 3, 2, 1) = 5 - 4 + 3 \cdot 3 - 5 \cdot 2 + 2 \cdot 1 = 2$$
$$h(1, 2, 3, 4, 5) = 1 - 2 + 3 \cdot 3 - 5 \cdot 4 + 2 \cdot 5 = -2$$

As in the case for linear functions, the definition of linear inequalities in n variables is a direct extension of the definition of linear inequalities in two variables.

Example 8.1.2 Consider the linear equation in four variables

$$3x_1 + 5x_2 - 6x_3 + 8x_4 = 7 \tag{8.1.2}$$

If the equality in Eq. (8.1.2) is replaced by an inequality, there are four possibilities:

$$3x_1 + 5x_2 - 6x_3 + 8x_4 < 7 \tag{8.1.3}$$
$$3x_1 + 5x_2 - 6x_3 + 8x_4 > 7 \tag{8.1.4}$$
$$3x_1 + 5x_2 - 6x_3 + 8x_4 \le 7 \tag{8.1.5}$$
$$3x_1 + 5x_2 - 6x_3 + 8x_4 \ge 7 \tag{8.1.6}$$

Each of these expressions is referred to as a linear inequality (in four variables).

Values for the variables x_1, x_2, x_3, and x_4 which satisfy a particular inequality are called solutions to the linear inequality. For example, $x_1 = 2, x_2 = -4, x_3 = 5, x_4 = 4$ is a solution to the linear inequality (8.1.3), because

$$3 \cdot 2 + 5 \cdot (-4) - 6 \cdot 5 + 8 \cdot 4 = -12 < 7$$

On the other hand, $x_1 = 3, x_2 = 6, x_3 = 2, x_4 = -2$ is *not* a solution to Eq. (8.1.3), because

$$3 \cdot 3 + 5 \cdot 6 - 6 \cdot 2 + 8 \cdot (-2) = 11 \not< 7$$

But, of course, $x_1 = 3, x_2 = 6, x_3 = 2, x_4 = -2$ *is* a solution to Eq. (8.1.4), because

$$3 \cdot 3 + 5 \cdot 6 - 6 \cdot 2 + 8 \cdot (-2) = 11 > 7$$

Finally, note that $x_1 = 2, x_2 = 3, x_3 = 1, x_4 = -1$ is a solution to Eq. (8.1.5), because

$$3 \cdot 2 + 5 \cdot 3 - 6 \cdot 1 + 8 \cdot (-1) = 7 \le 7$$

and similarly it is a solution to Eq. (8.1.6). However, it is not a solution to either Eq. (8.1.3) or (8.1.4).

Definition

A *linear inequality* in n variables, $x_1, x_2, \ldots, x_n$, is an expression of one of the following four types:

$$a_1x_1 + a_2x_2 + \cdots + a_nx_n < b$$
$$a_1x_1 + a_2x_2 + \cdots + a_nx_n > b$$
$$a_1x_1 + a_2x_2 + \cdots + a_nx_n \leq b$$
$$a_1x_1 + a_2x_2 + \cdots + a_nx_n \geq b$$

Here $a_1, a_2, \ldots, a_n$ and b are constants. Values for $x_1, x_2, \ldots, x_n$ which satisfy a particular linear inequality are called *solutions* to that linear inequality. The set of all solutions to a linear inequality is called its *solution set*.

As in the case for a linear equation or inequality in two variables, the solution set of a linear equation or inequality in n variables has a geometric interpretation. However, we shall not require this interpretation in this text.

We conclude this section by introducing two examples of linear programming problems which will be solved following the presentation of the simplex algorithm.

Example 8.1.3 Cabinet Making A cabinet manufacturer makes three styles of cabinets. The simplest type requires 50 square feet of lumber per cabinet. The manufacturing process requires 3 hours of machine labor and 1 hour of hand labor per cabinet. The profit is $70 per cabinet. The intermediate style requires 60 square feet of lumber, 4 hours of machine labor, and 2 hours of hand labor per cabinet. The profit is $80 per cabinet. The decorative style requires 60 square feet of lumber, 6 hours of machine labor, and 3 hours of hand labor per cabinet. The profit is $100 per cabinet.

If the manufacturer has 1,000 square feet of lumber, 72 hours of machine time, and 40 hours of hand labor available per week, how many of each type should he manufacturer to obtain the maximum profit?

Example 8.1.4 Rental Service Problem A rental service provides caps and gowns to universities for graduation ceremonies. The manager knows that on three successive days he will need 400, 700, and 600 caps and gowns for three universities. The manager can purchase the caps and gowns from a distributor for $2 each, after which he can have the caps and gowns dry-cleaned by a 1-day cleaner (ready for the next day) for $1.50 each and by a 2-day cleaner for $.80 each. How many caps and gowns should be purchased from the distributor and how many should be dry-cleaned on each of the two days following the first day by each of the cleaners to minimize the cost?

Exercises for 8.1

1. Give two examples of linear functions in
   (a) one variable: x_1
   (b) two variables: x_1 and x_2
   (c) three variables: y_1, y_2, and y_3
   (d) four variables: u_1, u_2, u_3, and u_4

In each of problems 2–5, evaluate the given linear function at the values indicated.

2. $f(x_1, x_2) = 3x_1 - 7x_2$
   (a) $x_1 = 2, x_2 = 3$
   (b) $x_1 = 3, x_2 = 2$
   (c) $x_1 = 5, x_2 = -2$

3. $g(y_1, y_2, y_3) = 7y_1 - 4y_2 + 2y_3$
   (a) $y_1 = 1, y_2 = 2, y_3 = 3$
   (b) $y_1 = -2, y_2 = -3, y_3 = 6$
   (c) $y_1 = 3, y_2 = 0, y_3 = -5$

4. $h(x_1, x_2, x_3, x_4) = 2x_1 + 3x_2 + 6x_3 - 8x_4$
   (a) $x_1 = 2, x_2 = 3, x_3 = 1, x_4 = -1$
   (b) $x_1 = x_2 = x_3 = x_4 = 0$
   (c) $x_1 = 5, x_2 = 4, x_3 = \frac{1}{3}, x_4 = -\frac{1}{2}$

5. $w(u_1, u_2, u_3) = \frac{1}{4}u_1 - u_2 + \frac{1}{3}u_3$
   (a) $u_1 = u_2 = 0, u_3 = 6$
   (b) $u_1 = 8, u_2 = -3, u_3 = -9$
   (c) $u_1 = 2, u_2 = 3, u_3 = -1$

6. Indicate which of the following are linear functions and which are not.
   (a) $f(x_1, x_2) = 2x_1 - 3x_2$
   (b) $g(y_1, y_2, y_3) = 3y_1 + 2y_2^3 - 5y_3$
   (c) $h(x_1, x_2, x_3, x_4) = \frac{1}{4}x_1 - \frac{3}{2}x_2 + 6x_3 - 7x_4$
   (d) $f(u_1, u_2, u_3) = 3u_1u_2 - 7u_3$
   (e) $g(y_1, y_2, y_3, y_4) = \sqrt{2}y_1 + 3^2y_2 - 4y_3 + 5y_4$
   (f) $h(x_1, x_2, x_3) = 5\sqrt{x_1} + 2x_2 - 3x_3$

7. Which of the following are linear functions?
   (a) $h(x_1, x_2, x_3) = x_1 - x_2x_3$
   (b) $g(y_1, y_2) = 7\sqrt{y_1} - 4y_2$
   (c) $f(x_1, x_2, x_3, x_4) = \sqrt{7}x_1 - (\frac{3}{2})^2x_2 + 2x_3 - \frac{4}{5}x_4$
   (d) $f(x_1, x_2, x_3) = x_1^2 - 3x_2 + 4x_3$
   (e) $g(u_1, u_2, u_3, u_4) = u_1 + u_2 + u_3 + u_4$
   (f) $h(x_1, x_2) = (3x_1 + 2x_2)^3$

8. Indicate to which of the following linear inequalities $x_1 = 2, x_2 = -1, x_3 = 4$ is a solution.
   (a) $3x_1 + 2x_2 + 5x_3 \le 10$ (b) $4x_1 + 2x_2 - x_3 > 2$
   (c) $-2x_1 - 4x_2 + 3x_3 \ge 12$ (d) $x_1 - 5x_2 - 6x_3 < 14$
   (e) $-4x_1 + 6x_2 + 4x_3 > -8$

9. Which of the following linear inequalities has $x_1 = 4, x_2 = 3, x_3 = 1, x_4 = 0, x_5 = -2$ as a solution?
   (a) $2x_1 + 4x_2 - 3x_3 + x_4 + x_5 \le 15$ (b) $x_1 + x_2 + x_3 - 5x_4 - 6x_5 > 12$
   (c) $3x_1 - 2x_2 + 3x_3 - x_4 + 6x_5 \ge -2$ (d) $-x_1 + x_2 - 3x_3 + x_4 - 4x_5 < 10$

10. Determine five solutions to the linear inequality

$$3x_1 - 5x_2 + 6x_3 + 8x_4 \le 6$$

11. Find four solutions to the linear inequality

$$5x_1 - 3x_2 + 4x_3 + x_4 - x_5 + x_6 \ge 7$$

12. Let f and g be two linear functions of three variables, x_1, x_2, x_3.
    (a) Show that the function $f + g$ defined by

$$(f + g)(x_1, x_2, x_3) = f(x_1, x_2, x_3) + g(x_1, x_2, x_3)$$

is a linear function of the three variables x_1, x_2, x_3.
    (b) If

$$f(x_1, x_2, x_3) = a_1x_1 + a_2x_2 + a_3x_3$$
$$g(x_1, x_2, x_3) = b_1x_1 + b_2x_2 + b_3x_3$$

and

$$(f + g)(x_1, x_2, x_3) = c_1 x_1 + c_2 x_2 + c_3 x_3$$

then what is the relationship between the cs, as, and bs?

(c) If

$$f(x_1, x_2, x_3) = 2x_1 - 4x_2 + 5x_3$$
$$g(x_1, x_2, x_3) = 6x_1 + 2x_2 + 4x_3$$

find the linear function $(f + g)(x_1, x_2, x_3)$.

13. Let f and g be two linear functions in the two variables x_1, x_2 and define $f \cdot g$ by

$$(f \cdot g)(x_1, x_2) = f(x_1, x_2) \cdot g(x_1, x_2)$$

(a) If

$$f(x_1, x_2) = 3x_1 - 2x_2$$
$$g(x_1, x_2) = 6x_1 + 4x_2$$

then

$$(f \cdot g)(x_1, x_2) = ?$$

(b) If f and g are two linear functions in the two variables x_1, x_2, is $f \cdot g$ a linear function in x_1, x_2?

14. A person has x_1 pennies, x_2 nickels, x_3 dimes, x_4 quarters, and x_5 half-dollars. Let $f(x_1, x_2, x_3, x_4, x_5)$ be the amount of money (in cents) that this person has in change.
    (a) Determine explicitly the linear function f.
    (b) In the notation of Eq. (8.1.1), what are the a_is?
    (c) If the person is known to have less than \$1.25, express this fact as a linear inequality in x_1, x_2, x_3, x_4, and x_5.
    (d) In part (c) find three possibilities for the number of each denomination of coin that the person has.
    (e) If the person is known to have at least \$2.00, express this fact as a linear inequality in x_1, x_2, x_3, x_4, and x_5.
    (f) In part (e) find three possibilities for the number of each denomination of coin that the person has.

15. Suppose that milk costs x_1 cents per half-gallon, eggs cost x_2 cents per dozen, lettuce costs x_3 cents per head, and hamburger costs x_4 cents per pound. A particular family buys 5 half-gallons of milk, 2 dozen eggs, 4 heads of lettuce, and 3 pounds of hamburger per week.
    (a) Write the total cost (in cents) per week of these four items for this family as a linear function $c(x_1, x_2, x_3, x_4)$.
    (b) If the family has at most \$10.30 per week to spend on these four items, express this condition as a linear inequality in x_1, x_2, x_3, and x_4.
    (c) If milk costs 60 cents a half-gallon, a dozen eggs 70 cents, and a head of lettuce 35 cents, how much per pound can hamburger cost and still have the family be able to satisfy the requirement in part (b)?

16. Refer to Example 8.1.3. Let

$$x_1 = \text{no. of plain cabinets made per week}$$
$$x_2 = \text{no. of intermediate cabinets made per week}$$
$$x_3 = \text{no. of decorative cabinets made per week}$$

(a) Write the total profit per week as a linear function of x_1, x_2, and x_3.
(b) Write the lumber, machine-labor, and hand-labor restrictions as three linear inequalities in x_1, x_2, and x_3.

17. Refer to Example 8.1.4. Let

$$y_1 = \text{no. of caps and gowns purchased}$$
$$y_2 = \text{no. cleaned by the 1-day cleaner after the first ceremony}$$

y_3 = no. cleaned by the 1-day cleaner after the second ceremony

y_4 = no. cleaned by the 2-day cleaner after the first ceremony

(a) Write the total cost to the rental service (in dollars) as a linear function of y_1, y_2, y_3, and y_4.

*(b) Find the restrictions (in terms of linear inequalities) on y_1, y_2, y_3, and y_4 so that there will be enough caps and gowns for each of the three ceremonies.

Section 8.2   Vector-Matrix Form of a Linear Program

To begin with we shall need a convenient method for writing a system of linear inequalities. This is provided by matrices. In Chapter 6 we defined two vectors to be equal if they are of the same length and all the corresponding entries are equal. We now need the notion of one vector being less than or equal to another. The definition is a natural extension from that of the equality of two vectors.

Definition

Let V and W be two column or row vectors of the *same length*. Then we say that $V \leq W$ if and only if each entry of V is less than or equal to the corresponding entry of W. For column vectors this means that if

$$V = \begin{bmatrix} v_1 \\ v_2 \\ \vdots \\ v_n \end{bmatrix} \quad \text{and} \quad W = \begin{bmatrix} w_1 \\ w_2 \\ \vdots \\ w_n \end{bmatrix}$$

then $V \leq W$ if and only if $v_i \leq w_i$ for all i. For row vectors this means that if

$$V = [v_1, v_2, \ldots, v_n] \quad \text{and} \quad W = [w_1, w_2, \ldots, w_n]$$

then $V \leq W$ if and only if $v_i \leq w_i$ for all i.

Example 8.2.1   The following examples illustrate the above definition.

1. $\begin{bmatrix} -1 \\ 3 \\ 1 \\ 5 \end{bmatrix} \leq \begin{bmatrix} 1 \\ 5 \\ 1 \\ 6 \end{bmatrix}$

2. $\begin{bmatrix} -1 \\ 3 \\ 1 \\ 5 \end{bmatrix} \nleq \begin{bmatrix} -1 \\ 2 \\ 1 \\ 5 \end{bmatrix}$

3. $\begin{bmatrix} 2 \\ -1 \\ 4 \end{bmatrix} \leq \begin{bmatrix} 2 \\ 5 \\ \frac{9}{2} \end{bmatrix}$

4. $\begin{bmatrix} 2 \\ -1 \\ 4 \end{bmatrix} \nleq \begin{bmatrix} \frac{3}{2} \\ 2 \\ 7 \end{bmatrix}$

5. $[1, 2] \leq [7, 10]$

6. $[4, 7, -3] \nleq [6, 6, 6]$

Needless to say, if V and W are vectors of the same length, we say that $V \geq W$ if and only if $W \leq V$. For example,

$$\begin{bmatrix} 1 \\ 3 \\ -5 \end{bmatrix} \geq \begin{bmatrix} 0 \\ 2 \\ -10 \end{bmatrix} \quad \text{and} \quad [\tfrac{1}{2}, 7, -3, 5] \geq [0, 2, -8, 1]$$

In Section 6.9 it was shown that a system of linear equations can be written in the *vector-matrix form* $AX = B$. We shall now obtain similar notations for linear functions and systems of linear inequalities. There are two main types. One used for linear functions and systems of linear inequalities that arise in maximum problems in linear programs and one used for those that arise in minimum problems.

The pertinent concepts are illustrated in the following examples.

Example 8.2.2 Consider the maximum problem arising in the solution of Example 7.1.2. In Eqs. (7.7.5) and (7.7.6) we saw that the problem could be phrased in the form: *Maximize* the linear function

$$f(x_1, x_2) = 10x_1 + 25x_2 \tag{8.2.1}$$

subject to the conditions

$$\begin{aligned}
2x_1 + 3x_2 &\le 72 \\
2x_1 + 10x_2 &\le 100 \\
x_1 &\ge 0 \\
x_2 &\ge 0
\end{aligned} \tag{8.2.2}$$

Recalling the definition of matrix multiplication we have that

$$10x_1 + 25x_2 = [10, 25]\begin{bmatrix} x_1 \\ x_2 \end{bmatrix} \tag{8.2.3}$$

Consequently, Eq. (8.2.1) can be rewritten as

$$f(X) = CX$$

where

$$X = \begin{bmatrix} x_1 \\ x_2 \end{bmatrix} \quad \text{and} \quad C = [10, 25]$$

Next consider the first two linear inequalities in Eq. (8.2.2). By the definition of vector inequality this can be expressed as

$$\begin{bmatrix} 2x_1 + 3x_2 \\ 2x_1 + 10x_2 \end{bmatrix} \le \begin{bmatrix} 72 \\ 100 \end{bmatrix} \tag{8.2.4}$$

The left side of Eq. (8.2.4) can be written as the product of two matrices:

$$\begin{bmatrix} 2 & 3 \\ 2 & 10 \end{bmatrix}\begin{bmatrix} x_1 \\ x_2 \end{bmatrix} \tag{8.2.5}$$

Combining Eqs. (8.2.4) and (8.2.5) we have that the first two linear inequalities can be expressed in the vector-matrix form

$$AX \le B$$

where

$$A = \begin{bmatrix} 2 & 3 \\ 2 & 10 \end{bmatrix} \quad \text{and} \quad B = \begin{bmatrix} 72 \\ 100 \end{bmatrix}$$

Finally, using the definition of vector inequality again, it follows that the last two linear inequalities in Eq. (8.2.2) can be written as

$$\begin{bmatrix} x_1 \\ x_2 \end{bmatrix} \ge \begin{bmatrix} 0 \\ 0 \end{bmatrix}$$

In other words,

$$X \geq \theta$$

where

$$\theta = \begin{bmatrix} 0 \\ 0 \end{bmatrix}$$

In summary, then, the maximum problem of Example 7.1.2 can be expressed in the form

Maximize: CX
subject to: $AX \leq B$, $X \geq \theta$

where

$$A = \begin{bmatrix} 2 & 3 \\ 2 & 10 \end{bmatrix} \qquad B = \begin{bmatrix} 72 \\ 100 \end{bmatrix} \qquad C = [10, 25] \qquad \theta = \begin{bmatrix} 0 \\ 0 \end{bmatrix} \qquad X = \begin{bmatrix} x_1 \\ x_2 \end{bmatrix}$$

Example 8.2.3 Consider the minimum problem arising in the solution of Example 7.1.3. In Section 7.7 [see Eqs. (7.7.11) and (7.7.12)] the problem was expressed as follows: *Minimize* the linear function

$$g(y_1, y_2) = 15y_1 + 25y_2 \qquad (8.2.6)$$

subject to the conditions

$$\begin{aligned} 2y_1 + 5y_2 &\geq 24 \\ 3y_1 + 4y_2 &\geq 29 \\ y_1 &\geq 0 \\ y_2 &\geq 0 \end{aligned} \qquad (8.2.7)$$

For a minimum problem we use the definition of matrix multiplication to write the right-hand side of Eq. (8.2.6) as

$$15y_1 + 25y_2 = [y_1, y_2] \begin{bmatrix} 15 \\ 25 \end{bmatrix}$$

so Eq. (8.2.6) can be rewritten as

$$g(Y) = YB$$

where

$$Y = [y_1, y_2] \qquad \text{and} \qquad B = \begin{bmatrix} 15 \\ 25 \end{bmatrix}$$

By using arguments as in the previous example, the first two linear inequalities in Eq. (8.2.7) can be expressed in the vector-matrix form

$$YA \geq C$$

where

$$A = \begin{bmatrix} 2 & 3 \\ 5 & 4 \end{bmatrix} \qquad \text{and} \qquad C = [24, 29]$$

(Notice that for a minimum problem the rows of A are obtained by reading down the columns of the appropriate linear inequalities.) The last two linear inequalities in Eq. (8.2.7) can be rewritten in the form

$$Y \geq \theta$$

where

$$\theta = [0, 0]$$

In summary, the minimum problem of Example 7.1.3 can be expressed in the form

Minimize: YB
subject to: $YA \geq C,\ Y \geq \theta$

where

$$A = \begin{bmatrix} 2 & 3 \\ 5 & 4 \end{bmatrix} \qquad B = \begin{bmatrix} 15 \\ 25 \end{bmatrix} \qquad C = [24, 29] \qquad \theta = [0, 0] \qquad Y = [y_1, y_2]$$

The situations illustrated in the above two examples give the general procedure for writing maximum and minimum problems in *vector-matrix form*.

Maximize: CX
subject to: $AX \leq B,\ X \geq \theta$ $\Big\}$ Maximum Problem

Minimize: YB
subject to: $YA \geq C,\ Y \geq \theta$ $\Big\}$ Minimum Problem

Example 8.2.4 Write the following linear programming problem in vector-matrix form: Maximize the linear function

$$f(x_1, x_2, x_3) = 3x_1 + 2x_2 + 6x_3$$

subject to the conditions

$$4x_1 + \quad - 8x_3 \leq 40$$
$$x_1 + x_2 + 6x_3 \leq 80$$
$$x_1 \geq 0$$
$$x_2 \geq 0$$
$$x_3 \geq 0$$

The vector-matrix form is

Maximize: CX
subject to: $AX \leq B,\ X \geq \theta$

where

$$A = \begin{bmatrix} 4 & 0 & -8 \\ 1 & 1 & 6 \end{bmatrix} \qquad B = \begin{bmatrix} 40 \\ 80 \end{bmatrix} \qquad C = [3, 2, 6] \qquad \theta = \begin{bmatrix} 0 \\ 0 \\ 0 \end{bmatrix} \qquad X = \begin{bmatrix} x_1 \\ x_2 \\ x_3 \end{bmatrix}$$

Example 8.2.5 Express the following linear program in vector-matrix form: Minimize the linear function

$$g(y_1, y_2, y_3) = 5y_1 + 3y_2 + 2y_3$$

subject to the conditions

$$y_1 + y_2 + \quad y_3 \geq 24$$
$$y_1 \quad - 2y_3 \geq 0$$
$$y_1 - y_2 + \quad y_3 \geq 0$$
$$2y_1 \quad + 2y_3 \geq 19$$
$$y_1 \geq 0$$
$$y_2 \geq 0$$
$$y_3 \geq 0$$

The vector-matrix form is

Minimize: YB
subject to: $YA \geq C,\ Y \geq \theta$

where

$$A = \begin{bmatrix} 1 & 1 & 1 & 2 \\ 1 & 0 & -1 & 0 \\ 1 & -2 & 1 & 2 \end{bmatrix} \qquad B = \begin{bmatrix} 5 \\ 3 \\ 2 \end{bmatrix} \qquad C = [24, 0, 0, 19]$$

$$\theta = [0, 0, 0] \qquad Y = [y_1, y_2, y_3]$$

In general, for a maximum problem involving n variables, $x_1, x_2, \ldots, x_n$, and $n + m$ linear inequalities (including the constraints $x_1 \geq 0,\ x_2 \geq 0,\ \ldots,\ x_n \geq 0$), the matrix A will be $m \times n$, B will be $m \times 1$, C will be $1 \times n$, θ will be $n \times 1$, and X will be $n \times 1$. For a minimum problem involving m variables $y_1, y_2, \ldots, y_m$ and $m + n$ linear inequalities, the matrix A will be $m \times n$, B will be $m \times 1$, C will be $1 \times n$, θ will be $1 \times m$, and Y will be $1 \times m$.

Notice that in both cases A is $m \times n$, B is $m \times 1$, and C is $1 \times n$. This fact will be used in the next few sections when the simplex algorithm for solving linear programs is presented.

Exercises for 8.2

1. Fill in the blank with the appropriate symbol, $\leq$ or $\geq$.
   (a) $[2, 1, -4]$ ____ $[3, 2, 0]$
   (b) $[1, -5, 6, 8]$ ____ $[1, -6, 6, 8]$
   (c) $[3, -2, 1, 4, -8]$ ____ $[3, -1, 4, 6, -7]$
   (d) $[1, 0, -3, 4]$ ____ $[1, 1, -3, 4]$
2. Indicate which of the following are true and which are false.

(a) $\begin{bmatrix} 1 \\ 5 \\ -3 \end{bmatrix} \leq \begin{bmatrix} 2 \\ 7 \\ -1 \end{bmatrix}$

(b) $[1, -3] \geq [0, -2]$

(c) $\begin{bmatrix} 1 \\ -7 \\ 4 \\ 5 \end{bmatrix} \leq \begin{bmatrix} 1 \\ -7 \\ 4 \\ 5 \end{bmatrix}$

(d) $[1, 6, -2] \leq [2, 8, -1]$

(e) $\begin{bmatrix} 2 \\ 7 \\ -1 \\ 6 \end{bmatrix} \geq \begin{bmatrix} 1 \\ -5 \\ 0 \\ 2 \end{bmatrix}$

(f) $3 \cdot [2, 4] \geq [7, 12]$

(g) $- \begin{bmatrix} 5 \\ 2 \\ -3 \\ 1 \end{bmatrix} \leq \begin{bmatrix} 5 \\ 2 \\ -3 \\ 1 \end{bmatrix}$

(h) $[1, 2, -3] \leq -2 \cdot [-3, -1, 1]$

In each of problems 3–10, express the given linear programming problem in vector-matrix form.

3. Maximize: $f(x_1, x_2) = 3x_1 + 5x_2$
   subject to:

$$6x_1 + 7x_2 \leq 10$$
$$2x_1 + x_2 \leq 4$$
$$x_1 \geq 0$$
$$x_2 \geq 0$$

4. Maximize: $f(x_1, x_2) = 4x_1 - x_2$
   subject to:

$$3x_1 - 5x_2 \leq 6$$
$$2x_1 + x_2 \leq 3$$
$$-8x_1 + 10x_2 \leq 1$$
$$x_1 \geq 0$$
$$x_2 \geq 0$$

5. Minimize: $g(y_1, y_2) = 2y_1 + 4y_2$
   subject to:

$$7y_1 + 4y_2 \geq 15$$
$$3y_1 - 6y_2 \geq 5$$
$$y_1 \geq 0$$
$$y_2 \geq 0$$

6. Minimize: $g(y_1, y_2) = 5y_1 + y_2$
   subject to:

$$y_1 - 7y_2 \geq 5$$
$$2y_1 + 3y_2 \geq 6$$
$$8y_1 + 6y_2 \geq -4$$
$$-4y_1 + y_2 \geq 8$$
$$y_1 \geq 0$$
$$y_2 \geq 0$$

7. Maximize: $f(x_1, x_2, x_3) = 7x_1 - 5x_2 + 3x_3$
   subject to:

$$x_1 - x_2 + 4x_3 \leq 8$$
$$3x_1 + 5x_2 - 2x_3 \leq 6$$
$$2x_1 + 3x_2 + 4x_3 \leq 5$$
$$-7x_1 + 6x_2 + x_3 \leq -2$$
$$x_1 \geq 0$$
$$x_2 \geq 0$$
$$x_3 \geq 0$$

8. Maximize: $f(x_1, x_2, x_3, x_4) = 8x_1 + 6x_2 - 3x_3 + 5x_4$
   subject to:

$$3x_1 - 2x_2 + 5x_3 + 7x_4 \leq 15$$
$$-2x_1 + x_2 + 3x_3 - 5x_4 \leq 1$$
$$x_1 \geq 0$$
$$x_2 \geq 0$$
$$x_3 \geq 0$$
$$x_4 \geq 0$$

9. Minimize: $g(y_1, y_2, y_3) = 5y_1 + 3y_2 - 7y_3$
   subject to:
$$3y_1 - 6y_2 + 4y_3 \geq -8$$
$$2y_1 + 4y_2 - y_3 \geq 3$$
$$y_1 \geq 0$$
$$y_2 \geq 0$$
$$y_3 \geq 0$$

10. Minimize: $g(y_1, y_2, y_3, y_4, y_5) = 2y_1 - 3y_2 + 4y_3 + y_4 - y_5$
    subject to:
$$6y_1 + 5y_2 - 4y_3 \qquad\qquad + 3y_5 \geq 8$$
$$4y_2 + 6y_3 - y_4 + 5y_5 \geq 2$$
$$7y_1 - 6y_2 \qquad\qquad + 2y_4 \qquad\qquad \geq -3$$
$$y_1 \geq 0$$
$$y_2 \geq 0$$
$$y_3 \geq 0$$
$$y_4 \geq 0$$
$$y_5 \geq 0$$

In each of problems 11–14, express the given linear programming problem in vector-matrix form. Be sure to first rewrite the given inequalities (if necessary) so that the problem is in standard form. For example, the maximization problem

Maximize: $f(x_1, x_2) = 3x_1 + 5x_2$
subject to:
$$2x_1 - 4x_2 \leq 7$$
$$3x_1 - 2x_2 \geq 5$$
$$x_1 \geq x_2$$
$$x_1 \geq 0$$
$$x_2 \geq 0$$

must first be rewritten in standard form:

Maximize: $f(x_1, x_2) = 3x_1 + 5x_2$
subject to:
$$2x_1 - 4x_2 \leq 7$$
$$-3x_1 + 2x_2 \leq -5$$
$$-x_1 + x_2 \leq 0$$
$$x_1 \geq 0$$
$$x_2 \geq 0$$

11. Maximize: $f(x_1, x_2) = -x_1 + 2x_2$
    subject to:
$$3x_1 + 5x_2 \leq 8$$
$$2x_2 \geq 3x_1$$
$$x_1 \geq 0$$
$$x_2 \geq 0$$

12. Maximize: $f(x_1, x_2, x_3) = 2x_1 + 4x_2 + 5x_3$
    subject to:
$$8x_1 - 7x_2 \geq 4 - 2x_3$$
$$2x_1 + 3 \leq 5x_2$$
$$x_2 \leq 2x_1 + 3x_3$$
$$6x_1 + x_3 \geq -10$$
$$\geq 0$$
$$x_2 \geq 0$$
$$x_3 \geq 0$$

13. Minimize: $g(y_1, y_2, y_3) = y_1 + 2y_2 - 3y_3$
    subject to:
$$2y_1 + 4y_2 + 8y_3 \geq 7$$
$$3y_1 - 6y_2 + 5 \leq y_3$$
$$y_3 \geq 2y_2$$
$$y_1 \geq 0$$
$$y_2 \geq 0$$
$$y_3 \geq 0$$

14. Minimize: $g(y_1, y_2, y_3, y_4) = 6y_1 - 2y_3 + y_4$
    subject to:
$$10y_1 + 4y_2 \geq -3y_3 + 5y_4 + 1$$
$$y_3 \leq 2y_4$$
$$y_1 - 4y_4 \leq y_2 - y_3 + 6$$
$$y_1 \geq 0$$
$$y_2 \geq 0$$
$$y_3 \geq 0$$
$$y_4 \geq 0$$

15. Let V_1, V_2, V_3 be column (or row) vectors all of the same length.
    (a) If $V_1 \leq V_2$ and $V_2 \leq V_3$, prove that $V_1 \leq V_3$.
    (b) If $V_1 \geq \theta$ and $V_2 \geq \theta$, prove that $V_1 + V_2 \geq \theta$.
    (c) If $V_1 \leq V_2$ and $c \geq 0$, prove that $c \cdot V_1 \leq c \cdot V_2$.

In each of problems 16–19, determine whether the statement given is true or whether it is false. If it is true, prove that it is true; if it is false, give a counterexample to the statement.

16. If $V \leq W$, then $V - W \leq \theta$.
17. Either $V > \theta$ or $V < \theta$ or $V = \theta$.
18. If $V \leq \theta$ and c is a real number, then $c \cdot V \leq \theta$.
19. If $V_1 \geq V_2$ and $V_3 \geq V_4$ and if V_1, V_2, V_3, and V_4 are all row vectors of the same size, $V_1 + V_3 \geq V_2 + V_4$.

Section 8.3   Tucker Tableau

In the next few sections an analytic (as opposed to geometric) method will be developed for solving linear programming problems. This method will be applicable to those problems involving an arbitrary (finite) number of variables, whereas the geometric method is generally useful only for those involving two variables. The method is called the *simplex algorithm*. The simplex algorithm that we shall present is actually a simplification of the general algorithm. However, it will suffice for all problems that we shall consider. The restriction is simply that the matrix (vector) B in the vector-matrix form of the linear program have *nonnegative* entries (i.e., $B \geq \theta$).

The initial setup required for the use of the simplex algorithm involves the construction of the *Tucker tableau*.

Example 8.3.1   Consider the linear program described in Example 8.2.2:

$$\text{Maximize: } f(x_1, x_2) = 10x_1 + 25x_2 \qquad (8.3.1)$$
subject to:
$$2x_1 + 3x_2 \leq 72 \qquad (8.3.2)$$
$$2x_1 + 10x_2 \leq 100 \qquad (8.3.3)$$
$$x_1 \geq 0$$
$$x_2 \geq 0$$

We first transform the inequalities in Eqs. (8.3.2) and (8.3.3) into equalities by introducing auxiliary variables which "take up the slack" in these inequalities. That is, we define *slack variables* t_1 and t_2 by

$$t_1 = 72 - (2x_1 + 3x_2)$$
$$t_2 = 100 - (2x_1 + 10x_2)$$

(8.3.4)

In view of Eqs. (8.3.2)–(8.3.4) we must have $t_1 \geq 0$, $t_2 \geq 0$. It will be useful for us to rewrite Eq. (8.3.4) as

$$2x_1 + 3x_2 - 72 = -t_1$$

(8.3.5)

$$2x_1 + 10x_2 - 100 = -t_2$$

(8.3.6)

Next recall [see Eq. (8.3.1)] that the problem is to *maximize* $f(x_1, x_2) = 10x_1 + 25x_2$, which for convenience we write as

$$10x_1 + 25x_2 = f$$

(8.3.7)

Equations (8.3.5)–(8.3.7) can be combined in a tableau as in Figure 8.3.1. To obtain

Figure 8.3.1

x_1	x_2	-1	
2	3	72	$= -t_1$
2	10	100	$= -t_2$
10	25	0	$= f$

Eq. (8.3.5) from this tableau, simply multiply the entries of the first row of the tableau by the corresponding column headings, add these terms together, and set the resulting expression equal to the indicated value at the right of the tableau. Doing this we obtain

$$2(x_1) + 3(x_2) + 72(-1) = -t_1$$

or

$$2x_1 + 3x_2 - 72 = -t_1$$

which is Eq. (8.3.5). Similarly, we obtain Eqs. (8.3.6) and (8.3.7) from the tableau. Now, recall that the vector-matrix form for this linear programming problem is

Maximize: CX
subject to: $AX \leq B$, $X \geq \theta$

where

$$A = \begin{bmatrix} 2 & 3 \\ 2 & 10 \end{bmatrix} \quad B = \begin{bmatrix} 72 \\ 100 \end{bmatrix} \quad C = [10, 25] \quad \theta = \begin{bmatrix} 0 \\ 0 \end{bmatrix} \quad X = \begin{bmatrix} x_1 \\ x_2 \end{bmatrix}$$

Thus we see that in the upper left-hand corner of the tableau in Figure 8.3.1 is the matrix A, in the upper right-hand corner is the column vector B, in the lower left-hand corner is the row vector C, and in the lower right-hand corner is the number 0. In the above notation Figure 8.3.1 can be displayed as in Figure 8.3.2.

Figure 8.3.2

	x_1	x_2	-1	
	A	B		$= -t_1$
				$= -t_2$
	C		0	$= f$

Example 8.3.2 Consider the linear programming problem of Example 8.2.3:

$$\text{Minimize: } g(y_1, y_2) = 15y_1 + 25y_2 \tag{8.3.8}$$

subject to:

$$2y_1 + 5y_2 \geq 24 \tag{8.3.9}$$
$$3y_1 + 4y_2 \geq 29 \tag{8.3.10}$$
$$y_1 \geq 0$$
$$y_2 \geq 0$$

As in the previous example, we first transform the inequalities in Eqs. (8.3.9) and (8.3.10) into equalities by the introduction of slack variables. We define

$$s_1 = 2y_1 + 5y_2 - 24 \tag{8.3.11}$$

$$s_2 = 3y_1 + 4y_2 - 29 \tag{8.3.12}$$

Because of Eqs. (8.3.9)–(8.3.12) we have the requirement that $s_1 \geq 0$, $s_2 \geq 0$.

Recall that the problem here is to *minimize* $g(y_1, y_2) = 15y_1 + 25y_2$. For convenience we write this as

$$15y_1 + 25y_2 = g \tag{8.3.13}$$

We can combine Eqs. (8.3.11)–(8.3.13) into the tableau shown in Figure 8.3.3. To

Figure 8.3.3

	2	3	15
y_1			
y_2	5	4	25
-1	24	29	0
	$\parallel$	$\parallel$	$\parallel$
	s_1	s_2	g

obtain Eq. (8.3.11) from the tableau, multiply the entries of the first column of the tableau by the corresponding row headings, add these terms together, and set the resulting expression equal to the indicated value at the bottom of the tableau. Doing this we obtain

$$2(y_1) + 5(y_2) + 24(-1) = s_1$$

or

$$2y_1 + 5y_2 - 24 = s_1$$

which is Eq. (8.3.11). By similar reasoning we obtain Eqs. (8.3.12) and (8.3.13) from the tableau.

Now, the vector-matrix form for this linear programming problem is given by

Minimize: YB
subject to: $YA \geq C,\ Y \geq \theta$

where

$$A = \begin{bmatrix} 2 & 3 \\ 5 & 4 \end{bmatrix} \qquad B = \begin{bmatrix} 15 \\ 25 \end{bmatrix} \qquad C = [24,\ 29] \qquad \theta = [0,\ 0] \qquad Y = [y_1, y_2]$$

As in the previous example, the tableau in Figure 8.3.3 can be written schematically as in Figure 8.3.4.

Figure 8.3.4

$\begin{matrix} y_1 \\ y_2 \end{matrix}$	A	B
-1	C	0

$$\begin{matrix} \| & \| & \| \\ s_1 & s_2 & g \end{matrix}$$

Example 8.3.3   Consider again the linear programming problem of Example 8.3.1. If we label the rows and bottom of the tableau for this maximum problem (Figure 8.3.1) in the same way as we did the rows and bottom of the tableau for the minimum problem of Example 8.3.2 (Figure 8.3.3), we get the Tucker tableau in Figure 8.3.5.

Figure 8.3.5

	x_1	x_2	-1	
y_1	2	3	72	$= -t_1$
y_2	2	10	100	$= -t_2$
-1	10	25	0	$= f$

$$\begin{matrix} \| & \| & \| \\ s_1 & s_2 & g \end{matrix}$$

In this form we see that the tableau not only contains the original maximum linear programming problem, but it also contains the minimum linear programming problem:

Minimize: $g(y_1, y_2) = 72y_1 + 100y_2$
subject to:
$$2y_1 + 2y_2 \geq 10$$
$$3y_1 + 10y_2 \geq 25$$
$$y_1 \geq 0$$
$$y_2 \geq 0$$

This is called the *dual* (minimum) problem of the maximum problem in Example 8.3.1.

Example 8.3.4 We again consider the linear programming problem of Example 8.3.2. If we label the columns and right-hand side of the tableau for this minimum problem (Figure 8.3.3) in the same way as we did the columns and right-hand side of the tableau for the maximum problem of Example 8.3.1 (Figure 8.3.1), we obtain the Tucker tableau of Figure 8.3.6.

Figure 8.3.6

	x_1	x_2	-1	
y_1	2	3	15	$= -t_1$
y_2	5	4	25	$= -t_2$
-1	24	29	0	$= f$
	$\parallel$	$\parallel$	$\parallel$	
	s_1	s_2	g	

Consequently, we see that in this form the tableau not only contains the original minimum linear programming problem but also contains the maximum linear programming problem

Maximize: $f(x_1, x_2) = 24x_1 + 29x_2$
subject to:
$$2x_1 + 3x_2 \leq 15$$
$$5x_1 + 4x_2 \leq 25$$
$$x_1 \geq 0$$
$$x_2 \geq 0$$

This is called the *dual* (maximum) problem of the minimum problem in Example 8.3.2.

In summary, if a linear programming problem has the Tucker tableau of Figure 8.3.7, the tableau contains both the original linear program and its dual problem,

Figure 8.3.7

	x_1	x_2	$\cdots$	x_n	-1	
y_1						$= -t_1$
y_2			A		B	$= -t_2$
$\vdots$						$\vdots$
y_m						$= -t_m$
-1			C		0	$= f$
	$\parallel$	$\parallel$		$\parallel$	$\parallel$	
	s_1	s_2	$\cdots$	s_n	g	

which is a minimum problem if the original is a maximum problem and is a maximum problem if the original is a minimum problem.

The simplex algorithm will give us a method for solving both the original linear programming problem and its dual problem simultaneously.

Definition
The entries of the row vector C in the Tucker tableau are called the *indicators* of the tableau.

For example, the indicators of the tableau in Figure 8.3.5 are 10 and 25; those of Figure 8.3.6 are 24 and 29.

Example 8.3.5 Find the Tucker tableau for the simplex algorithm of the linear programming problem (Example 8.2.4)

$$\text{Maximize: } f(x_1, x_2, x_3) = 3x_1 + 2x_2 + 6x_3$$
subject to:
$$4x_1 \quad\quad - 8x_3 \le 40$$
$$x_1 + x_2 + 6x_3 \le 80$$
$$x_1 \ge 0$$
$$x_2 \ge 0$$
$$x_3 \ge 0$$

The vector-matrix form is

$$\text{Maximize: } CX$$
$$\text{subject to: } AX \le B, X \ge \theta$$

where

$$A = \begin{bmatrix} 4 & 0 & -8 \\ 1 & 1 & 6 \end{bmatrix} \quad B = \begin{bmatrix} 40 \\ 80 \end{bmatrix} \quad C = [3, 2, 6] \quad \theta = \begin{bmatrix} 0 \\ 0 \\ 0 \end{bmatrix} \quad X = \begin{bmatrix} x_1 \\ x_2 \\ x_3 \end{bmatrix}$$

The Tucker tableau for this linear program is therefore as shown in Figure 8.3.8, and the indicators are 3, 2, and 6.

Figure 8.3.8

	x_1	x_2	x_3	-1	
y_1	4	0	-8	40	$= -t_1$
y_2	1	1	6	80	$= -t_2$
-1	3	2	6	0	$= f$
	$\parallel$	$\parallel$	$\parallel$	$\parallel$	
	s_1	s_2	s_3	g	

Finally, the dual to the given maximum problem is the minimum problem

$$\text{Minimize: } g(y_1, y_2) = 40y_1 + 80y_2$$
subject to:
$$4y_1 + y_2 \ge 3$$
$$y_2 \ge 2$$
$$-8y_1 + 6y_2 \ge 6$$
$$y_1 \ge 0$$
$$y_2 \ge 0$$

Example 8.3.6 Consider the linear program (Example 8.2.5) given by

Minimize: $g(y_1, y_2, y_3) = 5y_1 + 3y_2 + 2y_3$
subject to:

$$y_1 + y_2 + \ y_3 \geq 24$$
$$y_1 \qquad\quad - 2y_3 \geq \ 0$$
$$y_1 - y_2 + \ y_3 \geq \ 0$$
$$2y_1 \qquad + 2y_3 \geq 19$$
$$y_1 \geq \ 0$$
$$y_2 \geq \ 0$$
$$y_3 \geq \ 0$$

The vector-matrix form is

Minimize: YB
subject to: $YA \geq C, \ Y \geq \theta$

where

$$A = \begin{bmatrix} 1 & 1 & 1 & 2 \\ 1 & 0 & -1 & 0 \\ 1 & -2 & 1 & 2 \end{bmatrix} \qquad B = \begin{bmatrix} 5 \\ 3 \\ 2 \end{bmatrix} \qquad C = [24, 0, 0, 19]$$

$$\theta = [0, 0, 0] \qquad Y = [y_1, y_2, y_3]$$

Consequently, the Tucker tableau for this linear program is given by Figure 8.3.9, and the indicators are 24, 0, 0, and 19.

Figure 8.3.9

	x_1	x_2	x_3	x_4	-1	
y_1	1	1	1	2	5	$= -t_1$
y_2	1	0	-1	0	3	$= -t_2$
y_3	1	-2	1	2	2	$= -t_3$
-1	24	0	0	19	0	$= f$
	$\parallel$	$\parallel$	$\parallel$	$\parallel$	$\parallel$	
	s_1	s_2	s_3	s_4	g	

Also, the dual to the given minimum problem is the maximum problem

Maximize: $f(x_1, x_2, x_3, x_4) = 24x_1 + 19x_4$
subject to:

$$x_1 + \ x_2 + x_3 + 2x_4 \leq 5$$
$$x_1 \qquad - x_3 \qquad\quad \leq 3$$
$$x_1 - 2x_2 + x_3 + 2x_4 \leq 2$$
$$x_1 \geq 0$$
$$x_2 \geq 0$$
$$x_3 \geq 0$$
$$x_4 \geq 0$$

Exercises for 8.3

In each of problems 1–6, construct the Tucker tableau for the given linear programming problem and determine the indicators for the tableau.

1. Maximize: $f(x_1, x_2) = 3x_1 - 7x_2$
   subject to:
   $$5x_1 + 2x_2 \leq 6$$
   $$4x_1 - 6x_2 \leq 1$$
   $$x_1 \geq 0$$
   $$x_2 \geq 0$$

2. Maximize: $f(x_1, x_2, x_3) = x_1 - x_2 + 4x_3$
   subject to:
   $$3x_1 - 4x_2 + x_3 \leq 2$$
   $$5x_1 + 6x_2 \qquad \leq 1$$
   $$x_1 \geq 0$$
   $$x_2 \geq 0$$
   $$x_3 \geq 0$$

3. Minimize: $g(y_1, y_2) = y_1 + 4y_2$
   subject to:
   $$4y_1 + 3y_2 \geq \quad 7$$
   $$2y_1 - \quad y_2 \geq -8$$
   $$-3y_1 + 5y_2 \geq \quad 1$$
   $$y_1 \geq \quad 0$$
   $$y_2 \geq \quad 0$$

4. Minimize: $g(y_1, y_2, y_3, y_4) = 2y_1 + y_2 + 3y_3 + y_4$
   subject to:
   $$-y_1 + 6y_2 + 7y_3 + 5y_4 \geq \quad 6$$
   $$2y_1 \qquad + \quad y_3 - \quad y_4 \geq -2$$
   $$8y_2 \qquad + 6y_4 \geq \quad 1$$
   $$y_1 \geq \quad 0$$
   $$y_2 \geq \quad 0$$
   $$y_3 \geq \quad 0$$
   $$y_4 \geq \quad 0$$

5. Maximize: $f(x_1, x_2, x_3) = -5x_1 + x_2 + x_3$
   subject to:
   $$2x_1 + 3x_2 - 4x_3 \leq \quad 1$$
   $$x_1 \qquad - \quad x_3 \leq \quad 4$$
   $$6x_1 - 5x_2 \qquad \leq 16$$
   $$x_1 \geq \quad 0$$
   $$x_2 \geq \quad 0$$
   $$x_3 \geq \quad 0$$

6. Minimize: $g(y_1, y_2, y_3) = y_1 + y_2 + \frac{3}{2}y_3$
   subject to:
   $$3y_1 - 5y_2 + 7y_3 \geq -2$$
   $$2y_1 \qquad + 5y_3 \geq \quad 1$$
   $$4y_2 - \quad y_3 \geq 10$$
   $$y_1 \geq \quad 0$$
   $$y_2 \geq \quad 0$$
   $$y_3 \geq \quad 0$$

In each of problems 7–10, determine the Tucker tableau for the given linear programming problem and also find the indicators for the tableau.

7. Maximize: $f(x_1, x_2, x_3) = 3x_1 + x_2 - 6x_3$
   subject to:

$$3x_1 - 4x_2 + x_3 \leq 2$$
$$x_1 \leq 4 + 6x_3$$
$$6x_2 + 5x_1 \geq 2x_2 - 5$$
$$x_2 \geq 4x_3$$
$$x_1 \geq 0$$
$$x_2 \geq 0$$
$$x_3 \geq 0$$

8. Maximize: $f(x_1, x_2, x_3, x_4) = x_1 - x_2 + x_3 + x_4$
   subject to:

$$x_1 \geq 3x_2 - 5x_4$$
$$x_2 + x_3 \leq 6 + 2x_1 - 4x_4$$
$$4 - 2x_4 \geq 3 - 8x_1 + 7x_3$$
$$x_1 \geq 0$$
$$x_2 \geq 0$$
$$x_3 \geq 0$$
$$x_4 \geq 0$$

9. Minimize: $g(y_1, y_2) = 5y_1 + 4y_2$
   subject to:

$$2y_1 + 5y_2 \geq 7$$
$$6y_2 - 3y_1 \geq -2$$
$$3 + 2y_2 \geq -y_1$$
$$y_1 \geq 0$$
$$y_2 \geq 0$$

10. Minimize: $g(y_1, y_2, y_3, y_4) = y_1 + 6y_2 + 3y_3 + 10y_4$
    subject to:

$$y_1 - 3y_2 + 4y_3 - 6y_4 \leq 5$$
$$6 + 7y_1 - 8y_3 \geq 11$$
$$y_1 \geq 0$$
$$y_2 \geq 0$$
$$y_3 \geq 0$$
$$y_4 \geq 0$$

11. Determine the Tucker tableau and indicators for each of the following linear programming problems.

(a) Maximize: $f(x_1, x_2, x_3, x_4) = 4x_1 - 2x_2 + x_3 + 5x_4$
    subject to:

$$2x_1 + 6x_2 + 3x_3 - 4x_4 \leq 3$$
$$8x_2 - 3x_3 + x_4 \leq 1$$
$$-x_1 + 4x_3 + 2x_4 \leq 4$$
$$x_1 \geq 0$$
$$x_2 \geq 0$$
$$x_3 \geq 0$$
$$x_4 \geq 0$$

(b) Minimize: $g(y_1, y_2, y_3) = 3y_1 + y_2 + 4y_3$
   subject to:
$$
\begin{aligned}
2y_1 \quad\quad\quad - y_3 &\geq 4 \\
6y_1 + 8y_2 \quad\quad &\geq -2 \\
3y_1 - 3y_2 + 4y_3 &\geq 1 \\
-4y_1 + y_2 + 2y_3 &\geq 5 \\
y_1 &\geq 0 \\
y_2 &\geq 0 \\
y_3 &\geq 0
\end{aligned}
$$

12. Determine the Tucker tableau and indicators for each of the following linear programming problems.

(a) Maximize: $f(x_1, x_2, x_3) = -2x_1 + 4x_2 + 6x_3$
   subject to:
$$
\begin{aligned}
-x_1 + 3x_2 \quad\quad &\leq 1 \\
5x_1 + 2x_2 - 3x_3 &\leq 2 \\
6x_1 \quad\quad + 8x_3 &\leq 4 \\
2x_1 + 6x_2 - 2x_3 &\leq 3 \\
x_1 &\geq 0 \\
x_2 &\geq 0 \\
x_3 &\geq 0
\end{aligned}
$$

(b) Minimize: $g(y_1, y_2, y_3, y_4) = y_1 + 2y_2 + 4y_3 + 3y_4$
   subject to:
$$
\begin{aligned}
-y_1 + 5y_2 + 6y_3 + 2y_4 &\geq -2 \\
3y_1 + 2y_2 \quad\quad + 6y_4 &\geq 4 \\
-3y_2 + 8y_3 - 2y_4 &\geq 6 \\
y_1 &\geq 0 \\
y_2 &\geq 0 \\
y_3 &\geq 0 \\
y_4 &\geq 0
\end{aligned}
$$

In each of problems 13–18, determine both the maximum and minimum linear programming problems contained in the given Tucker tableau.

13.

	x_1	x_2	-1	
y_1	2	-5	8	$= -t_1$
y_2	3	6	4	$= -t_2$
-1	-5	7	0	$= f$
	$\shortparallel$	$\shortparallel$	$\shortparallel$	
	s_1	s_2	g	

14.

	x_1	x_2	x_3	-1	
y_1	-3	5	4	2	$= -t_1$
y_2	1	-1	2	6	$= -t_2$
-1	7	-3	5	0	$= f$
	$\shortparallel$	$\shortparallel$	$\shortparallel$	$\shortparallel$	
	s_1	s_2	s_3	g	

15.

	x_1	x_2	-1	
y_1	$\frac{1}{4}$	-3	2	$= -t_1$
y_2	-5	$\frac{2}{3}$	1	$= -t_2$
y_3	6	-8	3	$= -t_3$
-1	4	6	0	$= f$
	$\parallel$	$\parallel$	$\parallel$	
	s_1	s_2	g	

16.

	x_1	x_2	x_3	-1	
y_1	3	$-\frac{1}{2}$	7	3	$= -t_1$
y_2	2	4	0	0	$= -t_2$
y_3	0	$\frac{3}{4}$	1	5	$= -t_3$
-1	-2	6	4	0	$= f$
	$\parallel$	$\parallel$	$\parallel$	$\parallel$	
	s_1	s_2	s_3	g	

17.

	x_1	x_2	x_3	x_4	-1	
y_1	$\frac{3}{4}$	2	6	-4	6	$= -t_1$
y_2	-8	3	1	5	4	$= -t_2$
-1	3	2	5	-5	0	$= f$
	$\parallel$	$\parallel$	$\parallel$	$\parallel$	$\parallel$	
	s_1	s_2	s_3	s_4	g	

18.

	x_1	x_2	x_3	-1	
y_1	3	0	-5	4	$= -t_1$
y_2	2	1	0	1	$= -t_2$
y_3	0	-6	7	3	$= -t_3$
y_4	1	2	3	0	$= -t_4$
y_5	-8	-4	1	6	$= -t_5$
-1	2	-5	7	0	$= f$
	$\parallel$	$\parallel$	$\parallel$	$\parallel$	
	s_1	s_2	s_3	g	

Section 8.4   Simplex Method: An Example

In this section we shall illustrate how the simplex method is applied to solve a maximum linear programming problem. We will see in Section 8.6 that it will not be necessary to consider minimum linear programming problems separately because the solution to such a problem can be obtained by solving its dual maximum problem.

Example 8.4.1 Consider again the linear programming problem of Examples 8.2.2 and 8.3.1:

$$\text{Maximize: } f(x_1, x_2) = 10x_1 + 25x_2$$
subject to:
$$2x_1 + 3x_2 \leq 72$$
$$2x_1 + 10x_2 \leq 100$$
$$x_1 \geq 0$$
$$x_2 \geq 0$$

In Example 8.3.1 [see Eqs. (8.3.5) and (8.3.6)] we found that the problem can be reexpressed as

$$\text{Maximize: } f(x_1, x_2) = 10x_1 + 25x_2 \tag{8.4.1}$$
subject to:
$$2x_1 + 3x_2 - 72 = -t_1 \tag{8.4.2}$$
$$2x_1 + 10x_2 - 100 = -t_2 \tag{8.4.3}$$
$$x_1 \geq 0 \tag{8.4.4}$$
$$x_2 \geq 0 \tag{8.4.5}$$
$$t_1 \geq 0 \tag{8.4.6}$$
$$t_2 \geq 0 \tag{8.4.7}$$

The tableau for this problem was determined in Figure 8.3.1 and is given in Figure 8.4.1. Values for the x_1, x_2, t_1, t_2 which satisfy the constraints (8.4.2)–(8.4.7) are called *feasible values* for these variables.

Figure 8.4.1

x_1	x_2	-1	
2	3	72	$= -t_1$
2	10	100	$= -t_2$
10	25	0	$= f$

Now, if we set $x_1 = x_2 = 0$, we find [by Eqs. (8.4.2) and (8.4.3) or by Figure 8.4.1] that we must have $t_1 = 72$ and $t_2 = 100$. Hence, when $x_1 = 0$, $x_2 = 0$, $t_1 = 72$, and $t_2 = 100$, all the constraints (8.4.2)–(8.4.7) are satisfied (i.e., these are feasible values for the variables). However, when $x_1 = x_2 = 0$, it follows from Eq. (8.4.1) (or the tableau in Figure 8.4.1) that $f = 0$.

It seems clear that we should be able to increase the value of f, in this case, by increasing either x_1 or x_2 (or both). For instance, if we set $x_1 = 2$, $x_2 = 0$, then, by Eqs. (8.4.2) and (8.4.3), we must have $t_1 = 68$ and $t_2 = 96$. Again these values for the variables are feasible and by Eq. (8.4.1) we have $f = 20$ (>0) in this case. We see that by keeping $x_2 = 0$ and increasing x_1 from 0 to 2 we obtain feasible values for the variables which result in a larger value for f.

Now, although we can increase the value of f by keeping $x_2 = 0$ and increasing the value of x_1, we must be careful not to make x_1 too large. For by doing so we may violate one or more of the inequalities (8.4.6) and (8.4.7). For instance, if we take $x_1 = 50$ and $x_2 = 0$ we see that to satisfy Eqs. (8.4.2) and (8.4.3) we must take $t_1 = -28$ and $t_2 = 0$. Thus, even though Eqs. (8.4.2)–(8.4.5) and (8.4.7) are satisfied, Eq. (8.4.6) is not satisfied. Hence these are not feasible values for the variables.

So, the question now is: If we set $x_2 = 0$, how large can x_1 be made and still have feasible values for the variables? The answer to this question can be obtained by examining Eqs. (8.4.2) and (8.4.3). Because we are setting $x_2 = 0$, these equations become

$$2x_1 - 72 = -t_1 \tag{8.4.8}$$
$$2x_1 - 100 = -t_2 \tag{8.4.9}$$

Since we want $t_1 \geq 0$, $t_2 \geq 0$ [Eqs. (8.4.6) and (8.4.7)], it follows that we must have

$$2x_1 - 72 \leq 0$$
$$2x_1 - 100 \leq 0$$

or

$$2x_1 \leq 72$$
$$2x_1 \leq 100$$

or

$$x_1 \leq \tfrac{72}{2} = 36$$
$$x_1 \leq \tfrac{100}{2} = 50 \tag{8.4.10}$$

Both of these inequalities will be satisfied if we set x_1 equal to the smaller ratio on the right-hand side of (8.4.10), namely, $\tfrac{72}{2} = 36$. This is as large as x_1 can be made (having $x_2 = 0$) and still have feasible values for the variables.

Now, when $x_1 = 36$ and $x_2 = 0$ we have $t_1 = 0$ and $t_2 = 28$. Also, $f = 360$. This is quite an improvement over the value $f = 0$ obtained by setting $x_1 = x_2 = 0$. However, can f still be made larger? To answer this question we first solve for x_1 in terms of t_1 and x_2 (the two variables currently set equal to 0) in Eq. (8.4.2). The result is

$$x_1 = -\tfrac{1}{2}t_1 - \tfrac{3}{2}x_2 + 36$$

In other words,

$$\tfrac{1}{2}t_1 + \tfrac{3}{2}x_2 - 36 = -x_1 \tag{8.4.11}$$

Substituting this into Eq. (8.4.3) gives

$$2(-\tfrac{1}{2}t_1 - \tfrac{3}{2}x_2 + 36) + 10x_2 - 100 = -t_2$$

or

$$-t_1 + 7x_2 - 28 = -t_2 \tag{8.4.12}$$

Finally, using Eq. (8.4.11) in (8.4.1) yields

$$f = 10(-\tfrac{1}{2}t_1 - \tfrac{3}{2}x_2 + 36) + 25x_2$$

or

$$f = -5t_1 + 10x_2 + 360 \tag{8.4.13}$$

Thus, by Eqs. (8.4.11)–(8.4.13) we can reexpress the problem in Eqs. (8.4.1)–(8.4.7)

as

Maximize: $f = -5t_1 + 10x_2 + 360$ $\qquad$ (8.4.14)

subject to:

$$\tfrac{1}{2}t_1 + \tfrac{3}{2}x_2 - 36 = -x_1 \tag{8.4.15}$$
$$-t_1 + 7x_2 - 28 = -t_2 \tag{8.4.16}$$
$$x_1 \geq 0 \tag{8.4.17}$$
$$x_2 \geq 0 \tag{8.4.18}$$
$$t_1 \geq 0 \tag{8.4.19}$$
$$t_2 \geq 0 \tag{8.4.20}$$

The tableau for this reexpression of the original problem is obtained as usual and is given by Figure 8.4.2.

Figure 8.4.2

t_1	x_2	-1	
$\frac{1}{2}$	$\frac{3}{2}$	36	$= -x_1$
-1	7	28	$= -t_2$
-5	10	-360	$= f$

Let us examine Eq. (8.4.14) for a moment. First, it is clear that to make f large, we should set $t_1 = 0$. This is because of the negative coefficient (-5) of t_1 and the fact that we must have $t_1 \geq 0$. On the other hand, since x_2 has a positive coefficient (10), we can still increase the value of f by increasing x_2. As before, we must take care not to make x_2 too large. For by doing so we could obtain values for the variables which are not feasible.

To see how large x_2 can be made, we proceed as before. Setting $t_1 = 0$ in Eqs. (8.4.15) and (8.4.16), we get the equations

$$\tfrac{3}{2}x_2 - 36 = -x_1$$
$$7x_2 - 28 = -t_2$$

and since we want $x_1 \geq 0$, $t_2 \geq 0$, this means that

$$\tfrac{3}{2}x_2 - 36 \leq 0$$
$$7x_2 - 28 \leq 0$$

or

$$\tfrac{3}{2}x_2 \leq 36$$
$$7x_2 \leq 28$$

or

$$x_2 \leq 36/\tfrac{3}{2} = 24$$
$$x_2 \leq \tfrac{28}{7} = 4 \tag{8.4.21}$$

We then set x_2 equal to the smaller of the values on the right-hand side of Eq. (8.4.21), $\frac{28}{7} = 4$. This is as large as x_2 can be made and still have feasible values for the variables.

When $t_1 = 0$ and $x_2 = 4$, we have [see Eqs. (8.4.15) and (8.4.16)] $x_1 = 30$ and $t_2 = 0$. Also, by Eq. (8.4.14),

$$f = -5 \cdot 0 + 10 \cdot 4 + 360 = 400$$

which is an improvement over our last value for f, which was 360.

Once more we ask whether or not f can still be made larger? To answer this question we solve for x_2 in terms of t_1 and t_2 (the two values currently set equal to 0) in Eq. (8.4.16). The result is

$$x_2 = \tfrac{1}{7}t_1 - \tfrac{1}{7}t_2 + 4$$

or

$$-\tfrac{1}{7}t_1 + \tfrac{1}{7}t_2 - 4 = -x_2 \tag{8.4.22}$$

Substituting this into Eq. (8.4.15) gives

$$\tfrac{1}{2}t_1 + \tfrac{3}{2}(\tfrac{1}{7}t_1 - \tfrac{1}{7}t_2 + 4) - 36 = -x_1$$

or

$$\tfrac{5}{7}t_1 - \tfrac{3}{14}t_2 - 30 = -x_1 \tag{8.4.23}$$

Finally, using Eq. (8.4.22) in (8.4.14) we obtain

$$f = -5t_1 + 10(\tfrac{1}{7}t_1 - \tfrac{1}{7}t_2 + 4) + 360$$

or

$$f = -\tfrac{25}{7}t_1 - \tfrac{10}{7}t_2 + 400 \tag{8.4.24}$$

Consequently, as before, we can reexpress our problem as

Maximize: $f = -\tfrac{25}{7}t_1 - \tfrac{10}{7}t_2 + 400$ \hfill (8.4.25)

subject to:

$$\tfrac{5}{7}t_1 - \tfrac{3}{14}t_2 - 30 = -x_1 \tag{8.4.26}$$
$$-\tfrac{1}{7}t_1 + \tfrac{1}{7}t_2 - 4 = -x_2 \tag{8.4.27}$$
$$x_1 \ge 0$$
$$x_2 \ge 0$$
$$t_1 \ge 0$$
$$t_2 \ge 0$$

and the tableau for this reexpression is shown in Figure 8.4.3.

Figure 8.4.3

t_1	t_2	-1	
$\tfrac{5}{7}$	$-\tfrac{3}{14}$	30	$= -x_1$
$-\tfrac{1}{7}$	$\tfrac{1}{7}$	4	$= -x_2$
$-\tfrac{25}{7}$	$-\tfrac{10}{7}$	-400	$= f$

Now, from Eq. (8.4.25) (or the indicators of the tableau in Figure 8.4.3) we see that the coefficients of t_1 and t_2 in the expression for f are both nonpositive $(-\tfrac{25}{7}$ and $-\tfrac{10}{7})$. Thus f can be made largest by setting $t_1 = t_2 = 0$ (remember that we must have $t_1 \ge 0$, $t_2 \ge 0$). Using Eqs. (8.4.26) and (8.4.27), this means that $x_1 = 30$ and $x_2 = 4$, and, by Eq. (8.4.25), $f = 400$.

In summary, the maximum value of f, subject to the given constraints, is 400, and this occurs when $x_1 = 30$ and $x_2 = 4$ (and $t_1 = t_2 = 0$).

Let us interpret our results in terms of the tableau. First, we saw that because the coefficients of the variables in the expression for f were nonpositive [see Eq. (8.4.24)] we obtained the maximum value of f by setting these variables equal to zero. In terms of the tableau in Figure 8.4.3, the coefficients of the variables in the expression for f being nonpositive corresponds to the fact that *the indicators of the tableau are nonpositive.*

Second, setting $t_1 = t_2 = 0$ we found by using Eqs. (8.4.26), (8.4.27), and (8.4.25) that $x_1 = 30$, $x_2 = 4$, and $f = 400$. This can be obtained directly from the last column of the tableau in Figure 8.4.3. Indeed, by interpreting the tableau as usual and setting

$t_1 = t_2 = 0$, we get

$$(\tfrac{5}{7}) \cdot 0 - (\tfrac{3}{14}) \cdot 0 - 30 = -x_1$$
$$-(\tfrac{1}{7}) \cdot 0 + (\tfrac{1}{7}) \cdot 0 - 4 = -x_2$$
$$-(\tfrac{25}{7}) \cdot 0 - (\tfrac{10}{7}) \cdot 0 + 400 = f$$

or, in other words $x_1 = 30$, $x_2 = 4$, and $f = 400$.

Hence, once a tableau corresponding to a reexpression of a maximum linear programming problem has only nonpositive indicators, the solution to the problem is contained in the tableau: the variables labeling the columns should be set equal to zero, and those on the right-hand side of the tableau have the values indicated by the last column of the tableau.

The reader may recall that the above linear programming problem was solved in Section 7.7 by using the geometric method, with much less effort! So, why go through all this work when we can get the answer much easier by the other (geometric) method? There are several justifications.

First, the method developed in the example above applies not only to linear programs in two variables (which can be solved geometrically), but also applies to linear programs in an arbitrary (finite) number of variables (which, in practice, cannot be solved by the geometric method).

Second, although the amount of writing was greater using the simplex method to solve the linear program in the example above than using the geometric method of Chapter 7, conceptually the amount of work was less. The reason is that using the geometric method, the function f in the example above had to be evaluated at all four extreme points: $(0, 0)$, $(0, 10)$, $(30, 4)$, and $(36, 0)$ (see page 329). However, in the simplex method the function f was really only evaluated at three of the extreme points: $(0, 0)$, $(36, 0)$, and $(30, 4)$.

Third, as we shall see, the simplex method solves a problem and its dual simultaneously and the solution to the dual of the original linear program has important mathematical (as well as applied) interpretations.

Finally, by carefully analyzing the steps used in the example above, we can reduce considerably the amount of writing and effort required and in fact can give a relatively simple, systematic procedure for use of the simplex method.

Exercises for 8.4

Use the simplex method as illustrated in Example 8.4.1 to solve the following linear programming problems.

1. Maximize: $f(x_1, x_2) = 2x_1 + 3x_2$
   subject to:
   $$3x_1 + x_2 \le 15$$
   $$3x_1 + 4x_2 \le 24$$
   $$x_1 \ge 0$$
   $$x_2 \ge 0$$

2. Maximize: $f(x_1, x_2) = 3x_1 + 2x_2$
   subject to:
   $$3x_1 + x_2 \le 15$$
   $$3x_1 + 4x_2 \le 24$$
   $$x_1 \ge 0$$
   $$x_2 \ge 0$$

3. Maximize: $f(x_1, x_2) = 5x_1 + 2x_2$
   subject to:
   $$x_1 + 3x_2 \leq 6$$
   $$x_1 + x_2 \leq 4$$
   $$x_1 \geq 0$$
   $$x_2 \geq 0$$

4. Maximize: $f(x_1, x_2) = 4x_1 + 5x_2$
   subject to:
   $$x_1 + 3x_2 \leq 6$$
   $$x_1 + x_2 \leq 4$$
   $$x_1 \geq 0$$
   $$x_2 \geq 0$$

5. Maximize: $f(x_1, x_2, x_3) = 3x_1 + 2x_2 + 6x_3$
   subject to:
   $$4x_1 \qquad - 8x_3 \leq 40$$
   $$x_1 + x_2 + 6x_3 \leq 80$$
   $$x_1 \geq 0$$
   $$x_2 \geq 0$$
   $$x_3 \geq 0$$

   (*Hint:* Begin by setting two of the three variables x_1, x_2, and x_3 equal to zero and making the third as large as possible.)

6. Maximize: $f(x_1, x_2) = 24x_1 + 29x_2$
   subject to:
   $$2x_1 + 3x_2 \leq 15$$
   $$5x_1 + 4x_2 \leq 25$$
   $$x_1 \geq 0$$
   $$x_2 \geq 0$$

7. Maximize: $f(x_1, x_2, x_3, x_4) = 24x_1 + 19x_4$
   subject to:
   $$x_1 + x_2 + x_3 + 2x_4 \leq 5$$
   $$x_1 \qquad - x_3 \qquad \leq 3$$
   $$x_1 - 2x_2 + x_3 + 2x_4 \leq 2$$
   $$x_1 \geq 0$$
   $$x_2 \geq 0$$
   $$x_3 \geq 0$$
   $$x_4 \geq 0$$

Section 8.5 Pivoting Operation

In Section 8.4 we applied the simplex method for solving a maximum linear programming problem. In doing so we found that on several occasions it was necessary to solve for certain variables in terms of others. This was not difficult but did require quite a few calculations. We saw that the solving of certain variables in terms of others led to a reexpression of the linear programming problem, which, of course, could be represented by a new tableau.

Our aim here is to present a method for going from one tableau to another without having to bother doing all the details of the intermediate computations. The method is obtained simply by examining carefully the effect on a tableau resulting from the solution of some variables in terms of others. We call the method *the pivoting operation*.

Before presenting the pivoting operation, we remark that we have stated previously that the simplex method solves a linear program and its dual simultaneously. Thus, in explaining the pivoting operation, we shall use the Tucker tableau. When the pivoting operation is performed on the Tucker tableau, it will not only yield the new tableau corresponding to the reexpression of the maximum problem, but it will also give the new tableau corresponding to the reexpression of the dual minimum problem.

To describe the pivoting operation we first write a general tableau in the form of Figure 8.5.1. In the figure, p is to represent some *nonzero* entry in the tableau not

Figure 8.5.1

in the last column or row (i.e., p is some entry of the matrix A). The entry q is to represent any other entry in the same row as p, *including* the entry in the last column. Also, r is to represent any other entry in the same column as p, *including* the entry in the last row. Finally, s is to represent any entry not in the same row or column as p.

Pivoting Operation

The *pivoting operation* (on p) can then be described by the following steps.

1. Exchange the variable labels x_j and t_i and also exchange y_i and s_j.
2. Replace p by $1/p$.
3. Replace the entries q by q/p. In other words, the entries in the same row as p, other than p itself, are divided by p.
4. Replace r by $-r/p$. That is, divide by $-p$ the entries in the same column as p, other than p itself.
5. Replace each entry s by $(ps - rq)/p$. That is, for each entry s not in the same row or same column as p, let q be the entry in the same row as p and the same column as s. Also, let r be the entry in the same row as s and in the same column as p. Then s is replaced by $(ps - rq)/p$.

In this operation, the entry p is referred to as the *pivot entry* and the change from the original tableau to the one obtained via steps 1–5 is called a *pivot step*.

It can be proved that the tableau obtained after the pivot step is equivalent to the original tableau in the sense that it leads to a reexpression of the original linear programs contained in the tableau.

A pivot box is useful for illustrating the pivoting operation. It gives the tableau in Figure 8.5.2, which results from the tableau in Figure 8.5.1 after pivoting on p.

Figure 8.5.2

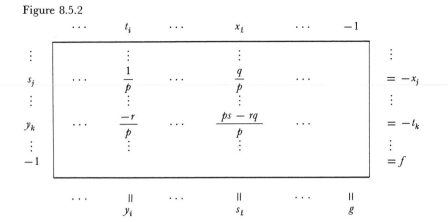

The pivoting operation will now be illustrated by the following examples.

Example 8.5.1   Consider again the linear programming problem of Example 8.4.1.

Maximize: $f(x_1, x_2) = 10x_1 + 25x_2$
subject to:

$$2x_1 + 3x_2 \leq 72$$
$$2x_1 + 10x_2 \leq 100$$
$$x_1 \geq 0$$
$$x_2 \geq 0$$

The Tucker tableau is shown in Figure 8.5.3. This corresponds to Figure 8.4.1 in

Figure 8.5.3

	x_1	x_2	-1	
y_1	2*	3	72	$= -t_1$
y_2	2	10	100	$= -t_2$
-1	10	25	0	$= f$
	$\shortparallel$	$\shortparallel$	$\shortparallel$	
	s_1	s_2	g	

Example 8.4.1. In that example we found it necessary to solve for x_1 and t_2 in terms of t_1 and x_2 (see page 357). This corresponds to pivoting on the 2 in the upper left-hand corner of the tableau in Figure 8.5.3.

We now carry out the steps in the pivoting operation:

1. Exchange the variables x_1 and t_1 as well as the variables y_1 and s_1.
2. Replace the 2 (marked with an asterisk) by $\frac{1}{2}$.
3. Replace 3 and 72 by $\frac{3}{2}$ and $\frac{72}{2} = 36$.
4. Replace 2 and 10 by $-\frac{2}{2} = -1$ and $-\frac{10}{2} = -5$.
5. 2nd $\begin{cases} \text{Replace 10 by } (2 \cdot 10 - 2 \cdot 3)/2 = 7. \\ \text{Replace 100 by } (2 \cdot 100 - 2 \cdot 72)/2 = 28. \end{cases}$
   row
   3rd $\begin{cases} \text{Replace 25 by } (2 \cdot 25 - 10 \cdot 3)/2 = 10. \\ \text{Replace 0 by } (2 \cdot 0 - 10 \cdot 72)/2 = -360. \end{cases}$
   row

Figure 8.5.4

	t_1	x_2	-1	
s_1	$\frac{1}{2}$	$\frac{3}{2}$	36	$= -x_1$
y_2	-1	7	28	$= -t_2$
-1	-5	10	-360	$= f$
	$\parallel$	$\parallel$	$\parallel$	
	y_1	s_2	g	

The tableau after the pivot step is shown in Figure 8.5.4. Notice that this corresponds to the tableau in Figure 8.4.2 but was obtained with much less effort. Moreover, it also contains the corresponding reexpression of the dual minimum problem.

Example 8.5.2 Consider the tableau of Example 8.3.4,

	x_1	x_2	-1	
y_1	2	3	15	$= -t_1$
y_2	$5*$	4	25	$= -t_2$
-1	24	29	0	$= f$
	$\parallel$	$\parallel$	$\parallel$	
	s_1	s_2	g	

We will apply the pivoting operation with 5 as the pivot. To remember that it is the pivot entry, we mark it with an asterisk. The steps in the pivoting operation are now applied.

1. Exchange the variables x_1 and t_2 as well as y_2 and s_1.
2. Replace 5 by $\frac{1}{5}$.
3. Replace 4 and 25 by $\frac{4}{5}$ and $\frac{25}{5} = 5$.
4. Replace 2 and 24 by $-\frac{2}{5}$ and $-\frac{24}{5}$.
5. 1st $\begin{cases} \text{Replace 3 by } (5 \cdot 3 - 2 \cdot 4)/5 = \frac{7}{5}. \\ \text{Replace 15 by } (5 \cdot 15 - 2 \cdot 25)/5 = 5. \end{cases}$
   row
   3rd $\begin{cases} \text{Replace 29 by } (5 \cdot 29 - 24 \cdot 4)/5 = \frac{49}{5}. \\ \text{Replace 0 by } (5 \cdot 0 - 24 \cdot 25)/5 = -120. \end{cases}$
   row

The result after the pivot step is the tableau

	t_2	x_2	-1	
y_1	$-\frac{2}{5}$	$\frac{7}{5}$	5	$= -t_1$
s_1	$\frac{1}{5}$	$\frac{4}{5}$	5	$= -x_1$
-1	$-\frac{24}{5}$	$\frac{49}{5}$	-120	$= f$
	$\parallel$	$\parallel$	$\parallel$	
	y_2	s_2	g	

Example 8.5.3 Consider the tableau given in Figure 8.5.5. Let the entry in the second row and fourth column of the tableau be the *pivot*. Applying 1–5 we obtain:

Figure 8.5.5

	x_1	x_2	x_3	x_4	-1	
y_1	2	1	0	2	8	$= -t_1$
y_2	4	-8	4	4*	8	$= -t_2$
y_3	3	-4	1	3	7	$= -t_3$
-1	24	0	0	19	0	$= f$
	$\parallel$	$\parallel$	$\parallel$	$\parallel$	$\parallel$	
	s_1	s_2	s_3	s_4	g	

1. Exchange x_4 and t_2 as well as y_2 and s_4.
2. Replace 4 by $\frac{1}{4}$.
3. Replace 4, -8, 4, and 8 by $\frac{4}{4} = 1$, $-\frac{8}{4} = -2$, $\frac{4}{4} = 1$, and $\frac{8}{4} = 2$.
4. Replace 2, 3, and 19 by $-\frac{2}{4} = -\frac{1}{2}$, $-\frac{3}{4}$, and $-\frac{19}{4}$.
5.
1st row $\begin{cases} \text{Replace 2 by } (4 \cdot 2 - 2 \cdot 4)/4 = 0 \\ \text{Replace 1 by } (4 \cdot 1 - 2 \cdot (-8))/4 = 5. \\ \text{Replace 0 by } (4 \cdot 0 - 2 \cdot 4)/4 = -2. \\ \text{Replace 8 by } (4 \cdot 8 - 2 \cdot 8)/4 = 4. \end{cases}$

3rd row $\begin{cases} \text{Replace 3 by } (4 \cdot 3 - 3 \cdot 4)/4 = 0. \\ \text{Replace } -4 \text{ by } (4 \cdot (-4) - 3 \cdot (-8))/4 = 2. \\ \text{Replace 1 by } (4 \cdot 1 - 3 \cdot 4)/4 = -2. \\ \text{Replace 7 by } (4 \cdot 7 - 3 \cdot 8)/4 = 1. \end{cases}$

4th row $\begin{cases} \text{Replace 24 by } (4 \cdot 24 - 19 \cdot 4)/4 = 5. \\ \text{Replace 0 by } (4 \cdot 0 - 19 \cdot (-8))/4 = 38. \\ \text{Replace 0 by } (4 \cdot 0 - 19 \cdot 4)/4 = -19. \\ \text{Replace 0 by } (4 \cdot 0 - 19 \cdot 8)/4 = -38. \end{cases}$

The tableau after the pivot step is

	x_1	x_2	x_3	t_2	-1	
y_1	0	5	-2	$-\frac{1}{2}$	4	$= -t_1$
s_4	1	-2	1	$\frac{1}{4}$	2	$= -x_4$
y_3	0	2	-2	$-\frac{3}{4}$	1	$= -t_3$
-1	5	38	-19	$-\frac{19}{4}$	-38	$= f$
	$\parallel$	$\parallel$	$\parallel$	$\parallel$	$\parallel$	
	s_1	s_2	s_3	y_2	g	

Exercises for 8.5

Perform the pivoting operation on the given tableau with the entry marked with an asterisk as the pivot entry.

1.

	x_1	x_2	-1	
y_1	1	-4	2	$= -t_1$
y_2	5*	8	3	$= -t_2$
-1	4	-6	0	$= f$
	$\shortparallel$	$\shortparallel$	$\shortparallel$	
	s_1	s_2	g	

2.

	x_1	x_2	-1	
y_1	15	3*	6	$= -t_1$
y_2	1	0	4	$= -t_2$
-1	4	12	0	$= f$
	$\shortparallel$	$\shortparallel$	$\shortparallel$	
	s_1	s_2	g	

3.

	x_1	x_2	-1	
y_1	8*	-2	1	$= -t_1$
y_2	1	4	5	$= -t_2$
-1	2	-6	0	$= f$
	$\shortparallel$	$\shortparallel$	$\shortparallel$	
	s_1	s_2	g	

4.

	x_1	x_2	x_3	-1	
y_1	-1	3	2	3	$= -t_1$
y_2	4	-5	7*	1	$= -t_2$
-1	2	-1	5	0	$= f$
	$\shortparallel$	$\shortparallel$	$\shortparallel$	$\shortparallel$	
	s_1	s_2	s_3	g	

5.

	x_1	x_2	-1	
y_1	0	-2	6	$= -t_1$
y_2	16	8^*	2	$= -t_2$
y_3	4	3	3	$= -t_3$
-1	-5	4	0	$= f$
	$\shortparallel$	$\shortparallel$	$\shortparallel$	
	s_1	s_2	g	

6.

	x_1	x_2	x_3	-1	
y_1	5	-2	0	8	$= -t_1$
y_2	2	6^*	-4	6	$= -t_2$
y_3	-1	3	5	5	$= -t_3$
-1	3	12	-2	0	$= f$
	$\shortparallel$	$\shortparallel$	$\shortparallel$	$\shortparallel$	
	s_1	s_2	s_3	g	

7.

	x_1	x_2	x_3	-1	
y_1	$\frac{1}{4}$	$\frac{1}{2}$	0	1	$= -t_1$
y_2	0	-3	$\frac{3}{4}$	2	$= -t_2$
y_3	$-\frac{1}{2}$	$\frac{1}{4}^*$	2	$\frac{1}{8}$	$= -t_3$
-1	2	5	$-\frac{1}{4}$	0	$= f$
	$\shortparallel$	$\shortparallel$	$\shortparallel$	$\shortparallel$	
	s_1	s_2	s_3	g	

8.

	x_1	x_2	x_3	-1	
y_1	$\frac{1}{5}^*$	$\frac{1}{2}$	$-\frac{2}{5}$	1	$= -t_1$
y_2	$-\frac{2}{5}$	$\frac{3}{5}$	$\frac{3}{10}$	$\frac{2}{5}$	$= -t_2$
-1	$\frac{1}{10}$	$-\frac{1}{5}$	$\frac{3}{5}$	0	$= f$
	$\shortparallel$	$\shortparallel$	$\shortparallel$	$\shortparallel$	
	s_1	s_2	s_3	g	

9.

	x_1	x_2	-1	
y_1	0	$\frac{1}{8}$	1	$= -t_1$
y_2	$\frac{1}{4}$	-1	2	$= -t_2$
y_3	$-\frac{3}{4}$	$\frac{1}{2}^*$	$\frac{1}{4}$	$= -t_3$
y_4	1	2	4	$= -t_4$
-1	3	1	0	$= f$
	$\shortparallel$	$\shortparallel$	$\shortparallel$	
	s_1	s_2	g	

10.

	x_1	x_2	x_3	x_4	-1	
y_1	$\frac{1}{2}$	0	-1	2	1	$= -t_1$
y_2	1	$\frac{1}{2}$	1^*	-1	$\frac{1}{4}$	$= -t_2$
y_3	2	1	$-\frac{1}{4}$	0	$-\frac{1}{2}$	$= -t_3$
y_4	$\frac{1}{8}$	$\frac{1}{4}$	2	$\frac{1}{4}$	1	$= -t_4$
-1	-1	$-\frac{1}{4}$	2	$\frac{1}{2}$	0	$= f$
	$\parallel$	$\parallel$	$\parallel$	$\parallel$	$\parallel$	
	s_1	s_2	s_3	s_4	g	

Section 8.6 Simplex Algorithm

In Section 8.4 we illustrated the simplex method for solving a maximum linear programming problem. Using the pivoting operation we can now state the simplex algorithm, which accomplishes the work done in Example 8.4.1 with considerably less writing and effort by concentrating on the tableaux obtained during the various steps of the simplex method. The motivation for the sequence of steps in the simplex algorithm can be found by referring to Example 8.4.1.

Before presenting the simplex algorithm, which is based upon the solution of a maximum linear programming problem by the simplex method (see Section 8.4), we must make some remarks concerning minimum linear programming problems. We have seen that to each minimum linear programming problem there corresponds a dual maximum problem and that these two problems have the same Tucker tableau. By applying several of the fundamental theorems of linear programming, it can be shown that if we use the simplex method to solve the dual maximum problem of a minimum problem, the solution to the minimum problem will be contained in the final tableau (i.e., the tableau with all nonpositive indicators). The method for obtaining the solution to the minimum problem from the final tableau will be given presently.

Recall that for a maximum problem involving n variables, $x_1, x_2, \ldots, x_n$, and $n + m$ linear inequalities or a minimum problem involving m variables, $y_1, y_2, \ldots, y_m$, and $m + n$ linear inequalities, the vector-matrix form is

$$\left.\begin{array}{l} \text{Maximize: } CX \\ \text{subject to: } AX \leq B, X \geq 0 \end{array}\right\} \begin{array}{l} \text{Maximum} \\ \text{Problem} \end{array}$$

or

$$\left.\begin{array}{l} \text{Minimize: } YB \\ \text{subject to: } YA \geq C, Y \geq 0 \end{array}\right\} \begin{array}{l} \text{Minimum} \\ \text{Problem} \end{array}$$

and the Tucker tableau is given in Figure 8.6.1. Also recall that the entries of the row vector C are called the indicators for the tableau.

To solve the linear programming problem in question, it suffices to transform the initial tableau into one in which all the indicators are nonpositive (i.e., less than or equal to zero). The method for doing this is called the simplex algorithm, and the steps in the algorithm are listed below:

Figure 8.6.1

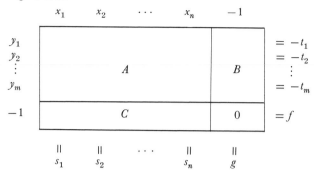

The Simplex Algorithm

1. Examine the indicators of the tableau. If they are all nonpositive, then the solution to the linear program is contained in the tableau (we shall see later exactly how to find the solution). If there is a positive indicator in the tableau, proceed to step 2.
2. Choose any column of the tableau in which there is a positive indicator. If all the entries in this column, other than the indicator, are nonpositive, the linear program has no solution. Otherwise, call this the *pivotal column* and continue to step 3.
3. For each *positive* entry (other than the indicator) in the pivotal column chosen at step 2, consider the ratio of the entry in the last column lying in the same row, to the positive entry (i.e., if p is the positive entry in question and q is the entry in the last column which lies in the same row as p, consider q/p). Mark by an asterisk the element in the pivotal column for which this ratio is the smallest (ties may be broken arbitrarily).
4. Pivot on the entry marked with the asterisk (i.e., perform the pivoting operation on the tableau with the entry marked with the asterisk as the pivot entry).
5. Return to step 1.

Once the initial tableau has been transformed into one with all nonpositive indicators, the solutions to both the maximum and minimum problems contained in the initial Tucker tableau are obtained as follows: Set the variables labeling the rows and columns of the (final) tableau equal to zero. The values of the other variables in the tableau can then be obtained directly from the last column and last row of the tableau (see Example 8.4.1 for the motivation behind this).

Example 8.6.1   Use the simplex algorithm to solve Example 8.2.2. This example was solved by the geometric method in Section 7.7 and in detail using the simplex method in Example 8.4.1. The problem is to

Maximize: $f(x_1, x_2) = 10x_1 + 25x_2$
subject to:
$$2x_1 + 3x_2 \leq 72$$
$$2x_1 + 10x_2 \leq 100$$
$$x_1 \geq 0$$
$$x_2 \geq 0$$

The Tucker tableau for this problem is given by Figure 8.6.2. We now apply the simplex algorithm to this tableau.

Figure 8.6.2

	x_1	x_2	-1	
y_1	2*	3	72	$= -t_1$
y_2	2	10	100	$= -t_2$
-1	10	25	0	$= f$
	$\shortparallel$	$\shortparallel$	$\shortparallel$	
	s_1	s_2	g	

1. The indicators are 10 and 25, so we proceed to step 2 of the simplex algorithm.
2. Choose any column in the tableau with a positive indicator, say the first column (the indicator here is 10). This will be the pivotal column. The entries in this column, other than the indicator, are 2 and 2. We proceed to step 3 of the simplex algorithm.
3. For step 3 we consider the ratios $\frac{72}{2} = 36$ and $\frac{100}{2} = 50$. [*Note:* This is precisely what we did in Example 8.4.1. See, in particular, Eq. (8.4.10).] Since $\frac{72}{2} < \frac{100}{2}$, we mark the 2 in the upper left-hand corner of the tableau in Figure 8.6.2 with an asterisk.
4. In step 4 we pivot on the entry 2 marked with an asterisk in Figure 8.6.2. The resulting tableau is (see Figure 8.4.2) shown in Figure 8.6.3.

Figure 8.6.3

	t_1	x_2	-1	
s_1	$\frac{1}{2}$	$\frac{3}{2}$	36	$= -x_1$
y_2	-1	7*	28	$= -t_2$
-1	-5	10	-360	$= f$
	$\shortparallel$	$\shortparallel$	$\shortparallel$	
	y_1	s_2	g	

5. We now return to step 1 of the simplex algorithm.
  1′. The indicators in the new tableau are -5 and 10, and so there is still a positive indicator. Thus we proceed to step 2.
  2′. There is only one positive indicator, and this is in column 2. The nonindicator entries are $\frac{3}{2}$ and 7, and so we proceed to step 3 of the simplex algorithm.
  3′. For this step we consider the ratios $36/\frac{3}{2} = 24$ and $\frac{28}{7} = 4$. [Again, this is exactly what we did in Example 8.4.1, specifically in Eq. (8.4.21).] Since $4 < 24$, the entry 7 in Figure 8.6.3 is marked with an asterisk.
  4′. Next we pivot on the entry 7 marked with an asterisk. The resulting tableau is (see Figure 8.4.3) shown in Figure 8.6.4.
  5′. We now return to step 1 of the simplex algorithm.
    1″. Since the indicators in this last tableau are $-\frac{25}{7}$ and $-\frac{10}{7}$, which are both nonpositive, the solution to the linear program (and its dual) is now contained in the tableau.

Figure 8.6.4

	t_1	t_2	-1	
s_1	$\frac{5}{7}$	$-\frac{3}{14}$	30	$= -x_1$
s_2	$-\frac{1}{7}$	$\frac{1}{7}$	4	$= -x_2$
-1	$-\frac{25}{7}$	$-\frac{10}{7}$	-400	$= f$
	$\parallel$	$\parallel$	$\parallel$	
	y_1	y_2	g	

To obtain the solution to the maximum problem we set the variables labeling the columns of this last tableau equal to zero (i.e., we set $t_1 = t_2 = 0$). Reading the rows of the tableau with these values for t_1 and t_2 we find that $-30 = -x_1$, $-4 = -x_1$, and $-(-400) = f$. In other words, the maximum value of the linear function $f(x_1, x_2) = 10x_1 + 25x_2$, subject to the given linear inequalities, is equal to 400, and this occurs when $x_1 = 30$ and $x_2 = 4$.

We remark, in passing, that the dual of the given maximum problem, which is

Minimize: $g(y_1, y_2) = 72y_1 + 100y_2$
subject to:
$$2y_1 + 2y_2 \geq 10$$
$$3y_1 + 10y_2 \geq 25$$
$$y_1 \geq 0$$
$$y_2 \geq 0$$

has a solution that can also be obtained from the tableau in Figure 8.6.4, as explained previously. First set the variables labeling the rows equal to zero (i.e., $s_1 = s_2 = 0$) and then read the columns of the tableau in the usual manner with these values for s_1 and s_2. The result is $-(-\frac{25}{7}) = y_1$, $-(-\frac{10}{7}) = y_2$, and $-(-400) = g$. In other words, the solution to the dual minimum problem of the given maximum problem is as follows: the minimum value of the linear function $g(y_1, y_2) = 72y_1 + 100y_2$ subject to the given linear inequalities is 400, and this occurs when $y_1 = \frac{25}{7}$ and $y_2 = \frac{10}{7}$.

Example 8.6.2   Use the simplex algorithm to solve Example 7.1.3. This example was also solved in Section 7.7 by the geometric method. There it was seen that the appropriate formulation for the problem could be phrased as follows [see Eqs. (7.7.11) and (7.7.12)]:

Minimize: $g(y_1, y_2) = 15y_1 + 25y_2$
subject to:
$$2y_1 + 5y_2 \geq 24$$
$$3y_1 + 4y_2 \geq 29$$
$$y_1 \geq 0$$
$$y_2 \geq 0$$

The vector-matrix form for this problem is

Minimize: YB
subject to: $YA \geq C$, $Y \geq \theta$

where

$$A = \begin{bmatrix} 2 & 3 \\ 5 & 4 \end{bmatrix} \qquad B = \begin{bmatrix} 15 \\ 25 \end{bmatrix} \qquad C = [24, 29] \qquad Y = [y_1, y_2] \qquad \theta = [0, 0]$$

The Tucker tableau is given in Figure 8.6.5.

Figure 8.6.5

	x_1	x_2	-1	
y_1	2	3	15	$= -t_1$
y_2	5	4	25	$= -t_2$
-1	24	29	0	$= f$
	$\shortparallel$	$\shortparallel$	$\shortparallel$	
	s_1	s_2	g	

If at the second step of the simplex algorithm the first column is chosen as the pivotal column, the simplex algorithm yields the sequence of tableaux shown in Figure 8.6.6.

Figure 8.6.6

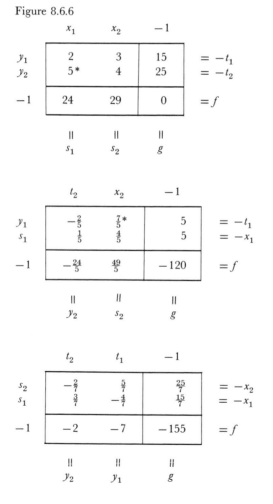

	x_1	x_2	-1	
y_1	2	3	15	$= -t_1$
y_2	5*	4	25	$= -t_2$
-1	24	29	0	$= f$
	$\shortparallel$	$\shortparallel$	$\shortparallel$	
	s_1	s_2	g	

	t_2	x_2	-1	
y_1	$-\frac{2}{5}$	$\frac{7}{5}*$	5	$= -t_1$
s_1	$\frac{1}{5}$	$\frac{4}{5}$	5	$= -x_1$
-1	$-\frac{24}{5}$	$\frac{49}{5}$	-120	$= f$
	$\shortparallel$	$\shortparallel$	$\shortparallel$	
	y_2	s_2	g	

	t_2	t_1	-1	
s_2	$-\frac{2}{7}$	$\frac{5}{7}$	$\frac{25}{7}$	$= -x_2$
s_1	$\frac{3}{7}$	$-\frac{4}{7}$	$\frac{15}{7}$	$= -x_1$
-1	-2	-7	-155	$= f$
	$\shortparallel$	$\shortparallel$	$\shortparallel$	
	y_2	y_1	g	

Since all the indicators in the last tableau of Figure 8.6.6 are nonpositive, this is the final tableau for the simplex algorithm. To obtain the solution to the *minimum problem* from the tableau, we set the variables labeling the rows equal to zero (i.e., set $s_1 = s_2 = 0$) and then read the columns of the tableau in the usual way with these values for s_1 and s_2. The result is $-(-2) = y_2$, $-(-7) = y_1$, and $-(-155) = g$. In other words, subject to the given linear inequalities, the minimum value of the linear function $g(y_1, y_2) = 15y_1 + 25y_2$ is 155, and this occurs when $y_1 = 7$ and $y_2 = 2$.

Example 8.6.3 Consider the linear programming problem presented in Example 8.2.4:

Maximize: $f(x_1, x_2, x_3) = 3x_1 + 2x_2 + 6x_3$
subject to:

$$4x_1 \quad - 8x_3 \le 40$$
$$x_1 + x_2 + 6x_3 \le 80$$
$$x_1 \ge 0$$
$$x_2 \ge 0$$
$$x_3 \ge 0$$

The Tucker tableau is

	x_1	x_2	x_3	-1	
y_1	4	0	-8	40	$= -t_1$
y_2	1	1	6	80	$= -t_2$
-1	3	2	6	0	$= f$
	$\|\|$	$\|\|$	$\|\|$	$\|\|$	
	s_1	s_2	s_3	g	

Applying the simplex algorithm, we obtain the following tableaux:

	x_1	x_2	x_3	-1	
y_1	4*	0	-8	40	$= -t_1$
y_2	1	1	6	80	$= -t_2$
-1	3	2	6	0	$= f$
	$\|\|$	$\|\|$	$\|\|$	$\|\|$	
	s_1	s_2	s_3	g	

	t_1	x_2	x_3	-1	
s_1	$\frac{1}{4}$	0	-2	10	$= -x_1$
y_2	$-\frac{1}{4}$	1*	8	70	$= -t_2$
-1	$-\frac{3}{4}$	2	12	-30	$= f$
	$\|\|$	$\|\|$	$\|\|$	$\|\|$	
	y_1	s_2	s_3	g	

	t_1	t_2	x_3	-1	
s_1	$\frac{1}{4}$	0	-2	10	$= -x_1$
s_2	$-\frac{1}{4}$	1	8	70	$= -x_2$
-1	$-\frac{1}{4}$	-2	-4	-170	$= f$
	$\parallel$	$\parallel$	$\parallel$	$\parallel$	
	y_1	y_2	s_3	g	

Since all the indicators in this last tableau are nonpositive, this is the final tableau for the simplex algorithm. To obtain the solution to the maximum problem from the tableau, we proceed as usual. First set the variables labeling the columns of the tableau equal to zero (i.e., $t_1 = t_2 = x_3 = 0$) and then read the rows of the tableau in the usual manner with these values for t_1, t_2, and x_3. The result is $-10 = -x_1$, $-70 = -x_2$, and $-(-170) = f$. In other words, the maximum value of the linear function $f(x_1, x_2, x_3) = 3x_1 + 2x_2 + 6x_3$, subject to the given linear inequalities is 170, and this occurs when $x_1 = 10$, $x_2 = 70$, and $x_3 = 0$.

Example 8.6.4 Solve the linear programming problem given in Example 8.2.5 by using the simplex algorithm. The problem is to

Minimize: $g(y_1, y_2, y_3) = 5y_1 + 3y_2 + 2y_3$
subject to:

$$y_1 + y_2 + y_3 \geq 24$$
$$y_1 \qquad - 2y_3 \geq 0$$
$$y_1 - y_2 + y_3 \geq 0$$
$$2y_1 \qquad + 2y_3 \geq 19$$
$$y_1 \geq 0$$
$$y_2 \geq 0$$
$$y_3 \geq 0$$

The Tucker tableau for this linear program is

	x_1	x_2	x_3	x_4	-1	
y_1	1	1	1	2	5	$= -t_1$
y_2	1	0	-1	0	3	$= -t_2$
y_3	1	-2	1	2	2	$= -t_3$
-1	24	0	0	19	0	$= f$
	$\parallel$	$\parallel$	$\parallel$	$\parallel$	$\parallel$	
	s_1	s_2	s_3	s_4	g	

Applying the simplex algorithm yields

	x_1	x_2	x_3	x_4	-1	
y_1	1	1	1	2	5	$= -t_1$
y_2	1	0	-1	0	3	$= -t_2$
y_3	1^*	-2	1	2	2	$= -t_3$
-1	24	0	0	19	0	$= f$
	$\parallel$	$\parallel$	$\parallel$	$\parallel$	$\parallel$	
	s_1	s_2	s_3	s_4	g	

	t_3	x_2	x_3	x_4	-1	
y_1	-1	3	0	0	3	$= -t_1$
y_2	-1	2^*	-2	-2	1	$= -t_2$
s_1	1	-2	1	2	2	$= -x_1$
-1	-24	48	-24	-29	-48	$= f$
	$\parallel$	$\parallel$	$\parallel$	$\parallel$	$\parallel$	
	y_3	s_2	s_3	s_4	g	

	t_3	t_2	x_3	x_4	-1	
y_1	$\frac{1}{2}$	$-\frac{3}{2}$	3^*	3	$\frac{3}{2}$	$= -t_1$
s_2	$-\frac{1}{2}$	$\frac{1}{2}$	-1	-1	$\frac{1}{2}$	$= -x_2$
s_1	0	1	-1	0	3	$= -x_1$
-1	0	-24	24	19	-72	$= f$
	$\parallel$	$\parallel$	$\parallel$	$\parallel$	$\parallel$	
	y_3	y_2	s_3	s_4	g	

	t_3	t_2	t_1	x_4	-1	
s_3	$\frac{1}{6}$	$-\frac{1}{2}$	$\frac{1}{3}$	1	$\frac{1}{2}$	$= -x_3$
s_2	$-\frac{1}{3}$	0	$\frac{1}{3}$	0	1	$= -x_2$
s_1	$\frac{1}{6}$	$\frac{1}{2}$	$\frac{1}{3}$	1	$\frac{7}{2}$	$= -x_1$
-1	-4	-12	-8	-5	-84	$= f$
	$\parallel$	$\parallel$	$\parallel$	$\parallel$	$\parallel$	
	y_3	y_2	y_1	s_4	g	

Since all the indicators in this last tableau are nonpositive, this is the final tableau for the simplex algorithm. To obtain the solution to the minimum problem from the tableau, we proceed as usual. First, set the variables labeling the rows of the tableau equal to zero (i.e., $s_3 = s_2 = s_1 = 0$) and then, using these values for s_3, s_2, and s_1, read the columns of the tableau in the usual way. The result of this is that $-(-4) = y_3$, $-(-12) = y_2$, $-(-8) = y_1$, $-(-5) = s_4$, and $-(-84) = g$. In other words, the minimum value of the linear function $g(y_1, y_2, y_3) = 5y_1 + 3y_2 + 2y_3$, subject to the given linear inequalities, is 84, and this occurs when $y_1 = 8$, $y_2 = 12$, and $y_3 = 4$.

Exercises for 8.6

In each of problems 1–14, use the simplex algorithm to solve the given linear programming problem.

1. Maximize: $f(x_1, x_2) = 6x_1 - 2x_2$
   subject to:
   $$3x_1 + 4x_2 \leq 15$$
   $$-x_1 + 2x_2 \leq 5$$
   $$x_1 \geq 0$$
   $$x_2 \geq 0$$

2. Maximize: $f(x_1, x_2) = -x_1 + 4x_2$
   subject to:
   $$3x_1 + 4x_2 \leq 15$$
   $$-x_1 + 2x_2 \leq 5$$
   $$x_1 \geq 0$$
   $$x_2 \geq 0$$

3. Minimize: $g(y_1, y_2) = 3y_1 + 2y_2$
   subject to:
   $$4y_1 + 2y_2 \geq 20$$
   $$y_1 + 4y_2 \geq 12$$
   $$y_1 \geq 0$$
   $$y_2 \geq 0$$

4. Minimize: $g(y_1, y_2) = 3y_1 + y_2$
   subject to:
   $$4y_1 + 2y_2 \geq 20$$
   $$y_1 + 4y_2 \geq 12$$
   $$y_1 \geq 0$$
   $$y_2 \geq 0$$

5. Minimize: $g(y_1, y_2) = 7y_1 + 2y_2$
   subject to:
   $$2y_1 + 3y_2 \geq 6$$
   $$4y_1 + 3y_2 \geq 12$$
   $$y_1 \geq 0$$
   $$y_2 \geq 0$$

6. Maximize: $f(x_1, x_2) = 3x_1 + 2x_2$
   subject to:
   $$x_1 + x_2 \leq 45$$
   $$5x_1 + 2x_2 \leq 180$$
   $$x_1 \geq 0$$
   $$x_2 \geq 0$$

7. Minimize: $g(y_1, y_2) = 5y_1 + 4y_2$
   subject to:
$$y_1 + 3y_2 \geq 6$$
$$y_1 + y_2 \geq 4$$
$$3y_1 + y_2 \geq 6$$
$$y_1 \geq 0$$
$$y_2 \geq 0$$

8. Maximize: $f(x_1, x_2, x_3) = 3x_1 + 2x_2 + x_3$
   subject to:
$$3x_1 + x_2 + 2x_3 \leq 100$$
$$x_1 + x_2 + 6x_3 \leq 80$$
$$x_1 \geq 0$$
$$x_2 \geq 0$$
$$x_3 \geq 0$$

9. Maximize: $f(x_1, x_2, x_3) = 4x_1 + 6x_2 + 5x_3$
   subject to:
$$-x_1 + x_2 - x_3 \leq 0$$
$$x_1 + x_2 + x_3 \leq 27$$
$$-x_1 + 2x_3 \leq 0$$
$$x_1 \geq 0$$
$$x_2 \geq 0$$
$$x_3 \geq 0$$

10. Minimize: $g(y_1, y_2) = 2y_1 + 3y_2$
    subject to:
$$3y_1 + y_2 \geq 4$$
$$y_1 + 5y_2 \geq 4$$
$$y_1 + y_2 \leq 4$$
$$y_1 \leq 2$$
$$y_2 \leq 3$$
$$y_1 \geq 0$$
$$y_2 \geq 0$$

(Be careful to set up the inequalities in proper form.)

11. Minimize: $g(y_1, y_2, y_3) = 24y_1 + 24y_2 + 12y_3$
    subject to:
$$4y_1 + 2y_2 + 3y_3 \geq 1$$
$$6y_1 + 3y_2 + y_3 \geq 12$$
$$3y_1 + 6y_2 \geq 10$$
$$y_1 \geq 0$$
$$y_2 \geq 0$$
$$y_3 \geq 0$$

12. Minimize: $g(y_1, y_2, y_3) = 5y_1 + 3y_2 + 2y_3$
    subject to:
$$y_1 - y_2 + y_3 \geq 0$$
$$y_1 + y_2 + y_3 \geq 24$$
$$2y_1 - 4y_3 \geq 0$$
$$-y_1 - y_2 - y_3 \geq -27$$
$$y_1 \geq 0$$
$$y_2 \geq 0$$
$$y_3 \geq 0$$

13. Maximize: $f(x_1, x_2, x_3, x_4) = 2x_1 - 3x_2 + 4x_3 + x_4$
subject to:
$$2x_1 + 3x_2 - 7x_3 + 8x_4 \leq 0$$
$$-6x_1 + 2x_2 - 2x_3 - 6x_4 \geq -20$$
$$-x_1 - 5x_2 - 9x_3 + 6x_4 \leq 2$$
$$x_1 \geq 0$$
$$x_2 \geq 0$$
$$x_3 \geq 0$$
$$x_4 \geq 0$$

14. Maximize: $f(x_1, x_2, x_3) = x_1 + 50x_2 + 10x_3$
subject to:
$$x_1 + 100x_2 + 10x_3 \leq 100$$
$$x_1 + 10x_2 + 100x_3 \leq 110$$
$$x_1 + x_2 + x_3 \leq 5$$
$$x_1 \geq 0$$
$$x_2 \geq 0$$
$$x_3 \geq 0$$

In each of problems 15–24, solve both of the linear programming problems contained in the given Tucker tableau by applying the simplex algorithm.

15.

	x_1	x_2	-1	
y_1	3	1	12	$= -t_1$
y_2	3	5	15	$= -t_2$
-1	2	1	0	$= f$
	$\parallel$	$\parallel$	$\parallel$	
	s_1	s_2	g	

16.

	x_1	x_2	x_3	-1	
y_1	5	1	0	5	$= -t_1$
y_2	2	1	1	3	$= -t_2$
-1	300	90	90	0	$= f$
	$\parallel$	$\parallel$	$\parallel$	$\parallel$	
	s_1	s_2	s_3	g	

17.

	x_1	x_2	-1	
y_1	1	1	6	$= -t_1$
y_2	1	-5	0	$= -t_2$
y_3	5	-1	0	$= -t_3$
-1	3	2	0	$= f$
	$\parallel$	$\parallel$	$\parallel$	
	s_1	s_2	g	

18.

	x_1	x_2	x_3	-1	
y_1	3	1	6	36	$= -t_1$
y_2	5	3	2	75	$= -t_2$
y_3	3	2	5	30	$= -t_3$
-1	20	9	30	0	$= f$
	$\parallel$	$\parallel$	$\parallel$	$\parallel$	
	s_1	s_2	s_3	g	

19.

	x_1	x_2	x_3	-1	
y_1	4	0	-8	40	$= -t_1$
y_2	1	1	6	80	$= -t_2$
-1	3	2	6	0	$= f$
	$\parallel$	$\parallel$	$\parallel$	$\parallel$	
	s_1	s_2	s_3	g	

20.

	x_1	x_2	x_3	x_4	-1	
y_1	1	1	1	2	5	$= -t_1$
y_2	1	0	-1	0	3	$= -t_2$
y_3	1	-2	1	2	2	$= -t_3$
-1	24	0	0	19	0	$= f$
	$\parallel$	$\parallel$	$\parallel$	$\parallel$	$\parallel$	
	s_1	s_2	s_3	s_4	g	

21.

	x_1	x_2	x_3	-1	
y_1	50	60	60	1,000	$= -t_1$
y_2	3	4	6	72	$= -t_2$
y_3	1	2	3	40	$= -t_3$
-1	70	80	100	0	$= f$
	$\parallel$	$\parallel$	$\parallel$	$\parallel$	
	s_1	s_2	s_3	g	

22.

	x_1	x_2	-1	
y_1	2	9	18	$= -t_1$
y_2	1	1	3	$= -t_2$
y_3	7	2	14	$= -t_3$
-1	4	2	0	$= f$
	$\parallel$	$\parallel$	$\parallel$	
	s_1	s_2	g	

23.

	x_1	x_2	x_3	x_4	-1	
y_1	6	18	3	15	9	$= -t_1$
y_2	4	16	20	8	32	$= -t_2$
y_3	8	3	4	1	7	$= -t_3$
-1	6	8	2	14	0	$= f$
	$\parallel$	$\parallel$	$\parallel$	$\parallel$	$\parallel$	
	s_1	s_2	s_3	s_4	g	

24.

	x_1	x_2	x_3	x_4	x_5	-1	
y_1	1	0	1	0	1	2	$= -t_1$
y_2	0	-1	1	-1	1	$\frac{3}{2}$	$= -t_2$
y_3	0	0	0	-1	1	$\frac{3}{2}$	$= -t_3$
y_4	0	-1	0	-1	1	$\frac{4}{5}$	$= -t_4$
-1	700	-400	1,100	$-1,100$	1,700	0	$= f$
	$\parallel$	$\parallel$	$\parallel$	$\parallel$	$\parallel$	$\parallel$	
	s_1	s_2	s_3	s_4	s_5	g	

Section 8.7 Examples and Applications

As our final illustrations we solve Examples 8.1.3 and 8.1.4. The reader should now return to Section 8.1 and reread these examples.

Solution to Example 8.1.3 The problem is to determine what quantity of each type of cabinet the manufacturer should produce in order to obtain the maximum profit. Let

$x_1 = $ no. of plain cabinets made per week
$x_2 = $ no. of intermediate cabinets made per week
$x_3 = $ no. of decorative cabinets made per week

The plain, intermediate, and decorative cabinets require 50, 60, and 60 square feet of lumber per cabinet, respectively. Consequently, the total square feet of lumber used per week is

$$50x_1 + 60x_2 + 60x_3$$

Since the total amount of lumber available per week is 1,000 square feet, we must have

$$50x_1 + 60x_2 + 60x_3 \leq 1,000 \tag{8.7.1}$$

The amount of machine labor required per cabinet for the plain, intermediate, and decorative styles, is 3, 4, and 6 hours, respectively. Thus the total machine-labor time required per week is $3x_1 + 4x_2 + 6x_3$, and this must not exceed 72:

$$3x_1 + 4x_2 + 6x_3 \leq 72 \tag{8.7.2}$$

Next, we know that the plain, intermediate, and decorative styles require 1, 2, and 3 hours of hand labor, respectively, per cabinet. Since the total hand-labor time available per week is 40 hours, we require that

$$x_1 + 2x_2 + 3x_3 \leq 40 \tag{8.7.3}$$

Finally, the profit, per cabinet, for the three respective styles is $70, $80, and $100. Thus the total profit per week is

$$70x_1 + 80x_2 + 100x_3 \tag{8.7.4}$$

This is the quantity to be maximized.

In view of Eqs. (8.7.1)–(8.7.4), the problem at hand can be stated as follows:

Maximize: $f(x_1, x_2, x_3) = 70x_1 + 80x_2 + 100x_3$
subject to:
$$\begin{aligned}
50x_1 + 60x_2 + 60x_3 &\leq 1{,}000 \\
3x_1 + 4x_2 + 6x_3 &\leq 72 \\
x_1 + 2x_2 + 3x_3 &\leq 40 \\
x_1 &\geq 0 \\
x_2 &\geq 0 \\
x_3 &\geq 0
\end{aligned}$$

The vector-matrix form for this linear program is

Maximize: CX
subject to: $AX \leq B, X \geq \theta$

where

$$A = \begin{bmatrix} 50 & 60 & 60 \\ 3 & 4 & 6 \\ 1 & 2 & 3 \end{bmatrix} \quad B = \begin{bmatrix} 1{,}000 \\ 72 \\ 40 \end{bmatrix} \quad C = [70, 80, 100] \quad \theta = \begin{bmatrix} 0 \\ 0 \\ 0 \end{bmatrix} \quad X = \begin{bmatrix} x_1 \\ x_2 \\ x_3 \end{bmatrix}$$

The Tucker tableau is given by

	x_1	x_2	x_3	-1	
y_1	50	60	60	1,000	$= -t_1$
y_2	3	4	6	72	$= -t_2$
y_3	1	2	3	40	$= -t_3$
-1	70	80	100	0	$= f$
	$\parallel$	$\parallel$	$\parallel$	$\parallel$	
	s_1	s_2	s_3	g	

Using the simplex algorithm, the following sequence of tableaux is obtained:

	x_1	x_2	x_3	-1	
y_1	50*	60	60	1,000	$= -t_1$
y_2	3	4	6	72	$= -t_2$
y_3	1	2	3	40	$= -t_3$
-1	70	80	100	0	$= f$
	$\parallel$	$\parallel$	$\parallel$	$\parallel$	
	s_1	s_2	s_3	g	

	t_1	x_2	x_3	-1	
s_1	$\frac{1}{50}$	$\frac{6}{5}$	$\frac{6}{5}$	20	$=-x_1$
y_2	$-\frac{3}{50}$	$\frac{2}{5}$	$\frac{12}{5}$ *	12	$=-t_2$
y_3	$-\frac{1}{50}$	$\frac{4}{5}$	$\frac{9}{5}$	20	$=-t_3$
-1	$-\frac{7}{5}$	-4	16	$-1,400$	$=f$
	$\|\|$	$\|\|$	$\|\|$	$\|\|$	
	y_1	s_2	s_3	g	

	t_1	x_2	t_2	-1	
s_1	$\frac{1}{20}$	1	$-\frac{1}{2}$	14	$=-x_1$
s_3	$-\frac{1}{40}$	$\frac{1}{6}$	$\frac{5}{12}$	5	$=-x_3$
y_3	$\frac{1}{40}$	$\frac{1}{2}$	$-\frac{3}{4}$	11	$=-t_3$
-1	-1	$-\frac{20}{3}$	$-\frac{20}{3}$	$-1,480$	$=f$
	$\|\|$	$\|\|$	$\|\|$	$\|\|$	
	y_1	s_2	y_2	g	

Since all the indicators in this last tableau are nonpositive, this is the final tableau for the simplex algorithm. To obtain the solution to the maximum problem from the tableau, we proceed as usual. Setting $t_1 = x_2 = t_2 = 0$ and using these values to read the rows of the tableau, we find that $-14 = -x_1$, $-5 = -x_3$, $-11 = -t_3$, and $-(-1,480) = f$. Consequently, subject to the given linear inequalities, the maximum value of the linear function $f(x_1, x_2, x_3) = 70x_1 + 80x_2 + 100x_3$ is equal to 1,480, and this occurs when $x_1 = 14$, $x_2 = 0$, and $x_3 = 5$.

In terms of the original problem, the cabinet manufacturer should make 14 of his plain cabinets, none of his intermediate cabinets, and 5 of his decorative cabinets per week. The profit will be $1,480 per week, which is the maximum that he can attain under the constraints on his resources.

Solution to Example 8.1.4 The problem is to determine how many caps and gowns should be purchased initially and how many, on each day, should be dry-cleaned by the various cleaners in order to minimize cost. Let

y_1 = no. of caps and gowns purchased
y_2 = no. cleaned by the 1-day cleaner after the first ceremony
y_3 = no. cleaned by the 1-day cleaner after the second ceremony
y_4 = no. cleaned by the 2-day cleaner after the first ceremony

First, since the number of caps and gowns required on the three successive days is 400, 700, and 600, respectively, it is clear that

$$y_1 \geq 700 \tag{8.7.5}$$

Also, notice that because $y_2 + y_4$ caps and gowns are turned in to be dry-cleaned after the first ceremony, which uses 400, it must be that

$$y_2 + y_4 \leq 400 \tag{8.7.6}$$

After the first ceremony the service will have $y_1 - 400$ unused caps and gowns. Since y_2 will be dry-cleaned and ready for the next ceremony, which requires 700 caps and gowns, we must have

$$y_1 - 400 + y_2 \geq 700 \tag{8.7.7}$$

Now, the number of uncleaned caps and gowns after the second ceremony is equal to 700 plus the number of uncleaned caps and gowns not sent to the cleaners after the first ceremony, which is $400 - y_2 - y_4$. Since y_3 is the number sent to the dry cleaners after the second ceremony, we must have

$$y_3 \leq 700 + 400 - y_2 - y_4 \tag{8.7.8}$$

Also, after the second ceremony the service will have $y_1 - 400 + y_2 - 700$ clean caps and gowns. Since $y_3 + y_4$ will be dry-cleaned and ready for the next ceremony and there are 600 caps and gowns required for that ceremony, it is necessary that

$$y_1 - 400 + y_2 - 700 + y_3 + y_4 \geq 600 \tag{8.7.9}$$

Finally, because the caps and gowns cost \$2 each from the distributor, because the 1-day cleaner charges \$1.50 each for cleaning, and because the 2-day cleaner charges \$.80 each for cleaning, the total cost to the rental service will be

$$2y_1 + 1.5y_2 + 1.5y_3 + .8y_4 \tag{8.7.10}$$

This is the quantity to be minimized. In view of Eqs. (8.7.6)–(8.7.10), the problem is to

Minimize: $g(y_1, y_2, y_3, y_4) = 2y_1 + 1.5y_2 + 1.5y_3 + .8y_4$
subject to:

$$
\begin{aligned}
y_1 & & & & &\geq & 700 \\
-y_2 & & &-y_4 & &\geq & -400 \\
y_1 + y_2 & & & & &\geq & 1{,}100 \\
-y_2 &-y_3 &-y_4 & & &\geq & -1{,}100 \\
y_1 + y_2 &+y_3 &+y_4 & & &\geq & 1{,}700 \\
& & &y_1 & &\geq & 0 \\
& & &y_2 & &\geq & 0 \\
& & &y_3 & &\geq & 0 \\
& & &y_4 & &\geq & 0
\end{aligned}
$$

The vector-matrix form for this linear program is

Minimize: YB
subject to: $YA \geq C,\ Y \geq \theta$

where

$$
A = \begin{bmatrix}
1 & 0 & 1 & 0 & 1 \\
0 & -1 & 1 & -1 & 1 \\
0 & 0 & 0 & -1 & 1 \\
0 & -1 & 0 & -1 & 1
\end{bmatrix}
\qquad
B = \begin{bmatrix}
2 \\
\frac{3}{2} \\
\frac{3}{2} \\
\frac{4}{5}
\end{bmatrix}
$$

$C = [700, -400, 1{,}100, -1{,}100, 1{,}700]$ \qquad $\theta = [0, 0, 0, 0]$ \qquad $Y = [y_1, y_2, y_3, y_4]$

The Tucker tableau is

	x_1	x_2	x_3	x_4	x_5	-1	
y_1	1	0	1	0	1	2	$= -t_1$
y_2	0	-1	1	-1	1	$\frac{3}{2}$	$= -t_2$
y_3	0	0	0	-1	1	$\frac{3}{2}$	$= -t_3$
y_4	0	-1	0	-1	1	$\frac{4}{5}$	$= -t_4$
-1	700	-400	1,100	$-1,100$	1,700	0	$= f$
	$\parallel$	$\parallel$	$\parallel$	$\parallel$	$\parallel$	$\parallel$	
	s_1	s_2	s_3	s_4	s_5	g	

Using the simplex algorithm, the problem can be solved (this is left as an exercise). The results are $y_1 = 1,100$, $y_2 = 0$, $y_3 = 200$, $y_4 = 400$, and $g = 2,820$. In other words, the minimum possible cost to the service is $2,820, and this is obtained by purchasing 1,100 caps and gowns from the distributor, having none cleaned by the 1-day cleaner after the first ceremony, having 200 cleaned by the 1-day cleaner after the second ceremony, and having 400 cleaned by the 2-day cleaner after the first ceremony.

Exercises for 8.7

1. Solve both parts of problem 1, Exercises 7.7 by using the simplex algorithm.
2. Use the simplex algorithm to solve both parts of problem 2, Exercises 7.7.
3. A manufacturer of hand calculators produces three types, the XL-25, XL-40, and XL-85. The numbers of hours of hand-labor time required per calculator are, respectively, 2, 4, and 6. The inspection times per calculator are given, respectively, by 1, 2, and 5 hours. The respective profits per calculator are $30, $50, and $100. How many of each type should the manufacturer produce per week to maximize profit if the total number of hours available per week for hand-labor time is 300 and that for inspection time is 200?
4. Use the simplex algorithm to solve problem 3, Exercises 7.7 (both parts).
5. Use the simplex algorithm to verify the solution of Example 8.1.4.
6. Three carpenters work *together* in the construction of certain prefabricated units to be used for home building. There are three types of units constructed, one for each of the three types of elevations the builder offers. Each of the carpenters handles a particular facet in the construction of the prefabricated units. Carpenter A needs 3, 6, and 4 hours, respectively, to finish his part of a prefabricated unit of type I, II, and III; carpenter B requires 2, 6, and 5 hours, respectively; and carpenter C needs 5, 2, and 4 hours, respectively. If the profits per unit are $30, $60, and $50 for types I, II, and III, respectively, and if each carpenter works at most 40 hours per week, how many of each type of pre-fabricated unit should be constructed per week to maximize profit?
7. By applying the simplex algorithm, determine the solutions to (1)–(3) of problem 4, Exercises 7.7.
8. Solve both parts of problem 6, Exercises 7.7 by applying the simplex algorithm.
9. A certain diet consists of meat, salad, and bread. Assume that 1 pound of meat contains 10 units of protein, 4 units of carbohydrate, and 2 units of vitamins. One pound of the salad contains 1 unit of protein, 2 units of carbohydrate, and 4 units of vitamins. Also 1 pound of bread contains 1 unit of protein, 8 units of carbohydrate, and 1 unit of vitamins. The minimum daily requirements are 6 units of protein, 4 units of carbohydrate, and 5 units of vitamins. The meat costs $2 a pound, the salad costs 70 cents a pound, and

bread costs 40 cents a pound. How much of each should be purchased per day to meet the minimum daily requirements at a minimum cost?

10. Use the simplex algorithm to solve problem 7, Exercises 7.7.

11. A merchandiser stocks four items, say I, II, III, and IV. The net profits per unit of each item are, respectively, $12, $15, $20, and $20. The amounts of storage space required per unit of each item are, respectively, 3, 6, 12, and 4 cubic feet. The amounts of time required for unpacking and shelving per unit of each item are given by 2, 3, 3, and 4 minutes, respectively. Because of past experience the merchandiser always buys at least as many units of item I as the other three combined. Assume that the merchandiser purchases his supplies monthly and that he has 4,900 cubic feet of storage and 3,600 minutes of unpacking and shelving time available per month. How many units of each item should be purchased per month to maximize the net profit?

Markov Chains

9

In this chapter the theory of probability will be combined with the methods of linear algebra to study the subject of Markov chains. Markov chains have become more and more important in the management, life, and social sciences as these areas have become increasingly quantitative in nature.

Section 9.1   Definitions and Examples

Consider a system that can be in any one of several states. The state of the system will, in general, change through time, and we assume that the state of the system is observed at fixed time intervals (e.g., every second, every hour).

We have already discussed a system of this type when Bernoulli trials were presented in Section 4.15. If the state of the system at a given time (trial) is considered as being the outcome of the experiment on that trial, the system has the following property: *The future state of the system is independent of the present and past states of the system.* In other words, the probability of the system being in a particular state at the next observation period is independent of the present and past states of the system.

Example 9.1.1 Coin Tossing Consider the random experiment of repeatedly tossing a coin (not necessarily a fair coin). Let the state of the system at a given time be the outcome of the toss at that time. Then there are two states for this system (H or T). The results after 10 time periods (trials) might be

Toss (time)	1	2	3	4	5	6	7	8	9	10
Outcome (state)	H	T	H	H	T	T	T	H	T	H

In this case the state of the system would be H at time 1, T at time 2, H at time 3, H at time 4, and so on.

Because the tosses are independent we know, for example, that the probability of being in state H at time 8 (i.e., a head on the eighth toss) does not depend on the states of the system before that time (i.e., does not depend on the outcomes of previous tosses).

In various applications it is no longer reasonable to assume that the state of the system at a future time is independent of the present and past states of the system. The simplest system of this sort is a Markov chain.

Definition

A *Markov chain* is a process in which the probability of being in a particular state at a future time may depend on the state of the system at the present time but not on any past times. In other words, in a *Markov chain, given the present state of the system, the future state is independent of the past* (but may depend upon the present).

The following examples should help to clarify the concepts involved.

Example 9.1.2 7s in Craps Consider the experiment of repeatedly rolling a pair of *fair* dice. Suppose that we are only interested in whether or not a 7 comes up on any given roll. Here the state of the system at any time is either S (a 7 comes up) or F (a 7 does not come up). The results after 10 trials might be as follows:

Time (trial)	1	2	3	4	5	6	7	8	9	10
Outcome	Not 7	7	Not 7	7	7	Not 7	Not 7	Not 7	7	Not 7
State	F	S	F	S	S	F	F	F	S	F
Probability	$\frac{5}{6}$	$\frac{1}{6}$	$\frac{5}{6}$	$\frac{1}{6}$	$\frac{1}{6}$	$\frac{5}{6}$	$\frac{5}{6}$	$\frac{5}{6}$	$\frac{1}{6}$	$\frac{5}{6}$

Since the result at any given trial has no influence on that of any other trial (the rolls are independent), we have, in this case, a sequence of independent trials. That is, the future state of the system is independent of the present and past states of the system. For example, the probability of being in state S at time 5 is $\frac{1}{6}$ (= probability of a 7 when a pair of fair dice is rolled), regardless of the past states of the system.

However, suppose that we are interested in the *total* number of 7s rolled by any given time. Here, then, the state of the system at any given time is the number of 7s rolled up to and including that time. Some typical results after 10 rolls could be the following:

I

Time (trials)	1	2	3	4	5	6	7	8	9	10
Outcome	Not 7	7	Not 7	7	7	Not 7	Not 7	Not 7	7	Not 7
State (no. of 7s)	0	1	1	2	3	3	3	3	4	4
Probability	$\frac{5}{6}$	$\frac{1}{6}$	$\frac{5}{6}$	$\frac{1}{6}$	$\frac{1}{6}$	$\frac{5}{6}$	$\frac{5}{6}$	$\frac{5}{6}$	$\frac{1}{6}$	$\frac{5}{6}$

II

Time	1	2	3	4	5	6	7	8	9	10
Outcome	7	Not 7	7	Not 7	7	7	Not 7	Not 7	Not 7	7
State	1	1	2	2	3	4	4	4	4	5
Probability	$\frac{1}{6}$	$\frac{5}{6}$	$\frac{1}{6}$	$\frac{5}{6}$	$\frac{1}{6}$	$\frac{1}{6}$	$\frac{5}{6}$	$\frac{5}{6}$	$\frac{5}{6}$	$\frac{1}{6}$

III

Time	1	2	3	4	5	6	7	8	9	10
Outcome	7	7	Not 7	7	Not 7	Not 7	Not 7	Not 7	Not 7	7
State	1	2	2	3	3	3	3	3	3	4
Probability	$\frac{1}{6}$	$\frac{1}{6}$	$\frac{5}{6}$	$\frac{1}{6}$	$\frac{5}{6}$	$\frac{5}{6}$	$\frac{5}{6}$	$\frac{5}{6}$	$\frac{5}{6}$	$\frac{1}{6}$

IV

Time	1	2	3	4	5	6	7	8	9	10
Outcome	Not 7	7	Not 7	Not 7	7	Not 7	Not 7	Not 7	Not 7	Not 7
State	0	1	1	1	2	2	2	2	2	2
Probability	$\frac{5}{6}$	$\frac{1}{6}$	$\frac{5}{6}$	$\frac{5}{6}$	$\frac{1}{6}$	$\frac{5}{6}$	$\frac{5}{6}$	$\frac{5}{6}$	$\frac{5}{6}$	$\frac{5}{6}$

It should be clear to the reader that the future state of the system *depends* on the present state (but not on any past states).

For example, the probability of the system being in *state 3 at time 5* (i.e., three 7s in five rolls) *given* that it is in *state 2 at time 4* (i.e., two 7s in four rolls) is just the probability of a 7 on the fifth roll, which is $\boxed{\frac{1}{6}}$. The states of the system before time 4 have no effect on this (conditional) probability (see tables I and II).

On the other hand, the probability of the system being in *state 3 at time 5* (i.e., three 7s in five rolls) *given* that it is in *state 3 at time 4* (i.e., three 7s in four rolls) is just the probability of not rolling a 7 on the fifth roll, which is $\boxed{\frac{5}{6}}$. Again the states of the system before time 4 have no effect on this conditional probability (see table III).

Finally, the probability that the system is in *state 3 at time 5* given that it is in *state 1 at time 4* (i.e., one 7 in four rolls) is $\boxed{0}$, since it is impossible to do this. Indeed, given that the system is in state 1 at time 4, there are only two possibilities for the state of the system at time 5. The system will be either in state 2 (if a 7 is rolled on roll 5) or in state 1 (if a 7 is not rolled on roll 5).

The process we have just discussed is an example of a Markov chain.

Exercises for 9.1

1. A fair coin is tossed repeatedly and the total number of heads tossed by any given time is observed. Let the state of the system at any given time be the total number of heads tossed up to, and including, that time.
   (a) Explain why the process is a Markov chain.
   (b) Given that the system is in state 3 at a given time (i.e., given that a total of three heads have been tossed up to, and including, that time), what is the probability that in one time period the system will be in state (1) 4? (2) 3? (3) 2? (4) 5?
2. Suppose that we have two urns, labeled I and II, and four balls labeled 1, 2, 3, and 4. Initially some of the balls are in urn I and the rest are in urn II. At certain time intervals, say every 10 seconds, a number is selected at random from 1, 2, 3, and 4, and the ball labeled by that number is removed from its urn and put in the opposite urn. Suppose that we regard the state of the system at any given time as being the number of balls in urn I at that time.

(a) Explain why the process defines a Markov chain. (A Markov chain of this type is called an *Ehrenfest chain*.)

(b) If the process is in state 3 at a given time (i.e., if there are 3 balls in urn I at a given time), what is the probability that in one time period (1) the system is in state 2? (2) the system is in state 4? (3) the system is in state 3? (4) the system is in state 1?

3. Three boys, 1, 2, and 3, are throwing a ball to each other. Boy 1 always throws the ball to 2, and 2 always throws the ball to 3. However, 3 is just as likely to throw the ball to 2 as to 1. Assume that none of the boys keeps the ball once it is thrown to him. Let the state of the system at any given time be the boy to which the ball is thrown at that time.

(a) Given that the process is in state 2 at a given time, what is the probability that in one time period (1) it is in state 1? (2) it is in state 3?

(b) Given that the process is in state 3 at a given time, what is the probability that in one time period (1) it is in state 1? (2) it is in state 2? (3) it is in state 3?

4. Consider the random experiment of repeatedly rolling a fair die. Let the state of the system at any given time be the maximum of the numbers rolled up to and including that time. Does the process define a Markov chain? Explain.

5. Two boys, Mark and David, find $6. Rather than split the money evenly, they decide to make a series of $1 bets to determine who will keep all the money. The winner of each bet is determined by tossing a fair coin. They begin by giving each other theoretical interests of $3. Suppose that we consider only the possible values of Mark's interest in the $6. Then the state of the system at any given time is the value of Mark's interest in the $6 up to and including that time.

(a) Does this system define a Markov chain?

(b) Given that the process is in state 4 at a given time, what is the probability that in one time period (1) it is in state 3? (2) it is in state 4? (3) it is in state 5?

(c) Given that the process is in state 0 at a given time, what is the probability that in one time period (1) it is in state 0? (2) it is in state 1? (3) it is in state 2?

6. Imagine a particle that moves in a straight line in unit steps on a line with the positions 0, 1, 2, 3, and 4 labeled. If the particle is at position 1, 2, or 3, it moves to the right one unit with probability $\frac{1}{3}$, and it moves to the left one unit with probability $\frac{2}{3}$. If the particle is at position 4, it moves to position 3 with probability 1, but if it reaches position 0 it remains there for the next two time units, and at the third time unit it moves to position 1 with probability 1. Let the state of the system at any given time be the position of the particle at that time. Explain why the process cannot be a Markov chain.

7. A fair coin is tossed until three heads occur in a row. Let the state of the system at any given time be the number of heads that have occurred in succession up to and including that time; that is, the state of the system at time k is j if the last tail occurred at the $(k - j)$th toss. Since the coin is not tossed after the third head occurs in succession, we make the convention that the state of the system from that time on is 3. Does the process define a Markov chain? Explain.

8. A fair coin is tossed until three heads occur in a row. Let the state of the system at any given time be the longest string of heads that have been tossed up to and including that time. Does the process define a Markov chain? Explain.

9. Consider the following random experiment. A fair coin is tossed until a tail comes up and then a coin with probability $\frac{1}{3}$ of coming up heads is tossed repeatedly. Let the state of the system at any given time be the outcome of the toss at that time. Explain why this process is not a Markov chain.

10. Suppose that the experiment in problem 9 is modified in the following way: We have two coins, one fair and one biased with probability $\frac{1}{3}$ of coming up heads. We start by tossing the fair coin. Whenever the outcome of a toss is a head, the fair coin is tossed, but if the outcome of a toss is a tail, the biased coin is tossed. Let the states of the system be as in problem 9. Does the process define a Markov chain? Explain.

11. A school contains 100 boys and 150 girls. Students are selected at random, one after another, to take an eye examination. Let the state of the system at any given time be the sex of the student who takes the examination at that time. Explain why this process does not define a Markov chain.

Section 9.2 Transition Probabilities

Before proceeding to the next example we introduce some notation that will be used throughout the chapter. In a Markov chain the symbol

$$p_{ij} \text{ (read "the probability of going from } i \text{ to } j \text{ in one step")}$$

is used to represent the following (conditional) probability: given that the system is in state i at a particular time, the (conditional) probability that the system is in state j at the next time is denoted by p_{ij}.

For instance, in the previous example (Example 9.1.2) we have

$$p_{23} = \tfrac{1}{6} \ (i = 2, j = 3)$$
$$p_{33} = \tfrac{5}{6} \ (i = 3, j = 3)$$
$$p_{13} = 0 \ (i = 1, j = 3)$$

In terms of the notation of Section 4.9, if

$$A = \text{event the system is in state } i \text{ at time } n$$
$$B = \text{event the system is in state } j \text{ at time } n + 1$$

then

$$p_{ij} = \Pr(B|A)$$

In general the p_{ij}s are called the *transition probabilities* of the Markov chain. Indeed, p_{ij} is the probability of a transition from state i to state j.

Example 9.2.1 Social Mobility Suppose that a person's social or financial status is considered to be either lower, middle, or upper class. It is then of interest to determine the mobility between classes from generation to generation. Conceivably, the class of an individual will depend on that of his immediate predecessor. For convenience, the present generation will be referred to as the "father," the immediate past as the "grandfather," the immediate future as the "son," and so on.

For simplicity, the following correspondence will be made:

State	Class
1	Lower
2	Middle
3	Upper

If we start with a given individual and follow a particular line of descent (e.g., first-born male), this can be considered as a system changing throughout time, with the state of the system at a particular time being the class of the individual in the corresponding generation. For example, one possibility might begin as follows:

Generation (time)	0	1	2	3	4	5	6	7
Class (state)	2	1	3	3	3	2	2	1

In this case the father (generation 0) is middle class, his son (generation 1) is lower class, his grandson (generation 2) is upper class, and so on.

The assumption that this system is a Markov chain is that the class of the son of a given individual (father) depends only on the class of the father and not on the classes of any of the father's ancestors. In other words, given the class of the father, the son's status is independent of the classes of any of his grandparents. The Markovian assumption may or may not be valid.

The transition probabilities for this system might be as follows:

		Next generation		
	State	1	2	3
Present generation	1	.6	.3	.1
	2	.1	.8	.1
	3	.1	.2	.7

(9.2.1)

The ith row and jth column of this table gives the probability of transition from state i to j in one generation (p_{ij}). For example, the probability that the son is middle class (state 2) *given* that the father is lower class (state 1) is

$$p_{12} = .3 \qquad \text{(here } i = 1, j = 2)$$

Similarly,

$$p_{13} = .1 \qquad p_{22} = .8 \qquad p_{32} = .2$$

The preceding example already indicates [see Eq. (9.2.1)] that matrices will play a role in the study of Markov chains.

Example 9.2.2 Word Structure It has been determined that in the Samoan language the probability of occurrence of a vowel or consonant in a sequence of letters depends only upon the preceding letter and not on any letters before that.[1] Moreover, analysis of the data indicates that the following holds:

		Next letter	
	Letter	Vowel	Consonant
Present letter	Vowel	0	1
	Consonant	.49	.51

(9.2.2)

[1] E. B. Newman, "The Patterns of Vowels and Consonants in Various Languages," *Amer. Jour. Psychol.*, Vol. 64, 1951, pp. 369–379.

In other words, the probability of a vowel following a vowel is 0, the probability of a consonant following a vowel is 1, the probability of a vowel following a consonant is .49, and the probability of a consonant following a consonant is .51.

The facts of the preceding paragraph imply that the occurrence of vowels and consonants in the Samoan language forms a Markov chain. If the correspondence

State	Type of letter
1	Vowel
2	Consonant

is made, the transition probabilities of the Markov chain are

$$p_{11} = 0 \qquad p_{12} = 1$$
$$p_{21} = .49 \qquad p_{22} = .51$$

The state of the system at a given time is, of course, 1 if the letter observed is a vowel and 2 if the letter observed is a consonant.

The transition probabilities indicate that it is impossible for a vowel to follow a vowel ($p_{11} = 0$) and that it is slightly more likely to have a consonant follow a consonant ($p_{22} = .51$) than to have a vowel follow a consonant ($p_{21} = .49$).

Again, Eq. (9.2.2) reveals that matrices will play an important part in analyzing Markov chains.

Example 9.2.3 Gambling   An example of the classical gambling situation is as follows: Two players, say player I and player II, are indulging in a game of chance such as tossing a coin. The player calling the outcome of the toss correctly wins $1 from the other player. If either of the players goes broke, the game ends with the other player winning.

In this example we shall assume that the coin is unbiased [i.e., $\Pr(\{H\}) = \Pr(\{T\}) = \frac{1}{2}$], so the game is "fair." To analyze the situation, consider the game as a system changing through time. One way to do this is to regard the state of the system at a given time as being the amount of capital player I has at that time. The reader should convince himself that this system is a Markov chain (the capital of player I after the next toss of the coin depends on his capital at the present time but not on his capital at times before the present one).

To be specific, let us suppose that initially player I has $2 and player II has $4. Then the system has seven states. For the capital of player I can be 0, 1, 2, 3, 4, 5, or 6 dollars.

If the state of the system at a given time is 0, it stays forever after in that state (player I is broke). If the state of the system at a given time is 6, it remains in that state from that time on (player II is broke). In terms of transition probabilities the last two sentences mean that

$$p_{00} = 1, \quad p_{01} = 0, \quad p_{02} = 0, \quad p_{03} = 0, \quad p_{04} = 0, \quad p_{05} = 0, \quad p_{06} = 0$$
$$p_{60} = 0, \quad p_{61} = 0, \quad p_{62} = 0, \quad p_{63} = 0, \quad p_{64} = 0, \quad p_{65} = 0, \quad p_{66} = 1$$

However, if the state of the system at a given time is *not* 0 or 6, then in one time period (i.e., the next toss of the coin) the state of the system must change by either -1 (player I loses on that toss) or $+1$ (player I wins on that toss). Because the coin is *fair*, each of these two possibilities is equally likely. Thus the transition probabilities of this Markov chain are as follows:

Capital of player I

State	0	1	2	3	4	5	6
			Capital after next toss				
0	1	0	0	0	0	0	0
1	$\frac{1}{2}$	0	$\frac{1}{2}$	0	0	0	0
2	0	$\frac{1}{2}$	0	$\frac{1}{2}$	0	0	0
3	0	0	$\frac{1}{2}$	0	$\frac{1}{2}$	0	0
4	0	0	0	$\frac{1}{2}$	0	$\frac{1}{2}$	0
5	0	0	0	0	$\frac{1}{2}$	0	$\frac{1}{2}$
6	0	0	0	0	0	0	1

Present capital

(9.2.3)

Exercises for 9.2

1. In Example 9.2.1, find
   (a) p_{11} (b) p_{21}
   (c) p_{23} (d) p_{33}

2. Let a Markov chain have states 1, 2, and 3. Suppose that whenever the process is in state 1 at a given time it will still be in state 1 in one time period with probability 1. If the process is in state 2 at a given time it will be in state 1 with probability $\frac{1}{2}$, in state 2 with probability $\frac{1}{3}$, and in state 3 with probability $\frac{1}{6}$ in one time period. If the process is in state 3 at a given time it will be in state 2 with probability $\frac{1}{3}$ and in state 3 with probability $\frac{2}{3}$ in one time period. Find the transition probabilities for this Markov chain.

3. Find the transition probabilities for the Ehrenfest chain of problem 2, Exercises 9.1.

4. A man is playing three slot machines. The first machine pays off with probability $\frac{1}{5}$, the second with probability $\frac{1}{2}$, and the third with probability $\frac{1}{4}$. He plays a machine until he wins and then he changes machines. If he is playing the first machine when he wins, he changes to the third machine. If he is playing the second machine when he wins, he changes to the first machine. If he is playing the third machine when he wins, he changes to the second machine. Let the state of the system at any given time be the machine that the man is playing at that time. Find the transition probabilities corresponding to this system.

5. Find the transition probabilities for the process defined in problem 3, Exercises 9.1.

6. An urn contains five balls, two of which are red and three of which are black. At a sequence of times a ball is chosen at random. If the ball chosen is red, it is painted black and then put back. If the ball chosen is black, it is painted red and then put back. Let the state of the system at any given time be the number of red balls in the urn at that time.
   (a) Find the transition probabilities for this Markov chain.
   (b) List them in matrix form as in the table in Eq. (9.2.3).

7. Suppose that we have two urns, each containing three balls. Three of the six balls are painted red and three black. At a sequence of times a ball is chosen at random from each urn. The ball chosen from the first urn is put into the second, and the ball chosen

from the second urn is put into the first. Let the state of the system at any given time be the number of red balls in the first urn at that time.

(a) Find the transition probabilities for this Markov chain.

(b) List them in matrix form.

8. Find the transition probabilities of the process defined in problem 5, Exercises 9.1.

9. In Example 9.2.1 it was tacitly assumed that every man has a son. Suppose we do not assume that every man has a son but assume instead that the probability of a man having a son is .5. Then a new process can be formed having four states, where the first three states are as in Example 9.2.1 and the fourth state corresponds to the outcome that a man has no son. This state represents families whose male line has died out, and we make the convention that once the process reaches this state, the state of the system from that time on is 4. Find the transition probabilities corresponding to this process. (Assume that *if a man has a son*, the probabilities of transition are given by Eq. (9.2.1).]

10. Consider a Markov chain with states 1, 2, and 3, and let p_{ij}, with $i = 1, 2, 3$, and $j = 1, 2, 3$, be the transition probabilities for this chain. Show that

$$p_{11} + p_{12} + p_{13} = 1$$

with a similar result holding for

$$p_{i1} + p_{i2} + p_{i3} \qquad \text{where } i = 2, 3$$

[*Hint:* Recall that if E = event the system is in state 1 at time k, and E_j = event the system is in state j at time $k + 1$, $j = 1, 2, 3$, then $p_{1j} = \Pr(E_j|E)$. Note that exactly one of E_1, E_2, E_3 must occur. Use problem 11, Exercises 4.10.]

11. Consider the following modified version of problem 6, Exercises 9.1. If the particle is at position 1, 2, or 3, it has equal probability of moving one unit to the right, moving one unit to the left, or staying at its present position. If it is at position 0 or 4, it cannot stay, but has equal probability of moving to any of the other four positions. Find the transition probabilities for this system.

12. Joe's luck at playing poker follows a certain pattern. If he wins a game, the probability of winning the next game is $\frac{1}{6}$, the probability of breaking even on the next game is $\frac{1}{3}$, and the probability of losing the next game is $\frac{1}{2}$. If he breaks even on a game, there is equal probability of winning, breaking even, or losing on the next game. If he loses a game, the probability of winning the next game is $\frac{2}{5}$, the probability of losing is $\frac{1}{5}$, and the probability of breaking even is $\frac{2}{5}$. Let the state of the system at any given time be the outcome of winning, losing, or breaking even on that particular poker game, and let 1 correspond to the state "wins," 2 correspond to the state "loses," and 3 correspond to the state "breaks even." Find the transition probabilities that correspond to this process.

13. In the Ehrenfest chain of problem 2, Exercises 9.1, suppose that we have d balls, labeled $1, 2, \ldots, d$. Find the transition probabilities for this Markov chain.

Section 9.3   Transition Matrix

It was indicated in Section 9.2 that matrices will prove useful in the study of Markov chains. We begin with an example that will illustrate the general situation. While proceeding through this example, we shall pause at various places to state general results concerning Markov chains which have been demonstrated to be valid in this particular example.

Example 9.3.1   Social Mobility   Consider, again, Example 9.2.1 and assume that the process is Markovian (i.e., given the class of the father, the class of the son is independent of those of previous generations). From the table in (9.2.1) it is natural to form the following matrix:

$$P = \begin{bmatrix} .6 & .3 & .1 \\ .1 & .8 & .1 \\ .1 & .2 & .7 \end{bmatrix}$$

This is a 3×3 matrix. The element in the ith row and jth column of the matrix is p_{ij}—the probability of transition from state i to state j (i.e., the conditional probability of being in state j in the next time period *given* that the present state of the system is i).

Definition

Consider a Markov chain with states $1, 2, \ldots, N$. Let the transition probability from state i to state j be p_{ij}. Then the $N \times N$ matrix $P = [p_{ij}]$ is called the *transition matrix* of the Markov chain.

For example, if the Markov chain has four states, 1, 2, 3, and 4, the transition matrix can be displayed as

$$P = \begin{bmatrix} p_{11} & p_{12} & p_{13} & p_{14} \\ p_{21} & p_{22} & p_{23} & p_{24} \\ p_{31} & p_{32} & p_{33} & p_{34} \\ p_{41} & p_{42} & p_{43} & p_{44} \end{bmatrix}$$

Example 9.3.2

1. The transition matrix for the social-mobility chain is

$$P = \begin{bmatrix} .6 & .3 & .1 \\ .1 & .8 & .1 \\ .1 & .2 & .7 \end{bmatrix}$$

2. The transition matrix for the word-structure chain (Example 9.2.2) is

$$P = \begin{bmatrix} 0 & 1 \\ .49 & .51 \end{bmatrix}$$

In some cases it is convenient to number the states starting with 0 instead of 1 (e.g., the gambling Markov chain of Example 9.2.3). In this case a zeroth row and column are used. For example, if the Markov chain has the four states 0, 1, 2, and 3, the transition matrix is represented as

$$P = \begin{bmatrix} p_{00} & p_{01} & p_{02} & p_{03} \\ p_{10} & p_{11} & p_{12} & p_{13} \\ p_{20} & p_{21} & p_{22} & p_{23} \\ p_{30} & p_{31} & p_{32} & p_{33} \end{bmatrix}$$

The transition matrix of the gambling chain (Example 9.2.3) with states 0, 1, 2, 3, 4, 5, and 6 is given by the 7×7 matrix

$$P = \begin{bmatrix} 1 & 0 & 0 & 0 & 0 & 0 & 0 \\ \frac{1}{2} & 0 & \frac{1}{2} & 0 & 0 & 0 & 0 \\ 0 & \frac{1}{2} & 0 & \frac{1}{2} & 0 & 0 & 0 \\ 0 & 0 & \frac{1}{2} & 0 & \frac{1}{2} & 0 & 0 \\ 0 & 0 & 0 & \frac{1}{2} & 0 & \frac{1}{2} & 0 \\ 0 & 0 & 0 & 0 & \frac{1}{2} & 0 & \frac{1}{2} \\ 0 & 0 & 0 & 0 & 0 & 0 & 1 \end{bmatrix}$$

As an aid in reading the transition probabilities of a Markov chain from its transition matrix, the states of the system are frequently placed adjacent to the matrix, as illustrated by the following examples.

Example 9.3.3

1. Social mobility:

$$P = \begin{array}{c} \\ 1 \\ 2 \\ 3 \end{array} \begin{array}{ccc} 1 & 2 & 3 \\ \begin{bmatrix} .6 & .3 & .1 \\ .1 & .8 & .1 \\ .1 & .2 & .7 \end{bmatrix} \end{array}$$

For example, $p_{11} = .6$, $p_{32} = .2$, and $p_{33} = .7$.

2. Word structure:

$$P = \begin{array}{c} \\ 1 \\ 2 \end{array} \begin{array}{cc} 1 & 2 \\ \begin{bmatrix} 0 & 1 \\ .49 & .51 \end{bmatrix} \end{array}$$

Then it is easy to see, for example, that $p_{12} = 1$ and $p_{21} = .49$.

3. Gambling:

$$P = \begin{array}{c} \\ 0 \\ 1 \\ 2 \\ 3 \\ 4 \\ 5 \\ 6 \end{array} \begin{array}{ccccccc} 0 & 1 & 2 & 3 & 4 & 5 & 6 \\ \begin{bmatrix} 1 & 0 & 0 & 0 & 0 & 0 & 0 \\ \frac{1}{2} & 0 & \frac{1}{2} & 0 & 0 & 0 & 0 \\ 0 & \frac{1}{2} & 0 & \frac{1}{2} & 0 & 0 & 0 \\ 0 & 0 & \frac{1}{2} & 0 & \frac{1}{2} & 0 & 0 \\ 0 & 0 & 0 & \frac{1}{2} & 0 & \frac{1}{2} & 0 \\ 0 & 0 & 0 & 0 & \frac{1}{2} & 0 & \frac{1}{2} \\ 0 & 0 & 0 & 0 & 0 & 0 & 1 \end{bmatrix} \end{array}$$

From this representation it is easy to read off the transition probabilities. For example, $p_{01} = 0$, $p_{10} = \frac{1}{2}$, and $p_{66} = 1$.

Example 9.3.4 Social Mobility We continue our study of the social-mobility chain introduced in Example 9.2.1. Now, according to the data, the probability of a transition from state 2 to state 3 in *one generation* is $p_{23} = .1$. Suppose, however, that the following question is asked: What is the probability of a transition from state 2 to state 3 in *two generations*? In other words, if the father is middle class (2), what is the probability that his grandson is upper class (3)?

Before proceeding to answer this question, we illustrate, via a tree diagram (Figure 9.3.1), the possible transitions in *two generations* starting from state 2.

Figure 9.3.1

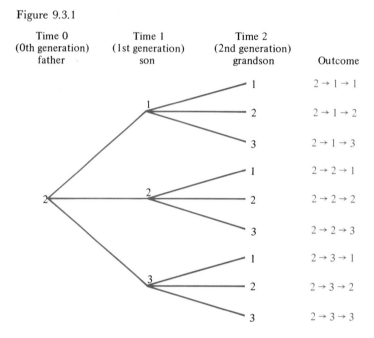

Time 0 (0th generation) father	Time 1 (1st generation) son	Time 2 (2nd generation) grandson	Outcome
		1	$2 \to 1 \to 1$
		2	$2 \to 1 \to 2$
		3	$2 \to 1 \to 3$
		1	$2 \to 2 \to 1$
		2	$2 \to 2 \to 2$
		3	$2 \to 2 \to 3$
		1	$2 \to 3 \to 1$
		2	$2 \to 3 \to 2$
		3	$2 \to 3 \to 3$

We now illustrate how to calculate the probabilities that are associated with each of the transitions portrayed in Figure 9.3.1. As a typical example, consider the transition $2 \to 3 \to 3$. This means that the father's son is upper class and so is his grandson.

First we proceed intuitively. According to the transition matrix P, the probability of a transition (in one generation) from 2 to 3 is .1. Once in state 3 the probability of transition to state 3 in the next generation is .7. Hence it seems clear that the transition $2 \to 3 \to 3$ should have probability

$$(.1) \cdot (.7) = .07 \tag{9.3.1}$$

To give a rigorous verification of this fact we proceed in the following way. Let

A = event the initial state is 2
B = event the system is in state 3 at time 1
C = event the system is in state 3 at time 2

Then the probability of the transition $2 \to 3 \to 3$ is just $\Pr(C \cap B | A)$. But by problem 6(b), Exercises 4.11,

$$\Pr(C \cap B | A) = \Pr(B | A)\Pr(C | B \cap A) \tag{9.3.2}$$

Now, $\Pr(B | A) = p_{23} = .1$. To handle $\Pr(C | B \cap A)$, note that because the process is a Markov chain, the transition probability from state 3 in the first generation to state 3 in the second generation does not depend on the fact that the initial (0th) generation was in state 2. In other words, the Markovian assumption implies that

$$\Pr(C | B \cap A) = \Pr(C | B) \tag{9.3.3}$$

But $\Pr(C|B) = p_{33} = .7$. Thus, by Eqs. (9.3.2) and (9.3.3),

$$\begin{aligned} \Pr(C \cap B | A) &= \Pr(B|A)\Pr(C|B \cap A) \\ &= \Pr(B|A)\Pr(C|B) \\ &= p_{23} \cdot p_{33} = (.1) \cdot (.7) = .07 \end{aligned} \qquad (9.3.4)$$

This verifies, rigorously, the result of Eq. (9.3.1).

Before proceeding with this example we take a moment to summarize the results obtained so far.

Formula (9.3.4) indicates that the general procedure for calculating probabilities of transitions through *two* time periods is as follows.

Theorem 9.3.1

In a Markov chain with transition matrix $P = [p_{ij}]$, the probability of transition from state i to state k to state j is given by $p_{ik} \cdot p_{kj}$. Schematically,

$$\begin{array}{ccc} i \to k, & k \to j \\ \downarrow & \downarrow \\ p_{ik} & \cdot & p_{kj} \end{array} \qquad (9.3.5)$$

Exercises for 9.3

1. Let

$$P = \begin{array}{c} \\ 1 \\ 2 \\ 3 \\ 4 \end{array} \begin{array}{cccc} 1 & 2 & 3 & 4 \\ \left[\begin{array}{cccc} \frac{3}{8} & \frac{5}{32} & \frac{1}{4} & \frac{7}{32} \\ \frac{1}{4} & 0 & \frac{1}{2} & \frac{1}{4} \\ \frac{1}{4} & \frac{1}{4} & \frac{3}{8} & \frac{1}{8} \\ \frac{3}{8} & \frac{5}{16} & \frac{3}{16} & \frac{1}{8} \end{array}\right] \end{array}$$

be the transition matrix of a Markov chain with states 1, 2, 3, and 4. Find

    (a) p_{13} (b) p_{22}

    (c) p_{31} (d) p_{43}

2. Two men are competing in a shooting contest. The first man hits the target 90 percent of the time, and the second man hits the target 80 percent of the time. Each man fires until he misses the target, and then it is the other man's turn. Let the state of the system at any given time be the man who is shooting at that time, and assume that the process is Markovian. Find the transition matrix for this Markov chain.

3. Suppose that a machine is either in operating condition or is broken down at the start of each day. If the machine is broken down at the start of a day, there is probability $\frac{2}{3}$ that it will be repaired and in operating condition by the start of the next day. However, if the machine is in operating condition at the start of a day, there is probability $\frac{1}{8}$ that it will be broken down at the start of the next day. Let 1 correspond to the state that the machine is broken down and 2 correspond to the state that the machine is in operating condition, and assume that the process is Markovian. Find the transition matrix for this Markov chain.

4. A man either drives or rides a bus to work each day. He never drives to work on two successive days, but if he rides a bus to work one day he is just as likely to ride a bus the next day as he is to drive his car. Let the state of the system at any given time be the outcome of either driving or riding a bus to work on that day, and let 1 correspond to the state of driving to work and 2 correspond to the state of riding a bus. Find the transition matrix for this process.

5. Find the transition matrix for the process defined in problem 3, Exercises 9.1.

6. A maze is constructed in such a way that at each junction there is a choice of turning left, turning right, or going straight ahead. A rat is released in the maze. If he turns left at a junction there is a probability $\frac{1}{3}$ that he will turn left at the next junction and a probability $\frac{2}{3}$ that he will turn right. If he turns right at a junction there is a probability $\frac{1}{4}$ that he will turn right at the next junction, a probability $\frac{1}{4}$ that he will turn left, and a probability $\frac{1}{2}$ that he will go straight ahead. If he goes straight ahead at a junction, there is a probability $\frac{1}{3}$ that he will go straight ahead at the next junction, a probability $\frac{1}{3}$ that he will turn left, and a probability $\frac{1}{3}$ that he will turn right. Let 1 correspond to the state the rat turns left, 2 the state the rat turns right, and 3 the state the rat goes straight ahead. Find the transition matrix for this process.

7. Find the transition matrix for the Ehrenfest chain defined in problem 2, Exercises 9.1.

8. Find the transition matrix for the generalized Ehrenfest chain of problem 13, Exercises 9.2.

9. Find the transition matrix for the Markov chain defined in problem 4, Exercises 9.1.

10. Find the transition matrix for the Markov chain defined in problem 7, Exercises 9.1.

11. In Example 9.2.3, find the probability of transition from state 1 to state 2 to state 3.

12. A matrix A is called a *stochastic matrix* if its entries are all nonnegative and the sum of the entries in every row is 1. Which of the following matrices are stochastic matrices?

(a) $\begin{bmatrix} 0 & 1 & 0 \\ \frac{1}{2} & 0 & \frac{1}{2} \\ \frac{1}{3} & \frac{1}{3} & \frac{1}{3} \end{bmatrix}$

(b) $\begin{bmatrix} 1 & 0 & 0 \\ \frac{1}{2} & 1 & -\frac{1}{2} \end{bmatrix}$

(c) $\begin{bmatrix} \frac{1}{4} & \frac{1}{4} & \frac{1}{4} & \frac{1}{4} \\ .3 & .2 & .1 & .3 \\ \frac{1}{6} & \frac{1}{6} & \frac{1}{3} & \frac{1}{3} \\ .2 & .2 & .1 & .6 \end{bmatrix}$

(d) $\begin{bmatrix} .4 & .4 & .2 \\ .3 & .5 & .1 \\ .3 & .2 & .5 \end{bmatrix}$

(e) $[0 \quad 0 \quad 1 \quad 0]$

(f) $\begin{bmatrix} -1 & 2 \\ \frac{1}{2} & .5 \end{bmatrix}$

(g) $\begin{bmatrix} 1 \\ 0 \\ 1 \end{bmatrix}$

(h) $\begin{bmatrix} \frac{1}{2} & \frac{1}{3} & \frac{1}{6} \\ 0 & 1 & 0 \\ \frac{1}{3} & \frac{1}{3} & \frac{1}{3} \end{bmatrix}$

13. By arguing as in problem 10, Exercises 9.2, one can show that the transition matrix P of a Markov chain with N states is an $N \times N$, square, stochastic matrix. Conversely, it can be shown that a square, stochastic matrix is the transition matrix for some Markov chain. Which of the matrices in problem 12 are transition matrices?

14. Let A and B be stochastic matrices such that AB is defined. Prove that AB is a stochastic matrix.

15. Find the transition matrix of the process defined in problem 9, Exercises 9.2.

Section 9.4   Two-Step Transition Matrix

As we saw in Example 9.3.4, it is important to consider the probabilities associated with transitions between states involving *two* time periods. In this section we shall develop a simple method for determining these two-step transition probabilities. The development of the method will proceed through the following example.

Example 9.4.1   Social Mobility   By using Eqs. (9.2.1) and (9.3.5), the probabilities for the various transitions in *two* generations starting from state 2 can now be obtained. The results are presented in the last column of the tree diagram in Figure 9.4.1.

Figure 9.4.1

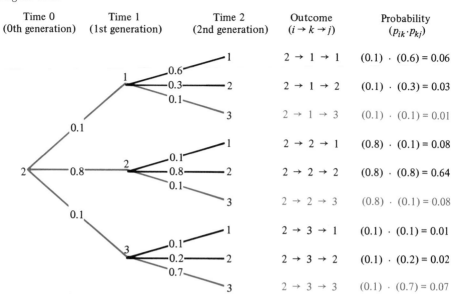

Time 0 (0th generation)	Time 1 (1st generation)	Time 2 (2nd generation)	Outcome $(i \to k \to j)$	Probability $(p_{ik} \cdot p_{kj})$
		1	$2 \to 1 \to 1$	$(0.1) \cdot (0.6) = 0.06$
		2	$2 \to 1 \to 2$	$(0.1) \cdot (0.3) = 0.03$
		3	$2 \to 1 \to 3$	$(0.1) \cdot (0.1) = 0.01$
		1	$2 \to 2 \to 1$	$(0.8) \cdot (0.1) = 0.08$
		2	$2 \to 2 \to 2$	$(0.8) \cdot (0.8) = 0.64$
		3	$2 \to 2 \to 3$	$(0.8) \cdot (0.1) = 0.08$
		1	$2 \to 3 \to 1$	$(0.1) \cdot (0.1) = 0.01$
		2	$2 \to 3 \to 2$	$(0.1) \cdot (0.2) = 0.02$
		3	$2 \to 3 \to 3$	$(0.1) \cdot (0.7) = 0.07$

Recall that the original question posed in Example 9.3.4 was: What is the probability of a transition from state 2 to state 3 in *two* generations? Intuitively, the answer to this question can be obtained as follows. In two generations a transition from state 2 to state 3 can occur in three mutually exclusive ways (see Figure 9.4.1):

$$\begin{array}{cccc} \textit{Time:}\ 0 & 1 & 2 \\ 2 & \to 1 & \to 3 \\ 2 & \to 2 & \to 3 \\ 2 & \to 3 & \to 3 \end{array} \tag{9.4.1}$$

In other words, a transition from state 2 to state 3 in *two* generations must occur via a transition in the first generation to either state 1, 2, or 3. According to Figure 9.4.1 the probabilities associated with the transitions in Eq. (9.4.1) are, respectively,

$$\begin{aligned} p_{21} \cdot p_{13} &= (.1) \cdot (.1) = .01 \\ p_{22} \cdot p_{23} &= (.8) \cdot (.1) = .08 \\ p_{23} \cdot p_{33} &= (.1) \cdot (.7) = .07 \end{aligned} \tag{9.4.2}$$

Because these transitions are mutually exclusive, it should follow that (problem 12, Exercises 4.5) the probability of transition from state 2 to state 3 in *two* generations is the sum of the probabilities in Eq. (9.4.2):

$$p_{21} \cdot p_{13} + p_{22} \cdot p_{23} + p_{23} \cdot p_{33} = .01 + .08 + .07 = .16 \tag{9.4.3}$$

To prove this rigorously it is only necessary to follow the "intuitive" procedure just used to obtain Eq. (9.4.3). Let

F = event the initial state (zeroth generation) is 2
G = event the system is in state 3 in the second generation
E_1 = event the system is in state 1 in the first generation
E_2 = event the system is in state 2 in the first generation
E_3 = event the system is in state 3 in the first generation

The problem is to determine $\Pr(G|F)$. First notice that *exactly one* of E_1, E_2, and E_3 must occur and consequently (see problem 12, Exercises 4.10)

$$\Pr(G|F) = \Pr(G \cap E_1|F) + \Pr(G \cap E_2|F) + \Pr(G \cap E_3|F)$$

Now, notice that, for example, $\Pr(G \cap E_1|F)$ is just the probability of transition from state 2 to state 1 to state 3. By Theorem 9.3.1 this is just $p_{21} \cdot p_{13}$. Thus

$$
\begin{array}{cccccc}
2 \to 1, & 1 \to 3 & 2 \to 2, & 2 \to 3 & 2 \to 3, & 3 \to 3 \\
\downarrow & \downarrow & \downarrow & \downarrow & \downarrow & \downarrow
\end{array}
$$

$$
\begin{aligned}
\Pr(G|F) = \quad & p_{21} \quad \cdot \quad p_{13} \quad + \quad p_{22} \quad \cdot \quad p_{23} \quad + \quad p_{23} \quad \cdot \quad p_{33} \\
& = .01 + .08 + .07 = .16
\end{aligned}
\tag{9.4.4}
$$

This is a rigorous justification of Eq. (9.4.3).

For convenience we write $i \overset{2}{\to} j$ to indicate a transition from state i to state j in *two* time periods.

Definition

Consider a Markov chain with transition matrix $P = [p_{ij}]$. The probability of transition from state i to state j in two time periods is denoted by $p_{ij}^{(2)}$. The matrix, $P^{(2)} = [p_{ij}^{(2)}]$, obtained is called the *two-step transition matrix of the Markov chain.*

If, for example, the Markov chain has four states, 1, 2, 3, and 4, the two-step transition matrix can be displayed as

$$
P^{(2)} = \begin{bmatrix}
p_{11}^{(2)} & p_{12}^{(2)} & p_{13}^{(2)} & p_{14}^{(2)} \\
p_{21}^{(2)} & p_{22}^{(2)} & p_{23}^{(2)} & p_{24}^{(2)} \\
p_{31}^{(2)} & p_{32}^{(2)} & p_{33}^{(2)} & p_{34}^{(2)} \\
p_{41}^{(2)} & p_{42}^{(2)} & p_{43}^{(2)} & p_{44}^{(2)}
\end{bmatrix}
$$

Example 9.4.2 Social Mobility In Example 9.4.1 we just showed [Eq. (9.4.3) or (9.4.4)] that the probability of a transition from state 2 to state 3 in two generations is .16. Hence in the notation of the definition just given

$$p_{23}^{(2)} = .16$$

In order to determine the two-step transition matrix, $P^{(2)}$, of a Markov chain, the argument leading up to Eq. (9.4.4) can be used to establish the following general result.

Theorem 9.4.1

Consider a Markov chain with N states (say, $1, 2, \ldots, N$), so that the transition matrix $P = [p_{ij}]$ is an $N \times N$ matrix. Then the probability of transition from state i to state j in *two* time periods is given by

$$p_{ij}^{(2)} = p_{i1} \cdot p_{1j} + p_{i2} \cdot p_{2j} + \cdots + p_{iN} \cdot p_{Nj} \tag{9.4.5}$$

Example 9.4.3 Word Structure Consider the Markov chain introduced in Example 9.2.2. The transition matrix is

$$P = \begin{array}{cc} & \begin{array}{cc} 1 & 2 \end{array} \\ \begin{array}{c} 1 \\ 2 \end{array} & \begin{bmatrix} 0 & 1 \\ .49 & .51 \end{bmatrix} \end{array}$$

which is a 2×2 matrix. To calculate the two-step transition matrix we apply Eq. (9.4.5). The results are

$$p_{11}^{(2)} = p_{11} \cdot p_{11} + p_{12} \cdot p_{21} = 0 \cdot 0 + 1 \cdot .49 = .49$$
$$p_{12}^{(2)} = p_{11} \cdot p_{12} + p_{12} \cdot p_{22} = 0 \cdot 1 + 1 \cdot .51 = .51$$
$$p_{21}^{(2)} = p_{21} \cdot p_{11} + p_{22} \cdot p_{21} = .49 \cdot 0 + .51 \cdot .49 = .2499$$
$$p_{22}^{(2)} = p_{21} \cdot p_{12} + p_{22} \cdot p_{22} = .49 \cdot 1 + .51 \cdot .51 = .7501$$

Consequently,

$$P^{(2)} = \begin{array}{cc} & \begin{array}{cc} 1 & 2 \end{array} \\ \begin{array}{c} 1 \\ 2 \end{array} & \begin{bmatrix} .49 & .51 \\ .2499 & .7501 \end{bmatrix} \end{array}$$

Then, for example, the probability of going from state 2 to state 1 in two time periods is .2499. This means that the probability is .2499 ($\doteq \frac{1}{4}$) that the *second* letter following a consonant will be a vowel.

Fortunately, there is an efficient and easy-to-remember method for calculating the two-step transition matrix of a Markov chain. The key to this method lies in Theorem 9.4.1. Formula (9.4.5) should remind the reader of the formula for matrix multiplication [see Eq. (6.8.5)]. In fact, the right side of Eq. (9.4.5) represents the element in the ith row and jth column of the matrix $P \cdot P = P^2$. On the other hand, the left side of Eq. (9.4.5) represents the element in the ith row and jth column of the two-step transition matrix, $P^{(2)}$, of the Markov chain. This means that the $N \times N$ matrices P^2 and $P^{(2)}$ are equal.

Theorem 9.4.2

Consider a Markov chain with transition matrix P. Then the two-step transition matrix, $P^{(2)}$, is just the product of the matrix P with itself. That is,

$$P^{(2)} = P^2 \tag{9.4.6}$$

Example 9.4.4

1. Consider the word-structure chain in Example 9.4.3. The transition matrix P is

$$P = \begin{array}{cc} & \begin{array}{cc} 1 & 2 \end{array} \\ \begin{array}{c} 1 \\ 2 \end{array} & \begin{bmatrix} 0 & 1 \\ .49 & .51 \end{bmatrix} \end{array}$$

According to Eq. (9.4.6) the two-step transition matrix is

$$P^{(2)} = P^2 = \begin{bmatrix} 0 & 1 \\ .49 & .51 \end{bmatrix} \begin{bmatrix} 0 & 1 \\ .49 & .51 \end{bmatrix}$$

$$= \begin{bmatrix} .49 & .51 \\ .51 \cdot .49 & .49 + (.51)^2 \end{bmatrix} = \begin{bmatrix} .49 & .51 \\ .2499 & .7501 \end{bmatrix}$$

This agrees with the results of Example 9.4.3.

2. The social-mobility chain has transition matrix

$$P = \begin{array}{c} \\ 1 \\ 2 \\ 3 \end{array} \begin{array}{ccc} 1 & 2 & 3 \\ \begin{bmatrix} .6 & .3 & .1 \\ .1 & .8 & .1 \\ .1 & .2 & .7 \end{bmatrix} \end{array}$$

In order to find the two-step transition probabilities we use Eq. (9.4.6) to obtain

$$P^{(2)} = \begin{bmatrix} .6 & .3 & .1 \\ .1 & .8 & .1 \\ .1 & .2 & .7 \end{bmatrix} \cdot \begin{bmatrix} .6 & .3 & .1 \\ .1 & .8 & .1 \\ .1 & .2 & .7 \end{bmatrix}$$

$$= \begin{bmatrix} .40 & .44 & .16 \\ .15 & .69 & .16 \\ .15 & .33 & .52 \end{bmatrix}$$

Now it is an easy matter to read off the two-step transition probabilities. For example, the probability of a transition in *two* generations from upper class to middle class $(3 \xrightarrow{2} 2)$ is

$$p_{32}^{(2)} = .33$$

3. As we have seen, the transition matrix for the gambling chain in Example 9.2.3 is

$$P = \begin{array}{c} \\ 0 \\ 1 \\ 2 \\ 3 \\ 4 \\ 5 \\ 6 \end{array} \begin{array}{ccccccc} 0 & 1 & 2 & 3 & 4 & 5 & 6 \\ \begin{bmatrix} 1 & 0 & 0 & 0 & 0 & 0 & 0 \\ \frac{1}{2} & 0 & \frac{1}{2} & 0 & 0 & 0 & 0 \\ 0 & \frac{1}{2} & 0 & \frac{1}{2} & 0 & 0 & 0 \\ 0 & 0 & \frac{1}{2} & 0 & \frac{1}{2} & 0 & 0 \\ 0 & 0 & 0 & \frac{1}{2} & 0 & \frac{1}{2} & 0 \\ 0 & 0 & 0 & 0 & \frac{1}{2} & 0 & \frac{1}{2} \\ 0 & 0 & 0 & 0 & 0 & 0 & 1 \end{bmatrix} \end{array}$$

In order to calculate the probabilities associated with the change in the capital of player I in *two* tosses of the coin, we use Eq. (9.4.6) to get

$$P^{(2)} = P \cdot P = \begin{array}{c} \\ 0 \\ 1 \\ 2 \\ 3 \\ 4 \\ 5 \\ 6 \end{array} \begin{array}{ccccccc} 0 & 1 & 2 & 3 & 4 & 5 & 6 \\ \begin{bmatrix} 1 & 0 & 0 & 0 & 0 & 0 & 0 \\ \frac{1}{2} & \frac{1}{4} & 0 & \frac{1}{4} & 0 & 0 & 0 \\ \frac{1}{4} & 0 & \frac{1}{2} & 0 & \frac{1}{4} & 0 & 0 \\ 0 & \frac{1}{4} & 0 & \frac{1}{2} & 0 & \frac{1}{4} & 0 \\ 0 & 0 & \frac{1}{4} & 0 & \frac{1}{2} & 0 & \frac{1}{4} \\ 0 & 0 & 0 & \frac{1}{4} & 0 & \frac{1}{4} & \frac{1}{2} \\ 0 & 0 & 0 & 0 & 0 & 0 & 1 \end{bmatrix} \end{array}$$

So, for example, the probability that player I's capital goes from 2 to 4 in two tosses of the coin $(2 \xrightarrow{2} 4)$ is

$$p_{24}^{(2)} = \frac{1}{4}$$

The probability that his capital goes from 3 to 3 in two tosses of the coin $(3 \xrightarrow{2} 3)$ is

$$p_{33}^{(2)} = \tfrac{1}{2}$$

Exercises for 9.4

1. Let

$$
P^{(2)} = \begin{array}{c} \\ 1 \\ 2 \\ 3 \\ 4 \end{array}
\begin{array}{cccc} 1 & 2 & 3 & 4 \\ \end{array}
\begin{bmatrix}
\tfrac{1}{3} & 0 & \tfrac{2}{3} & 0 \\
0 & \tfrac{7}{9} & 0 & \tfrac{2}{9} \\
\tfrac{2}{9} & 0 & \tfrac{7}{9} & 0 \\
0 & \tfrac{2}{3} & 0 & \tfrac{1}{3}
\end{bmatrix}
$$

be the two-step transition matrix of a Markov chain with states 1, 2, 3, and 4. Find

(a) $p_{13}^{(2)}$ (b) $p_{21}^{(2)}$

(c) $p_{33}^{(2)}$ (d) $p_{24}^{(2)}$

(e) $p_{44}^{(2)}$ (f) $p_{43}^{(2)}$

2. Let

$$
P = \begin{array}{c} \\ 1 \\ 2 \end{array}
\begin{array}{cc} 1 & 2 \\ \end{array}
\begin{bmatrix}
\tfrac{1}{4} & \tfrac{3}{4} \\
\tfrac{1}{3} & \tfrac{2}{3}
\end{bmatrix}
$$

be the transition matrix of a Markov chain with states 1 and 2.

(a) Find $P^{(2)}$ by means of Eq. (9.4.5).

(b) Use matrix multiplication to verify the results in part (a).

(c) Define and find $p_{21}^{(2)}$.

3. Find the two-step transition matrix of the Markov chain with transition matrix

$$
P = \begin{array}{c} \\ 1 \\ 2 \end{array}
\begin{array}{cc} 1 & 2 \\ \end{array}
\begin{bmatrix}
1 & 0 \\
0 & 1
\end{bmatrix}
$$

4. Find the two-step transition matrix of the Markov chain with transition matrix

$$
P = \begin{array}{c} \\ 1 \\ 2 \end{array}
\begin{array}{cc} 1 & 2 \\ \end{array}
\begin{bmatrix}
0 & 1 \\
1 & 0
\end{bmatrix}
$$

5. Let

$$
P = \begin{array}{c} \\ 1 \\ 2 \end{array}
\begin{array}{cc} 1 & 2 \\ \end{array}
\begin{bmatrix}
p & 1-p \\
0 & 1
\end{bmatrix}
$$

be the transition matrix of a Markov chain with states 1 and 2, where $0 \le p \le 1$.

(a) Find $P^{(2)}$ by means of Eq. (9.4.5).

(b) Verify the results in part (a) by calculating $P^{(2)}$ using matrix multiplication.

6. Find the two-step transition matrix of the Markov chain in problem 2, Exercises 9.3.

7. (a) Find the two-step transition matrix of the Markov chain in problem 3, Exercises 9.3.

   (b) If the machine is in operating condition at the start of a certain day, what is the probability that it is broken down 2 days later?

8. Find the two-step transition matrix of the Markov chain in problem 6, Exercises 9.3.

9. Each year a man leases a new car. He always leases a Ford, Chevrolet, or a Dodge. If he has a Ford, he leases a Ford again the next year with probability 1. If he has a Chevrolet,

the probability is $\frac{1}{2}$ that he leases a Ford and $\frac{1}{2}$ that he leases a Dodge the next year. If he has a Dodge, he will lease a Dodge again next year with probability $\frac{1}{3}$ and a Chevrolet with probability $\frac{2}{3}$. Let the state of the system at any given time be the make of car that was leased during that year, and let 1 correspond to the state a Ford was leased, 2 to the state a Chevrolet was leased, and 3 to the state a Dodge was leased. Assume that the process is Markovian and let P be the transition matrix.

(a) Find $P^{(2)}$.

(b) If he has a 1974 Dodge, what is the probability that he leases a 1976 Ford?

(c) If he has a 1974 Chevrolet, what is the probability that he leases a 1976 Chevrolet?

10. The football coach of a local university tells individual A his intentions of either accepting or declining an offer made to him by another university. A, in turn, relays the coaches intentions to B, B to C, etc., each time to some new person. Suppose that there is a probability p that a person will change the answer that was given to him from "yes" to "no" in passing it on to the next person and a probability q that he will change it from "no" to "yes." Let the state of the system at any given time be the reply "yes" or the reply "no" that was given at that time, and let 1 correspond to the state "yes" and 2 correspond to the state "no."

(a) Find the two-step transition matrix.

(b) If A is told by the coach that he is going to accept the offer, what is the probability that C is told that the coach is not going to accept the offer?

11. Find the two-step transition matrix of the Markov chain defined in problem 2, Exercises 9.2.

12. (a) Assuming that the process is Markovian, find the two-step transition matrix of the Markov chain defined in problem 9, Exercises 9.2.

(b) Given that a father is middle class, what is the probability that his grandson is upper class?

13. Find the two-step transition matrix of the Markov chain defined in problem 2, Exercises 9.1.

14. Find the two-step transition matrix of the Markov chain defined in problem 12, Exercises 9.2.

15. Let P be the transition matrix of a Markov chain with three states. Then recall that P is a 3×3 stochastic matrix. Prove that the two-step transition matrix P is also a 3×3 stochastic matrix. (*Hint:* See problem 10, Exercises 9.2 and problems 12 and 14, Exercises 9.3.)

16. Show that the results of problem 15 hold for the general case of a Markov chain with N states.

*17. Find the two-step transition matrix for the generalized Ehrenfest chain of problem 13, Exercises 9.2.

18. Find the two-step transition matrix for the Markov chain defined in problem 7, Exercises 9.1.

Section 9.5   *n*-Step Transition Matrix

The result of Theorem 9.4.2 is easily extended to the case where the number of transitions is three or more. We indicate the details in this section.

Definition
Suppose that a Markov chain has transition matrix $P = [p_{ij}]$. The probability of transition from state i to state j in *three* time periods is denoted by $p_{ij}^{(3)}$. The matrix

$$P^{(3)} = [p_{ij}^{(3)}]$$

is called the *three-step transition matrix* of the Markov chain. We write $i \xrightarrow{3} j$ to indicate a transition from state i to state j in three time periods.

The problem now is to determine a formula for $P^{(3)}$ in terms of the transition matrix P. As you probably suspect, $P^{(3)}$ is just the third power of the matrix P.

Example 9.5.1 Rainfall In certain areas of the world a reasonable approximation of the occurrence of wet and dry days is given by a two-state Markov chain. A day is considered to be a wet day if there is any precipitation during any part of that day.

Suppose it has been determined that in a certain city the probability of a wet day following a dry day is $\frac{1}{4}$ and the probability of a wet day following a wet day is $\frac{1}{2}$. For convenience the following association is made:

State	Day
1	Dry
2	Wet

Then the transition matrix for the Markov chain is

$$P = \begin{array}{cc} & \begin{array}{cc} 1 & 2 \end{array} \\ \begin{array}{c} 1 \\ 2 \end{array} & \begin{bmatrix} \frac{3}{4} & \frac{1}{4} \\ \frac{1}{2} & \frac{1}{2} \end{bmatrix} \end{array}$$

If it is raining on a given day, what is the probability that it will be dry 3 days later? In terms of the terminology we have developed, the problem is to determine $p_{21}^{(3)}$. That is, what is the probability of a transition from state 2 to state 1 in *three* time periods?

The possible transitions in 3 days, starting in state 2, are illustrated by the tree diagram shown in Figure 9.5.1.

Figure 9.5.1

Day 0	Day 1	Day 2	Day 3	Outcome

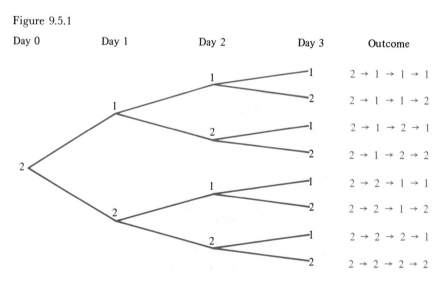

$$
\begin{aligned}
&2 \to 1 \to 1 \to 1 \\
&2 \to 1 \to 1 \to 2 \\
&2 \to 1 \to 2 \to 1 \\
&2 \to 1 \to 2 \to 2 \\
&2 \to 2 \to 1 \to 1 \\
&2 \to 2 \to 1 \to 2 \\
&2 \to 2 \to 2 \to 1 \\
&2 \to 2 \to 2 \to 2
\end{aligned}
$$

However, to calculate the probability in question we can reason as follows: A transition in 3 days from state 2 to state 1 can occur in the following mutually exclusive ways:

Day 0		Day 2		Day 3
2	$\xrightarrow{2}$	1	$\xrightarrow{1}$	1
2	$\xrightarrow{2}$	2	$\xrightarrow{1}$	1

$$(9.5.1)$$

Notice that the transitions at the first day are not included. We are just using the fact that a transition from state 2 to state 1 in 3 days must occur by way of a transition to either state 1 or state 2 at the *second* day.

The probabilities associated with the transitions in Eq. (9.5.1) can be calculated without too much difficulty. For example, to determine the probability of the transition

$$2 \xrightarrow{2} 1 \xrightarrow{1} 1 \qquad (9.5.2)$$

first notice that the probability of a transition from state 2 to state 1 in *2 days* is by definition $p_{21}^{(2)}$. Once in state 1 the probability of being in state 1 on the *next day* is just p_{11}. Thus the transition in Eq. (9.5.2) has probability $p_{21}^{(2)} \cdot p_{11}$. Similarly, the transition $2 \xrightarrow{2} 2 \xrightarrow{1} 1$ has probability $p_{22}^{(2)} \cdot p_{21}$. Because the transitions in Eq. (9.5.1) are mutually exclusive (it cannot both be dry on day 2 and rain on day 2) and because a transition from state 2 to state 1 in 3 days must occur via one of these (it either is dry on day 2 or rains on day 2), we conclude that

$$
\begin{array}{cccc}
2 \xrightarrow{2} 1, & 1 \xrightarrow{1} 1 & \text{or } 2 \xrightarrow{2} 2, & 2 \xrightarrow{1} 1 \\
\downarrow & \downarrow & \downarrow & \downarrow \\
p_{21}^{(3)} = & p_{21}^{(2)} \cdot p_{11} & + \quad p_{22}^{(2)} \cdot & p_{21}
\end{array}
\qquad (9.5.3)
$$

To actually obtain a numerical answer we first need to calculate $P^{(2)}$. But

$$
P^{(2)} = P^2 = \begin{array}{c} 1 \\ 2 \end{array} \begin{bmatrix} \frac{11}{16} & \frac{5}{16} \\ \frac{10}{16} & \frac{6}{16} \end{bmatrix}
$$

So, $p_{21}^{(2)} = \frac{10}{16}$ and $p_{22}^{(2)} = \frac{6}{16}$. Consequently, by Eq. (9.5.3), if it is raining on a given day, the probability that it will be dry 3 days later is

$$
p_{21}^{(3)} = \frac{10}{16} \cdot \frac{3}{4} + \frac{6}{16} \cdot \frac{1}{2} = \frac{21}{32} \doteq .66
$$

The same argument just given to obtain Eq. (9.5.3) can be applied to get the following general result.

Theorem 9.5.1

Consider a Markov chain with N possible states, say $1, 2, \ldots, N$, so that the transition matrix $P = [p_{ij}]$ is $N \times N$. The probability of a transition from state i to state j in *three* time periods $(i \xrightarrow{3} j)$ is given by

$$
p_{ij}^{(3)} = p_{i1}^{(2)} \cdot p_{1j} + p_{i2}^{(2)} \cdot p_{2j} + \cdots + p_{iN}^{(2)} \cdot p_{Nj} \qquad (9.5.4)
$$

Formula (9.5.4) shows that the matrix $P^{(3)}$ is just the product of the matrices $P^{(2)}$ and P. But $P^{(2)} = P^2$, so $P^{(3)} = P^{(2)} \cdot P = P^2 \cdot P = P^3$.

Theorem 9.5.2

Consider a Markov chain with transition matrix P. Then the *three-step* transition matrix, $P^{(3)}$, is just the third power of the matrix P. That is,

$$P^{(3)} = P^3 \tag{9.5.5}$$

Example 9.5.2 Rainfall In the rainfall model of Example 9.5.1,

$$P = \begin{bmatrix} \frac{3}{4} & \frac{1}{4} \\ \frac{1}{2} & \frac{1}{2} \end{bmatrix} \qquad P^2 = \begin{bmatrix} \frac{11}{16} & \frac{5}{16} \\ \frac{10}{16} & \frac{6}{16} \end{bmatrix}$$

so

$$P^{(3)} = P^3 = P^2 \cdot P = \begin{matrix} 1 \\ 2 \end{matrix} \begin{bmatrix} \frac{43}{64} & \frac{21}{64} \\ \frac{21}{32} & \frac{11}{32} \end{bmatrix} \begin{matrix} \\ \end{matrix}$$

From this it follows immediately that $p^{(3)}_{21} = \frac{21}{32}$, which is the result obtained in Example 9.5.1.

Of course, the result of Theorem 9.5.2 can be extended to transitions in any number of time periods.

Theorem 9.5.3

Consider a Markov chain with transition matrix $P = [p_{ij}]$ and let $p^{(n)}_{ij}$ denote the probability of a transition from state i to state j in n time periods ($i \xrightarrow{n} j$). Then the matrix $P^{(n)} = [p^{(n)}_{ij}]$ is called the *n-step transition matrix* of the Markov chain and is just the nth power of the matrix P. That is,

$$P^{(n)} = P^n \tag{9.5.6}$$

With the aid of a computer it is a simple matter to calculate the n-step transition matrix of a Markov chain because of Eq. (9.5.6). Calculations, of course, can be done by hand, but this is, in general, an extremely tedious process.

For future reference the first six powers of the transition matrices with which we have worked before are listed below. (The entries are given to five decimal places.)

Social Mobility

$$P = \begin{bmatrix} .60000 & .30000 & .10000 \\ .10000 & .80000 & .10000 \\ .10000 & .20000 & .70000 \end{bmatrix}$$

$$P^2 = \begin{bmatrix} .40000 & .44000 & .16000 \\ .15000 & .69000 & .16000 \\ .15000 & .33000 & .52000 \end{bmatrix}$$

$$P^3 = \begin{bmatrix} .30000 & .50400 & .19600 \\ .17500 & .62900 & .19600 \\ .17500 & .41300 & .41200 \end{bmatrix}$$

$$P^4 = \begin{bmatrix} .25000 & .53240 & .21760 \\ .18750 & .59490 & .21760 \\ .18750 & .46530 & .34720 \end{bmatrix}$$

$$P^5 = \begin{bmatrix} .22500 & .54444 & .23056 \\ .19375 & .57569 & .23056 \\ .19375 & .49793 & .30832 \end{bmatrix}$$

$$P^6 = \begin{bmatrix} .21250 & .54916 & .23834 \\ .19687 & .56479 & .23834 \\ .19687 & .51813 & .28499 \end{bmatrix}$$

Word Structure

$$P = \begin{bmatrix} .00000 & 1.00000 \\ .49000 & .51000 \end{bmatrix}$$

$$P^2 = \begin{bmatrix} .49000 & .51000 \\ .24990 & .75010 \end{bmatrix}$$

$$P^3 = \begin{bmatrix} .24990 & .75010 \\ .36755 & .63245 \end{bmatrix}$$

$$P^4 = \begin{bmatrix} .36755 & .63245 \\ .30990 & .69010 \end{bmatrix}$$

$$P^5 = \begin{bmatrix} .30990 & .69010 \\ .33815 & .66185 \end{bmatrix}$$

$$P^6 = \begin{bmatrix} .33815 & .66185 \\ .32431 & .67569 \end{bmatrix}$$

Gambling

$$P = \begin{bmatrix} 1.00000 & .00000 & .00000 & .00000 & .00000 & .00000 & .00000 \\ .50000 & .00000 & .50000 & .00000 & .00000 & .00000 & .00000 \\ .00000 & .50000 & .00000 & .50000 & .00000 & .00000 & .00000 \\ .00000 & .00000 & .50000 & .00000 & .50000 & .00000 & .00000 \\ .00000 & .00000 & .00000 & .50000 & .00000 & .50000 & .00000 \\ .00000 & .00000 & .00000 & .00000 & .50000 & .00000 & .50000 \\ .00000 & .00000 & .00000 & .00000 & .00000 & .00000 & 1.00000 \end{bmatrix}$$

$$P^2 = \begin{bmatrix} 1.00000 & .00000 & .00000 & .00000 & .00000 & .00000 & .00000 \\ .50000 & .25000 & .00000 & .25000 & .00000 & .00000 & .00000 \\ .25000 & .00000 & .50000 & .00000 & .25000 & .00000 & .00000 \\ .00000 & .25000 & .00000 & .50000 & .00000 & .25000 & .00000 \\ .00000 & .00000 & .25000 & .00000 & .50000 & .00000 & .25000 \\ .00000 & .00000 & .00000 & .25000 & .00000 & .25000 & .50000 \\ .00000 & .00000 & .00000 & .00000 & .00000 & .00000 & 1.00000 \end{bmatrix}$$

$$P^3 = \begin{bmatrix} 1.00000 & .00000 & .00000 & .00000 & .00000 & .00000 & .00000 \\ .62500 & .00000 & .25000 & .00000 & .12500 & .00000 & .00000 \\ .25000 & .25000 & .00000 & .37500 & .00000 & .12500 & .00000 \\ .12500 & .00000 & .37500 & .00000 & .37500 & .00000 & .12500 \\ .00000 & .12500 & .00000 & .37500 & .00000 & .25000 & .25000 \\ .00000 & .00000 & .12500 & .00000 & .25000 & .00000 & .62500 \\ .00000 & .00000 & .00000 & .00000 & .00000 & .00000 & 1.00000 \end{bmatrix}$$

$$P^4 = \begin{bmatrix} 1.00000 & .00000 & .00000 & .00000 & .00000 & .00000 & .00000 \\ .62500 & .12500 & .00000 & .18750 & .00000 & .06250 & .00000 \\ .37500 & .00000 & .31250 & .00000 & .25000 & .00000 & .06250 \\ .12500 & .18750 & .00000 & .37500 & .00000 & .18750 & .12500 \\ .06250 & .00000 & .25000 & .00000 & .31250 & .00000 & .37500 \\ .00000 & .06250 & .00000 & .18750 & .00000 & .12500 & .62500 \\ .00000 & .00000 & .00000 & .00000 & .00000 & .00000 & 1.00000 \end{bmatrix}$$

$$P^5 = \begin{bmatrix} 1.00000 & .00000 & .00000 & .00000 & .00000 & .00000 & .00000 \\ .68750 & .00000 & .15625 & .00000 & .12500 & .00000 & .03125 \\ .37500 & .15625 & .00000 & .28125 & .00000 & .12500 & .06250 \\ .21875 & .00000 & .28125 & .00000 & .28125 & .00000 & .21875 \\ .06250 & .12500 & .00000 & .28125 & .00000 & .15625 & .37500 \\ .03125 & .00000 & .12500 & .00000 & .15625 & .00000 & .68750 \\ .00000 & .00000 & .00000 & .00000 & .00000 & .00000 & 1.00000 \end{bmatrix}$$

$$P^6 = \begin{bmatrix} 1.00000 & .00000 & .00000 & .00000 & .00000 & .00000 & .00000 \\ .68750 & .07812 & .00000 & .14062 & .00000 & .06250 & .03125 \\ .45312 & .00000 & .21875 & .00000 & .20312 & .00000 & .12500 \\ .21875 & .14062 & .00000 & .28125 & .00000 & .14062 & .21875 \\ .12500 & .00000 & .20312 & .00000 & .21875 & .00000 & .45312 \\ .03125 & .06250 & .00000 & .14062 & .00000 & .07812 & .68750 \\ .00000 & .00000 & .00000 & .00000 & .00000 & .00000 & 1.00000 \end{bmatrix}$$

Rainfall

$$P = \begin{bmatrix} .75000 & .25000 \\ .50000 & .50000 \end{bmatrix}$$

$$P^2 = \begin{bmatrix} .68750 & .31250 \\ .62500 & .37500 \end{bmatrix}$$

$$P^3 = \begin{bmatrix} .67187 & .32812 \\ .65625 & .34375 \end{bmatrix}$$

$$P^4 = \begin{bmatrix} .66797 & .33203 \\ .66406 & .33594 \end{bmatrix}$$

$$P^5 = \begin{bmatrix} .66699 & .33301 \\ .66602 & .33398 \end{bmatrix}$$

$$P^6 = \begin{bmatrix} .66675 & .33325 \\ .66650 & .33350 \end{bmatrix}$$

Exercises for 9.5

1. Let

$$P^{(3)} = \begin{matrix} & \begin{matrix} 1 & 2 & 3 & 4 \end{matrix} \\ \begin{matrix} 1 \\ 2 \\ 3 \\ 4 \end{matrix} & \begin{bmatrix} 0 & \frac{7}{9} & 0 & \frac{2}{9} \\ \frac{7}{27} & 0 & \frac{20}{27} & 0 \\ 0 & \frac{20}{27} & 0 & \frac{7}{27} \\ \frac{2}{9} & 0 & \frac{7}{9} & 0 \end{bmatrix} \end{matrix}$$

be the three-step transition matrix of a Markov chain with states 1, 2, 3, and 4. Find

(a) $p_{12}^{(3)}$ (b) $p_{13}^{(3)}$
(c) $p_{21}^{(3)}$ (d) $p_{33}^{(3)}$
(e) $p_{32}^{(3)}$ (f) $p_{43}^{(3)}$

2. In Example 9.5.1, find

(a) $p_{12}^{(4)}$ (b) $p_{22}^{(4)}$

3. In Example 9.3.1, find

(a) $p_{12}^{(5)}$ (b) $p_{21}^{(5)}$
(c) $p_{23}^{(5)}$ (d) $p_{33}^{(5)}$

4. In Example 9.2.3, find

(a) $p_{11}^{(6)}$ (b) $p_{24}^{(6)}$
(c) $p_{56}^{(6)}$ (d) $p_{60}^{(6)}$

5. Let

$$P = \begin{array}{c} \\ 1 \\ 2 \end{array}\begin{array}{cc} 1 & 2 \\ \begin{bmatrix} 1 & 0 \\ 0 & 1 \end{bmatrix} \end{array}$$

be the transition matrix of a Markov chain with states 1 and 2.
(a) Find $P^{(3)}$. (b) Find $P^{(n)}$, $n \geq 1$.

6. Let

$$P = \begin{array}{c} \\ 1 \\ 2 \end{array}\begin{array}{cc} 1 & 2 \\ \begin{bmatrix} 0 & 1 \\ 1 & 0 \end{bmatrix} \end{array}$$

be the transition matrix of a Markov chain with states 1 and 2.
(a) Find $P^{(3)}$. (b) Find $P^{(n)}$, $n \geq 1$.

7. Let

$$P = \begin{array}{c} \\ 1 \\ 2 \end{array}\begin{array}{cc} 1 & 2 \\ \begin{bmatrix} p & 1-p \\ 0 & 1 \end{bmatrix} \end{array}$$

be the transition matrix of a Markov chain with states 1 and 2; $0 \leq p \leq 1$.
(a) Find $P^{(3)}$. (b) Find $P^{(n)}$, $n \geq 1$.

8. Let

$$P = \begin{array}{c} \\ 1 \\ 2 \\ 3 \end{array}\begin{array}{ccc} 1 & 2 & 3 \\ \begin{bmatrix} 0 & 1 & 0 \\ p & 0 & 1-p \\ 0 & 1 & 0 \end{bmatrix} \end{array}$$

be the transition matrix of a Markov chain with states 1, 2, and 3; $0 \leq p \leq 1$.
(a) Find $P^{(2)}$.
(b) Show that $P^{(4)} = P^{(2)}$.
(c) Find $P^{(n)}$, $n \geq 1$.

9. (a) Find the three-step transition matrix of the Markov chain in problem 2, Exercises 9.3.
   (b) If the first man starts the contest, what is the probability that the second man will take the fourth shot at the target?

10. (a) Find the three-step transition matrix of the Markov chain in problem 3, Exercises 9.3.
    (b) If the machine is operating at the start of a given day, what is the probability that it will be broken down three days later?

11. (a) Find the three-step transition matrix of the Markov chain in problem 12, Exercises 9.2.

(b) If Joe won the last poker game, what is the probability that he will win three games later?

12. Let P be the transition matrix of the Markov chain defined in problem 4, Exercises 9.3.
   (a) Find $P^{(3)}$.
   (b) Given that he drives to work on Tuesday, what is the probability that he drives to work on Friday?

13. In problem 10, Exercises 9.4, let $p = 0$ and let $q = \frac{1}{2}$, and let P be the transition matrix for this Markov chain.
   (a) Find $P^{(3)}$.   (b) Find $P^{(n)}$, $n \geq 1$.

14. Let P be an $N \times N$ stochastic matrix. Prove that $P^{(3)}$ is also an $N \times N$ stochastic matrix. (See problem 12, Exercises 9.3.)

15. A buyer for a supermarket must decide at the beginning of each month whether to buy brand 1, brand 2, or brand 3 of milk for that month. Let p_{ij} denote the probability that the buyer will select brand j at the beginning of any month given that he bought brand i the preceding month, and suppose that $p_{11} = 0$, $p_{12} = p_{13} = \frac{1}{2}$, $p_{21} = p_{22} = p_{23} = \frac{1}{3}$, $p_{31} = p_{33} = \frac{1}{4}$, and $p_{32} = \frac{1}{2}$.
   (a) Set up the transition matrix P for this chain.
   (b) Find $P^{(2)}$ and $P^{(3)}$.
   (c) If the buyer selects brand 1 for January, what is the probability that he will select brand 2 for March?
   (d) If the buyer selects brand 2 for January, what is the probability that he will select brand 3 for April?

*16. Let P be the transition matrix for the generalized Ehrenfest chain of problem 13, Exercises 9.2.
   (a) Find $P^{(3)}$.
   (b) Show that $p_{ii}^{(n)} = 0$ for n odd, $n \geq 1$, where $i = 0, 1, 2, \ldots, d$.

Section 9.6   Distribution of a Markov Chain: Introduction and Motivation

In the preceding pages we have discovered how to calculate the probabilities associated with transitions between states in n time periods. To determine the probability, $p_{ij}^{(n)}$, of a transition from state i to state j in n time periods ($i \xrightarrow{n} j$) calculate the nth power, P^n, of the transition matrix P. The i–j entry of P^n is $p_{ij}^{(n)}$.

Now, *given* that the initial (time 0) state of the system is i, the probability that the system is in state j at time n is $p_{ij}^{(n)}$. As we have just mentioned, this probability can be determined by taking powers of the transition matrix P. Suppose, however, that the initial state of the system is not known and that only the various probabilities of being in any particular state at time 0 are available. Then, how can the probability that the system is in a particular state j at time n be calculated? The following example is presented to illustrate the procedure involved in making this calculation.

Example 9.6.1   Busy Signals   At a switchboard it has been determined that the line to a certain company satisfies the following conditions: If at time intervals of 5 minutes it is observed whether or not the line is busy:

(1) The state of the line at a future time depends only on the present state and not on any past states (Markov property).
(2) The probabilities of transition between states in a time interval of 5 minutes are given by the following table:

		Next state	
	State	Not busy	Busy
Present state	Not busy	$\frac{3}{4}$	$\frac{1}{4}$
	Busy	$\frac{5}{8}$	$\frac{3}{8}$

So, for example, given that the line is not busy at a certain time, the probability that it will be busy 5 minutes later is $\frac{1}{4}$.

(3) The probability that the line is busy at 8:00 A.M. is $\frac{1}{10}$, and so the probability that it is not busy at 8:00 A.M. is $\frac{9}{10}$.

If a person calls the company at 8:10 A.M., what is the probability that the line is not busy?

To solve this problem, it is first convenient to associate numbers with the conditions of the line:

State	Condition of line
1	Not busy
2	Busy

If time intervals are measured in units of 5 minutes, the assumptions (1) and (2) imply that the condition of the line is a Markov chain with the transition matrix

$$P = \begin{array}{c} \\ 1 \\ 2 \end{array}\begin{array}{cc} 1 & 2 \\ \left[\begin{array}{cc} \frac{3}{4} & \frac{1}{4} \\ \frac{5}{8} & \frac{3}{8} \end{array}\right] \end{array}$$

The two-step transition matrix is

$$P^2 = \begin{array}{c} \\ 1 \\ 2 \end{array}\begin{array}{cc} 1 & 2 \\ \left[\begin{array}{cc} \frac{23}{32} & \frac{9}{32} \\ \frac{45}{64} & \frac{19}{64} \end{array}\right] \end{array} \tag{9.6.1}$$

If 8:00 A.M. is considered as time 0, then 8:10 A.M. is time 2, since the time intervals are 5 minutes each. The problem is then to determine the probability that the system is in state 1 at time 2.

The method of solution is to *condition* on the initial state of the system (i.e., the state of the system at 8:00 A.M.). The system can be in state 1 at time 2 in either one of two mutually exclusive ways:

1. It is initially in state 1 and is again in state 1 two time periods later.
2. It is initially in state 2 and is then in state 1 two time periods later.

Thus the problem is to calculate the probabilities of the events in 1 and 2.

Let $\pi_i^{(0)}$ denote the probability that the system is in state i initially (i.e., at time 0) and let $\pi_1^{(2)}$ denote the probability that the system is in state 1 at time 2. According to condition (3),

$$\pi_1^{(0)} = \frac{9}{10} \qquad \pi_2^{(0)} = \frac{1}{10} \tag{9.6.2}$$

Intuitively, the probability, $\pi_1^{(2)}$, of being in state 1 at time 2 equals the probability of being in state 1 initially times the probability of transition from state 1 to state 1 in two time periods,

$$1, \quad 1 \xrightarrow{2} 1$$
$$\downarrow \qquad \downarrow$$
$$\pi_1^{(0)} \quad \cdot \quad p_{11}^{(2)}$$

plus the probability of being in state 2 initially times the probability of transition from state 2 to state 1 in two time periods,

$$2, \quad 2 \xrightarrow{2} 1$$
$$\downarrow \qquad \downarrow$$
$$\pi_2^{(0)} \quad \cdot \quad p_{21}^{(2)}$$

That is,

$$1, \quad 1 \xrightarrow{2} 1 \text{ or } 2, \quad 2 \xrightarrow{2} 1$$
$$\downarrow \qquad \downarrow \qquad \qquad \downarrow \qquad \downarrow$$
$$\pi_1^{(2)} = \pi_1^{(0)} \cdot p_{11}^{(2)} + \pi_2^{(0)} \cdot p_{21}^{(2)} \qquad\qquad (9.6.3)$$

This result can be illustrated by a tree diagram (Figure 9.6.1).

Figure 9.6.1

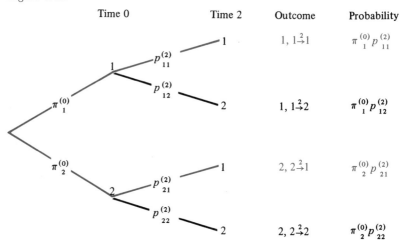

Time 0		Time 2	Outcome	Probability
		1	$1, 1 \xrightarrow{2} 1$	$\pi_1^{(0)} p_{11}^{(2)}$
		2	$1, 1 \xrightarrow{2} 2$	$\pi_1^{(0)} p_{12}^{(2)}$
		1	$2, 2 \xrightarrow{2} 1$	$\pi_2^{(0)} p_{21}^{(2)}$
		2	$2, 2 \xrightarrow{2} 2$	$\pi_2^{(0)} p_{22}^{(2)}$

To obtain Eq. (9.6.3) rigorously, let

E = event the system is in state 1 at time 2
F_1 = event the system is in state 1 at time 0
F_2 = event the system is in state 2 at time 0

As was mentioned above,

$$E = (E \cap F_1) \cup (E \cap F_2)$$

The two events on the right of the above equation are mutually exclusive, and consequently, by the addition principle of probability,

$$\Pr(E) = \Pr(E \cap F_1) + \Pr(E \cap F_2)$$

Now, by the multiplication principle of probability,

$$\Pr(E \cap F_1) = \Pr(F_1)\Pr(E|F_1)$$
$$\Pr(E \cap F_2) = \Pr(F_2)\Pr(E|F_2)$$

Thus

$$\Pr(E) = \Pr(F_1)\Pr(E|F_1) + \Pr(F_2)\Pr(E|F_2)$$

But

$$\Pr(F_1) = \pi_1^{(0)} \qquad \Pr(F_2) = \pi_2^{(0)}$$
$$\Pr(E|F_1) = p_{11}^{(2)} \qquad \Pr(E|F_2) = p_{21}^{(2)}$$

Since $\Pr(E) = \pi_1^{(2)}$, we conclude that

$$\pi_1^{(2)} = \pi_1^{(0)} p_{11}^{(2)} + \pi_2^{(0)} p_{21}^{(2)}$$

which is Eq. (9.6.3).

From Eqs. (9.6.1) and (9.6.2) it follows that

$$\pi_1^{(0)} = \tfrac{9}{10} \qquad \pi_2^{(0)} = \tfrac{1}{10}$$
$$p_{11}^{(2)} = \tfrac{23}{32} \qquad p_{21}^{(2)} = \tfrac{45}{64}$$

Thus the probability that the line is not busy at 8:10 A.M. is

$$\pi_1^{(2)} = \tfrac{9}{10} \cdot \tfrac{23}{32} + \tfrac{1}{10} \cdot \tfrac{45}{64} = \tfrac{459}{640} \doteq .727$$

Exercises for 9.6

1. In Example 9.6.1, what is the probability that the line is busy at 8:10 A.M.?
2. Let

$$P = \begin{array}{c} \\ 1 \\ 2 \end{array} \begin{array}{cc} 1 & 2 \\ \left[\begin{array}{cc} \tfrac{1}{4} & \tfrac{3}{4} \\ \tfrac{2}{3} & \tfrac{1}{3} \end{array} \right] \end{array}$$

be the transition matrix of a Markov chain with states 1 and 2, and let $\pi_1^{(0)} = \tfrac{8}{17}$. Find
(a) $\pi_1^{(2)}$ (b) $\pi_2^{(2)}$

3. Let

$$P = \begin{array}{c} \\ 1 \\ 2 \end{array} \begin{array}{cc} 1 & 2 \\ \left[\begin{array}{cc} \tfrac{1}{2} & \tfrac{1}{2} \\ 0 & 1 \end{array} \right] \end{array}$$

be the transition matrix of a two-state Markov chain with states 1 and 2, and let $\pi_1^{(0)} = \pi_2^{(0)} = \tfrac{1}{2}$. Find
(a) $\pi_1^{(2)}$ (b) $\pi_2^{(2)}$

4. In problem 2, Exercises 9.3, the man who starts the shooting contest is determined by tossing a fair coin. What is the probability that the second man takes the third shot at the target?

5. In problem 10, Exercises 9.4, let $p = \tfrac{1}{2}$ and $q = \tfrac{2}{3}$, and suppose the probability that the coach accepts the offer is $\tfrac{4}{7}$. Find the probability that C is told that the coach turned down the offer.

6. The buyer for a new supermarket makes the following assumptions concerning the buying habits of its customers. During any given week, 70 percent of the customers that bought brand A soap last week will buy brand A this week, and 60 percent of the customers that bought brand B soap last week will buy brand A this week. For convenience we

assume that the number of customers remains constant and that given the brand of soap purchased by a customer during the present week, the brand of soap he purchases in the future is not influenced by the brand he purchased during past weeks. If 50 percent of the customers bought brand A during the first week the supermarket was open, what percent of the customers will be buying brand A soap during the third week the store is open?

7. In problem 4, Exercises 9.3, suppose the probability that the man rides a bus to work on Monday is $\frac{1}{3}$. What is the probability that he drives to work on Wednesday?

8. Suppose that the latest census indicates that people are moving from rural areas to urban areas at the rate of 5 percent each year, and that people from urban areas are moving to rural areas at the rate of 2 percent each year. Suppose the census also shows that 80 percent of the population is presently living in urban areas and 20 percent is living in rural areas. Assume that the population remains constant and that the above process satisfies the Markov property. What percent of the population will be living in rural areas 2 years from the latest census?

9. A rat is put into a box with two compartments labeled 1 and 2. The rat's movements are checked every 5 minutes. It is observed that if the rat is in compartment 1 at any given time, 5 minutes later it will be in compartment 2 with probability $\frac{2}{5}$, but if it is in compartment 2 at any given time, 5 minutes later it will be in compartment 1 with probability $\frac{1}{2}$. Also, given the present location of the rat, its future location is independent of its past locations. Suppose that each compartment is equally likely to be chosen as the one in which the rat is put initially. What is the probability that the rat will be in compartment 2 after the first 10 minutes?

10. In problem 3, Exercises 9.3, suppose that the company using the machine orders it by freight, and suppose there is a probability $\frac{2}{3}$ that the machine arrives in operating condition. Assume also that freight deliveries are made before the start of each day and that the machine is put into use the morning it arrives, provided it is in operating condition. What is the probability that it is broken down 2 days after it arrives?

11. A cigarette company is promoting a new brand of filter cigarettes. Of those people smoking other brands of cigarettes during a given month, 55 percent change over to the promoted brand the next month, and of those people, already using the promoted brand during a given month, 70 percent continue to use it the next month. Assuming that the above process is Markovian, what percentage of the smokers will be smoking the promoted brand after 2 months given that 45 percent of the people are using it now?

Section 9.7 Distribution of a Markov Chain: Definitions, Theorems, and Examples

Using Example 9.6.1 as motivation, we now state the following definitions and theorems.

Definition

For each $n \geq 0$, let $\pi_j^{(n)}$ denote the probability that a Markov chain is in state j at time n. In particular, then, $\pi_j^{(0)}$ denotes the probability that the Markov chain is initially in state j. If the Markov chain has N states, say $1, 2, \ldots, N$, it will be convenient to form the following row vectors of length N:

$$\Pi^{(n)} = [\pi_1^{(n)}, \pi_2^{(n)}, \ldots, \pi_N^{(n)}]$$

The vector $\Pi^{(n)}$ is called the *distribution of the Markov chain at time n*. $\Pi^{(0)}$ is also called the *initial distribution* of the Markov chain.

The arguments used in the previous example to obtain Eq. (9.6.3) can be applied to prove the next theorem.

Theorem 9.7.1

Consider a Markov chain with the states $1, 2, \ldots, N$. Let its initial distribution be $\Pi^{(0)}$ and its transition matrix be P. Then the probability that the system is in state j at time n is given by

$$\pi_j^{(n)} = \pi_1^{(0)} p_{1j}^{(n)} + \pi_2^{(0)} p_{2j}^{(n)} + \cdots + \pi_N^{(0)} p_{Nj}^{(n)} \qquad (9.7.1)$$

Let us examine Eq. (9.7.1) a little more closely. The left side is just the entry in the jth column of the row vector ($1 \times N$ matrix) $\Pi^{(n)}$. On the other hand, the right side of Eq. (9.7.1) represents the entry in the jth column of the row vector ($1 \times N$ matrix) obtained by multiplying the $1 \times N$ matrix $\Pi^{(0)}$ by the $N \times N$ matrix $P^{(n)} = P^n$. Consequently, $\Pi^{(n)} = \Pi^{(0)} P^n$.

Theorem 9.7.2

Consider a Markov chain with initial distribution $\Pi^{(0)}$ and transition matrix P. Then the distribution of the Markov chain at any time n is given by

$$\Pi^{(n)} = \Pi^{(0)} P^n \qquad (9.7.2)$$

By using Eq. (9.7.2) it is quite simple to determine, in a Markov chain, the probability of the system being in any particular state at any particular time, once the initial distribution and transition matrix are known.

Example 9.7.1 Social Mobility In Example 9.2.1 assume that at a given time (which is taken as time 0) it is known that the percentages of individuals in each class are given by

Class	Percent	
Lower	40	(9.7.3)
Middle	50	
Upper	10	

Using the results just obtained we can answer the following question: What will be the percentages of individuals in each class *three generations from now?*

The data translated into probabilities means that the initial distribution of the Markov chain is

$$\Pi^{(0)} = [.4, .5, .1]$$

That is, $\pi_1^{(0)} = .4$, $\pi_2^{(0)} = .5$, $\pi_3^{(0)} = .1$.

The problem at hand is to determine $\Pi^{(3)}$. By Eq. (9.7.2),

$$\Pi^{(3)} = \Pi^{(0)} P^3$$

On page 409 it was determined that

$$P^3 = \begin{bmatrix} .300 & .504 & .196 \\ .175 & .629 & .196 \\ .175 & .413 & .412 \end{bmatrix}$$

Using this fact, calculations show that

$$\Pi^{(3)} = \Pi^{(0)}P^3 = [.2250, .5574, .2176]$$

In other words,

$$\pi_1^{(3)} = .2250 \qquad \pi_2^{(3)} = .5574 \qquad \pi_3^{(3)} = .2176$$

Translated back into percentages this means that the percentages of individuals in each class in the *third generation* are

Class	Percent
Lower	22.50
Middle	55.74
Upper	21.76

Example 9.7.2 Gambling   Consider, again, the gambling chain introduced in Example 9.2.3. If player I begins with \$2 and player II begins with \$4, what is the probability that player I will have \$3 after *five* wagers?

This Markov chain has the seven states 0, 1, 2, 3, 4, 5, and 6. The transition matrix of this Markov chain is given on page 410. In terms of our notation the problem is to find $\pi_3^{(5)}$.

By assumption the initial state of the system is 2. In terms of the initial distribution this means

$$\pi_0^{(0)} = 0, \ \pi_1^{(0)} = 0, \ \pi_2^{(0)} = 1, \ \pi_3^{(0)} = 0, \ \pi_4^{(0)} = 0, \ \pi_5^{(0)} = 0, \ \pi_6^{(0)} = 0$$

or, more simply,

$$\begin{matrix} 0 \ 1 \ 2 \ 3 \ 4 \ 5 \ 6 \\ \Pi^{(0)} = [0, 0, 1, 0, 0, 0, 0] \end{matrix}$$

By Eq. (9.7.2)

$$\Pi^{(5)} = \Pi^{(0)}P^5$$

The matrix P^5 is given on page 411. Consequently, after multiplying $\Pi^{(0)}$ by P^5, we obtain

$$\begin{matrix} 0 \quad\ 1 \quad 2 \quad\ 3 \quad\ 4 \quad 5 \quad\ 6 \\ \Pi^{(5)} = [.375, .15625, 0, .28125, 0, .125, .0625] \end{matrix}$$

In particular, then, $\pi_3^{(5)} = .28125$. This is the probability that player I will have \$3 after five wagers.

Example 9.7.3 Business Trends   Assume that a product is manufactured by two companies, say company A and company B. At the present time, company A enjoys 75 percent of the market and B enjoys 25 percent of the market. A survey analysis over the past several years indicates that from one year to another 15 percent of company A's customers switch to company B and 10 percent of company B's customers switch to company A. Moreover, it has been determined that the Markov property holds for this process (i.e., given the company with which an individual does his business at the present, the company he will do business with next year is independent of those with which he did business in past years).

What percentage of the market will company B have 4 years from now?

To answer this question, consider the system obtained as follows: at time intervals of 1 year, observe the company with which a *particular* person does his business. At any time let the state of the system be 1 if this person is doing business with company A at that time, and let the state of the system be 2 if this person is doing business with company B at that time. Briefly,

State	Company
1	A
2	B

According to the assumptions, the system forms a Markov chain with transition matrix

$$P = \begin{matrix} & 1 & 2 \\ 1 & \\ 2 & \end{matrix} \begin{bmatrix} .85 & .15 \\ .10 & .90 \end{bmatrix}$$

and initial distribution

$$\begin{matrix} & 1 & 2 \end{matrix}$$
$$\Pi^{(0)} = [.75, .25]$$

The problem at hand is to calculate $\pi_2^{(4)}$. Calculations which were done on the computer, but which can also be verified by hand without too much trouble, show that

$$P^4 = \begin{matrix} & 1 & 2 \\ 1 & \\ 2 & \end{matrix} \begin{bmatrix} .58984 & .41016 \\ .27344 & .72656 \end{bmatrix}$$

By Eq. (9.7.2), the distribution of the Markov chain after four time periods (4 years) is

$$\Pi^{(4)} = \Pi^{(0)} P^4$$

Multiplication of these two matrices gives

$$\begin{matrix} & 1 & 2 \end{matrix}$$
$$\Pi^{(4)} = [.51074, \quad .48926]$$

In particular, $\pi_2^{(4)} = .48926$. In other words, 4 years from now company B will have approximately 49 percent of the market.

Exercises for 9.7

1. What is the initial distribution of the Markov chain defined in Example 9.6.1?
2. Let

$$P = \begin{array}{c} 1 \\ 2 \end{array}\begin{array}{cc} 1 & 2 \\ \begin{bmatrix} .4 & .6 \\ .5 & .5 \end{bmatrix} \end{array}$$

   be the transition matrix of a Markov chain with states 1 and 2, and suppose that $\pi_1^{(0)} = .3$.
   (a) What is the initial distribution?
   (b) What is the distribution of the Markov chain at time 2?
   (c) Find $\Pi^{(3)}$.
3. A family's eating habits are as follows: if they have steak one day, the probability is .8 that they do not have steak the next day. However, the probability that they do not have steak one day given that they did not have steak the previous day is .6. Moreover, it has been determined that the Markov property holds for this process. Given that they have steak on Monday, with probability .1, what is probability that they have steak on Thursday?
4. Let

$$P = \begin{array}{c} 1 \\ 2 \end{array}\begin{array}{cc} 1 & 2 \\ \begin{bmatrix} 1 & 0 \\ 0 & 1 \end{bmatrix} \end{array}$$

   be the transition matrix of a Markov chain with states 1 and 2, and let $\Pi^{(0)} = [\frac{1}{2}, \frac{1}{2}]$.
   (a) Find $\Pi^{(2)}$.
   (b) Find $\Pi^{(3)}$.
   (c) Find $\Pi^{(n)}$, $n \geq 1$.
5. Let

$$P = \begin{array}{c} 1 \\ 2 \end{array}\begin{array}{cc} 1 & 2 \\ \begin{bmatrix} p & 1-p \\ 0 & 1 \end{bmatrix} \end{array} \qquad 0 < p < 1$$

   be the transition matrix of a Markov chain with states 1 and 2, and let $\Pi^{(0)} = [\frac{1}{2}, \frac{1}{2}]$.
   (a) Find $\Pi^{(2)}$.
   (b) Find $\Pi^{(3)}$.
   (c) Find $\Pi^{(n)}$, $n \geq 1$.
6. (a) What is the initial distribution of the Markov chain defined in problem 8, Exercises 9.6?
   (b) What is the distribution of the population with respect to urban and rural living 3 years after the latest census?
7. A local television station has three different commercials advertising a certain product. They never use the same commercial twice in a row. If the first commercial was used last time, there is equal probability that either the second or the third will be used next time. If the second commercial was used, they use the first commercial next time with probability $\frac{3}{4}$. If the third commercial was used, they use the first commercial next time with probability $\frac{1}{8}$. Suppose it has been determined that the Markov property holds for this process, and assume also that there is equal probability that any one of the three commercials is picked as the first one used.
   (a) Find the initial distribution of this chain.
   (b) What is the probability that the first commercial is used the second time?
   (c) What is the probability that the third commercial is used the second time?
8. In problem 3, Exercises 9.1, suppose that boy 1 has the ball initially.
   (a) What is the probability that boy 2 is the third person to receive the ball?
   (b) What is the probability that boy 1 is the third person to receive the ball?

9. In problem 9, Exercises 9.4, suppose there is equal probability that the man will lease a 1974 Ford, Dodge, or Chevrolet. What is the probability that he leases a 1977 Dodge?

10. Suppose the probability that a father with blue eyes has a son with blue eyes is .7 and the probability that he has a son with brown eyes is .1; the probability that a father with brown eyes has a son with brown eyes is .6 and the probability that he has a son with hazel eyes is .2; and the probability that a father with hazel eyes has a son with hazel eyes is .5 and the probability that he has a son with blue eyes is .4. Assume that the initial distribution of men with respect to the color of their eyes is 30 percent blue, 30 percent hazel, and 40 percent brown, and suppose that the above process is Markovian. What is the distribution of men with respect to the color of their eyes three generations from now? (Consider only blue, brown, and hazel as possible eye colors.)

11. Consider the Ehrenfest chain of problem 2, Exercises 9.1. A fair die is rolled to determine how many balls are to be placed initially in urn I. If a 1 or 2 is rolled, zero balls are placed initially in urn I. If a 3, 4, 5, or 6 is rolled, the number of balls placed in urn I initially is, respectively, 1, 2, 3, or 4. What is the probability that after 30 seconds there are

    (a) 2 balls in urn I?   (b) 4 balls in urn I?

12. A gambler has $2. At each play of the game, he loses $1 with probability $\frac{2}{3}$. On the other hand, he wins $2 with probability $\frac{1}{3}$ at each play of the game. He stops playing when he has lost his $2 or when he has won at least $2.

    (a) Set up the transition matrix for this Markov chain.

    (b) What is the probability that he has lost his $2 at the end of, at most, 3 plays?

13. In problem 12, what is the probability that the game lasts more than 6 plays?

Section 9.8   Regular Markov Chains: Introduction and Motivation

One of the most important features that many Markov chains display is a long-run equilibrium behavior. In other words, "after a long time" the distribution of the Markov chain will remain about the same from time period to time period. This means that in the long run the probabilities of being in the various states will not change very much, if any, as time goes on. The best way to illustrate this property is via an example.

Example 9.8.1 Social Mobility We return again to Example 9.2.1. The comments made in the previous paragraph lead us to ask the following question: Is there a long-run tendency toward stabilization of the percentages of each class in the population?

To get a feeling for this, let us assume that the initial distribution of the Markov chain is the one given on page 418:

$$\Pi^{(0)} = [.4, .5, .1]$$

As we have seen, the distribution of the Markov chain (social classes) at time n is given by the product of the two matrices $\Pi^{(0)}$ and P^n. That is,

$$\Pi^{(n)} = \Pi^{(0)} P^n$$

The first six powers of P are given on pages 409 and 410. Using these we obtain the distribution of the Markov chain at times 1–6. They are (to five decimal places)

$$\Pi^{(1)} = [.3, .54, .16]$$
$$\Pi^{(2)} = [.25, .554, .196]$$
$$\Pi^{(3)} = [.225, .5574, .2176]$$
$$\Pi^{(4)} = [.2125, .55694, .23056]$$
$$\Pi^{(5)} = [.20625, .55541, .23834]$$
$$\Pi^{(6)} = [.20312, .55387, .24300]$$

By using the computer it is easy to obtain the distributions of the Markov chain at various times (Table 9.8.1). Again these calculations can be done by hand.

Table 9.8.1

Time	Distribution at time		
0	.40000	.50000	.10000
1	.30000	.54000	.16000
2	.25000	.55400	.19600
3	.22500	.55740	.21760
4	.21250	.55694	.23056
5	.20625	.55541	.23834
6	.20312	.55387	.24300
7	.20156	.55264	.24580
8	.20078	.55174	.24748
9	.20039	.55112	.24849
10	.20020	.55071	.24909
11	.20010	.55045	.24946
12	.20005	.55028	.24967
13	.20002	.55017	.24980
14	.20001	.55011	.24988
15	.20001	.55006	.24993
16	.20000	.55004	.24996
17	.20000	.55002	.24997
18	.20000	.55001	.24998
19	.20000	.55001	.24999
20	.20000	.55001	.24999
21	.20000	.55000	.25000
22	.20000	.55000	.25000
23	.20000	.55000	.25000
24	.20000	.55000	.25000
25	.20000	.55000	.25000
26	.20000	.55000	.25000
27	.20000	.55000	.25000
28	.20000	.55000	.25000
29	.20000	.55000	.25000
30	.20000	.55000	.25000

According to the computer data, the distribution of the Markov chain remains the same after time 20. In fact, the data indicate that for $n \geq 21$,

$$\Pi^{(n)} = [.20, .55, .25]$$

or $\pi_1^{(n)} = .20$, $\pi_2^{(n)} = .55$, $\pi_3^{(n)} = .25$. Translated into percentages this means that after 20 generations the percentages in each class remain the same and are given by the following table:

Class	Percentage
Lower	20
Middle	55
Upper	25

For convenience this "equilibrium" distribution will be denoted by

$$V = [.20, .55, .25] \tag{9.8.1}$$

What we have shown so far is that if the initial distribution of individuals in the various classes is

$$\Pi^{(0)} = [.4, .5, .1] \tag{9.8.2}$$

then in the *long run* the distribution at time n will be

$$\Pi^{(n)} \doteq V \tag{9.8.3}$$

What happens in the long run if the initial distribution is something other than the one in Eq. (9.8.2)?

With the aid of the computer we tried two additional initial distributions,

$$\Pi^{(0)} = [.60, .25, .15] \text{ (see Table 9.8.2)}$$

Table 9.8.2

Time	Distribution at time		
0	.60000	.25000	.15000
1	.40000	.41000	.19000
2	.30000	.48600	.21400
3	.25000	.52160	.22840
4	.22500	.53796	.23704
5	.21250	.54528	.24222
6	.20625	.54842	.24533
7	.20312	.54967	.24720
8	.20156	.55012	.24832
9	.20078	.55023	.24899
10	.20039	.55021	.24940
11	.20020	.55017	.24964
12	.20010	.55012	.24978
13	.20005	.55008	.24987
14	.20002	.55005	.24992
15	.20001	.55003	.24995
16	.20001	.55002	.24997
17	.20000	.55001	.24998
18	.20000	.55001	.24999
19	.20000	.55001	.24999
20	.20000	.55000	.25000
21	.20000	.55000	.25000
22	.20000	.55000	.25000
23	.20000	.55000	.25000
24	.20000	.55000	.25000
25	.20000	.55000	.25000

and

$$\Pi^{(0)} = [.15, .75, .10] \text{ (see Table 9.8.3)}$$

Table 9.8.3

Time	Distribution at time		
0	.15000	.75000	.10000
1	.17500	.66500	.16000
2	.18750	.61650	.19600
3	.19375	.58865	.21760
4	.19687	.57256	.23066
5	.19844	.56323	.23834
6	.19922	.55778	.24300
7	.19961	.55459	.24580
8	.19980	.55271	.24748
9	.19990	.55161	.24849
10	.19995	.55096	.24909
11	.19998	.55057	.24946
12	.19999	.55034	.24967
13	.19999	.55020	.24930
14	.20000	.55012	.24988
15	.20000	.55007	.24993
16	.20000	.55004	.24996
17	.20000	.55003	.24997
18	.20000	.55002	.24998
19	.20000	.55001	.24999
20	.20000	.55001	.24999
21	.20000	.55000	.25000
22	.20000	.55000	.25000
23	.20000	.55000	.25000
24	.20000	.55000	.25000
25	.20000	.55000	.25000

In both cases, not only was there a long-run tendency toward stabilization of the percentages of individuals in each class, but the "equilibrium" distribution was the same in both cases and equal to V. That is, for any of the initial distributions tried so far, we have $\Pi^{(n)} \doteq V$ for sufficiently large n (i.e., after a long time).

Exercises for 9.8

1. Let

$$P = \begin{array}{c} \\ 1 \\ 2 \end{array} \begin{array}{cc} 1 & 2 \\ \begin{bmatrix} \frac{1}{2} & \frac{1}{2} \\ \frac{1}{2} & \frac{1}{2} \end{bmatrix} \end{array}$$

be the transition matrix of a two-state Markov chain, and let $\Pi^{(0)} = [\frac{1}{3}, \frac{2}{3}]$ be the initial distribution. Find the "equilibrium" distribution for this Markov chain by proceeding as in Example 9.8.1.

2. In the rainfall model of Example 9.5.1, the transition matrix P was given by

$$P = \begin{bmatrix} \frac{3}{4} & \frac{1}{4} \\ \frac{1}{2} & \frac{1}{2} \end{bmatrix}$$

(a) Find the "equilibrium" distribution for this Markov chain by proceeding as in Example 9.8.1. (*Hint:* Since the "equilibrium" distribution is independent of the initial distribution, let $\Pi^{(0)} = [1, 0]$. The first six powers of P are given on page 411.)

(b) Interpret this result.

3. Let P be the transition matrix of the word-structure model of Example 9.2.2. Then

$$P = \begin{bmatrix} 0 & 1 \\ .49 & .51 \end{bmatrix}$$

Find the "equilibrium" distribution for this Markov chain.

4. In the Markov chain defined in problem 10, Exercises 9.4, let $p = 0$ and $q = \frac{1}{2}$.

(a) Find the "equilibrium" distribution for this Markov chain.

(b) Interpret this result.

Section 9.9 Regular Markov Chains: The Equilibrium Distribution

From the results in Section 9.8 it is natural to make the following conjecture concerning the social-mobility chain: *In the long run the probability of being in any particular state* (i.e., the distribution of the Markov chain) *is given approximately by the row vector* $V = [.20, .55, .25]$ *regardless of the initial distribution.* This conjecture is not only valid for this Markov chain, but a similar result holds true for a large class of Markov chains.

Definition

Let P be the transition matrix of a Markov chain. Then P is said to be *regular* if some power of P contains only *positive entries*. A Markov chain is called *regular* if its transition matrix is regular.

Example 9.9.1

1. Social mobility. Here

$$P = \begin{bmatrix} .6 & .3 & .1 \\ .1 & .8 & .1 \\ .1 & .2 & .7 \end{bmatrix}$$

and so, in fact, $P(= P^1)$ itself contains only positive entries. Thus P is regular.

2. Word structure. In this case

$$P = \begin{bmatrix} 0 & 1 \\ .49 & .51 \end{bmatrix}$$

and so P has a 0 entry, $p_{11} = 0$. However,

$$P^2 = \begin{bmatrix} .49 & .51 \\ .2499 & .7501 \end{bmatrix}$$

and consequently P^2 (the second power of P) has only positive entries. Thus P is regular.

3. Gambling. On pages 410 and 411 we calculated several powers of the transition matrix of the Markov chain of Example 9.2.3. Notice that, for example, the 1–2 entry is 0 in all these powers of P. In fact, it is not too difficult to see that the 1–2 entry is 0 in all powers of P. Thus P is *not* regular.

We stress the fact that if the transition matrix P itself has no 0 entries, it is regular.

The following theorem states that if the transition matrix of a Markov chain is regular, it will behave in the same way as the social-mobility chain in the sense that there will be a long-run "equilibrium" distribution, which is the same regardless of the initial distribution.

Theorem 9.9.1

Suppose that the transition matrix P of a Markov chain is *regular*. As usual, let $\Pi^{(n)}$ denote the distribution of the Markov chain at time n. Then there is a unique vector V such that $\Pi^{(n)}$ approaches V, that is,

$$\Pi^{(n)} \doteq V \qquad \text{for large } n \tag{9.9.1}$$

regardless of the initial distribution, $\Pi^{(0)}$, of the Markov chain.

The vector V is called the *equilibrium distribution* of the Markov chain.

In Example 9.8.1 we found that the equilibrium distribution of the social-mobility chain is

$$V = [.20, .55, .25]$$

Example 9.9.2 Rainfall In Example 9.5.1 a specific rainfall model was discussed. Recall that on a given day the state of the system is 1 or 2 according as it is dry or wet on that day. The transition matrix for this Markov chain was given to be

$$P = \begin{bmatrix} \frac{3}{4} & \frac{1}{4} \\ \frac{1}{2} & \frac{1}{2} \end{bmatrix}$$

Since P has no 0 entries it is regular. Consequently, according to Theorem 9.9.1, regardless of the initial distribution, the distribution of the Markov chain will approach an equilibrium distribution V as time goes on.

In the present case this means that regardless of the probability of a wet or dry day when we begin our observations (time 0), the probability of a wet or dry day in the distant future will be given approximately by the entries of the vector V. In this case we can use the computer (or hand calculations) to determine V by specifying *any* initial distribution and then calculating $\Pi^{(n)}$ for various n. As n gets large $\Pi^{(n)}$ will approach the equilibrium distribution V. The results are given in Tables 9.9.1–9.9.3 for three different initial distributions.

Table 9.9.1

Time	Distribution at time	
0	1.00000	.00000
1	.75000	.25000
2	.68750	.31250
3	.67187	.32812
4	.66797	.33203
5	.66699	.33301
6	.66675	.33325
7	.66669	.33331
8	.66667	.33333
9	.66667	.33333
10	.66667	.33333
11	.66667	.33333
12	.66667	.33333
13	.66667	.33333
14	.66667	.33333
15	.66667	.33333

Table 9.9.2

Time	Distribution at time	
0	.10000	.90000
1	.52500	.47500
2	.63125	.36875
3	.65781	.34219
4	.66445	.33555
5	.66611	.33389
6	.66653	.33347
7	.66663	.33337
8	.66666	.33334
9	.66667	.33333
10	.66667	.33333
11	.66667	.33333
12	.66667	.33333
13	.66667	.33333
14	.66667	.33333
15	.66667	.33333

Thus the output indicates that the equilibrium distribution for this Markov chain is $V = [\frac{2}{3}, \frac{1}{3}]$. In the present case this can be interpreted as meaning that in the long run it will be dry $\frac{2}{3}$ of the time and wet (rain) $\frac{1}{3}$ of the time.

Examples 9.8.1 and 9.9.2 illustrate the significance of the vector V as the long-run equilibrium distribution of the probabilities of being in the various states of the system. In other words, the knowledge of the vector V allows one to predict the behavior of the system after a large number of transitions (time periods). Specifically, V gives us the approximate probabilities of being in the various states of the system after a sufficiently large number of time periods have elapsed (this is Theorem 9.9.1).

Table 9.9.3

Time	Distribution at time	
0	.50000	.50000
1	.62500	.37500
2	.65625	.34375
3	.66406	.33594
4	.66602	.33398
5	.66650	.33350
6	.66663	.33337
7	.66666	.33334
8	.66666	.33334
9	.66667	.33333
10	.66667	.33333
11	.66667	.33333
12	.66667	.33333
13	.66667	.33333
14	.66667	.33333
15	.66667	.33333

Because of the properties of the vector V it is clearly worthwhile to determine it. How can this be done? According to Theorem 9.9.1 the row vector $\Pi^{(n)}$ will approach the vector V as n gets large. So, one possible way to find V would be to calculate $\Pi^{(n)}$ $(= \Pi^{(0)}P^n)$ for $n = 1, 2, 3, \ldots$ and observe to what row vector it is converging. This latter row vector must be V (Theorem 9.9.1). This is, in fact, the way that we calculated V for the social-mobility and rainfall Markov chains. There are several problems with this approach.

1. The calculation of the vectors $\Pi^{(n)}$ is extremely laborious.
2. Even if these calculations are done with the aid of a computer, there will, in general, be "errors" involved.
3. It may take a "very long time" for the vectors $\Pi^{(n)}$ to approach V and, in fact, in the general situation, although $\Pi^{(n)} \doteq V$ for large n, it will never be the case that $\Pi^{(n)}$ is actually equal to V.

Because of the above comments it is clear that it is desirable to obtain an alternative, more exact method for determining the equilibrium distribution V for a Markov chain. As we shall see, the method involves solving a system of linear equations. The idea for the method is based on Theorem 9.9.1. According to that theorem $\Pi^{(n)} \doteq V$ for large n. But $\Pi^{(n)} = \Pi^{(0)}P^n$, so that, for large n,

$$\Pi^{(0)}P^n \doteq V$$

This, in turn, implies that $\Pi^{(0)}P^{n+1} \doteq V$ and $(\Pi^{(0)}P^n)P \doteq VP$ for large n. But $(\Pi^{(0)}P^n)P = \Pi^{(0)}P^nP = \Pi^{(0)}P^{n+1}$, so that, for large n,

$$\Pi^{(0)}P^{n+1} \doteq V \qquad \Pi^{(0)}P^{n+1} \doteq VP$$

Consequently, this argument indicates that

$$VP \doteq V \tag{9.9.2}$$

Definition

Let $W = [w_1, w_2, \ldots, w_N]$ be a row vector of length N. Then W is called a *probability vector* if all its entries are nonnegative and if $w_1 + \cdots + w_N = 1$.

Example 9.9.3

1. $W = [.2, .5, .3]$ is a probability vector of length 3, since all its entries are non-negative and

$$.2 + .5 + .3 = 1$$

2. $W = [\frac{1}{3}, 0, \frac{1}{6}, \frac{1}{2}, 0]$ is a probability vector of length 5 since all its entries are non-negative and

$$\frac{1}{3} + 0 + \frac{1}{6} + \frac{1}{2} + 0 = 1$$

The method we shall use to calculate the equilibrium distribution V of a Markov chain is contained in the following theorem. The motivation is Eq. (9.9.2).

Theorem 9.9.2

Let P be the transition matrix of a Markov chain and suppose that P is regular. Then the equilibrium distribution V of the Markov chain is the *unique probability vector* V that satisfies the matrix equation

$$VP = V \tag{9.9.3}$$

Thus Theorem 9.9.2 gives an explicit method for determining the equilibrium distribution of a Markov chain with a regular transition matrix. As was mentioned earlier, solving for a probability vector V, satisfying Eq. (9.9.3) consists of solving a system of linear equations. In the next section several examples will be given which illustrate the results of this section.

Exercises for 9.9

1. Which of the following transition matrices are regular?

(a) $\begin{bmatrix} \frac{1}{4} & \frac{3}{4} \\ 1 & 0 \end{bmatrix}$

(b) $\begin{bmatrix} \frac{1}{3} & \frac{2}{3} \\ \frac{1}{2} & \frac{1}{2} \end{bmatrix}$

(c) $\begin{bmatrix} 1 & 0 \\ \frac{1}{2} & \frac{1}{2} \end{bmatrix}$

(d) $\begin{bmatrix} 1 & 0 \\ 0 & 1 \end{bmatrix}$

(e) $\begin{bmatrix} \frac{4}{5} & \frac{1}{5} \\ 0 & 1 \end{bmatrix}$

(f) $\begin{bmatrix} \frac{1}{2} & 0 & \frac{1}{2} \\ 0 & 1 & 0 \\ 0 & \frac{1}{2} & \frac{1}{2} \end{bmatrix}$

(g) $\begin{bmatrix} \frac{2}{3} & \frac{1}{3} & 0 \\ 0 & \frac{1}{4} & \frac{3}{4} \\ \frac{1}{3} & \frac{1}{3} & \frac{1}{3} \end{bmatrix}$

(h) $\begin{bmatrix} 1 & 0 & 0 \\ \frac{1}{3} & \frac{1}{3} & \frac{1}{3} \\ 0 & 1 & 0 \end{bmatrix}$

2. In testing for regularity of a Markov chain, we are only interested in whether or not the entries in some power of its transition matrix are all positive. It is not necessary to compute the actual values of these entries. Thus an entry can be replaced by an x if it is positive and by a 0 otherwise. Also, in certain cases it is necessary to try large powers of the

transition matrix when checking for regularity. Therefore, it is convenient to square the result each time (i.e., raise the transition matrix to even powers). Use this technique to determine whether the Markov chain with transition matrix

$$P = \begin{bmatrix} 0 & 1 & 0 \\ 0 & 0 & 1 \\ \frac{1}{3} & \frac{2}{3} & 0 \end{bmatrix}$$

is regular or not.

3. Let

$$P = \begin{array}{c} \\ 1 \\ 2 \\ 3 \\ 4 \end{array} \begin{array}{cccc} 1 & 2 & 3 & 4 \\ \begin{bmatrix} \frac{1}{2} & \frac{1}{2} & 0 & 0 \\ \frac{1}{2} & \frac{1}{2} & 0 & 0 \\ \frac{1}{4} & \frac{1}{4} & \frac{1}{4} & \frac{1}{4} \\ \frac{1}{4} & \frac{1}{4} & \frac{1}{4} & \frac{1}{4} \end{bmatrix} \end{array}$$

be the transition matrix of a Markov chain with states 1, 2, 3, and 4. Is this Markov chain regular?

4. Is the Ehrenfest chain of problem 2, Exercises 9.1, a regular Markov chain?
5. Is the social-mobility model of problem 9, Exercises 9.2, a regular Markov chain?
6. For what values of p and q will the transition matrix

$$P = \begin{bmatrix} 1 - p & p \\ q & 1 - q \end{bmatrix}$$

be regular?

7. Which of the following row vectors are probability vectors?
   (a) $[\frac{1}{2}, \frac{1}{2}, 0]$
   (b) $[\frac{1}{3}, -1, \frac{2}{3}, 1]$
   (c) $[.7, 0, .2, .1]$
   (d) $[\frac{1}{3}, \frac{1}{2}, \frac{1}{6}]$

8. Note that if $V = [v_1, v_2, \ldots, v_N]$ is a row vector such that $v_i \geq 0$ and not all $v_i = 0$, $1 \leq i \leq N$, then there exists a scalar λ such that λV is a probability vector. For example, let $V = [1, 0, 5, 2]$. Then $1 + 5 + 2 = 8$, and so, let $\lambda = \frac{1}{8}$. Multiply each of the following row vectors by the appropriate scalar to form a probability vector.
   (a) $[1, 0, 2, 3]$
   (b) $[2, 3, 0, 1, 3]$
   (c) $[\frac{2}{3}, 0, 1, \frac{1}{2}]$
   (d) $[\frac{1}{4}, 1, \frac{1}{3}, 2]$

9. Let

$$P = \begin{bmatrix} p_{11} & p_{12} \\ p_{21} & p_{22} \end{bmatrix}$$

be a transition matrix and let $V = [v_1, v_2]$ be a probability vector.
   (a) Prove that VP is a probability vector.
   (b) State a similar result for an $N \times N$ transition matrix.

10. A nonzero row vector $V = [v_1, v_2, \ldots, v_N]$ is called a *fixed vector* for the $N \times N$ square matrix A if $VA = V$. Thus the equilibrium distribution of a regular Markov chain with transition matrix P is a fixed *probability* vector for P.
   (a) Show that $[1, 2, 2]$ is a fixed vector for the matrix

$$A = \begin{bmatrix} 0 & 1 & 0 \\ 0 & 0 & 1 \\ \frac{1}{2} & \frac{1}{2} & 0 \end{bmatrix}$$

   (b) Show that $[1, 0, \frac{1}{3}]$ and $[\frac{2}{3}, 0, 1]$ are both fixed vectors for the matrix

$$A = \begin{bmatrix} 1 & 0 & 0 \\ \frac{1}{3} & 0 & \frac{2}{3} \\ 0 & 0 & 1 \end{bmatrix}$$

11. If V is a fixed vector for a matrix A, show that for any scalar λ, $\lambda \neq 0$, λV is also a fixed vector for A. (See problem 10 for the definition of a fixed vector.)

12. Let

$$P = \begin{bmatrix} 1-p & p \\ q & 1-q \end{bmatrix} \qquad 0 \leq p \leq 1, \ 0 \leq q \leq 1$$

(a) Show that the vector $V = [q, p]$ is a fixed vector for P provided that p and q are not both zero.

(b) Use part (a) to find the unique equilibrium distribution for the Markov chain with transition matrix P given by

(1) $P = \begin{bmatrix} \frac{1}{2} & \frac{1}{2} \\ 1 & 0 \end{bmatrix}$

(2) $P = \begin{bmatrix} .6 & .4 \\ .3 & .7 \end{bmatrix}$

(3) $P = \begin{bmatrix} \frac{3}{4} & \frac{1}{4} \\ \frac{1}{3} & \frac{2}{3} \end{bmatrix}$

13. Let

$$P = \begin{bmatrix} \frac{1}{2} & \frac{1}{2} \\ 0 & 1 \end{bmatrix}$$

(a) Show that P is not regular.

(b) Show that the Markov chain with transition matrix P has a unique fixed probability vector. Thus it is possible for a Markov chain to have a unique fixed probability vector even though its transition matrix is not regular.

14. Let P be a regular transition matrix, and let V be its unique equilibrium distribution. Prove that as n gets large, $P^{(n)}$ approaches a matrix T whose rows are each the vector V.

*15. Consider a Markov chain such that for any two states i and j there is a positive integer n such that $p_{ij}^{(n)} > 0$; that is, it is possible to go from any state i to any state j. Also suppose that $p_{kk} \neq 0$ for at least one state k. Prove that the chain is regular.

Section 9.10   Regular Markov Chains: Examples

Example 9.10.1   In Example 9.8.1 it was determined that the equilibrium distribution of the social-mobility Markov chain is $V = [.20, .55, .25]$. We shall now illustrate how to obtain this fact by using Eq. (9.9.3). Let $V = [v_1, v_2, v_3]$. The transition matrix for the social-mobility Markov chain is

$$P = \begin{bmatrix} .6 & .3 & .1 \\ .1 & .8 & .1 \\ .1 & .2 & .7 \end{bmatrix}$$

Consequently, Eq. (9.9.3) can be written as

$$[v_1, v_2, v_3] \begin{bmatrix} .6 & .3 & .1 \\ .1 & .8 & .1 \\ .1 & .2 & .7 \end{bmatrix} = [v_1, v_2, v_3]$$

Multiplying the two matrices on the left side of this matrix equation yields

$$[.6v_1 + .1v_2 + .1v_3, \ .3v_1 + .8v_2 + .2v_3, \ .1v_1 + .1v_2 + .7v_3] = [v_1, v_2, v_3]$$

In other words, Eq. (9.9.3) in this case is equivalent to

$$.6v_1 + .1v_2 + .1v_3 = v_1$$
$$.3v_1 + .8v_2 + .2v_3 = v_2$$
$$.1v_1 + .1v_2 + .7v_3 = v_3$$

Combining terms this system becomes

$$-.4v_1 + .1v_2 + .1v_3 = 0$$
$$.3v_1 - .2v_2 + .2v_3 = 0$$
$$.1v_1 + .1v_2 - .3v_3 = 0$$

Finally, since V is to be a *probability vector* we must also have

$$v_1 + v_2 + v_3 = 1$$

Consequently, finding the probability vector V that satisfies $VP = V$ is equivalent to solving the system of equations

$$-.4v_1 + .1v_2 + .1v_3 = 0$$
$$.3v_1 - .2v_2 + .2v_3 = 0$$
$$.1v_1 + .1v_2 - .3v_3 = 0 \qquad (9.10.1)$$
$$v_1 + v_2 + v_3 = 1$$

To solve this system we use Gaussian elimination and augmented matrices. The augmented matrix associated with Eq. (9.10.1) is

$$\begin{bmatrix} -.4 & .1 & .1 & \vdots & 0 \\ .3 & -.2 & .2 & \vdots & 0 \\ .1 & .1 & -.3 & \vdots & 0 \\ 1 & 1 & 1 & \vdots & 1 \end{bmatrix}$$

To simplify this, first multiply each of the first three rows by 10 to obtain

$$\begin{bmatrix} -4 & 1 & 1 & \vdots & 0 \\ 3 & -2 & 2 & \vdots & 0 \\ 1 & 1 & -3 & \vdots & 0 \\ 1 & 1 & 1 & \vdots & 1 \end{bmatrix}$$

The system of linear equations corresponding to this augmented matrix was solved in Example 6.9.5. The result obtained was

$$v_1 = \tfrac{1}{5} \qquad v_2 = \tfrac{11}{20} \qquad v_3 = \tfrac{1}{4}$$

In other words,

$$V = [\tfrac{1}{5}, \tfrac{11}{20}, \tfrac{1}{4}] = [.20, .55, .25]$$

which agrees with Eq. (9.8.1).

Example 9.10.2 Consider again the business-trend illustration given in Example 9.7.3. The transition matrix associated with this Markov chain is

$$P = \begin{bmatrix} .85 & .15 \\ .10 & .90 \end{bmatrix}$$

Since all the entries of P are positive, P is regular. Hence, by Theorem 9.9.1, the

Markov chain has an equilibrium distribution V. By Theorem 9.9.2, V is the unique probability vector satisfying the matrix equation $VP = V$. If $V = [v_1, v_2]$, this matrix equation becomes

$$[v_1, v_2] \begin{bmatrix} .85 & .15 \\ .10 & .90 \end{bmatrix} = [v_1, v_2]$$

Multiplying this out gives

$$[.85v_1 + .10v_2, .15v_1 + .90v_2] = [v_1, v_2]$$

In other words,

$$.85v_1 + .10v_2 = v_1$$
$$.15v_1 + .90v_2 = v_2$$

Combining terms gives

$$-.15v_1 + .10v_2 = 0$$
$$.15v_1 - .10v_2 = 0$$

The condition that V is to be a probability vector is that

$$v_1 + v_2 = 1$$

Consequently, finding the unique probability vector satisfying $VP = V$ is equivalent to solving the system of equations

$$-.15v_1 + .10v_2 = 0$$
$$.15v_1 - .10v_2 = 0$$
$$v_1 + \quad v_2 = 1$$

The augmented matrix associated with this system is

$$\begin{bmatrix} -.15 & .10 & \vdots & 0 \\ .15 & -.10 & \vdots & 0 \\ 1. & 1 & \vdots & 1 \end{bmatrix} \quad \text{or} \quad \begin{bmatrix} -15 & 10 & \vdots & 0 \\ 15 & -10 & \vdots & 0 \\ 1 & 1 & \vdots & 1 \end{bmatrix}$$

Using Gaussian elimination we can solve the system

$$\begin{bmatrix} -15 & 10 & \vdots & 0 \\ 15 & -10 & \vdots & 0 \\ 1 & 1 & \vdots & 1 \end{bmatrix} \rightarrow \begin{bmatrix} 1 & 1 & \vdots & 1 \\ 15 & -10 & \vdots & 0 \\ -15 & 10 & \vdots & 0 \end{bmatrix}$$

$$-\tfrac{1}{25} \rightarrow \begin{bmatrix} 1 & 1 & \vdots & 1 \\ 0 & -25 & \vdots & -15 \\ 0 & 25 & \vdots & 15 \end{bmatrix} \rightarrow \begin{bmatrix} 1 & 1 & \vdots & 1 \\ 0 & 1 & \vdots & \frac{15}{25} \\ 0 & 25 & \vdots & 15 \end{bmatrix}$$

$$\begin{bmatrix} 1 & 0 & \vdots & \frac{10}{25} \\ 0 & 1 & \vdots & \frac{15}{25} \\ 0 & 0 & \vdots & 0 \end{bmatrix}$$

Consequently, $v_1 = \frac{10}{25}$, $v_2 = \frac{15}{25}$, or

$$V = [\tfrac{10}{25}, \tfrac{15}{25}] = [.4, .6] \tag{9.10.2}$$

For comparison, the result of Eq. (9.10.2) was also obtained, numerically, by using the computer (again, these calculations can be done by hand). The data are listed in Table 9.10.1.

Table 9.10.1

Time	Distribution at time	
0	.75000	.25000
1	.66250	.33750
2	.59687	.40312
3	.54766	.45234
4	.51074	.48926
5	.48306	.51694
6	.46229	.53771
7	.44672	.55328
8	.43504	.56496
9	.42628	.57372
10	.41971	.58029
11	.41478	.58522
12	.41109	.58891
13	.40832	.59168
14	.40624	.59376
15	.40468	.59532
16	.40351	.59649
17	.40263	.59737
18	.40197	.59803
19	.40148	.59852
20	.40111	.59889
21	.40083	.59917
22	.40062	.59938
23	.40047	.59953
24	.40035	.59965
25	.40026	.59974
26	.40020	.59980
27	.40015	.59985
28	.40011	.59989
29	.40008	.59992
30	.40006	.59994
31	.40005	.59995
32	.40004	.59996
33	.40003	.59997
34	.40002	.59998
35	.40001	.59999
36	.40001	.59999
37	.40001	.59999
38	.40001	.59999
39	.40000	.60000
40	.40000	.60000

By Theorem 9.9.1 we can conclude that no matter what the initial percentages of the market (i.e., the initial distribution), in the long run company A will have 40 percent of the market and company B 60 percent. For the data of the computer output, the initial distribution was assumed to be

$$\Pi^{(0)} = [.75, .25]$$

so that initially company A has 75 percent of the market and company B 25 percent of the market. The output in this case is very revealing. It indicates that somewhere in the fifth year (between time 4 and time 5) company B will catch and overtake company A in the total share of the market. The data also show that it will take about 40 years for the percentages of the market for each company to stabilize. After this time company A will have 40 percent of the market and B, 60 percent.

Example 9.10.3 As our final example we return to the busy-signal illustration of Example 9.6.1. The transition matrix is

$$P = \begin{bmatrix} \frac{3}{4} & \frac{1}{4} \\ \frac{5}{8} & \frac{3}{8} \end{bmatrix}$$

Since P is regular, this Markov chain will have an equilibrium distribution. To find it we need to solve the matrix equation $VP = V$, where V is a probability vector. If $V = [v_1, v_2]$, this means that

$$[v_1, v_2] \begin{bmatrix} \frac{3}{4} & \frac{1}{4} \\ \frac{5}{8} & \frac{3}{8} \end{bmatrix} = [v_1, v_2]$$

or
$$\tfrac{3}{4}v_1 + \tfrac{5}{8}v_2 = v_1$$
$$\tfrac{1}{4}v_1 + \tfrac{3}{8}v_2 = v_2$$

or
$$-\tfrac{1}{4}v_1 + \tfrac{5}{8}v_2 = 0$$
$$\tfrac{1}{4}v_1 - \tfrac{5}{8}v_2 = 0$$

Since V is to be a probability vector, it follows that the unique probability vector V, satisfying $VP = P$, can be obtained by solving the system of linear equations

$$-\tfrac{1}{4}v_1 + \tfrac{5}{8}v_2 = 0$$
$$\tfrac{1}{4}v_1 - \tfrac{5}{8}v_2 = 0$$
$$v_1 + v_2 = 1$$

The associated augmented matrix is

$$\begin{bmatrix} -\frac{1}{4} & \frac{5}{8} & \vdots & 0 \\ \frac{1}{4} & -\frac{5}{8} & \vdots & 0 \\ 1 & 1 & \vdots & 1 \end{bmatrix} \quad \text{or} \quad \begin{bmatrix} -2 & 5 & \vdots & 0 \\ 2 & -5 & \vdots & 0 \\ 1 & 1 & \vdots & 1 \end{bmatrix}$$

Gaussian elimination is now applied:

$$-\tfrac{1}{2} \rightarrow \begin{bmatrix} -2 & 5 & \vdots & 0 \\ 2 & -5 & \vdots & 0 \\ 1 & 1 & \vdots & 1 \end{bmatrix} \rightarrow \begin{matrix} -2 \\ -1 \end{matrix} \begin{bmatrix} 1 & -\frac{5}{2} & \vdots & 0 \\ 2 & -5 & \vdots & 0 \\ 1 & 1 & \vdots & 1 \end{bmatrix}$$

$$\begin{bmatrix} 1 & -\frac{5}{2} & \vdots & 0 \\ 0 & 0 & \vdots & 0 \\ 0 & \frac{7}{2} & \vdots & 1 \end{bmatrix} \rightarrow \tfrac{2}{7} \rightarrow \begin{bmatrix} 1 & -\frac{5}{2} & \vdots & 0 \\ 0 & \frac{7}{2} & \vdots & 1 \\ 0 & 0 & \vdots & 0 \end{bmatrix}$$

$$\tfrac{5}{2} \begin{bmatrix} 1 & -\frac{5}{2} & \vdots & 0 \\ 0 & 1 & \vdots & \frac{2}{7} \\ 0 & 0 & \vdots & 0 \end{bmatrix} \rightarrow \begin{bmatrix} 1 & 0 & \vdots & \frac{5}{7} \\ 0 & 1 & \vdots & \frac{2}{7} \\ 0 & 0 & \vdots & 0 \end{bmatrix}$$

Consequently, $v_1 = \frac{5}{7}$, $v_2 = \frac{2}{7}$, or

$$V = [\tfrac{5}{7}, \tfrac{2}{7}]$$

In the present situation Theorem 9.9.1 implies that no matter what the condition of the line at 8:00 A.M., as the day wears on, the probability of the line *not* being busy will be approximately $\frac{5}{7} \doteq .71$. In other words, if a person calls after several time periods (5 minutes each) have passed, he will find the line to be busy about 29 percent of the time.

If the line is assumed to be not busy initially (i.e., $\Pi^{(0)} = [1, 0]$), the computer output of Table 9.10.2 illustrates the situation. From these data we see that the Markov chain

Table 9.10.2

Time	Distribution at time	
0	1.00000	.00000
1	.75000	.25000
2	.71875	.28125
3	.71484	.28516
4	.71436	.28564
5	.71429	.28571
6	.71429	.28571
7	.71429	.28571
8	.71429	.28571
9	.71429	.28571
10	.71429	.28571

reaches equilibrium at about the fifth time period. This means that from about 8:25 A.M. on, the probability that the phone line is busy approximately equals $\frac{2}{7} \doteq .29$, so except for about the first half-hour in the day, the line will be busy about 29 percent of the time.

Exercises for 9.10

1. Find the equilibrium distribution for the Markov chain with transition matrix

$$P = \begin{bmatrix} \frac{1}{2} & \frac{1}{2} \\ \frac{1}{4} & \frac{3}{4} \end{bmatrix}$$

2. Find the equilibrium distribution for the Markov chain defined in the word structure illustration of Example 9.2.2.

3. Find the equilibrium distribution for the Markov chain with transition matrix

$$P = \begin{bmatrix} \frac{1}{4} & \frac{1}{4} & \frac{1}{2} \\ \frac{1}{2} & 0 & \frac{1}{2} \\ 0 & 1 & 0 \end{bmatrix}$$

4. (a) Find the equilibrium distribution for the Markov chain with transition matrix

$$P = \begin{bmatrix} 0 & 1 & 0 \\ \frac{1}{3} & \frac{1}{3} & \frac{1}{3} \\ 0 & \frac{1}{2} & \frac{1}{2} \end{bmatrix}$$

(b) According to problem 14, Exercises 9.9, what matrix does $P^{(n)}$ approach?

5. A student has the following study habits. If he studies one night, he is 75 percent sure of not studying the next night, but if he does not study one night, he is 60 percent sure of not studying the next night. Moreover, it has been determined that the above process satisfies the Markov property.
   (a) Find the equilibrium distribution for this Markov chain.
   (b) In the long run, how often does he study?

6. In problem 10, Exercises 9.4, let $p = \frac{1}{2}$ and $q = 1$.
   (a) Find the equilibrium distribution for this Markov chain.
   (b) In the long run, how often will the answer "yes" be given?

7. (a) Find the equilibrium distribution for the Markov chain defined in problem 3, Exercises 9.7.
   (b) In the long run, how often will the family eat steak?

8. A man has three different sport coats, a blue one, a plaid one, and a brown one. He never wears the same coat on two successive days. If he wears the blue one on a given day, he wears the plaid one the next day with probability 1. However, if he wears either the plaid one or the brown one on a given day, he is twice as likely to wear the blue one the next day as he is to wear the other one. Assume the above process is Markovian.
   (a) Find the equilibrium distribution for this Markov chain.
   (b) In the long run, how often does he wear each of the sport coats?

9. A man's drinking habits are as follows. If he drinks Scotch one week, he switches to bourbon the next week, with probability $\frac{1}{4}$. However, the probability that he drinks bourbon one week given that he drank it the previous week is $\frac{3}{5}$. Assume also that given what he is presently drinking, what he drinks in future weeks is independent of what he had to drink in past weeks.
   (a) Find the equilibrium distribution for this Markov chain.
   (b) In the long run, how often does he drink Scotch?

10. Let

$$ P = \begin{bmatrix} 1 - p & p \\ p & 1 - p \end{bmatrix} \qquad 0 < p < 1 $$

Show that every Markov chain having transition matrix P has the same equilibrium distribution (regardless of the value of p, as long as $0 < p < 1$).

11. A poker player's luck follows a certain pattern. If he wins a game, the probability of his winning the next game is .2 and the probability of his breaking even is .4. If he breaks even on a game, he has an equal probability of winning, breaking even, or losing on the next game. However, if he loses a game, the probability of losing the next game is $\frac{1}{4}$ and the probability of breaking even is $\frac{1}{2}$. Moreover, it has been determined that given the outcome of the present game, the outcome of future games is independent of past games.
   (a) Find the equilibrium distribution for this Markov chain.
   (b) In the long run, how often will he win, lose, and break even?

12. (a) Find the equilibrium distribution for the Markov chain defined in problem 3, Exercises 9.3.
   (b) In the long run, how often is the machine working and how often is it broken down?

13. (a) Find the equilibrium distribution for the Markov chain defined in problem 4, Exercises 9.3.
   (b) In the long run, how often does he ride the bus to work and how often does he drive?

14. Two boys and two girls are throwing a frisbee back and forth. Each boy throws the frisbee to the other boy with probability $\frac{1}{2}$ and to each girl with probability $\frac{1}{4}$. However, each girl throws the frisbee to each boy with probability $\frac{1}{2}$ and never to the other girl. Assume that the Markov property holds here. In the long run, how often does each person receive the frisbee?

15. A man leases a new car each year. He always leases a Ford, Chevrolet, or a Dodge. If he has a Ford, he leases a Ford, Chevrolet, or a Dodge the next year with equal probability. If he has a Chevrolet, next year he leases a Ford with probability $\frac{1}{2}$ and a Chevrolet or Dodge with probability $\frac{1}{4}$. However, if he has a Dodge, the next year he leases a Ford

with probability $\frac{1}{2}$, a Chevrolet with probability $\frac{1}{3}$, and a Dodge with probability $\frac{1}{6}$. Moreover, it has been determined that the Markov property holds for this process.

(a) Find the equilibrium distribution for the process.

(b) In the long run, how often does he lease each car?

16. (a) Show that the transition matrix

$$P = \begin{bmatrix} 1 & 0 & 0 \\ \frac{1}{3} & 0 & \frac{2}{3} \\ 0 & 0 & 1 \end{bmatrix}$$

has more than one probability vector V satisfying the equation $VP = P$.

(b) Explain why this shows that P cannot be regular.

17. Let

$$P = \begin{bmatrix} p_{11} & p_{12} & p_{13} \\ p_{21} & p_{22} & p_{23} \\ p_{31} & p_{32} & p_{33} \end{bmatrix}$$

be a regular 3×3 transition matrix such that its column sums are equal to 1. (Such a matrix is said to be *doubly stochastic*.)

(a) Show that any regular Markov chain having P as its transition matrix has the probability vector $V = [\frac{1}{3}, \frac{1}{3}, \frac{1}{3}]$ as its equilibrium distribution.

(b) State a similar result for an $N \times N$ regular transition matrix.

Section 9.11 Absorbing Markov Chains

In the last several sections we studied the class of Markov chains known as regular Markov chains. Their fundamental property is that they possess an equilibrium distribution; that is, in the long run the probabilities of being in the various states will settle down to some fixed positive values. In particular, then, after a (long) period of time there will be a positive probability of being in any of the states of the Markov chain.

In the next few sections we will study Markov chains that are, in a sense, the direct opposite of regular Markov chains. These are called absorbing Markov chains.

Definition

A state in a Markov chain is an *absorbing state* if once in it, it is impossible to leave it. In other words, a state i of a Markov chain is absorbing if and only if $p_{ii} = 1$ (so $p_{ij} = 0$ for $j \neq i$).

Example 9.11.1 Gambling Consider the gambling chain of Example 9.2.3. Its transition matrix is

$$
P = \begin{array}{c} \\ 0 \\ 1 \\ 2 \\ 3 \\ 4 \\ 5 \\ 6 \end{array}
\begin{array}{c} \begin{array}{ccccccc} 0 & 1 & 2 & 3 & 4 & 5 & 6 \end{array} \\
\begin{bmatrix}
1 & 0 & 0 & 0 & 0 & 0 & 0 \\
\frac{1}{2} & 0 & \frac{1}{2} & 0 & 0 & 0 & 0 \\
0 & \frac{1}{2} & 0 & \frac{1}{2} & 0 & 0 & 0 \\
0 & 0 & \frac{1}{2} & 0 & \frac{1}{2} & 0 & 0 \\
0 & 0 & 0 & \frac{1}{2} & 0 & \frac{1}{2} & 0 \\
0 & 0 & 0 & 0 & \frac{1}{2} & 0 & \frac{1}{2} \\
0 & 0 & 0 & 0 & 0 & 0 & 1
\end{bmatrix}
\end{array}
\qquad (9.11.1)
$$

The states 0 and 6 are absorbing. Formally this stems from the fact that $p_{00} = 1$ (or equivalently $p_{0j} = 0$ for $j = 1, 2, 3, 4, 5, 6$) and the fact that $p_{66} = 1$ (or equivalently $p_{6j} = 0$ for $j = 0, 1, 2, 3, 4, 5$). Also, as can be seen from Eq. (9.11.1), no other states are absorbing. This is true because for $i \neq 0, 6$, $p_{ii} < 1$ (or, equivalently, $p_{ij} > 0$ for some $j \neq i$).

Example 9.11.2 Social Mobility Consider the social-mobility chain of Example 9.2.1. The transition matrix of this chain is

$$
\begin{array}{ccc}
& \begin{array}{ccc} 1 & 2 & 3 \end{array} & \\
P = \begin{array}{c} 1 \\ 2 \\ 3 \end{array} & \begin{bmatrix} .6 & .3 & .1 \\ .1 & .8 & .1 \\ .1 & .2 & .7 \end{bmatrix} &
\end{array}
\tag{9.11.2}
$$

Since $p_{ii} < 1$ for all states $i = 1, 2, 3$, it follows that *no state* of this chain is absorbing.

Example 9.11.3 It is not too difficult to show (see problem 10, Exercises 9.11) that if i is an absorbing state ($p_{ii} = 1$) in a Markov chain, then $p_{ii}^{(n)} = 1$ for all n. In particular, then, $p_{ij}^{(n)} = 0$ for all n and all $j \neq i$. Consequently, if the Markov chain has more than one state, no power of P will have all positive entries. Thus a *Markov chain with an absorbing state cannot be regular.* Another way of putting this is, if a *Markov chain is regular* (with more than one state), *then it has no absorbing states.*

Example 9.11.4 Ehrenfest Chain This is an example of a Markov chain (used by physicists as a model for heat exchange and diffusion) that is neither regular nor has any absorbing states. Its transition matrix is (see problem 7, Exercises 9.3)

$$
\begin{array}{cccccc}
& \begin{array}{ccccc} 0 & 1 & 2 & 3 & 4 \end{array} & \\
P = \begin{array}{c} 0 \\ 1 \\ 2 \\ 3 \\ 4 \end{array} & \begin{bmatrix} 0 & 1 & 0 & 0 & 0 \\ \frac{1}{4} & 0 & \frac{3}{4} & 0 & 0 \\ 0 & \frac{1}{2} & 0 & \frac{1}{2} & 0 \\ 0 & 0 & \frac{3}{4} & 0 & \frac{1}{4} \\ 0 & 0 & 0 & 1 & 0 \end{bmatrix} &
\end{array}
\tag{9.11.3}
$$

Notice that $p_{ii} < 1$ (in fact, $p_{ii} = 0$) for all states i and so no state is absorbing. But, for example (see problem 16, Exercises 9.5), it is not difficult to show that $p_{22}^{(n)} = 0$ for n odd, and hence the Markov chain is not regular.

Definition
A Markov chain is said to be *absorbing* if it contains an absorbing state and if from each nonabsorbing state it is possible to go to some absorbing state. The latter condition means that for each nonabsorbing state i there is an absorbing state j such that for some n, $p_{ij}^{(n)} > 0$.

Example 9.11.5 Gambling The gambling chain of Example 9.11.1 is an absorbing Markov chain. Indeed the states 0 and 6 are absorbing, and the states 1–5 are nonabsorbing. Also, from the table of the powers of the transition matrix of this chain on pages 410 and 411 we see that from each nonabsorbing state it is possible to go to either absorbing state. In fact, if $i = 1, 2, 3, 4, 5$, then $p_{ij}^{(5)} > 0$ for $j = 0$ or 6.

Example 9.11.6 Genetics Chain In this example we introduce a Markov chain which arises in genetics. We shall not discuss the model explicitly but will only point out that the states of the system correspond to genotype pairs. For details, see Feller,[2] p. 380. Also see problems 8 and 9, Exercises 10.1.

The Markov chain in question has six states (1–6) and transition matrix

$$
P = \begin{array}{c} \\ 1 \\ 2 \\ 3 \\ 4 \\ 5 \\ 6 \end{array}
\begin{array}{c} \begin{array}{cccccc} 1 & 2 & 3 & 4 & 5 & 6 \end{array} \\
\begin{bmatrix}
1 & 0 & 0 & 0 & 0 & 0 \\
\frac{1}{4} & \frac{1}{2} & \frac{1}{4} & 0 & 0 & 0 \\
\frac{1}{16} & \frac{1}{4} & \frac{1}{4} & \frac{1}{4} & \frac{1}{16} & \frac{1}{8} \\
0 & 0 & \frac{1}{4} & \frac{1}{2} & \frac{1}{4} & 0 \\
0 & 0 & 0 & 0 & 1 & 0 \\
0 & 0 & 1 & 0 & 0 & 0
\end{bmatrix}
\end{array}
\qquad (9.11.4)
$$

States 1 and 5 are absorbing (corresponding to homozygosity in the population) and all other states are nonabsorbing. Also some computations show that the two-step transition matrix is

$$
P^2 = \begin{array}{c} \\ 1 \\ 2 \\ 3 \\ 4 \\ 5 \\ 6 \end{array}
\begin{array}{c} \begin{array}{cccccc} 1 & 2 & 3 & 4 & 5 & 6 \end{array} \\
\begin{bmatrix}
1 & 0 & 0 & 0 & 0 & 0 \\
\frac{25}{64} & \frac{5}{16} & \frac{3}{16} & \frac{1}{16} & \frac{1}{64} & \frac{1}{32} \\
\frac{9}{64} & \frac{3}{16} & \frac{5}{16} & \frac{3}{16} & \frac{9}{64} & \frac{1}{32} \\
\frac{1}{64} & \frac{1}{16} & \frac{3}{16} & \frac{5}{16} & \frac{25}{64} & \frac{1}{32} \\
0 & 0 & 0 & 0 & 1 & 0 \\
\frac{1}{16} & \frac{1}{4} & \frac{1}{4} & \frac{1}{4} & \frac{1}{16} & \frac{1}{8}
\end{bmatrix}
\end{array}
\qquad (9.11.5)
$$

This makes it clear that from each nonabsorbing state it is possible to reach an absorbing state. In fact, by Eq. (9.11.5) each nonabsorbing state can reach each absorbing state in two transitions [i.e., $p_{ij}^{(2)} > 0$ for $i = 2, 3, 4, 6$ and $j = 1, 5$]. Hence this Markov chain is absorbing.

One of the fundamental results concerning absorbing Markov chains is the following theorem, which is intuitively quite reasonable. The proof is omitted.

Theorem 9.11.1
In an absorbing Markov chain the state of the system will eventually be one of the absorbing states.

This means that regardless of the initial state of the absorbing Markov chain, the state of the Markov chain will, after a finite number of transitions, be in and remain forever in one of the absorbing states.

[2]William Feller, *An Introduction to Probability Theory and Its Applications,* 3rd ed., John Wiley & Sons, Inc., New York, 1950.

Exercises for 9.11

1. Let

$$
P = \begin{array}{c} \\ 1 \\ 2 \\ 3 \\ 4 \\ 5 \end{array}
\begin{array}{c}
\begin{array}{ccccc} 1 & 2 & 3 & 4 & 5 \end{array} \\
\begin{bmatrix}
\frac{1}{3} & 0 & \frac{2}{3} & 0 & 0 \\
0 & 1 & 0 & 0 & 0 \\
\frac{1}{2} & 0 & \frac{1}{4} & \frac{1}{4} & 0 \\
0 & 1 & 0 & 0 & 0 \\
0 & 0 & 0 & 0 & 1
\end{bmatrix}
\end{array}
$$

be the transition matrix of a Markov chain with states 1, 2, 3, 4, and 5. Which of the states are absorbing states?

2. Let

$$
P = \begin{array}{c} \\ 1 \\ 2 \\ 3 \\ 4 \\ 5 \end{array}
\begin{array}{c}
\begin{array}{ccccc} 1 & 2 & 3 & 4 & 5 \end{array} \\
\begin{bmatrix}
\frac{1}{4} & 0 & \frac{1}{4} & \frac{1}{4} & \frac{1}{4} \\
0 & 1 & 0 & 0 & 0 \\
0 & 0 & 1 & 0 & 0 \\
\frac{1}{3} & 0 & \frac{1}{3} & \frac{1}{3} & 0 \\
0 & 0 & 0 & 0 & 1
\end{bmatrix}
\end{array}
$$

be the transition matrix of a Markov chain with states 1, 2, 3, 4, and 5. Which of the states are absorbing states?

3. Which of the following matrices are transition matrices for an absorbing Markov chain?

(a) $\begin{array}{c} 1 \\ 2 \end{array} \begin{array}{c} \begin{array}{cc} 1 & 2 \end{array} \\ \begin{bmatrix} \frac{1}{3} & \frac{2}{3} \\ 0 & 1 \end{bmatrix} \end{array}$

(b) $\begin{array}{c} 1 \\ 2 \\ 3 \end{array} \begin{array}{c} \begin{array}{ccc} 1 & 2 & 3 \end{array} \\ \begin{bmatrix} 1 & 0 & 0 \\ \frac{1}{2} & \frac{1}{2} & 0 \\ 0 & 0 & 1 \end{bmatrix} \end{array}$

(c) $\begin{array}{c} 1 \\ 2 \\ 3 \end{array} \begin{array}{c} \begin{array}{ccc} 1 & 2 & 3 \end{array} \\ \begin{bmatrix} 1 & 0 & 0 \\ \frac{1}{3} & \frac{1}{3} & \frac{1}{3} \\ 0 & 0 & 1 \end{bmatrix} \end{array}$

(d) $\begin{array}{c} 1 \\ 2 \\ 3 \\ 4 \end{array} \begin{array}{c} \begin{array}{cccc} 1 & 2 & 3 & 4 \end{array} \\ \begin{bmatrix} \frac{1}{3} & 0 & \frac{2}{3} & 0 \\ 0 & 1 & 0 & 0 \\ 0 & 0 & 1 & 0 \\ 1 & 0 & 0 & 0 \end{bmatrix} \end{array}$

(e) $\begin{array}{c} 1 \\ 2 \\ 3 \\ 4 \end{array} \begin{array}{c} \begin{array}{cccc} 1 & 2 & 3 & 4 \end{array} \\ \begin{bmatrix} 0 & 1 & 0 & 0 \\ 1 & 0 & 0 & 0 \\ 0 & 0 & 1 & 0 \\ \frac{1}{2} & 0 & \frac{1}{2} & 0 \end{bmatrix} \end{array}$

(f) $\begin{array}{c} 1 \\ 2 \\ 3 \\ 4 \\ 5 \end{array} \begin{array}{c} \begin{array}{ccccc} 1 & 2 & 3 & 4 & 5 \end{array} \\ \begin{bmatrix} 0 & \frac{1}{3} & 0 & \frac{1}{3} & \frac{1}{3} \\ 0 & 1 & 0 & 0 & 0 \\ \frac{1}{2} & 0 & \frac{1}{2} & 0 & 0 \\ 0 & 0 & 0 & 1 & 0 \\ 0 & 0 & \frac{1}{4} & \frac{3}{4} & 0 \end{bmatrix} \end{array}$

4. List the absorbing states of the matrices in problem 3 that are transition matrices for absorbing Markov chains.

5. (a) What are the absorbing states for the Markov chain defined in problem 12, Exercises 9.7?

(b) Is this an absorbing Markov chain?

6. A fair coin is tossed until three heads occur in a row. Let the state of the system at any given time be the number of heads that have occurred in succession up to and including that time.

(a) What are the absorbing states for this Markov chain?

(b) Is the chain absorbing?

7. (a) Is the Markov chain corresponding to the transition matrix in problem 1 absorbing?

(b) Answer the same question for the transition matrix in problem 2.

8. Consider the modified social-mobility chain defined in problem 9, Exercises 9.2.
   (a) Does this chain have any absorbing states?
   (b) Is the chain absorbing?
9. Let

$$P = \frac{1}{2}\begin{bmatrix} \overset{1}{1-p} & \overset{2}{p} \\ q & 1-q \end{bmatrix} \qquad 0 \le p \le 1, \quad 0 \le q \le 1$$

be the transition matrix of a Markov chain with states 1 and 2. For what values of p and q is P the transition matrix for an absorbing Markov chain?
10. Let i be an absorbing state for a Markov chain. Show that $p_{ii}^{(n)} = 1$ for all n.

Section 9.12 Canonical and Fundamental Matrices

In Section 9.11 the class of absorbing Markov chains was introduced. In this and subsequent sections several interesting properties of such chains will be presented.

To begin, the notion of the canonical and fundamental matrices of an absorbing Markov chain are examined.

Example 9.12.1 Gambling Consider the gambling chain of Example 9.11.1. We first rearrange its transition matrix P given in Eq. (9.11.1) by placing the absorbing states in the first two rows to get the matrix

$$
P^* =
\begin{array}{c}
\begin{array}{ccccccc} 0 & 6 & 1 & 2 & 3 & 4 & 5 \end{array} \\
\begin{array}{c} 0 \\ 6 \\ 1 \\ 2 \\ 3 \\ 4 \\ 5 \end{array}
\left[
\begin{array}{cc:ccccc}
1 & 0 & 0 & 0 & 0 & 0 & 0 \\
0 & 1 & 0 & 0 & 0 & 0 & 0 \\ \hdashline
\frac{1}{2} & 0 & 0 & \frac{1}{2} & 0 & 0 & 0 \\
0 & 0 & \frac{1}{2} & 0 & \frac{1}{2} & 0 & 0 \\
0 & 0 & 0 & \frac{1}{2} & 0 & \frac{1}{2} & 0 \\
0 & 0 & 0 & 0 & \frac{1}{2} & 0 & \frac{1}{2} \\
0 & \frac{1}{2} & 0 & 0 & 0 & \frac{1}{2} & 0
\end{array}
\right]
\end{array}
\qquad (9.12.1)
$$

The submatrix in the upper left-hand corner of P^* is the 2×2 identity matrix

$$I_2 = \begin{bmatrix} 1 & 0 \\ 0 & 1 \end{bmatrix}$$

The matrix in the upper right-hand corner is the 2×5 zero matrix

$$\theta = \begin{bmatrix} 0 & 0 & 0 & 0 & 0 \\ 0 & 0 & 0 & 0 & 0 \end{bmatrix}$$

The matrix in the lower left-hand corner is a 5×2 matrix which we denote by R:

$$R = \begin{bmatrix} \frac{1}{2} & 0 \\ 0 & 0 \\ 0 & 0 \\ 0 & 0 \\ 0 & \frac{1}{2} \end{bmatrix}$$

Finally, the matrix in the lower right-hand corner is a 5×5 matrix which we denote by Q:

$$Q = \begin{bmatrix} 0 & \frac{1}{2} & 0 & 0 & 0 \\ \frac{1}{2} & 0 & \frac{1}{2} & 0 & 0 \\ 0 & \frac{1}{2} & 0 & \frac{1}{2} & 0 \\ 0 & 0 & \frac{1}{2} & 0 & \frac{1}{2} \\ 0 & 0 & 0 & \frac{1}{2} & 0 \end{bmatrix} \tag{9.12.2}$$

The matrix Q is called the *Q-matrix* of the Markov chain.

Using the above notation we can write the matrix $P*$ in the following way:

$$P* = \begin{bmatrix} I_2 & \theta \\ R & Q \end{bmatrix} \tag{9.12.3}$$

The matrix $P*$ written in this form is called the *canonical matrix* of the Markov chain. Using the above example as motivation, the following definition is made.

Definition

Consider an absorbing Markov chain with k absorbing states. If the rows of the transition matrix P are rearranged so that the absorbing states are in the first k rows, then the new matrix $P*$ has the form

$$P* = \begin{bmatrix} I_k & \theta \\ R & Q \end{bmatrix} \tag{9.12.4}$$

The matrix $P*$ is called the *canonical matrix* of the absorbing Markov chain and the matrix Q is called the *Q-matrix* of the absorbing Markov chain.

Example 9.12.2 Genetics Consider the absorbing Markov chain introduced in Example 9.11.6. Its transition matrix is

$$P = \begin{array}{c} \\ 1 \\ 2 \\ 3 \\ 4 \\ 5 \\ 6 \end{array} \begin{array}{c} \begin{array}{cccccc} 1 & 2 & 3 & 4 & 5 & 6 \end{array} \\ \begin{bmatrix} 1 & 0 & 0 & 0 & 0 & 0 \\ \frac{1}{4} & \frac{1}{2} & \frac{1}{4} & 0 & 0 & 0 \\ \frac{1}{16} & \frac{1}{4} & \frac{1}{4} & \frac{1}{4} & \frac{1}{16} & \frac{1}{8} \\ 0 & 0 & \frac{1}{4} & \frac{1}{2} & \frac{1}{4} & 0 \\ 0 & 0 & 0 & 0 & 1 & 0 \\ 0 & 0 & 1 & 0 & 0 & 0 \end{bmatrix} \end{array}$$

It has two absorbing states, 1 and 5. The *canonical matrix* is

$$P* = \begin{array}{c} \\ 1 \\ 5 \\ 2 \\ 3 \\ 4 \\ 6 \end{array} \begin{array}{c} \begin{array}{cccccc} 1 & 5 & 2 & 3 & 4 & 6 \end{array} \\ \begin{bmatrix} 1 & 0 & 0 & 0 & 0 & 0 \\ 0 & 1 & 0 & 0 & 0 & 0 \\ \frac{1}{4} & 0 & \frac{1}{2} & \frac{1}{4} & 0 & 0 \\ \frac{1}{16} & \frac{1}{16} & \frac{1}{4} & \frac{1}{4} & \frac{1}{4} & \frac{1}{8} \\ 0 & \frac{1}{4} & 0 & \frac{1}{4} & \frac{1}{2} & 0 \\ 0 & 0 & 0 & 1 & 0 & 0 \end{bmatrix} \end{array} \tag{9.12.5}$$

444 CHAPTER 9 MARKOV CHAINS

or

$$P^* = \begin{bmatrix} I_2 & 0 \\ R & Q \end{bmatrix}$$

The Q-matrix of the Markov chain is

$$Q = \begin{bmatrix} \frac{1}{2} & \frac{1}{4} & 0 & 0 \\ \frac{1}{4} & \frac{1}{4} & \frac{1}{4} & \frac{1}{8} \\ 0 & \frac{1}{4} & \frac{1}{2} & 0 \\ 0 & 1 & 0 & 0 \end{bmatrix} \qquad (9.12.6)$$

We shall discuss several problems in relation to absorbing Markov chains. The solutions to these problems all depend on the determination of a matrix known as the fundamental matrix.

Definition

Consider an absorbing Markov chain with Q-matrix Q. Then the *fundamental matrix* of the absorbing Markov chain is the matrix

$$F = [I - Q]^{-1} \qquad (9.12.7)$$

Example 9.12.3 Gambling Consider again the gambling chain of Example 9.12.1. The Q-matrix of this Markov chain is given by Eq. (9.12.2). Hence the fundamental matrix is

$$F = [I - Q]^{-1}$$

$$= \left(\begin{bmatrix} 1 & 0 & 0 & 0 & 0 \\ 0 & 1 & 0 & 0 & 0 \\ 0 & 0 & 1 & 0 & 0 \\ 0 & 0 & 0 & 1 & 0 \\ 0 & 0 & 0 & 0 & 1 \end{bmatrix} - \begin{bmatrix} 0 & \frac{1}{2} & 0 & 0 & 0 \\ \frac{1}{2} & 0 & \frac{1}{2} & 0 & 0 \\ 0 & \frac{1}{2} & 0 & \frac{1}{2} & 0 \\ 0 & 0 & \frac{1}{2} & 0 & \frac{1}{2} \\ 0 & 0 & 0 & \frac{1}{2} & 0 \end{bmatrix} \right)^{-1}$$

$$= \begin{bmatrix} 1 & -\frac{1}{2} & 0 & 0 & 0 \\ -\frac{1}{2} & 1 & -\frac{1}{2} & 0 & 0 \\ 0 & -\frac{1}{2} & 1 & -\frac{1}{2} & 0 \\ 0 & 0 & -\frac{1}{2} & 1 & -\frac{1}{2} \\ 0 & 0 & 0 & -\frac{1}{2} & 1 \end{bmatrix}^{-1}$$

By using the techniques of Section 6.10 this can be calculated and the result is that

$$F = \begin{array}{c} \\ 1 \\ 2 \\ 3 \\ 4 \\ 5 \end{array} \begin{array}{c} \begin{array}{ccccc} 1 & 2 & 3 & 4 & 5 \end{array} \\ \begin{bmatrix} \frac{5}{3} & \frac{4}{3} & 1 & \frac{2}{3} & \frac{1}{3} \\ \frac{4}{3} & \frac{8}{3} & 2 & \frac{4}{3} & \frac{2}{3} \\ 1 & 2 & 3 & 2 & 1 \\ \frac{2}{3} & \frac{4}{3} & 2 & \frac{8}{3} & \frac{4}{3} \\ \frac{1}{3} & \frac{2}{3} & 1 & \frac{4}{3} & \frac{5}{3} \end{bmatrix} \end{array} \qquad (9.12.8)$$

Example 9.12.4 Genetics Consider the genetics chain of Example 9.12.2. Its Q-matrix is given by Eq. (9.12.6). Consequently, its fundamental matrix is

$$F = [I - Q]^{-1}$$

$$= \left(\begin{bmatrix} 1 & 0 & 0 & 0 \\ 0 & 1 & 0 & 0 \\ 0 & 0 & 1 & 0 \\ 0 & 0 & 0 & 1 \end{bmatrix} - \begin{bmatrix} \frac{1}{2} & \frac{1}{4} & 0 & 0 \\ \frac{1}{4} & \frac{1}{4} & \frac{1}{4} & \frac{1}{8} \\ 0 & \frac{1}{4} & \frac{1}{2} & 0 \\ 0 & 1 & 0 & 0 \end{bmatrix} \right)^{-1}$$

$$= \begin{bmatrix} \frac{1}{2} & -\frac{1}{4} & 0 & 0 \\ -\frac{1}{4} & \frac{3}{4} & -\frac{1}{4} & -\frac{1}{8} \\ 0 & -\frac{1}{4} & \frac{1}{2} & 0 \\ 0 & -1 & 0 & 1 \end{bmatrix}^{-1}$$

and some calculations now show that

$$F = \begin{array}{c} \\ 2 \\ 3 \\ 4 \\ 6 \end{array} \begin{array}{cccc} 2 & 3 & 4 & 6 \\ \left[\begin{array}{cccc} \frac{8}{3} & \frac{4}{3} & \frac{2}{3} & \frac{1}{6} \\ \frac{4}{3} & \frac{8}{3} & \frac{4}{3} & \frac{1}{3} \\ \frac{2}{3} & \frac{4}{3} & \frac{8}{3} & \frac{1}{6} \\ \frac{4}{3} & \frac{8}{3} & \frac{4}{3} & \frac{4}{3} \end{array} \right] \end{array} \qquad (9.12.9)$$

Exercises for 9.12

1. Let

$$P = \begin{array}{c} \\ 1 \\ 2 \\ 3 \end{array} \begin{array}{ccc} 1 & 2 & 3 \\ \left[\begin{array}{ccc} \frac{1}{4} & \frac{1}{4} & \frac{1}{2} \\ 0 & 1 & 0 \\ \frac{1}{3} & \frac{1}{3} & \frac{1}{3} \end{array} \right] \end{array}$$

(a) Show that P is the transition matrix for an absorbing Markov chain.
(b) Find the Q-matrix and the canonical matrix.

2. Let

$$P = \begin{array}{c} \\ 1 \\ 2 \\ 3 \\ 4 \end{array} \begin{array}{cccc} 1 & 2 & 3 & 4 \\ \left[\begin{array}{cccc} 1 & 0 & 0 & 0 \\ \frac{2}{3} & 0 & 0 & \frac{1}{3} \\ \frac{1}{4} & \frac{1}{4} & \frac{1}{4} & \frac{1}{4} \\ 0 & 0 & 0 & 1 \end{array} \right] \end{array}$$

(a) Show that P is the transition matrix for an absorbing Markov chain.
(b) Find the Q-matrix and the canonical matrix.

3. (a) Find the Q-matrix and the canonical matrix for the Markov chain having the matrix P in problem 1, Exercises 9.11, as its transition matrix.
   (b) Find the fundamental matrix F for this chain.

4. Find the fundamental matrix F for the Markov chain having the matrix P in problem 2 as its transition matrix.

5. A particle moves in a straight line in unit steps on a line with the positions 0, 1, 2, 3, and 4 labeled. If the particle is at 1, 2, or 3, it moves to the right one unit with probability $\frac{1}{3}$ and it moves to the left one unit with probability $\frac{2}{3}$. If the particle ever reaches 0 or 4, it stays there.

(a) Show that this is an absorbing Markov chain.

(b) Find the Q-matrix and the canonical matrix.

(c) Find the fundamental matrix F for this chain.

6. Find the fundamental matrix F for the social-mobility chain defined in problem 9, Exercises 9.2.

7. Suppose that a student attending a certain university has a probability $\frac{1}{5}$ of flunking out during a given year, a probability $\frac{1}{10}$ of having to repeat the year, and a probability $\frac{7}{10}$ of passing on to the next year. Let 1 correspond to the state "has flunked out," 2 to the state "has graduated," 3 to the state "is a senior," 4 to the state "is a junior," 5 to the state "is a sophomore," and 6 to the state "is a freshman."

(a) Find the transition matrix for this Markov chain.

(b) Verify that the chain is absorbing.

(c) Find the Q-matrix and the canonical matrix for this chain.

(d) Find the fundamental matrix F.

8. (a) Find the Q-matrix and the canonical matrix for the absorbing Markov chain defined in problem 6, Exercises 9.11.

(b) Find the fundamental matrix F.

Section 9.13   Probabilities of Absorption

As we indicated in the preceding section, the fundamental matrix can be used to solve several interesting problems concerning absorbing Markov chains. Here we consider only one such problem.

Recall that, by Theorem 9.11.1, in an absorbing chain the state of the system will eventually be (and henceforth remain in) one of the absorbing states. Of course, if the system is initially in one of the absorbing states, it will remain there. However, if it is originally in a nonabsorbing state, it will eventually end up in one of the absorbing states (Theorem 9.11.1). A natural question is, therefore: Given that the state of the Markov chain is initially a certain nonabsorbing state, what probabilities are associated with eventually being in each of the absorbing states? The answer is contained in the following theorem.

Theorem 9.13.1

Consider an absorbing Markov chain with k absorbing states, canonical matrix

$$P^* = \begin{bmatrix} I_k & \theta \\ R & Q \end{bmatrix}$$

and fundamental matrix $F = [I - Q]^{-1}$. Let A be the product of F with R:

$$A = FR \tag{9.13.1}$$

Then the i-j entry of A (i.e., a_{ij}) gives the probability of the state of the system eventually being the absorbing state j given that the initial state of the system is the nonabsorbing state i. A is called the *matrix of absorption probabilities*.

Example 9.13.1   Gambling   We again consider the gambling chain of Example 9.12.1. The canonical matrix is given in Eq. (9.12.1) and the fundamental matrix in Eq. (9.12.8). We have

$$F = \begin{array}{c c} & \begin{array}{c c c c c} 1 & 2 & 3 & 4 & 5 \end{array} \\ \begin{array}{c} 1 \\ 2 \\ 3 \\ 4 \\ 5 \end{array} & \left[\begin{array}{c c c c c} \frac{5}{3} & \frac{4}{3} & 1 & \frac{2}{3} & \frac{1}{3} \\ \frac{4}{3} & \frac{8}{3} & 2 & \frac{4}{3} & \frac{2}{3} \\ 1 & 2 & 3 & 2 & 1 \\ \frac{2}{3} & \frac{4}{3} & 2 & \frac{8}{3} & \frac{4}{3} \\ \frac{1}{3} & \frac{2}{3} & 1 & \frac{4}{3} & \frac{5}{3} \end{array} \right] \end{array}$$

and

$$R = \begin{array}{c c} & \begin{array}{c c} 0 & 6 \end{array} \\ \begin{array}{c} 1 \\ 2 \\ 3 \\ 4 \\ 5 \end{array} & \left[\begin{array}{c c} \frac{1}{2} & 0 \\ 0 & 0 \\ 0 & 0 \\ 0 & 0 \\ 0 & \frac{1}{2} \end{array} \right] \end{array}$$

Consequently,

$$A = FR = \begin{array}{c c} & \begin{array}{c c} 0 & 6 \end{array} \\ \begin{array}{c} 1 \\ 2 \\ 3 \\ 4 \\ 5 \end{array} & \left[\begin{array}{c c} \frac{5}{6} & \frac{1}{6} \\ \frac{2}{3} & \frac{1}{3} \\ \frac{1}{2} & \frac{1}{2} \\ \frac{1}{3} & \frac{2}{3} \\ \frac{1}{6} & \frac{5}{6} \end{array} \right] \end{array} \qquad (9.13.2)$$

So, for example, if the state of the system is originally 2, the probability that the state of the system is eventually 6 is $\frac{1}{3}$ [see Eq. (9.13.2)].

Interpreting this in gambling terminology we have the following (see Example 9.2.3). Let the combined capital of two players (I and II) be \$6. Assume that the players bet \$1 at a time and each player is equally likely to win at each bet. Also assume that the state of the system at any given time is the capital of player I at that time.

That the state of the system is eventually 0 corresponds to the result that player I goes broke, and that the state of the system is eventually 6 corresponds to the result that player II goes broke.

Then, for example, it follows from Theorem 9.13.1 and Eq. (9.13.2) that if player I's initial capital is \$2, the probability that he breaks player II is $\frac{1}{3}$. As another example, if player I's initial capital is \$5, the probability that player I goes broke is $\frac{1}{6}$ [see Eq. (9.13.2)]. This corresponds to the probability of beginning in the nonabsorbing state 5 and eventually being in the absorbing state 0.

The probability of eventual absorption into state 0 is called the probability of the *gambler's ruin* (for player I). In this case the probabilities of the gambler's ruin with various initial capitals (initial states of the system) are given by the entries in the first column of the matrix A in Eq. (9.13.2). Notice that, of course, the second column of A gives the gambler's ruin probabilities for player II.

In Section 10.6 we shall present an alternative, more efficient method for calculating the gambler's ruin probabilities.

Example 9.13.2 Genetics From Eqs. (9.12.9) and (9.12.5) we see that the fundamental matrix of the genetics chain is

$$F = \begin{array}{c} \\ 2 \\ 3 \\ 4 \\ 6 \end{array} \begin{array}{cccc} 2 & 3 & 4 & 6 \\ \begin{bmatrix} \frac{8}{3} & \frac{4}{3} & \frac{2}{3} & \frac{1}{6} \\ \frac{4}{3} & \frac{8}{3} & \frac{4}{3} & \frac{1}{3} \\ \frac{2}{3} & \frac{4}{3} & \frac{8}{3} & \frac{1}{6} \\ \frac{4}{3} & \frac{8}{3} & \frac{4}{3} & \frac{4}{3} \end{bmatrix} \end{array}$$

and the R-matrix is

$$R = \begin{array}{c} \\ 2 \\ 3 \\ 4 \\ 6 \end{array} \begin{array}{cc} 1 & 5 \\ \begin{bmatrix} \frac{1}{4} & 0 \\ \frac{1}{16} & \frac{1}{16} \\ 0 & \frac{1}{4} \\ 0 & 0 \end{bmatrix} \end{array}$$

Thus the matrix A of absorption probabilities is

$$A = FR = \begin{bmatrix} \frac{8}{3} & \frac{4}{3} & \frac{2}{3} & \frac{1}{6} \\ \frac{4}{3} & \frac{8}{3} & \frac{4}{3} & \frac{1}{3} \\ \frac{2}{3} & \frac{4}{3} & \frac{8}{3} & \frac{1}{6} \\ \frac{4}{3} & \frac{8}{3} & \frac{4}{3} & \frac{4}{3} \end{bmatrix} \begin{bmatrix} \frac{1}{4} & 0 \\ \frac{1}{16} & \frac{1}{16} \\ 0 & \frac{1}{4} \\ 0 & 0 \end{bmatrix}$$

$$= \begin{array}{c} \\ 2 \\ 3 \\ 4 \\ 6 \end{array} \begin{array}{cc} 1 & 5 \\ \begin{bmatrix} \frac{3}{4} & \frac{1}{4} \\ \frac{1}{2} & \frac{1}{2} \\ \frac{1}{4} & \frac{3}{4} \\ \frac{1}{2} & \frac{1}{2} \end{bmatrix} \end{array} \qquad (9.13.3)$$

For example, if the initial state is 4, the probability of absorption into state 5 is $\frac{3}{4}$.

As in the previous example, the first column of A gives the probabilities of absorption into state 1 starting from the various nonabsorbing states, and the second column of A gives the probabilities of absorption into state 5, starting from the various nonabsorbing states.

In Section 10.5 another application of the fundamental matrix is presented in the context of paired associate learning.

Exercises for 9.13

1. Find the matrix of absorption probabilities for the absorbing Markov chain having

$$P = \begin{array}{c} \\ 1 \\ 2 \\ 3 \end{array} \begin{array}{ccc} 1 & 2 & 3 \\ \begin{bmatrix} 1 & 0 & 0 \\ \frac{1}{2} & 0 & \frac{1}{2} \\ 0 & 0 & 1 \end{bmatrix} \end{array}$$

as its transition matrix.

2. Let

$$P = \begin{array}{c} \\ 1 \\ 2 \\ 3 \\ 4 \end{array} \begin{array}{cccc} 1 & 2 & 3 & 4 \\ \begin{bmatrix} 1 & 0 & 0 & 0 \\ \frac{2}{3} & 0 & 0 & \frac{1}{3} \\ \frac{1}{4} & \frac{1}{4} & \frac{1}{4} & \frac{1}{4} \\ 0 & 0 & 0 & 1 \end{bmatrix} \end{array}$$

be the transition matrix for an absorbing Markov chain.

(a) Find the matrix of absorption probabilities.

(b) If the state of the system is originally 2, find the probability that the state of the system is eventually 4.

3. Four boys 1, 2, 3, and 4, are playing catch with a frisbee. If 1 receives the frisbee, he does not keep it but throws it to 2, 3, or 4 with equal probability. If 3 receives the frisbee, he also does not keep it, but throws it to 1 or 4 with equal probability. However, if either 2 or 4 receive the frisbee, they keep it.

(a) Find the matrix of absorption probabilities for the above process.

(b) Given that 3 originally has the frisbee, what is the probability that 4 eventually gets the frisbee?

(c) Given that 1 originally has the frisbee, what is the probability that 2 eventually gets the frisbee?

4. Two men, I and II, decide to play pool. They agree to bet $1 on each game. From past experience I has determined that he has probability $\frac{2}{3}$ of winning each game. He has $3 and decides to play until he has a total of $5 or has lost all his money. Let the state of the system at any given time be the capital of I at that time.

(a) Find the probability that I loses all his money.

(b) Find the probability that I wins $2.

5. In problem 4, suppose that the combined capital of the two men is $5, and they agree to play until either one is broke. Again, let the state of the system at any given time be the capital of I at that time.

(a) If I has initial capital of $2, what is the probability that he goes broke?

(b) If I has initial capital of $3, what is the probability that II goes broke?

(c) If II has initial capital of $4, what is the probability that I goes broke?

6. (a) Find the matrix of absorption probabilities for the social-mobility chain of problem 9, Exercises 9.2.

(b) If a father is lower class, what is the probability that the male line dies out in his family?

(c) If a father is upper class, what is the probability that the male line dies out in his family?

7. (a) Find the matrix of absorption probabilities for the Markov chain defined in problem 7, Exercises 9.12.

(b) What is the probability that a freshman will flunk out before he graduates?

(c) What is the probability that a sophomore will go on to graduate?

(d) What year must a student reach before he has a better-than-even chance of graduating?

Applications of Probability and Markov Chains

10

In this chapter we shall present several applications of probability and Markov chains to various subject areas. The first application is to genetics, the second application is to queuing (waiting-line) theory, the third application is to psychology, and the fourth application is to gambling.

We emphasize that these applications are just a few of the countless possible ones that could be presented, and, as mentioned previously, the number of applications of probability and Markov chains is increasing continually.

Section 10.1 Some Applications to Genetics

We consider, in this section and the next, some applications of probability and Markov chains to genetics. Certain characteristics in plants and animals are determined by a pair of genes, each of which may be of two types. We denote these types by A and a. There are three genotypes: AA, Aa, and aa. (The genotypes Aa and aA are the same.) In some instances these three genotypes result in three distinguishable characteristics, and in others the AA and Aa exhibit the same observable form. In the latter situation the A gene is said to *dominate* the a gene. Here an individual is called *dominant* with respect to the characteristic if he has the AA genotype, *heterozygous* if he has the Aa genotype, and *recessive* if he has the aa genotype.

As a matter of convenience, we will, in any case, denote an AA individual by D, an Aa by H, and an aa by R.

In a mating situation the offspring inherits one gene from each parent and we assume that an offspring is equally likely to inherit either one of the two genes from a particular parent. Furthermore, we assume that the gene inherited from one parent does not affect the gene inherited from the other parent (i.e., the gene inherited from one parent is independent of the gene inherited from the other parent).

Example 10.1.1 Assume that the mating parents are D and H. That is, one parent is AA and the other is Aa. Then the offspring can be either D or H, but not R. The probabilities associated with these two events can be obtained by using the tree diagram in Figure 10.1.1. Thus there is equal probability that the offspring of such parents will be D or H.

Figure 10.1.1

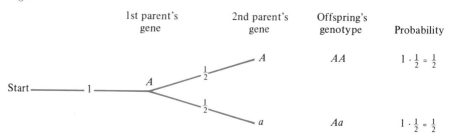

We remark that the above probabilities can also be computed directly by using the laws of probability and the assumptions discussed in the paragraph preceding this example.

Example 10.1.2 Suppose that the mating parents are both H. Then the offspring of such parents can be D, H, or R. The corresponding probabilities can be determined by consulting the tree diagram of Figure 10.1.2. The probability that the offspring

Figure 10.1.2

1st parent's gene	2nd parent's gene	Offspring's genotype	Probability
A	A	AA	$\frac{1}{2} \cdot \frac{1}{2} = \frac{1}{4}$
	a	Aa	$\frac{1}{2} \cdot \frac{1}{2} = \frac{1}{4}$
a	A	Aa	$\frac{1}{2} \cdot \frac{1}{2} = \frac{1}{4}$
	a	aa	$\frac{1}{2} \cdot \frac{1}{2} = \frac{1}{4}$

of such parents is D or R is $\frac{1}{4}$ each. Since the offspring can be H in two mutually exclusive ways, each with probability $\frac{1}{4}$, it follows, from the addition principle of probability, that there is probability $\frac{1}{2}$ that the offspring is H.

We leave it as an exercise (problem 1, Exercises 10.1) for the reader to show that if one parent is H and the other R, then the offspring is H with probability $\frac{1}{2}$ and R with probability $\frac{1}{2}$.

Example 10.1.3   Suppose that we consider an experiment of continued mating described as follows. At time 0 an individual is mated with an H individual. At time 1 the offspring of this mating is again mated with an H individual. The process is then repeated in the same manner. If we let the state of the system at time n be the genotype of the nth offspring, we obtain a Markov chain with three states.

From Examples 10.1.1 and 10.1.2 and problem 1, Exercises 10.1, it follows that the transition matrix for this Markov chain is

$$P = \begin{array}{c} \\ \\ \end{array} \begin{array}{ccc} D & H & R \\ \left[\begin{array}{ccc} \frac{1}{2} & \frac{1}{2} & 0 \\ \frac{1}{4} & \frac{1}{2} & \frac{1}{4} \\ 0 & \frac{1}{2} & \frac{1}{2} \end{array}\right] \end{array} \tag{10.1.1}$$

Notice that we have not specified the genotype of the individual mated with the H individual at time zero. That is, we have not specified the initial distribution of the Markov chain. It will not be necessary for us to do this at the moment.

Now, the two-step transition matrix for this Markov chain is

$$P^2 = P \cdot P = \begin{array}{c} D \\ H \\ R \end{array} \begin{array}{ccc} D & H & R \\ \left[\begin{array}{ccc} \frac{3}{8} & \frac{1}{2} & \frac{1}{8} \\ \frac{1}{4} & \frac{1}{2} & \frac{1}{4} \\ \frac{1}{8} & \frac{1}{2} & \frac{3}{8} \end{array}\right] \end{array}$$

which has all positive entries. Consequently, this Markov chain is regular and hence has an equilibrium distribution.

To determine the equilibrium distribution we proceed as usual to find a probability vector $V = [v_1, v_2, v_3]$ such that $VP = P$. The corresponding system of equations is

$$\begin{aligned}
\tfrac{1}{2}v_1 + \tfrac{1}{4}v_2 \qquad\quad &= v_1 \\
\tfrac{1}{2}v_1 + \tfrac{1}{2}v_2 + \tfrac{1}{2}v_3 &= v_2 \\
\tfrac{1}{4}v_2 + \tfrac{1}{2}v_3 &= v_3 \\
v_1 + v_2 + v_3 &= 1
\end{aligned}$$

In other words,

$$\begin{aligned}
-\tfrac{1}{2}v_1 + \tfrac{1}{4}v_2 \qquad\quad &= 0 \\
\tfrac{1}{2}v_1 - \tfrac{1}{2}v_2 + \tfrac{1}{2}v_3 &= 0 \\
\tfrac{1}{4}v_2 - \tfrac{1}{2}v_3 &= 0 \\
v_1 + v_2 + v_3 &= 1
\end{aligned}$$

Using Gaussian elimination we find that $v_1 = \frac{1}{4}$, $v_2 = \frac{1}{2}$, $v_3 = \frac{1}{4}$.

Thus, the equilibrium distribution is $V = [\frac{1}{4}, \frac{1}{2}, \frac{1}{4}]$. In other words, regardless of the genotype of the individual originally mated with the H individual, the probabilities of the various genotypes for the nth offspring (for large n) are given approximately by $\frac{1}{4}$ for D, $\frac{1}{2}$ for H, and $\frac{1}{4}$ for R.

Exercises for 10.1

1. (a) Assume that the mating parents are H and R. Show that the offspring is either H or R but cannot be D. Also, compute the probability that the offspring is (1) H, (2) R.
   (b) What is the situation if the mating parents are (1) D and R, (2) D and D, (3) R and R?

2. Refer to Example 10.1.3.
   (a) If the individual initially mated with the H individual is D, find the probability that the second offspring is D.
   (b) If the individual initially mated with the H individual is R, find the probability that the second offspring is D.
3. Refer to Example 10.1.3.
   (a) Find the three-step transition matrix for the Markov chain.
   (b) If the individual mated with the H individual at time 0 is H, find the probability that the third offspring is (1) D, (2) H, (3) R.
4. In Example 10.1.3 suppose that the individual who is to be mated with the H individual initially is chosen at random from a population in which 20 percent of the individuals are D, 70 percent are H, and 10 percent are R.
   (a) What is the initial distribution of the Markov chain?
   (b) Find the probability that the second offspring is (1) D, (2) H, (3) R.
   (c) What is the distribution of the Markov chain at the third generation (i.e., time 3)?
5. Suppose that in Example 10.1.3 the individual who is to be initially mated with the H individual has probability $\frac{1}{4}$ of being D and $\frac{3}{4}$ of being R.
   (a) What is the initial distribution of the Markov chain?
   (b) Determine the probability that the second offspring is (1) D, (2) H, (3) R.
   (c) What is the distribution of the Markov chain at time 3?
6. Suppose that Example 10.1.3 is modified so that instead of mating the individuals with an H individual each time, we mate them with a D individual each time.
   (a) Find the transition matrix for this Markov chain.
   (b) Determine the two- and three-step transition matrices for this Markov chain.
   (c) Show that this Markov chain is absorbing.
   (d) If the individual originally mated with the D individual is H, find the probability that the second offspring is (1) D, (2) H, (3) R.
   (e) If the individual originally mated with the D individual is chosen at random from a population in which 30 percent are D, 20 percent are H, and 50 percent are R, find the probability that the third offspring is (1) D, (2) H, (3) R.
7. If in Example 10.1.3 we use an R individual as the fixed mate instead of an H individual, answer (a)–(e) of problem 6.
*8. Suppose that we begin at time zero with two individuals of opposite sex and mate them. We then select, independently and at random, two offspring of these individuals and mate them. The process is then continued in this manner. Let the state of the system at time n be the pair of genotypes of the offspring selected to mate at that time. For example, if the original individuals are D and H, the state of the system at time 0 is (D, H) [or (H, D)]. We then obtain a Markov chain with six states for which the following correspondence is made:

   1—(D, D) 4—(H, H)
   2—(D, H) 5—(H, R)
   3—(D, R) 6—(R, R)

   (a) Find the transition matrix for this Markov chain.
   (b) What are the absorbing states?
   (c) Show that this Markov chain is absorbing.
   (d) Determine the two-step transition matrix for this Markov chain.
   (e) If the original individuals are both H, find the probability that the individuals selected to mate at the second generation are both H.
9. This is a continuation of problem 8.
   (a) Determine the canonical matrix of the Markov chain.
   (b) What is the fundamental matrix?
   (c) Find the matrix of absorption probabilities.
   (d) If the original individuals are H and R, what is the probability of eventually being in state 1?

Section 10.2 The Hardy–Weinberg Theorem

We continue our investigation of the genetics model introduced in Section 10.1. In Example 10.1.3 we considered a mating situation in which the genotype of one of the parents was fixed (namely, H). In this section we study the case in which both parents' genotypes are allowed to vary.

Specifically, we assume that in a large population:

1. The proportions of genotypes are the same for both males and females.
2. The mating is done at random.

Example 10.2.1 Suppose that the genotype proportions are initially (generation 0) $\frac{1}{6}$, $\frac{1}{3}$, and $\frac{1}{2}$ for D, H, and R, respectively. Let d_n, h_n, and r_n be the proportions of D, H, and R, respectively, in the nth generation. (Note, for example, that d_n can be interpreted as the probability of selecting a D individual from the nth generation.) So, by assumption,

$$d_0 = \tfrac{1}{6} \qquad h_0 = \tfrac{1}{3} \qquad r_0 = \tfrac{1}{2} \tag{10.2.1}$$

Figure 10.2.1

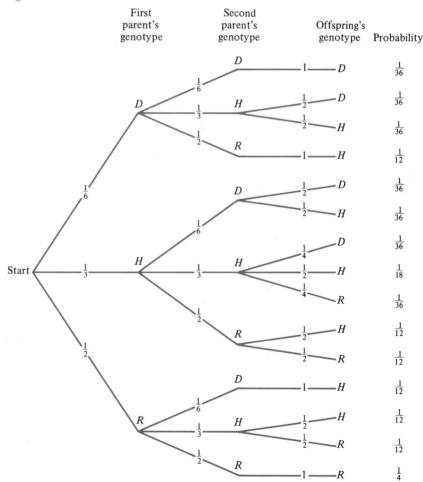

Using assumptions 1 and 2 along with results from Section 10.1 (see Examples 10.1.1 and 10.1.2 and problem 1, Exercises 10.1) we construct in Figure 10.2.1 a tree diagram to obtain the genotype proportions in the first generation. Adding the probabilities for the D, those for the H, and those for the R, we find that the genotype proportions in the first generation are given by

$$d_1 = \tfrac{1}{9} \qquad h_1 = \tfrac{4}{9} \qquad r_1 = \tfrac{4}{9} \tag{10.2.2}$$

Comparing Eqs. (10.2.1) and (10.2.2) we see that the genotype proportions have changed from the initial generation.

To determine the genotype proportions in the second generation we simply repeat the above procedure (see Figure 10.2.2). Adding the probabilities for the D, those

Figure 10.2.2

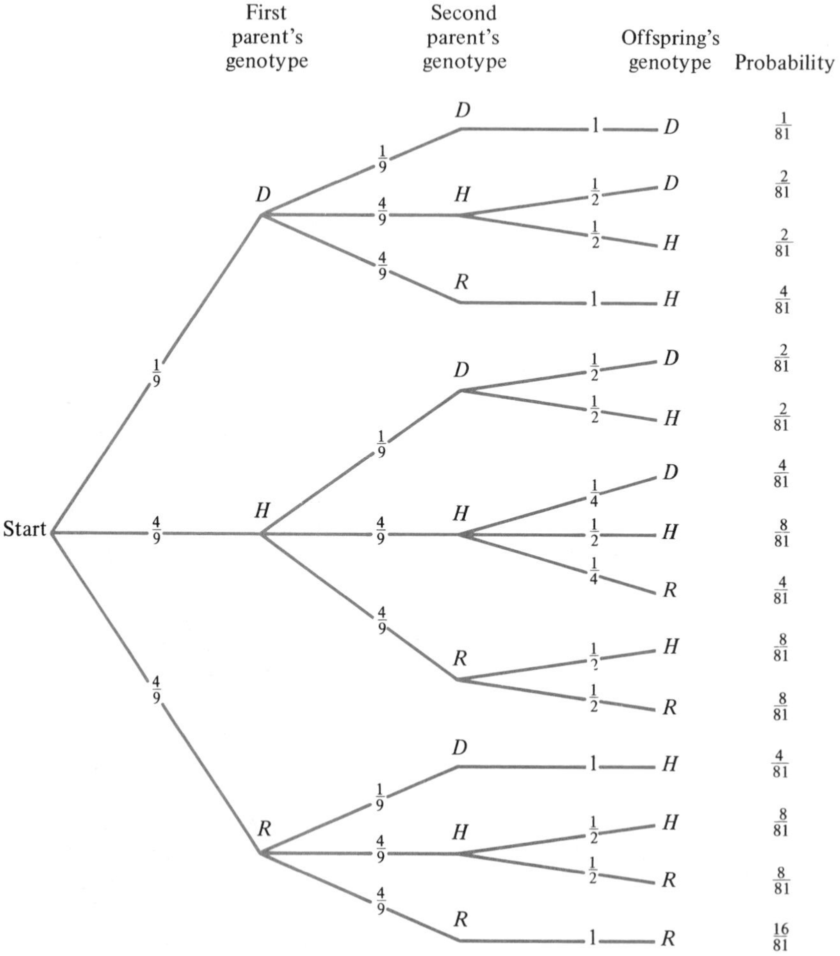

	First parent's genotype	Second parent's genotype	Offspring's genotype	Probability

for the H, and those for the R, we find that the genotype proportions in the second generation are

$$d_2 = \tfrac{1}{9} \qquad h_2 = \tfrac{4}{9} \qquad r_2 = \tfrac{4}{9} \tag{10.2.3}$$

Now, here is the crucial point: comparing Eqs. (10.2.2) and (10.2.3), we see that the genotype proportions have remained unchanged from the first to the second generations. Moreover, it is clear because of this that the tree diagram for obtaining the genotype proportions for the third generation from the second will be exactly the same as the one in Figure 10.2.2.

We conclude that in this case the genotype proportions remain unchanged after the first generation and in fact are given by Eq. (10.2.2).

The result obtained in Example 10.2.1 is typical of the general situation, as the following (Hardy–Weinberg) theorem indicates.

Theorem 10.2.1

Assume that 1 and 2 hold. Then the genotype proportions remain unchanged after one generation. That is, for $n \geq 1$,

$$d_n = d_1 \qquad h_n = h_1 \qquad r_n = r_1$$

The proof of this theorem follows exactly the same procedure as in Example 10.2.1. The only alteration is to use arbitrary d_0, h_0, and r_0 instead of the specified ones in Eq. (10.2.1). See problems 4 and 5, Exercises 10.2.

Exercises for 10.2

1. If the initial genotype proportions are given by $d_0 = \frac{1}{4}$, $h_0 = \frac{5}{8}$, and $r_0 = \frac{1}{8}$:
   (a) Determine the genotype proportions in the first generation. (*Hint:* Use the tree-diagram method of Example 10.2.1.)
   (b) What are the genotype proportions in the second generation?
2. Repeat the previous problem if $d_0 = \frac{2}{5}$, $h_0 = \frac{3}{5}$, and $r_0 = 0$.
3. Determine values for d_0, h_0, and r_0 so that the genotype proportions remain unchanged from the zeroth to the first generation.
*4. Use a tree-diagram argument to show that in general

$$d_1 = [d_0 + (h_0/2)]^2$$
$$h_1 = 2[d_0 + (h_0/2)][r_0 + (h_0/2)]$$
$$r_1 = [r_0 + (h_0/2)]^2$$

and, in fact, for $n \geq 1$,

$$d_n = [d_{n-1} + (h_{n-1}/2)]^2$$
$$h_n = 2[d_{n-1} + (h_{n-1}/2)][r_{n-1} + (h_{n-1}/2)]$$
$$r_n = [r_{n-1} + (h_{n-1}/2)]^2$$

*5. Use the result of problem 4 to verify that $d_2 = d_1$, $h_2 = h_1$, and $r_2 = r_1$. Conclude that Theorem 10.2.1 is valid.
6. Use the results of problem 4 to obtain Eqs. (10.2.2) and (10.2.3).
7. By applying problem 4, solve problem 1 without resorting to a tree diagram.
8. Solve problem 2 without using a tree diagram but by applying the results of problem 4.

Section 10.3   Application of Regular Markov Chains to Queuing Theory

In this section an application of the theory of regular Markov chains will be given to the theory of queues.

Example 10.3.1 Queuing Theory Markov chains have many applications to waiting-line (queuing) theory. Only a simplified case of the general situation will be presented here. However, the illustration will give the reader the flavor of the subject. Examples of queuing problems are numerous. Some typical ones are people arriving at a teller's window in a bank, waiting in line at a theater, sitting in the waiting room in a doctor's office, and waiting in line at a checkout stand in a supermarket.

Suppose that the length of the line at a particular checkout stand in a supermarket is observed at time intervals of 1 minute. The following assumptions will be made for the sake of simplicity.

During a time period of 1 minute *at most* one person (0 or 1) arrives at the checkout stand. The probability that no one arrives is $\frac{3}{4}$ and the probability that one person arrives is $\frac{1}{4}$. The probabilities are assumed to be independent of other arrivals.

If at the beginning of a time period a person is being served, it is supposed that the probability is $\frac{3}{10}$ that the person will be "checked out" by the beginning of the next time period (i.e., in the next minute) and that this probability is independent of the previous number of time units of service and of arrivals.

It is also assumed that no more than one person can be served in a single time period and that a customer cannot be checked out in the time period in which he arrives.

The manager of the market has observed that if more than five people are at the checkout stand, it is difficult for other customers to do their shopping because the people in line block the passageway between aisles. Therefore, the manager does not allow more than five people to be at this checkout stand during any one time period. In other words, if at the beginning of a time period there are five people at the checkout stand, no one is allowed to get in line at this stand during that time period.

As we have indicated, the above assumptions are made for the sake of simplicity. Much more complicated situations can be handled.

The case in point can be analyzed by using the theory of Markov chains. At the beginning of any time period the state of the system is considered to be the number of people waiting at the checkout stand, including the person who is in the process of being served.

The assumptions imply that this system is a Markov chain with six states. For at the beginning of a time period either 0, 1, 2, 3, 4, or 5 people are at the checkout stand (remember, no more than five people are permitted at this checkout stand). From the data given it is not too difficult to see that the transition matrix for this Markov chain is

$$P = \begin{array}{c c} & \begin{array}{cccccc} 0 & 1 & 2 & 3 & 4 & 5 \end{array} \\ \begin{array}{c} 0 \\ 1 \\ 2 \\ 3 \\ 4 \\ 5 \end{array} & \left[\begin{array}{cccccc} \frac{3}{4} & \frac{1}{4} & 0 & 0 & 0 & 0 \\ \frac{9}{40} & \frac{24}{40} & \frac{7}{40} & 0 & 0 & 0 \\ 0 & \frac{9}{40} & \frac{24}{40} & \frac{7}{40} & 0 & 0 \\ 0 & 0 & \frac{9}{40} & \frac{24}{40} & \frac{7}{40} & 0 \\ 0 & 0 & 0 & \frac{9}{40} & \frac{24}{40} & \frac{7}{40} \\ 0 & 0 & 0 & 0 & \frac{3}{10} & \frac{7}{10} \end{array} \right] \end{array}$$

For example, to show that $p_{00} = \frac{3}{4}$, just notice that a transition from state 0 to state 0 in one time period can occur if and only if no people arrive at the checkout stand during the time period. By assumption this event has probability $\frac{3}{4}$.

To show that $p_{54} = \frac{3}{10}$, observe that a transition from state 5 to state 4 in one time period occurs if and only if a person is served during the time period and this has probability $\frac{3}{10}$.

Now, $p_{23} = \frac{7}{40}$, because a transition from state 2 to state 3 can occur in one time period if and only if one person arrives and no person is served. The event E that one person arrives has probability $\frac{1}{4}$ and the event F that no one is served has probability $\frac{7}{10}$. The event that one person arrives and no person is served is $E \cap F$. By assumption E and F are independent, so

$$p_{23} = \Pr(E \cap F) = \Pr(E)\Pr(F) = \tfrac{1}{4} \cdot \tfrac{7}{10} = \tfrac{7}{40}$$

As a final illustration we indicate how to obtain $p_{33} = \frac{24}{40}$. A transition from state 3 to state 3 in one time period can occur in *two mutually exclusive* ways.

1. One person arrives and one person is served.
2. No one arrives and no one is served.

Let A be the first event and B be the second. To calculate $\Pr(A)$, let

$$E = \text{event one person arrives}$$
$$G = \text{event one person is served}$$

Then $A = E \cap G$. By assumption, E and G are independent, $\Pr(E) = \frac{1}{4}$, and $\Pr(G) = \frac{3}{10}$. Consequently,

$$\Pr(A) = \Pr(E)\Pr(G) = \tfrac{1}{4} \cdot \tfrac{3}{10} = \tfrac{3}{40}$$

A similar argument shows that

$$\Pr(B) = \tfrac{3}{4} \cdot \tfrac{7}{10} = \tfrac{21}{40}$$

Since A and B are mutually exclusive ($A \cap B = \varnothing$), it follows that

$$p_{33} = \Pr(A \cup B) = \Pr(A) + \Pr(B) = \tfrac{3}{40} + \tfrac{21}{40} = \tfrac{24}{40}$$

The other transition probabilities are calculated in a similar way.

The first six powers of the transition matrix are (to five decimal places):

$$P = \begin{bmatrix}
.75000 & .25000 & .00000 & .00000 & .00000 & .00000 \\
.22500 & .60000 & .17500 & .00000 & .00000 & .00000 \\
.00000 & .22500 & .60000 & .17500 & .00000 & .00000 \\
.00000 & .00000 & .22500 & .60000 & .17500 & .00000 \\
.00000 & .00000 & .00000 & .22500 & .60000 & .17500 \\
.00000 & .00000 & .00000 & .00000 & .30000 & .70000
\end{bmatrix}$$

$$P^2 = \begin{bmatrix}
.61875 & .33750 & .04375 & .00000 & .00000 & .00000 \\
.30375 & .45562 & .21000 & .03062 & .00000 & .00000 \\
.05062 & .27000 & .43875 & .21000 & .03062 & .00000 \\
.00000 & .05062 & .27000 & .43875 & .21000 & .03062 \\
.00000 & .00000 & .05062 & .27000 & .45187 & .22750 \\
.00000 & .00000 & .00000 & .06750 & .39000 & .54250
\end{bmatrix}$$

$$P^3 = \begin{bmatrix}
.54000 & .36703 & .08531 & .00766 & .00000 & .00000 \\
.33033 & .39656 & .21262 & .05512 & .00536 & .00000 \\
.09872 & .27337 & .35775 & .20967 & .05512 & .00536 \\
.01139 & .09112 & .26958 & .35775 & .21197 & .05819 \\
.00000 & .01139 & .09112 & .27253 & .38662 & .23833 \\
.00000 & .00000 & .01519 & .12825 & .40856 & .44800
\end{bmatrix}$$

$$P^4 = \begin{bmatrix} .48758 & .37441 & .11714 & .01952 & .00134 & .00000 \\ .33697 & .36836 & .20938 & .07149 & .01286 & .00094 \\ .13555 & .26920 & .30967 & .20081 & .07138 & .01340 \\ .02905 & .11818 & .25819 & .30952 & .20724 & .007783 \\ .00256 & .02734 & .11799 & .26646 & .35117 & .23449 \\ .00000 & .00342 & .03797 & .17153 & .40198 & .38510 \end{bmatrix}$$

$$P^5 = \begin{bmatrix} .44993 & .37290 & .14020 & .03252 & .00422 & .00023 \\ .33561 & .35237 & .20617 & .08243 & .02051 & .00291 \\ .16223 & .26508 & .27809 & .19074 & .08199 & .02187 \\ .04837 & .13626 & .24524 & .27752 & .20186 & .09075 \\ .00807 & .04359 & .13553 & .25953 & .32768 & .22560 \\ .00077 & .01059 & .06197 & .20001 & .38674 & .33992 \end{bmatrix}$$

$$P^6 = \begin{bmatrix} .42135 & .36777 & .15669 & .04499 & .00829 & .00090 \\ .33099 & .34171 & .20392 & .09015 & .02760 & .00562 \\ .18132 & .26218 & .25616 & .18156 & .08913 & .02966 \\ .06694 & .14903 & .23343 & .25485 & .19691 & .09885 \\ .01586 & .05867 & .14734 & .25317 & .30970 & .21526 \\ .00296 & .02049 & .08404 & .21787 & .36902 & .30562 \end{bmatrix}$$

Notice that P^5 has no zero entries, so the transition matrix of this Markov chain is regular. Consequently, according to Theorem 9.9.1 the Markov chain has an equilibrium distribution V. In this case the entries of the vector V represent the long-run probabilities of the length of the line at the checkout stand.

By Theorem 9.9.2, to obtain V it is only necessary to solve the matrix equation

$$VP = V$$

Letting $V = [v_0, v_1, v_2, v_3, v_4, v_5]$, this equation can be written as

$$[v_0, v_1, v_2, v_3, v_4, v_5] \begin{bmatrix} \frac{3}{4} & \frac{1}{4} & 0 & 0 & 0 & 0 \\ \frac{9}{40} & \frac{24}{40} & \frac{7}{40} & 0 & 0 & 0 \\ 0 & \frac{9}{40} & \frac{24}{40} & \frac{7}{40} & 0 & 0 \\ 0 & 0 & \frac{9}{40} & \frac{24}{40} & \frac{7}{40} & 0 \\ 0 & 0 & 0 & \frac{9}{40} & \frac{24}{40} & \frac{7}{40} \\ 0 & 0 & 0 & 0 & \frac{3}{10} & \frac{7}{10} \end{bmatrix} = [v_0, v_1, v_2, v_3, v_4, v_5]$$

Multiplying these matrices and setting corresponding entries equal yields the system of equations

$$\begin{aligned} \tfrac{3}{4}v_0 + \tfrac{9}{40}v_1 & = v_0 \\ \tfrac{1}{4}v_0 + \tfrac{24}{40}v_1 + \tfrac{9}{40}v_2 & = v_1 \\ \tfrac{7}{40}v_1 + \tfrac{24}{40}v_2 + \tfrac{9}{40}v_3 & = v_2 \\ \tfrac{7}{40}v_2 + \tfrac{24}{40}v_3 + \tfrac{9}{40}v_4 & = v_3 \\ \tfrac{7}{40}v_3 + \tfrac{24}{40}v_4 + \tfrac{3}{10}v_5 & = v_4 \\ \tfrac{7}{40}v_4 + \tfrac{7}{10}v_5 & = v_5 \end{aligned}$$

Combining terms and appending the equation $v_0 + v_1 + v_2 + v_3 + v_4 + v_5 = 1$ (V is a probability vector) gives

$$-\tfrac{1}{4}v_0 + \tfrac{9}{40}v_1 = 0$$
$$\tfrac{1}{4}v_0 - \tfrac{16}{40}v_1 + \tfrac{9}{40}v_2 = 0$$
$$\tfrac{7}{40}v_1 - \tfrac{16}{40}v_2 + \tfrac{9}{40}v_3 = 0$$
$$\tfrac{7}{40}v_2 - \tfrac{16}{40}v_3 + \tfrac{9}{40}v_4 = 0$$
$$\tfrac{7}{40}v_3 - \tfrac{16}{40}v_4 + \tfrac{3}{10}v_5 = 0$$
$$\tfrac{7}{40}v_4 - \tfrac{3}{10}v_5 = 0$$
$$v_0 + v_1 + v_2 + v_3 + v_4 + v_5 = 1$$

which in augmented matrix form is

$$
\left[
\begin{array}{cccccc|c}
-\tfrac{1}{4} & \tfrac{9}{40} & 0 & 0 & 0 & 0 & 0 \\
\tfrac{1}{4} & -\tfrac{16}{40} & \tfrac{9}{40} & 0 & 0 & 0 & 0 \\
0 & \tfrac{7}{40} & -\tfrac{16}{40} & \tfrac{9}{40} & 0 & 0 & 0 \\
0 & 0 & \tfrac{7}{40} & -\tfrac{16}{40} & \tfrac{9}{40} & 0 & 0 \\
0 & 0 & 0 & \tfrac{7}{40} & -\tfrac{16}{40} & \tfrac{3}{10} & 0 \\
0 & 0 & 0 & 0 & \tfrac{7}{40} & -\tfrac{3}{10} & 0 \\
1 & 1 & 1 & 1 & 1 & 1 & 1
\end{array}
\right]
$$

To simplify this slightly we can multiply the first five rows by 40 to get the equivalent augmented matrix form

$$
\left[
\begin{array}{cccccc|c}
-10 & 9 & 0 & 0 & 0 & 0 & 0 \\
10 & -16 & 9 & 0 & 0 & 0 & 0 \\
0 & 7 & -16 & 9 & 0 & 0 & 0 \\
0 & 0 & 7 & -16 & 9 & 0 & 0 \\
0 & 0 & 0 & 7 & -16 & 12 & 0 \\
0 & 0 & 0 & 0 & 7 & -12 & 0 \\
1 & 1 & 1 & 1 & 1 & 1 & 1
\end{array}
\right]
$$

By applying the method of Gaussian elimination the system of equations can now be solved. The result is (to three decimal places)

$$v_0 = .224, \quad v_1 = .248, \quad v_2 = .193, \quad v_3 = .150, \quad v_4 = .117, \quad v_5 = .068$$

In other words, the equilibrium distribution of the Markov chain is given (approximately) by

$$V = [.224, .248, .193, .150, .117, .068]$$

From this result several interesting conclusions can be drawn. First, we can conclude that after several time periods (minutes), there will be no one at the checkout stand about 22 percent of the time. This means that the person working at this checkout stand will be idle about 22 percent of the time. Second, it follows from the data that there will be five people at the checkout stand about 7 percent of the time. Consequently, people will be turned away from this stand relatively infrequently. Finally, the results indicate that the most frequent number of people at the checkout stand is one (about 25 percent of the time).

The computer was used to obtain the distribution of this Markov chain at various times (Table 10.3.1). Here it is assumed that initially (time 0) there is no one at the checkout stand (i.e., $\Pi^{(0)} = [1, 0, 0, 0, 0, 0]$). From the output we see that equilibrium (to three decimal places) is reached after about 100 time periods, which is 1 hour

Table 10.3.1

Time	Distribution at time					
0	1.000	.000	.000	.000	.000	.000
1	.750	.250	.000	.000	.000	.000
2	.619	.337	.044	.000	.000	.000
3	.540	.367	.085	.008	.000	.000
4	.488	.374	.117	.020	.001	.000
5	.450	.373	.140	.033	.004	.000
6	.421	.368	.157	.045	.008	.001
7	.399	.361	.168	.056	.013	.002
8	.380	.354	.177	.066	.018	.004
9	.365	.348	.183	.075	.024	.006
10	.352	.341	.188	.082	.029	.008
20	.281	.294	.197	.121	.071	.034
30	.252	.271	.196	.136	.094	.051
40	.238	.260	.194	.143	.105	.060
50	.231	.254	.194	.147	.111	.064
60	.227	.251	.193	.148	.114	.066
70	.225	.250	.193	.149	.115	.067
80	.224	.249	.193	.150	.116	.068
90	.224	.249	.193	.150	.116	.068
100	.224	.248	.193	.150	.117	.068
110	.224	.248	.193	.150	.117	.068
120	.224	.248	.193	.150	.117	.068

and 40 minutes. From that time on, the distribution of the number of customers at the checkout stand is given approximately by the vector V.

Exercises for 10.3

1. Patients arrive randomly at a doctor's office. The waiting room is small and will hold only three people at one time. In an interval of time, say, 15 minutes, at most one person will arrive at the office. If there are already three people waiting when a person arrives, he does not wait but comes back later. Also, no more than one patient will be seen by the doctor in any time interval, and a patient cannot be seen by the doctor in the time interval in which he arrives. Suppose that in an interval of 15 minutes there is a probability $\frac{3}{5}$ that a patient will arrive and a probability $\frac{2}{5}$ that no patient will arrive. The probabilities are assumed to be independent of other arrivals. Suppose also that if a patient is being examined by the doctor at the beginning of a time period, the probability that the doctor is done with this patient by the beginning of the next time period is $\frac{3}{4}$. This probability is assumed to be independent of the previous number of time units of service and of arrivals. Let the state of the system be the number of people in the doctor's office (waiting room plus examining room) at the beginning of a time period.
(a) Find the transition matrix for this Markov chain.
(b) What percentage of the time will there be no patients in the doctor's office?
(c) In the long run, what is the probability that a patient finds the waiting room full and so has to come back later?

2. Customers arrive at random at a teller's window in a bank. We assume that the line at the teller's window will hold only five people at one time, and that in an interval of time, say, one minute, at most one customer will arrive at the teller's window (although he may be turned away if at the beginning of the time period of his arrival there were already

five customers in the line) and at most one customer will be served. Suppose that in an interval of 1 minute there is a probability $\frac{2}{5}$ that a new customer will arrive at the teller's window and a probability $\frac{2}{3}$ that the customer at the head of the line will be served. Assume that arrivals are independent of other arrivals and that the probability of being served in a time period is independent of the previous number of time units of service, as well as other arrivals. Finally, assume that a person cannot be served in the time period of his arrival.

(a) Find the transition matrix for this Markov chain.

(b) In the long run, what is the probability that the teller is idle?

(c) In the long run, what is the probability that a customer is turned away?

Section 10.4 Paired Associate Learning

As an illustration of some of the applications of absorbing Markov chains we present the Bower model of paired associate learning.[1] Paired associate learning is of interest to psychologists studying verbal learning processes.

The basic assumptions and ideas involved will now be summarized. A list of stimuli is presented to a subject in random order. These stimuli may be words, numbers, nonsense syllables, pictures, or similar items. To each stimulus there corresponds a correct response that the subject is supposed to learn. Before the experiment actually begins, the subject may be informed of the set of responses in some way, or he may be exposed to them gradually during the course of the experiment.

The experiment consists of presenting the stimuli to the subject one at a time, for a brief exposure, during which time the subject is asked to try and state the correct response. After the subject replies, he is shown the correct response. This acts either as a confirmation to the correct response or a correction to an incorrect response.

After the complete list of stimuli is presented, it is again presented, but in a new random order. It should be pointed out that the responses can also be words, numbers, nonsense syllables, etc. Moreover, although the responses may be unique to each stimulus (i.e., different stimuli have different responses), this need not be the case.

For example, in the experimental situation modeled by Bower the stimuli consisted of 10 pairs of consonant letters while the responses were the numbers 1 and 2. The numbers were randomly assigned to the consonant pairs before the beginning of the experiment. The stimuli were each presented and the subject was asked to respond either 1 or 2. Following his reply he was informed of the correct response for that stimulus. After the 10 consonant pairs had been presented (constituting a trial), the deck of 10 stimulus cards was then reshuffled and again presented to the subject. This procedure was repeated until the subject had gone through the list twice in succession with no errors, at which time the subject was considered to have "learned" the proper responses.

Our purpose here is to apply the theory of Markov chains in order to analyze, mathematically, this type of experiment. For this to be permissible the following are taken as axioms.[2]

1. Each item (stimulus–response pair) is in one of two states on any trial n: conditioned (C_n) or guessing (G_n). Here conditioning of the stimulus–response pair is equated with the subject having learned the pairing. Otherwise the subject is simply guessing.

[1] G. H. Bower, "Applications of a Model to Paired-Associate Learning," *Psychometrika*, Vol. 26, 1961, pp. 255–280.

[2] G. Levine and C. J. Burke, *Mathematical Model Techniques for Learning Theories*, Academic Press, Inc., New York, 1972.

2. On any trial n, the probability of a transition from G_n to C_{n+1} (guessing at trial n, to conditioned at trial $n + 1$) is a constant c ($0 < c < 1$); and so on any trial n, the probability of a transition from G_n to G_{n+1} is $1 - c$.
3. On any trial n, the probability of a transition from C_n to C_{n+1} is 1 and hence from C_n to G_{n+1} is 0. This means that once the correct response is learned, it is not forgotten.
4. If in G_n on any trial n, then the probability of a success, S_n (correct response to stimulus), on trial n is $1/N$, where N is the total number of possible responses. This is just another way of saying that if the subject is guessing on trial n, he is equally likely to guess at any one of the possible responses.
5. Each item is in the nonconditioned (guessing) state at the initial trial.

In analyzing the experiment *we consider one fixed item* (stimulus–response pair) and consider its status on various trials as the state of a Markov chain at various times.

Under the above assumptions we shall construct two Markov chains corresponding to the experiment. For our first Markov chain we have two states, for which the following correspondence is made:

$\quad$ 1—conditioned
$\quad$ 2—guessing

Because of the axioms the status of the item in question on various trials forms a Markov chain. The state of the Markov chain at time n is defined to be the status of the item *during* the $(n + 1)$st trial of the experiment, or, equivalently, the status of the item *following* the nth trial of the experiment.

For example, the state of the Markov chain at time 0 ($n = 0$) is the status of the item during the first trial of the experiment. By axiom 5 the status is 2 (guessing). Hence the initial distribution of this Markov chain is

$$\begin{array}{cc} 1 & 2 \end{array}$$
$$\Pi^{(0)} = [0, \quad 1]$$

As another example, the state of the Markov chain at time 1 ($n = 1$) is the status of the item during the second trial, or, equivalently, the status of the item following the first trial. From axioms 2 and 5 it follows that the state of the Markov chain at time 1 will be 1 with probability c and 2 with probability $1 - c$.

By axioms 2 and 3 the transition matrix of the Markov chain is given by

$$\begin{array}{cc} & \begin{array}{cc} 1 & 2 \end{array} \\ P = \begin{array}{c} 1 \\ 2 \end{array} & \left[\begin{array}{cc} 1 & 0 \\ c & 1 - c \end{array} \right] \end{array}$$

To be more specific, let us fix a value of c, say $c = .3$. Then we have

$$P = \begin{bmatrix} 1 & 0 \\ .3 & .7 \end{bmatrix}$$

Using the computer the first 10 powers of the transition matrix P were calculated (see Figure 10.4.1). Again it is not too difficult to do these computations by hand.

Now, recall that the distribution of the Markov chain at time n gives the probabilities of being in the various states at that time and is given by $\Pi^{(n)} = \Pi^{(0)} \cdot P^n$. Using this, the distribution of the Markov chain at various times is easily obtained (Table 10.4.1). The results indicate, for example, that by time 13 (i.e., following the thirteenth trial) about 99 percent of the subjects tested will be in the conditioned state.

Figure 10.4.1

$$P = \begin{bmatrix} 1.00000 & .00000 \\ .30000 & .70000 \end{bmatrix}$$

$$P^2 = \begin{bmatrix} 1.00000 & .00000 \\ .51000 & .49000 \end{bmatrix}$$

$$P^3 = \begin{bmatrix} 1.00000 & .00000 \\ .65700 & .34300 \end{bmatrix}$$

$$P^4 = \begin{bmatrix} 1.00000 & .00000 \\ .75990 & .24010 \end{bmatrix}$$

$$P^5 = \begin{bmatrix} 1.00000 & .00000 \\ .83193 & .16807 \end{bmatrix}$$

$$P^6 = \begin{bmatrix} 1.00000 & .00000 \\ .88235 & .11765 \end{bmatrix}$$

$$P^7 = \begin{bmatrix} 1.00000 & .00000 \\ .91765 & .08235 \end{bmatrix}$$

$$P^8 = \begin{bmatrix} 1.00000 & .00000 \\ .94235 & .05765 \end{bmatrix}$$

$$P^9 = \begin{bmatrix} 1.00000 & .00000 \\ .95965 & .04035 \end{bmatrix}$$

$$P^{10} = \begin{bmatrix} 1.00000 & .00000 \\ .97175 & .02825 \end{bmatrix}$$

Table 10.4.1

Time	Distribution at time	
0	.00000	1.00000
1	.30000	.70000
2	.51000	.49000
3	.65700	.34300
4	.75990	.24010
5	.83193	.16807
6	.88235	.11765
7	.91765	.08235
8	.94235	.05765
9	.95965	.04035
10	.97175	.02825
11	.98023	.01977
12	.98616	.01384
→ 13	.99031	.00969
14	.99322	.00678
15	.99525	.00475
16	.99668	.00332
17	.99767	.00233
18	.99837	.00163
19	.99886	.00114
20	.99920	.00080

Exercises for 10.4

1. A teacher is teaching her class the multiplication tables for the integers between 1 and 10 by means of flash cards. On one side of the card the factors are listed and on the other side the product. A student is shown the factors and asked to give the product. Following his reply the card is turned over and he is shown the correct response. The teacher takes one student at a time and goes through all the cards with him until he can go through the whole deck twice in succession with no errors. Each time the deck has been gone through, the cards are reshuffled before going through it again. The following assumptions are made.
   (1) Either the student knows the answer or he is just guessing.
   (2) If he guesses at an answer in going through the deck, the probability is .2 that he will know the correct answer the next time through.
   (3) Once a student knows the answer, he does not forget it.
   (4) If a student is guessing at an answer, he is equally likely to guess at any one of the possible answers (in this case the possible products of the integers between 1 and 10).
   (5) To begin with, none of the students knows the correct answers.
   Suppose that we consider one fixed card and let 1 correspond to the state "has learned the correct answer" and 2 to the state "is guessing."
   (a) Set up the transition matrix P for this Markov chain.
   (b) Verify that the chain is absorbing.
   (c) What is the initial distribution?
   (d) What is the probability that the student will be in the conditioned state following the fourth time through the deck (i.e., in state 1 at time 4)?

2. In problem 1, suppose that if a student guesses at an answer in going through the deck, then the probability is $\frac{1}{2}$ that he will know the correct answer the next time through.
   (a) Set up the transition matrix P for this Markov chain.
   (b) What is the initial distribution?
   (c) What is the probability that a student will be in the conditioned state following the fourth time through the deck?

3. In a German vocabulary class the students are having trouble learning the English equivalent of a certain list of German words. To help them, the teacher selects these words from a box of German vocabulary cards and goes through the same process as did the teacher teaching the students the multiplication tables for the integers between 1 and 10 in problem 1. Suppose that we make the same assumptions as we did in (1)–(5) in problem 1, except in (2), suppose we assume that if a student guesses at an answer in going through the deck, the probability is .4 that he will know the correct answer the next time through. Let us consider one fixed German word on the list.
   (a) Set up the transition matrix P for this Markov chain.
   (b) What is the initial distribution?
   (c) What is the probability that a student will be in the conditioned state following the fifth time through the deck?

4. Let

$$P = \begin{bmatrix} 1 & 0 \\ c & 1 - c \end{bmatrix} \qquad 0 < c < 1$$

   (a) Find $P^{(2)}$.
   (b) Find $P^{(3)}$.
   (c) Show that for $n \geq 1$,

$$P^{(n)} = \begin{bmatrix} 1 & 0 \\ 1 - (1 - c)^n & (1 - c)^n \end{bmatrix}$$

   (d) If $\Pi^{(0)} = [0, 1]$, find $\Pi^{(n)}$, $n \geq 1$.

5. In problem 2, what is the minimum number of times the teacher must go through the deck to be at least .99 sure that a student will be in the conditioned state?

Section 10.5   Applications of the Fundamental Matrix to the Bower Model

We will now elaborate on the Bower model by considering it as a Markov chain with three instead of two states. This is done as follows. As before, state 1 corresponds to the "conditioned" status. However, if the subject (item) is in the guessing status on any given trial, this is decomposed into two states: "guessing with error" and "guessing with the correct response." These two states will be represented by the numbers 2 and 3, respectively:

> 1—conditioned
> 2—guessing with error
> 3—guessing the correct response

To determine the transition matrix for the corresponding Markov chain we use axiom 4 (see page 464) in conjunction with the other axioms. As before,

$$p_{11} = 1, \ p_{12} = 0, \ p_{13} = 0$$
$$p_{21} = c, \ p_{31} = c$$

To figure out, for example, p_{23}, we proceed as follows. Let G_{n+1} = event the subject is guessing on trial $n + 1$, S_{n+1} = event the subject responds correctly on trial $n + 1$, and T_n = event the subject is in state 2 on trial n (i.e., guesses with error). Then, by problem 6(b), Exercises 4.11,

$$p_{23} = \Pr(S_{n+1} \cap G_{n+1} \mid T_n)$$
$$= \Pr(S_{n+1} \mid G_{n+1} \cap T_n) \Pr(G_{n+1} \mid T_n)$$

Now, by axiom 2, $\Pr(G_{n+1} \mid T_n) = 1 - c$, and, by axiom 4, $\Pr(S_{n+1} \mid G_{n+1} \cap T_n) = 1/N$ (recall that N is the total number of possible responses). Consequently,

$$p_{23} = \frac{1}{N}(1 - c)$$

Similar arguments show that

$$p_{22} = \left(1 - \frac{1}{N}\right)(1 - c) \qquad p_{32} = \left(1 - \frac{1}{N}\right)(1 - c) \qquad p_{33} = \frac{1}{N}(1 - c)$$

Thus the transition matrix for this Markov chain is

$$P = \begin{array}{c} \\ 1 \\ 2 \\ 3 \end{array} \begin{array}{ccc} 1 & 2 & 3 \\ \left[\begin{array}{ccc} 1 & 0 & 0 \\ c & \left(1 - \dfrac{1}{N}\right)(1 - c) & \dfrac{1}{N}(1 - c) \\ c & \left(1 - \dfrac{1}{N}\right)(1 - c) & \dfrac{1}{N}(1 - c) \end{array}\right] \end{array}$$

which is an absorbing chain with state 1 absorbing and states 2 and 3 nonabsorbing. Axioms 4 and 5 imply that the initial distribution of the Markov chain is

$$\Pi^{(0)} = \left[0, 1 - \frac{1}{N}, \frac{1}{N}\right]$$

Again to be definite, let us fix values for c and N, say $c = .3$ and $N = 4$. Then the transition matrix is

$$P = \begin{bmatrix} 1 & 0 & 0 \\ .3 & .525 & .175 \\ .3 & .525 & .175 \end{bmatrix}$$

and the initial distribution is

$$\Pi^{(0)} = [0, .75, .25]$$

Using these facts, the distribution of the Markov chain can be calculated at various times, and the results are given in Table 10.5.1. The output indicates, for example, that following the thirtieth trial it is virtually certain (.99998) that the subject will be in the conditioned state.

Table 10.5.1

Time	Distribution at time		
0	.00000	.75000	.25000
1	.30000	.52500	.17500
2	.51000	.36750	.12250
3	.65700	.25725	.08575
4	.75990	.18007	.06002
5	.83193	.12605	.04202
6	.88235	.08824	.02941
7	.91765	.06177	.02059
8	.94235	.04324	.01441
9	.95965	.03027	.01009
10	.97175	.02119	.00706
11	.98023	.01483	.00494
12	.98616	.01038	.00346
13	.99031	.00727	.00242
14	.99322	.00509	.00170
15	.99525	.00356	.00119
16	.99668	.00249	.00083
17	.99767	.00174	.00058
18	.99837	.00122	.00041
19	.99886	.00085	.00028
20	.99920	.00060	.00020
21	.99944	.00042	.00014
22	.99961	.00029	.00010
23	.99973	.00021	.00007
24	.99981	.00014	.00005
25	.99987	.00010	.00003
26	.99991	.00007	.00002
27	.99993	.00005	.00002
28	.99995	.00003	.00001
29	.99997	.00002	.00001
30	.99998	.00002	.00001

An important question that arises in this model is, what is the expected number of times that the subject (item) is in state 2 or state 3? Notice, for example, that the number of times the state of the system is 2 is exactly the number of incorrect responses by the subject for the particular stimulus–response pair in question.

It can be proved by more advanced techniques that the subject will be in states 2 or 3 only finitely many times (this is Theorem 9.11.1). That is, the subject will eventually be in the conditioned state. This fact is intuitively clear and is supported by the output above.

In order to calculate the expected (average) number of times that the subject is in state 2 or state 3, first notice that the canonical matrix for this Markov chain is

$$P^* = \begin{bmatrix} 1 & 0 & 0 \\ \hline .3 & .525 & .175 \\ .3 & .525 & .175 \end{bmatrix}$$

and the Q-matrix is

$$Q = \begin{bmatrix} .525 & .175 \\ .525 & .175 \end{bmatrix}$$

It can be proved that the expected number of times that the subject (item) will be in state 2 or state 3 is given, respectively, by the entries of the row vector

$$[.75, .25]F$$

where F is the fundamental matrix (i.e., $F = [I - Q]^{-1}$).[3] Now, we have

$$I - Q = \begin{bmatrix} 1 & 0 \\ 0 & 1 \end{bmatrix} - \begin{bmatrix} .525 & .175 \\ .525 & .175 \end{bmatrix}$$

$$= \begin{bmatrix} .475 & -.175 \\ -.525 & .825 \end{bmatrix}$$

Using the results of Section 6.10, the inverse of $I - Q$ can be found. The result is

$$F = [I - Q]^{-1} = \begin{bmatrix} 2.75 & .5833 \cdots \\ 1.75 & 1.5833 \cdots \end{bmatrix}$$

or, in terms of fractions,

$$F = [I - Q]^{-1} = \begin{bmatrix} \frac{11}{4} & \frac{7}{12} \\ \frac{7}{4} & \frac{19}{12} \end{bmatrix}$$

Consequently,

$$[.75, .25]F = [\tfrac{3}{4}, \tfrac{1}{4}] \begin{bmatrix} \frac{11}{4} & \frac{7}{12} \\ \frac{7}{4} & \frac{19}{12} \end{bmatrix}$$

$$= [\tfrac{5}{2}, \tfrac{5}{6}]$$

Thus the expected number of times that the subject (item) is in state 2 is $\frac{5}{2} = 2.5$, and the expected number of times the subject (item) is in state 3 is $\frac{5}{6} \doteq .833$. In particular, then, the expected number of incorrect responses by the subject on the item in question is 2.5.

---

[3]For details, see the text by G. Levine and C. J. Burke, *Mathematical Model Techniques for Learning Theories,* Academic Press, Inc., New York, 1972.

Exercises for 10.5

1. Let $c = \frac{1}{2}$ and $N = 3$ in the Bower model of this section.
   (a) Find the transition matrix P for these values of c and N.
   (b) What is the initial distribution?
   (c) What is the expected number of incorrect responses by the subject?
2. In problem 3, Exercises 10.4, suppose that the number of German words the students are having trouble with is 5 (i.e., $N = 5$).
   (a) Find the transition matrix P for the three-state Markov chain corresponding to this experiment.
   (b) What is the initial distribution?
   (c) What is the probability that a student will know the English equivalent to a particular German word by the fourth time through the cards?
   (d) What is the expected number of incorrect responses by a student?
3. A psychologist is performing the following experiment with a rat. Three trays, A, B, and C, are set up for feeding with a specific tray specified for different meals. Tray A is used for the morning meal, B for the noon meal, and C for the evening meal. Food is put into all three trays each meal. However, the trays are equipped with an electrical shock device so that if the rat goes to the wrong tray for that meal, he receives an electrical shock. The experiment is continued until the rat goes to the proper tray for each meal 2 days in succession. Suppose that we make the assumptions that were made in axioms 1–5 of Section 10.4, except that in 2 we assume that if the rat guesses at a tray on any given day, the probability that he knows the correct tray the next day is .2. Let us observe the behavior of the rat with respect to the *noon* meal.
   (a) Find the transition matrix P for the three-state Markov chain corresponding to this experiment.
   (b) What is the initial distribution?
   (c) What is the probability that the rat will know the proper tray to go to following the fourth day?
   (d) What is the expected number of incorrect responses by the rat?
4. Let

$$P = \begin{bmatrix} 1 & 0 & 0 \\ c & \left(1 - \frac{1}{N}\right)(1 - c) & \frac{1}{N}(1 - c) \\ c & \left(1 - \frac{1}{N}\right)(1 - c) & \frac{1}{N}(1 - c) \end{bmatrix} \qquad 0 < c < 1$$

and N a positive integer.
   (a) Find $P^{(2)}$.
   (b) Find $P^{(3)}$.
   (c) Show that

$$P^{(n)} = \begin{bmatrix} 1 & 0 & 0 \\ 1 - (1 - c)^n & \left(1 - \frac{1}{N}\right)(1 - c)^n & \frac{1}{N}(1 - c)^n \\ 1 - (1 - c)^n & \left(1 - \frac{1}{N}\right)(1 - c)^n & \frac{1}{N}(1 - c)^n \end{bmatrix} \qquad n \geq 1$$

   (d) If $\Pi^{(0)} = \left[0, 1 - \frac{1}{N}, \frac{1}{N}\right]$, show that

$$\Pi^{(n)} = [1 - (1 - c)^n, \left(1 - \frac{1}{N}\right)(1 - c)^n, \frac{1}{N}(1 - c)^n] \qquad n \geq 1$$

5. In problem 3, suppose that if the rat guesses at a tray on any given day, the probability

that he knows the correct tray on the next day is .5. What is the minimum number of days the psychologist must perform the experiment to be at least 95 percent sure that the rat will be in the conditioned state?

6. Use arguments similar to those used in showing that $p_{23} = (1/N)(1 - c)$ to show that $p_{32} = (1 - 1/N)(1 - c)$.

Section 10.6   The Gambler's Ruin

In Section 9.13 it was mentioned that there is a more efficient method for calculating the gambler's ruin probabilities than by using the fundamental matrix approach. This method will be developed in this section.

Example 10.6.1   Suppose that two players, say player I and player II, are tossing a coin. Player I always calls heads. If the coin comes up heads, he wins a dollar from player II. If it comes up tails, he loses a dollar to player II. The game continues until either player I goes broke or player II goes broke.

For this illustration a somewhat extreme situation is considered. Assume that the initial capitals of players I and II are, respectively, $1,000,000 and $100.

If the coin is fair [i.e., $\Pr(\{H\}) = \Pr(\{T\}) = \frac{1}{2}$], it is not surprising that player I is much less likely to be cleaned out than player II. Indeed, by a formula to be developed presently, it can be calculated that the probability of ruin for player I (i.e., player II bankrupts player I) is approximately *.0001*.

Suppose, on the other hand, that the coin is biased slightly in favor of player II because the probability of a head is .49 instead of .50. Now what is the probability of ruin for player I? That is, what is the probability that player II wins player I's $1,000,000 before player I wins player II's $100?

What do you think? .001?, .01?, .10?, .15?, or what? Many people estimate the probability between about .001 and .30. Amazingly enough, the probability is approximately *.98*. That is, the *probability of ruin for player I* increases from almost nil (.0001) in the case where the coin is fair $[\Pr(\{H\}) = .5]$ to almost certainty (.98) in the case where the coin is biased "slightly" against player I $[\Pr(\{H\}) = .49]$. This means, in the long run, that about 98 times out of 100, player II will win $1,000,000 from player I before player I can win $100 from player II. The slight bias in the coin has overwhelming consequences.

The formulas for calculating probabilities such as the ones just encountered will now be developed.

In Example 9.2.3 a special case of the gambling situation was given. The general case that will be considered here is the following: player I and player II are gambling. The game is such that at each trial (bet) player I has probability p of winning $1[4] from player II and has probability $1 - p$ of losing $1 to player II. The trials are assumed to be independent of each other (e.g., coin tossing).

As in Example 9.2.3, if the state of the system at any time is the capital of player I at that time, the system is a Markov chain. To achieve sufficient generality let

$x = $ initial capital of player I
$d = $ total capital of players I and II

---

[4]The unit of wager at each trial does not have to be $1. It could be 1¢, $100, $1,000, and so on.

so that player II's initial capital is $d - x$. In Example 9.2.3 $x = 2$, $d = 6$, and $p = \frac{1}{2}$, while in Example 10.6.1, $x = 1{,}000{,}000$, $d = 1{,}000{,}100$, and $p = \frac{1}{2}$ for the unbiased coin; $x = 1{,}000{,}000$, $d = 1{,}000{,}100$, and $p = .49$ for the biased coin. The game ends whenever one of the players goes broke. This is when the state of the system first reaches 0 (player I goes broke) or d (player II goes broke). These are the absorbing states. To gamblers it is of course extremely important to know the probabilities associated with these two possibilities. As will be seen, the results are in many cases quite surprising.

Let E_x be the event that player I goes broke (i.e., player II cleans out player I) if his original capital is x. This is the event that starting at state x, the state of the system is 0 before it is d. The *probability* r_x *of ruin* for player I is then

$$r_x = \Pr(E_x) \tag{10.6.1}$$

It is this probability that will now be calculated. Following the derivation of the formula for r_x, some particular illustrations will be given.

From the statement of the problem, if neither of the players is broke at a given time, the state of the system, at the next time, changes by either $+1$ (if player I wins at that trial) or -1 (if player I loses at that trial). These two transitions have probabilities p and $1 - p$, respectively.

If the system is in state 0 at any time (player I is broke), it stays in state 0. If the system is in state d at any time (player II is broke), it stays in state d.

From the above facts it follows that the transition matrix of this absorbing Markov chain is

$$
P = \begin{array}{c} \\ 0 \\ 1 \\ 2 \\ 3 \\ \vdots \\ d-2 \\ d-1 \\ d \end{array}
\begin{array}{c}
\begin{array}{ccccccccc} 0 & \ 1 & \ 2 & \ 3 & \cdots & d-2 & d-1 & \ d \end{array} \\
\left[\begin{array}{cccccccc}
1 & 0 & 0 & 0 & \cdots & 0 & 0 & 0 \\
1-p & 0 & p & 0 & \cdots & 0 & 0 & 0 \\
0 & 1-p & 0 & p & \cdots & 0 & 0 & 0 \\
0 & 0 & 1-p & 0 & \cdots & 0 & 0 & 0 \\
\vdots & \vdots & \vdots & \vdots & \ddots & \vdots & \vdots & \vdots \\
0 & 0 & 0 & 0 & \cdots & 0 & p & 0 \\
0 & 0 & 0 & 0 & \cdots & 1-p & 0 & p \\
0 & 0 & 0 & 0 & \cdots & 0 & 0 & 1
\end{array} \right]
\end{array}
$$

For example, if player I's initial capital is 3, player II's is 2, and player I's success probability p at any given trial is $\frac{1}{4}$, then $x = 3$, $d = 5$, $p = \frac{1}{4}$, and

$$
P = \begin{array}{c} \\ 0 \\ 1 \\ 2 \\ 3 \\ 4 \\ 5 \end{array}
\begin{array}{c}
\begin{array}{cccccc} 0 & 1 & 2 & 3 & 4 & 5 \end{array} \\
\left[\begin{array}{cccccc}
1 & 0 & 0 & 0 & 0 & 0 \\
\frac{3}{4} & 0 & \frac{1}{4} & 0 & 0 & 0 \\
0 & \frac{3}{4} & 0 & \frac{1}{4} & 0 & 0 \\
0 & 0 & \frac{3}{4} & 0 & \frac{1}{4} & 0 \\
0 & 0 & 0 & \frac{3}{4} & 0 & \frac{1}{4} \\
0 & 0 & 0 & 0 & 0 & 1
\end{array} \right]
\end{array}
$$

Returning to the general situation we now indicate the procedure for determining r_x. The basic idea is this: if player I's initial capital is x, then after one time period (the first bet) his capital is either $x + 1$ (a win) or $x - 1$ (a loss) (Figure 10.6.1). The probabilities of these events are, respectively, p and $1 - p$.

Figure 10.6.1

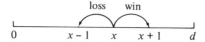

Given that player I wins the first bet, his capital then becomes $x + 1$. The probability of ruin for player I is now r_{x+1}. This is true because of the Markov property: given the present state of the system ($x + 1$ at time 1), the future states of the system (eventual ruin) are independent of the past (x at time 0).

Similarly, *given* that player I loses the first bet, his capital at time 1 is $x - 1$. From this position his probability of ruin is r_{x-1}.

The heuristic argument above leads to the formula

$$r_x = p r_{x+1} + (1 - p) r_{x-1} \tag{10.6.2}$$

To verify Eq. (10.6.2) rigorously, we proceed in the following manner. Let

A = event player I wins the first bet (so that the state of the system is $x + 1$ at time 1)

B = event player II wins the first bet (so that the state of the system is $x - 1$ at time 1)

E_y = event of ruin for player I given that his capital is at present equal to y

Since either A or B must occur and they are mutually exclusive, it follows from Eq. (4.11.9) that

$$r_x = \Pr(E_x) = \Pr(E_x|A)\Pr(A) + \Pr(E_x|B)\Pr(B) \tag{10.6.3}$$

By assumption, $\Pr(A) = p$. Also, by the Markov property and the definition of A and E_x, $\Pr(E_x|A) = \Pr(E_{x+1}) \equiv r_{x+1}$. Consequently,

$$\Pr(E_x|A)\Pr(A) = r_{x+1}p$$

Similarly,

$$\Pr(E_x|B)\Pr(B) = r_{x-1}(1 - p)$$

Substituting these results in Eq. (10.6.3) gives Eq. (10.6.2).

Using techniques from a more advanced course in mathematics, it is not too difficult to solve Eq. (10.6.2) for r_x. The result is

$$r_x = \frac{d - x}{d} \qquad \text{if } p = \tfrac{1}{2} \quad \text{(i.e., game is fair)} \tag{10.6.4}$$

and

$$r_x = \frac{\left(\dfrac{1 - p}{p}\right)^x - \left(\dfrac{1 - p}{p}\right)^d}{1 - \left(\dfrac{1 - p}{p}\right)^d} \qquad \text{if } p \neq \tfrac{1}{2} \quad \text{(i.e., game is not fair)} \tag{10.6.5}$$

The complicated nature of formula (10.6.5) should not be of concern to the reader. When particular numbers are substituted into the expression, there is considerable simplification.

For example, if $x = 3$, $d = 5$, and $p = \frac{1}{4}$, then $1 - p = \frac{3}{4}$, so $(1 - p)/p = 3$. Then Eq. (10.6.5) becomes

$$r_3 = \frac{3^3 - 3^5}{1 - 3^5} = \frac{216}{242} \doteq .89$$

In other words, the probability that player II wins player I's $3 before player I wins II's $2 is approximately .89. So, player I will be ruined about 90 percent of the time he plays this game.

In Example 10.6.1 the given data were $x = 1{,}000{,}000$ and $d = 1{,}000{,}100$. In the first case $p = \frac{1}{2}$. Then, according to Eq. (10.6.4), the probability of ruin for player I is

$$r_{1{,}000{,}000} = \frac{1{,}000{,}100 - 1{,}000{,}000}{1{,}000{,}100} \doteq .0001$$

In the second case $p = .49$, so $(1 - p)/p = \frac{51}{49}$. Here the probability of ruin for player I is given by Eq. (10.6.5) to be

$$r_{1{,}000{,}000} = \frac{\left(\frac{51}{49}\right)^{1{,}000{,}000} - \left(\frac{51}{49}\right)^{1{,}000{,}100}}{1 - \left(\frac{51}{49}\right)^{1{,}000{,}100}}$$

Using logarithms or an electronic calculator this last expression can be evaluated. The result is

$$r_{1{,}000{,}000} \doteq .98$$

This is the probability of ruin quoted in Example 10.6.1.

Using Eqs. (10.6.4) and (10.6.5), a table of the gambler's ruin probabilities was constructed for several different situations. In Table 10.6.1,

$x = $ player I's initial capital
$y = $ player II's initial capital
$p = $ probability of success for player I on a given trial
$f = $ probability of ruin for player I for a fair game ($p = .5$)
$r = $ probability of ruin for player I for the given value of p

Table 10.6.1

x	y	p	f	r
1,000	1,000	.499	.500	.982
100	100	.499	.500	.599
100	100	.490	.500	.982
10	1,000	.510	.990	.670
10	10	.510	.500	.481
10	10	.600	.500	.017
10	20	.510	.667	.528
10	20	.600	.667	.017
50	100	.510	.667	.133
1	1,000	.700	.999	.429

Note especially the difference between the fair and unfair game. For example, in the first row of the table, each of the players begins with $1,000, so $x = 1,000$ and $d = 2,000$. It is clear that for a fair game the probability of ruin for player I should be $\frac{1}{2}$. This is borne out by Eq. (10.6.4). Indeed,

$$r_{1,000} = \frac{2,000 - 1,000}{2,000} = .5$$

Now, if the game is only slightly favorable to player II, with $p = .499$, then the probability of ruin for player I skyrockets to about .982. This follows from Eq. (10.6.5). Here $(1 - p)/p = \frac{501}{499}$, so

$$r_{1,000} = \frac{\left(\frac{501}{499}\right)^{1,000} - \left(\frac{501}{499}\right)^{2,000}}{1 - \left(\frac{501}{499}\right)^{2,000}} \doteq .982$$

Exercises for 10.6

1. Two boys, Mark and David, find $6. Rather than split the money evenly, they decide to make a series of $1 bets to determine who will keep all the money. The winner of each bet is determined by tossing a fair coin. They begin by giving each other theoretical interests of $3. What is the probability that David goes home with the entire $6?

2. In problem 1, suppose the coin is biased with probability $\frac{2}{3}$ of coming up heads, and suppose that Mark always calls heads. What is the probability that Mark goes home with the entire $6?

3. Two men, I and II, decide to shoot pool. They agree to bet $1 on each game. From past experience I has determined that he has probability .6 of winning each game. He has $2 to begin with, and player II has $3. They decide to play until either one goes broke.
   (a) What is the probability that player I is ruined?
   (b) Suppose the two men are equally matched. What is the probability that player I is ruined?

4. You and a friend are matching fair pennies. You decide to play until either of you loses all his pennies. If you start with 50 pennies and your friend starts with 45, what is the probability that you lose all your pennies before your friend does?

5. Two players, I and II, are playing dice. Player I has $3 and player II has $2. They bet $1 on each game. If player I always throws the dice, he has probability .492 of winning each game. Suppose that they play until either player goes broke. What is the probability that player II goes broke before I does?

6. Two companies, A and B, compete against each other in a business that involves government contracts. Company A presently holds 4 of the 10 contracts released by the government each year and B holds the remaining 6. Each year the government takes one contract away from one of the companies and gives it to the other. If the chance of a shift of a contract from company A to company B is the same as a shift from company B to company A, what is the probability of each company surviving? (A company is ruined as soon as it has no contracts.)

7. In problem 6, suppose that $33\frac{1}{3}$ percent of the time the shift is from company A to company B. What is the probability of each company surviving?

8. A man leaves a bar in the state of intoxication. Twenty steps to the left of the bar his car is parked and 35 steps to the right is a ditch. What is the probability that the man will fall into the ditch before he reaches his car if at each step he is just as likely to take a step to the left as to the right?

Section 10.7 Applications to Roulette

There is another interesting application of formula (10.6.5) which will now be presented. Suppose that a person goes to Las Vegas with \$100 and plays roulette. He decides to bet on red and to continue betting until he loses his \$100 or wins \$100 from the house. He decides beforehand that the amount he will wager on any spin of the wheel will be the same, but he is not sure what that wager should be. For example, he could bet \$1 at each trial, \$5 at each trial, \$10 at each trial, and so on. What amount should he choose to wager at each trial to minimize his probability of ruin (i.e., losing his \$100 before winning \$100 from the house)?

Many people want to get a "play for their money" and so many would bet \$1 per spin of the wheel to ensure a relatively long playing time at the roulette wheel. Unfortunately, this strategy gives a person the poorest chance (i.e., maximizes the probability of ruin).

Now, few people would just bet the \$100 all at once and quit, win or lose; for, using this method, a person will have only one turn at the wheel. This strategy, however, gives a person the best chance (i.e., minimizes the probability of ruin).

The claims of the last two paragraphs can be justified by the use of formula (10.6.5). The formula gives the probability of ruin for a gambler under the following circumstances. The gambler has probability $p \neq \frac{1}{2}$ of winning at a particular trial. His initial capital is x units[5] and his opponent's initial capital is $d - x$ units, so the total capital is d units. The gambler is assumed to wager *1 unit per trial.*

In roulette there are 38 numbers on the wheel—1–36, 0, and 00. Of these 38 numbers, 18 are red. Since the ball is equally likely to land on each number, the probability of red at any given trial is

$$p = \tfrac{18}{38} = \tfrac{9}{19} \doteq .474$$

If the roulette player decides to bet the \$100 all at once, his probability of ruin is just the probability that the ball does not land on a red number. This is

$$1 - p = \tfrac{10}{19} \doteq .526$$

This result can also be derived by using Eq. (10.6.5). Here the unit of wager is \$100, so the player's original capital is 1 unit ($x = 1$). Since he intends to quit if he wins \$100, the opponent's capital is also taken to be 1 unit. In this case $x = 1$, $d = 2$, and $p = \tfrac{9}{19}$. Substituting these data in Eq. (10.6.5) yields the probability of ruin to be [note: $(1 - p)/p = \tfrac{10}{9}$]

$$r_1 = \frac{\left(\tfrac{10}{9}\right)^1 - \left(\tfrac{10}{9}\right)^2}{1 - \left(\tfrac{10}{9}\right)^2} = \tfrac{10}{19} \doteq .526$$

On the other hand, suppose that the roulette player decides to bet \$1 at a time. Then the unit of wager is \$1, so the gambler's initial capital is 100 units ($x = 100$). Again, since he quits if he wins \$100, the opponent's (player II's) capital is also taken to be 100 units. Consequently, in this case $x = 100$, $d = 200$, and $p = \tfrac{9}{19}$. According to Eq. (10.6.5), the probability of ruin for the player is, in this case,

$$r_{100} = \frac{\left(\tfrac{10}{9}\right)^{100} - \left(\tfrac{10}{9}\right)^{200}}{1 - \left(\tfrac{10}{9}\right)^{200}}$$

---

[5]In our previous examples the unit has always been taken to be \$1.

Using a calculating machine or logarithms this last expression can be calculated approximately. The result is

$$r_{100} \doteq .99997$$

Consequently, if the roulette player bets $1 at a time he is almost certain (.99997) to lose his $100 before winning $100 from the house. If, on the other hand, he bets the $100 all at once, his probability of losing his $100 before winning $100 from the house decreases to about .526.

Using the same types of arguments as employed above, a table of the probabilities of ruin for the roulette player can be constructed for various units of wager (Table 10.7.1).

Table 10.7.1

Unit of wager	Probability of ruin
1	.999
2	.995
5	.892
10	.741
25	.604
50	.552
100	.526

Exercises for 10.7

1. A man has $4 and decides to play roulette. He bets only on red and plays until he loses his $4 or wins $4 from the house.
   (a) What is his probability of ruin if he decides to bet the $4 all at once?
   (b) What is his probability of ruin if he decides to bet $1 at a time?
   (c) What is his probability of ruin if he decides to bet $2 at a time?
2. Suppose that a person with $10 is playing roulette. He decides to bet only on red and plays until he loses his $10 or wins $10 from the house.
   (a) What is his probability of ruin if he decides to bet the $10 all at once?
   (b) What is his probability of ruin if he decides to bet $1 at a time?
   (c) What is his probability of ruin if he decides to bet $2 at a time?
3. This problem is designed for those students who know how to operate a calculating machine or know how to work with logarithms. A gambler has $200. He decides to play roulette. He bets only on the red and plays until he loses his $200 or wins $200 from the house.
   (a) What is his probability of ruin if he decides to bet the $200 all at once?
   (b) What is his probability of ruin if he decides to bet $1 at a time?
   (c) What is his probability of ruin if he decides to bet $10 at a time?
   (d) What is his probability of ruin if he decides to bet $100 at a time?

Matrix Games

11

In this chapter we present an introduction to the mathematical theory of games. Most of the games studied here represent a simplified view of those which would arise in practice. However, by analyzing these simple games, insight into the more complicated situations can be developed.

We shall examine what are called *two-person, zero-sum* games and apply the methods of linear programming to obtain "optimal strategies."

Section 11.1 Two-Person, Zero-Sum Matrix Games

In order to motivate the development we begin by introducing some examples of what are referred to as two-person, zero-sum matrix games.

Example 11.1.1 Suppose that two people agree to play the following game. Each person places one hand behind his back and at a given signal "brings out" either one or two fingers. Call the people player I and player II. If the sum of the digits showing is even, player II pays player I that sum in dollars. For example, if each person shows two fingers, the sum is four and player II pays player I $4. On the other hand, if the sum of the digits showing is odd, player I pays player II that sum in dollars. For instance, if player I shows one finger and player II shows two fingers, the sum is three and player I pays player II $3.

Notice that the loss of one player is the gain of the other. For this reason such a game is called a *zero-sum game*. The reason that the game is called a *two-person game* is quite obvious—there are two players involved.

In order to analyze games such as this one it is convenient to represent the payments of one player to another in a matrix called the *payoff matrix*. For this game the payoff matrix is given in Figure 11.1.1. Notice that it is a 2 × 2 matrix. This is because each player has two options. Consequently, this is called a *2 × 2 matrix game*.

Figure 11.1.1

$$
\begin{array}{cc}
 & \text{Player II} \\
 & \begin{array}{cc} 1 & 2 \end{array} \\
\text{Player I} \quad \begin{array}{c} 1 \\ 2 \end{array} & \begin{bmatrix} 2 & -3 \\ -3 & 4 \end{bmatrix}
\end{array}
$$

To interpret this matrix in terms of the present game, note that the numbers bordering the matrix on the left correspond to the options of player I: option 1 corresponds to player I showing one finger, and option 2 corresponds to player I showing two fingers. Similarly, the numbers bordering the matrix on the top correspond to player II's options of showing one or two fingers, respectively.

All entries in the matrix correspond to payments from player II to player I. If for a particular choice of options player I pays player II, this is represented by the fact that the corresponding entry is negative. That is, a negative payment from player II to player I is a positive payment from player I to player II.

To illustrate this, first suppose that player I chooses option 1 (i.e., shows one finger) and player II chooses option 1. Then player II pays player I $2. This fact is represented in the matrix by placing a (positive) 2 in the 1–1 entry of the matrix. As another example, suppose that player I chooses option 1 and player II chooses option 2. Then player I must pay player II $3 (i.e., player II "pays" player I $−3.) Consequently, the 1–2 entry of the payoff matrix is −3. Similar arguments yield the other entries of the payoff matrix. We emphasize that the entries of the payoff matrix represent gains for player I and losses for player II.

There are several natural questions that arise in connection with this (and any other) matrix game. The first question is whether or not the game is "fair." This game certainly appears to be fair. However, surprisingly enough, we shall see in Section 11.3 that it is not fair. Can you guess which player has the advantage? Another question is: Are there "optimal" strategies for the players and, if so, how does one determine such optimal strategies? The answers to these and related questions will be the motivation for our mathematical development of matrix games.

Example 11.1.2 Consider the following game played by two people. Player I has the ace and king of spades; player II has the ace, king, and queen of hearts. If player I plays the ace of spades, he wins $1, $2, or $0, according as player II plays the ace, king, or queen of hearts. On the other hand, if player I plays the king of spades, he wins $4 if player II plays the ace of hearts, loses $3 if player II plays the king of hearts, and loses $1 if player II plays the queen of hearts.

Since player I has two options and player II has three options, this is an example of a *two-person, zero-sum, 2 × 3 matrix game*. The payoff matrix is as shown in Figure 11.1.2, where options 1 and 2 for player I correspond, respectively, to the play of the ace and king of spades, and for player II options 1, 2, and 3 correspond, respectively, to the play of the ace, king, and queen of hearts.

Figure 11.1.2

$$\begin{array}{c} & \begin{array}{ccc} 1 & 2 & 3 \end{array} \\ \begin{array}{c} 1 \\ 2 \end{array} & \left[\begin{array}{ccc} 1 & 2 & 0 \\ 4 & -3 & -1 \end{array}\right] \end{array}$$

At first glance this game might appear to favor player I. However, as we shall see, the game is "fair." Moreover, it seems that this game is more complicated than the one in Example 11.1.1. In point of fact, it is a much simpler game.

With the above examples in mind, we now make the following definitions and conventions. Consider a situation in which two persons play a game. Player I has m options available to him and player II has n options. Each player selects one of his possible plays. Once these selections are made, player II pays player I an amount

a_{ij}, based on player I choosing option i and player II choosing option j. If a_{ij} is negative, this corresponds to the fact that actually player I is paying player II an amount $-a_{ij}$. For example, if $a_{12} = 2$, this means that whenever player I chooses option 1 and player II chooses option 2, player II pays player I an amount 2. On the other hand, if, for example, $a_{23} = -1$, this implies that whenever player I chooses option 2 and player II chooses option 3, player I pays player II an amount 1. The *payoff matrix* for such a game is shown in Figure 11.1.3. The game is called a *two-person, zero-sum, $m \times n$ matrix game* for the reasons indicated in Examples 11.1.1 and 11.1.2.

Figure 11.1.3

$$
\begin{array}{cc}
 & \begin{array}{c} \text{Options for} \\ \text{player II} \end{array} \\
\end{array}
$$

$$
\begin{array}{cccccc}
 & & 1 & 2 & \cdots & n \\
\text{Options} & 1 & \begin{bmatrix} a_{11} & a_{12} & \cdots & a_{1n} \\ \text{for} & 2 & a_{21} & a_{22} & \cdots & a_{2n} \\ \text{player I} & \vdots & \vdots & \vdots & \ddots & \vdots \\ & m & a_{m1} & a_{m2} & \cdots & a_{mn} \end{bmatrix}
\end{array}
$$

In the development it is assumed that the game is being played repeatedly. Moreover, it is supposed that both players are "rational" and will do as well as they possibly can. The questions to be answered in the analysis of matrix games are the following:

1. Is the game fair? If it is not fair, which player has the advantage and how much of an advantage does this player have?
2. Do the players have "optimal" strategies and, if so, how are these optimal strategies determined?

Exercises for 11.1

1. Consider the two-person, zero-sum, 3×2 matrix game with payoff matrix

$$
\begin{array}{cc}
 & \begin{array}{cc} 1 & 2 \end{array} \\
\begin{array}{c} 1 \\ 2 \\ 3 \end{array} & \begin{bmatrix} 3 & -7 \\ -4 & 5 \\ 0 & 1 \end{bmatrix}
\end{array}
$$

Indicate how much is payed to which player if player I and player II select the following options, respectively.
(a) 1 and 1   (b) 2 and 2
(c) 2 and 1   (d) 3 and 2
(e) 3 and 1   (f) 1 and 2

2. Suppose that a two-person, zero-sum matrix game has payoff matrix

$$
\begin{array}{cc}
 & \begin{array}{cccc} 1 & 2 & 3 & 4 \end{array} \\
\begin{array}{c} 1 \\ 2 \\ 3 \end{array} & \begin{bmatrix} 0 & -1 & 4 & 2 \\ -6 & -2 & 1 & 5 \\ 7 & -3 & 2 & -4 \end{bmatrix}
\end{array}
$$

(a) How many options does player I have?
(b) How many options does player II have?
(c) What are the payoffs if player I and player II select the following options, respectively?
      (1) 2 and 3   (2) 3 and 2
      (3) 1 and 1   (4) 3 and 3
      (5) 3 and 4   (6) 2 and 4

3. Assume that two players indulge in the following game. Player I has the 2, 3, and 4 of hearts while player II has the 3, 4, 5, and 6 of diamonds. Each player selects one of his cards and at a given signal the players expose their choices. If the numerical sum of the cards is even, player II pays player I an amount equal to that sum. On the other hand, if the numerical sum of the cards is odd, then player I pays player II an amount equal to that sum. Determine the payoff matrix for this game.

4. A well-known game called "rock–paper–scissors" is played by two people as follows. The players place their hands behind their backs and at a given signal "come out" with either (1) a fist (rock), (2) an open palm (paper), or (3) two fingers (scissors). Now, we have the following hierarchy: (1) rock beats scissors, (2) scissors beats paper, (3) paper beats rock. Suppose that if one player beats another, the latter pays the former $1. If both players "come out" with the same option, the game is a tie. Set up the payoff matrix for this game. Do you think the game is fair?

5. (The Mississippi Gambler) On a Mississippi River boat a gambler offers a passenger the following game. The gambler takes a red deuce and black trey and gives the passenger a red ace and black deuce. They each choose one of their cards and display them simultaneously. If the colors match, the passenger wins; if they don't, the gambler wins. The payoffs are made according to the following rules.
   (1) If the passenger plays the red ace, the payment to be made consists of the difference of the numbers on the cards played (ace = 1).
   (2) If the passenger plays the black deuce, the payment to be made consists of the sum of the numbers on the cards.
   Let the gambler be player I and set up the payoff matrix for this game. Do you think the game is fair?

6. At the intersection of two streets there are four vacant corners available for gas stations. Two companies plan to locate, one station each, at this intersection. Company A has a choice of either the NW or SW corner; company B may select either the NE or SE corner. If they choose diagonally opposite corners, they will split the business 50–50. However, if they both locate on the north side, company A will get only 40 percent of the business; and if they both locate on the south side, company B will get 35 percent of the business.

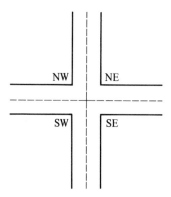

Suppose that payoffs are measured by the difference in percentage from 50 percent (e.g., if both companies locate on the south side, company B "pays" company A $15 = 50 - 35$). Let company A be player I and set up the payoff matrix for this game and explain your labeling.

7. Two clothing manufacturers (I and II) plan to locate in one of three suburbs of a large city. The distances between the suburbs are indicated in the diagram as well as the relative percentage of business to be expected from each town. If both companies locate in the same suburb, I, because it is larger, will get 60 percent of the total business. If they locate in different suburbs, (1) each will get 90 percent of the business from the suburb it is in, and (2) the suburb with no store will give 70 percent of its business to the store in the

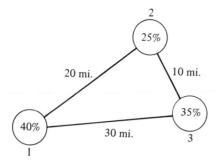

suburb closest to it and 30 percent of its business to the other store. Suppose that payoffs are measured by the difference in percentage from 50 percent. For example, suppose that I and II locate in suburbs 3 and 2, respectively. Then I gets 31.5 percent (= 90 percent of 35 percent) of the total business as a result of suburb 3, 2.5 percent (= 10 percent of 25 percent) of the total business as a result of suburb 2, and 12 percent (= 30 percent of 40 percent) of the total business as a result of suburb 3. Therefore, if I and II locate in suburbs 3 and 2, respectively, I will get $31.5 + 2.5 + 12 = 46$ percent of the total business and hence will "pay" II 4 (= 50 − 46). Set up this problem as a two-person, zero-sum, 3×3 matrix game and exhibit the payoff matrix.

*8. What happens to the payoff matrix of a two-person, zero-sum, $m \times n$ matrix game if player II becomes the row player and player I the column player, that is, if player II's options label the rows and the payoffs represent those from player I to player II?

Section 11.2 Strictly Determined Matrix Games

In this section the questions posed concerning matrix games at the end of Section 11.1 are answered for the simplest types of games. These are called strictly determined games.

Example 11.2.1 Consider the two-person, zero-sum, 4×3 matrix game with payoff matrix

$$
\begin{array}{c}
 \quad 1 \quad\; 2 \quad\;\; 3 \\
\begin{array}{c} 1 \\ 2 \\ 3 \\ 4 \end{array}
\left[
\begin{array}{rrr}
2 & -1 & 2 \\
-3 & -4 & -1 \\
3 & 1 & 2 \\
3 & 1 & -2
\end{array}
\right]
\end{array}
$$

What should player I do? If one examines the payoff matrix it is quite clear, in this case, what player I should do: he should always choose option 3. For, if he does, no matter which option player II selects, he will win at least as much as he would by choosing any other option. Thus, in this game, the optimal strategy for player I is to always select option 3.

Now, what should player II do? Since player II is rational, he realizes that because of the above facts player I will always choose his option 3. Therefore, the best that player II can do is to always select option 2. Notice that because of the preceding results, player II will pay player I $1 after each trial of the game. Thus the *value* of this game is said to be 1. The game is obviously biased in favor of player I and so is *unfair*.

In summary, then, the answers to questions 1 and 2 of Section 11.1 are, for this game, the following:

1. The game is unfair and is biased in favor of player I. His advantage is $1 per play (this is called the value of the game).
2. Each player has an optimal strategy. That for player I is to select option 3 every time and that for player II is to select option 2 every time.

These results are illustrated in Figure 11.2.1. Notice that the value of the game is the 3–2 entry of the payoff matrix and that this is an entry of the matrix which is *a minimum in its row and a maximum in its column.*

Figure 11.2.1

$$
\begin{array}{c}
\text{Optimal for} \\
\text{player II} \\
\downarrow \\
\begin{array}{ccc}
1 & 2 & 3
\end{array}
\end{array}
$$

Optimal for player I →

$$
\begin{array}{c}
1 \\
2 \\
3 \\
4
\end{array}
\left[
\begin{array}{ccc}
2 & -1 & 2 \\
-3 & -4 & -1 \\
3 & \boxed{1} & 2 \\
3 & 1 & -2
\end{array}
\right]
$$

Value of the game

Example 11.2.2 Consider, again, the two-person, zero-sum, 2×3 matrix game introduced in Example 11.1.2. Its payoff matrix is

$$
\begin{array}{c}
 \\
1 \\
2
\end{array}
\begin{array}{ccc}
1 & 2 & 3
\end{array}
\left[
\begin{array}{ccc}
1 & 2 & 0 \\
4 & -3 & -1
\end{array}
\right]
$$

What should player I do? He would, of course, like to win $4 by selecting option 2. However, since player II is rational, it is certain that he would protect himself against losses and select option 2 if player I always chose option 2. In this case player I would lose $3 instead of winning $4. But, if player I selects option 1, then no matter what player II does, the worst that could happen is that he would break even (i.e., win $0).

On the other hand, player II would like to win $3 by selecting option 2. However, if he always selected option 2, player I would choose his option 1, in which case player II would lose $2 instead of winning $3. But, if player II selects option 3, the worst he will do is break even.

Now, here is the crucial point. Suppose, as suggested above, that player I always selects option 1 and player II always chooses option 3. Then, *even if one player learns the other person's strategy, he cannot improve his own situation by switching to another.* Examination of the payoff matrix makes this last statement evident. Notice that by playing these strategies, the payoff will always be $0.

Consequently, for this game the answers to questions 1 and 2 of Section 11.1 are as follows:

1. The game is fair (i.e., the value of the game is 0).
2. Each player has an optimal strategy: that for player I is to always select option 1 and that for player II is to always select option 3.

Figure 11.2.2 illustrates the situation in terms of the payoff matrix. Note that the 1–3 entry is the value of the game, and, as in Example 11.2.1, this entry is a minimum in its row and a maximum in its column.

Figure 11.2.2

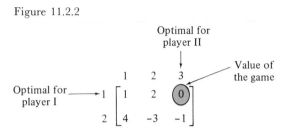

Examples 11.2.1 and 11.2.2 both illustrate what is referred to as a strictly determined matrix game.

Definition
Consider an $m \times n$ matrix game (i.e., player I has m options and player II has n options). Let the payoff matrix be $A = [a_{ij}]_{mn}$. Suppose there is an entry a_{pq} of A which is a minimum entry in its row and a maximum entry in its column. Formally, this means

$$a_{pq} = \text{minimum } \{a_{pj} | 1 \leq j \leq n\}$$
$$a_{pq} = \text{maximum } \{a_{iq} | 1 \leq i \leq m\}$$

Then the game is said to be *strictly determined*. The entry a_{pq} is called the *value* of the game and is also referred to as a *saddle point* of the payoff matrix.

As indicated in the above examples, the following fact is true.

Theorem 11.2.1
Let $A = [a_{ij}]_{mn}$ be the payoff matrix for a strictly determined matrix game and suppose a_{pq} is a saddle point of the payoff matrix. Then an optimal strategy for player I is to always choose option p and one for player II is to always select option q. If the players use their optimal strategies, then after each play of the game player II will pay player I an amount a_{pq} (if $a_{pq} < 0$, player I will pay player II an amount $-a_{pq}$). Finally, if $a_{pq} = 0$, the game is fair; if $a_{pq} > 0$, the game favors player I; and if $a_{pq} < 0$, the game favors player II.

In closing we point out that in analyzing the games in Examples 11.2.1 and 11.2.2, the players involved determined their optimal strategies by trying to minimize their maximum losses. In terms of the payoff matrix this means that *player I should maximize the minimum payoff from player II and that player II should minimize his maximum payoff to player I.*

In other words, for a strictly determined game, an optimal strategy for player I is a row whose smallest entry is largest and one for player II is a column whose largest entry is smallest.

Exercises for 11.2

In each of problems 1–8, determine whether or not the matrix has a saddle point (i.e., whether or not the game is strictly determined). In case the game is strictly determined, give the value of the game and the optimal strategies for the players.

1.
$$\begin{array}{cc} & \begin{array}{cc} 1 & 2 \end{array} \\ \begin{array}{c} 1 \\ 2 \end{array} & \begin{bmatrix} -1 & 3 \\ -4 & 10 \end{bmatrix} \end{array}$$

2.
$$\begin{array}{cc} & \begin{array}{cc} 1 & 2 \end{array} \\ \begin{array}{c} 1 \\ 2 \end{array} & \begin{bmatrix} 2 & -3 \\ -3 & 4 \end{bmatrix} \end{array}$$

3.
$$\begin{array}{cc} & \begin{array}{cc} 1 & 2 \end{array} \\ \begin{array}{c} 1 \\ 2 \\ 3 \end{array} & \begin{bmatrix} 3 & -7 \\ -4 & 5 \\ 0 & 1 \end{bmatrix} \end{array}$$

4.
$$\begin{array}{cc} & \begin{array}{cccc} 1 & 2 & 3 & 4 \end{array} \\ \begin{array}{c} 1 \\ 2 \\ 3 \end{array} & \begin{bmatrix} 0 & -1 & 4 & 2 \\ -6 & -2 & 1 & 5 \\ 7 & -3 & 2 & -4 \end{bmatrix} \end{array}$$

5.
$$\begin{array}{cc} & \begin{array}{ccccc} 1 & 2 & 3 & 4 & 5 \end{array} \\ \begin{array}{c} 1 \\ 2 \\ 3 \end{array} & \begin{bmatrix} 7 & -4 & 2 & -2 & 6 \\ -5 & -8 & 4 & -4 & 0 \\ 1 & 3 & 0 & 0 & 2 \end{bmatrix} \end{array}$$

6.
$$\begin{array}{cc} & \begin{array}{cc} 1 & 2 \end{array} \\ \begin{array}{c} 1 \\ 2 \end{array} & \begin{bmatrix} -2 & 5 \\ -2 & 30 \end{bmatrix} \end{array}$$

7.
$$\begin{array}{cc} & \begin{array}{cccc} 1 & 2 & 3 & 4 \end{array} \\ \begin{array}{c} 1 \\ 2 \\ 3 \end{array} & \begin{bmatrix} 5 & 3 & -7 & -5 \\ 3 & 4 & 3 & 3 \\ -3 & 6 & 0 & 3 \end{bmatrix} \end{array}$$

8.
$$\begin{array}{cc} & \begin{array}{ccc} 1 & 2 & 3 \end{array} \\ \begin{array}{c} 1 \\ 2 \\ 3 \\ 4 \end{array} & \begin{bmatrix} -4 & -2 & 3 \\ 6 & 2 & -5 \\ 7 & -1 & -8 \\ 3 & 4 & 1 \end{bmatrix} \end{array}$$

9. Suppose that each of two players (I and II) shows one or two fingers simultaneously. If the sum of the fingers showing is even, player II pays player I that sum. If the sum of the fingers showing is odd, player I pays player II that sum.
   (a) Find the payoff matrix for this game.
   (b) Is the game strictly determined?
   (c) If your answer in part (b) is "yes," what is the value of the game and what are the optimal strategies? Who has the advantage?
10. Two players each show one or two fingers at a given signal. Player II pays player I an amount equal to the sum of the fingers showing; player I pays player II an amount equal to the product of the fingers showing.
    (a) Find the payoff matrix of the game.
    (b) Is the game strictly determined?

(c) If your answer in part (b) is "yes," what is the value of the game and what are the optimal strategies? Who has the advantage?

11. Refer to problem 3, Exercises 11.1. The payoff matrix for the game is

$$\begin{bmatrix} -5 & 6 & -7 & 8 \\ 6 & -7 & 8 & -9 \\ -7 & 8 & -9 & 10 \end{bmatrix}$$

Is this game strictly determined? If so, what is the value of the game and what are the optimal strategies?

12. In the rock–paper–scissors game of problem 4, Exercises 11.1, the payoff matrix is given by

$$\begin{array}{c c c c} & R & P & S \\ R & \begin{bmatrix} 0 & -1 & 1 \\ P & 1 & 0 & -1 \\ S & -1 & 1 & 0 \end{bmatrix} \end{array}$$

Is this game strictly determined? If so, what is the value of the game and what are the optimal strategies?

13. This exercise refers to problem 5, Exercises 11.1. The payoff matrix is

$$\begin{array}{c c c} & RA & BD \\ RD & \begin{bmatrix} -1 & 4 \\ BT & 2 & -5 \end{bmatrix} \end{array}$$

where RD = red deuce, BT = black trey, etc. Is this game strictly determined? If so, what is the value of the game and whom does the game favor?

14. Refer to problem 6, Exercises 11.1. The payoff matrix for this "game" is given by

$$\begin{array}{c c c} & NE & SE \\ NW & \begin{bmatrix} -10 & 0 \\ SW & 0 & 15 \end{bmatrix} \end{array}$$

Is this game strictly determined? If so, what should each of the companies do and which one has the advantage?

15. Refer to problem 7, Exercises 11.1. The payoff matrix for this "game" is given by

$$\begin{array}{c c c c} & 1 & 2 & 3 \\ 1 & \begin{bmatrix} 10 & -1 & -3 \\ 2 & 1 & 10 & 4 \\ 3 & 3 & -4 & 10 \end{bmatrix} \end{array}$$

Is the game strictly determined? If so, what should the clothing manufacturers do, and which one has the advantage?

*16. Let

$$A = \begin{bmatrix} a & b \\ a & d \end{bmatrix}$$

be the payoff matrix for a two-person, zero-sum, 2×2 matrix game.
(a) Show that the game is strictly determined.
(b) What is the value of the game?
(c) What are the optimal strategies?

*17. Let

$$A = \begin{bmatrix} a & a \\ c & d \end{bmatrix}$$

be the payoff matrix for a 2×2 matrix game.
(a) Show that the game is strictly determined.
(b) What is the value of the game?
(c) What are the optimal strategies?

*18. Suppose that the payoff matrix for a 2×2 matrix game is given by

$$A = \begin{bmatrix} a & 0 \\ 0 & d \end{bmatrix}$$

(a) Determine necessary and sufficient conditions for the game to be strictly determined.
(b) If the game is strictly determined, what is its value?
(c) If the game is strictly determined, what are the optimal strategies?

Section 11.3   2 × 2 Matrix Games

In Section 11.2 we showed that for strictly determined games it is a fairly simple matter to determine the optimal strategies for the players and to find the value of the game. In this section we shall answer these questions for 2×2 matrix games that are not strictly determined.

Example 11.3.1   Consider the 2×2 matrix game with payoff matrix

$$A = \begin{array}{c} \\ 1 \\ 2 \end{array} \begin{matrix} 1 & 2 \\ \begin{bmatrix} 6 & -2 \\ -3 & 1 \end{bmatrix} \end{matrix}$$

First, this game is not strictly determined (i.e., A has no saddle point). To see this, first notice that the entry -2 is a minimum in the first row but is not a maximum in the second column. Hence -2 is not a saddle point. Also, -3 is a minimum in the second row, but it is not a maximum in the first column. Consequently, -3 is not a saddle point, and therefore the matrix A has no saddle point. This means that the game is not strictly determined.

Now, what should player I do? Let us apply the same reasoning to this game as we did to strictly determined games. Accordingly, player I should select the option that minimizes his maximum loss. This means that he should choose the row of the matrix whose minimum entry is largest. This is row 1, in which the minimum entry is -2, as opposed to row 2, in which the minimum entry is -3 (note: $-3 < -2$).

For player II, if he applies the criterion of minimizing his maximum loss, he should choose the column of the matrix whose maximum entry is smallest. This is column 2, in which the maximum entry is 1 as opposed to column 1, in which the maximum entry is 6. These results are summarized in Figure 11.3.1.

Figure 11.3.1

$$\begin{array}{c} \text{Player II} \\ \downarrow \\ \begin{array}{cc} 1 & 2 \end{array} \\ \text{Player I} \rightarrow \begin{array}{c} 1 \\ 2 \end{array} \begin{bmatrix} 6 & -2 \\ -3 & 1 \end{bmatrix} \end{array}$$

What will happen if the players select the options suggested by the above arguments—that player I always selects option 1 and player II always selects option 2? Then player I will, at each play, lose \$2 to player II (i.e., player II pays player I

$-2)$. This will make player I unhappy (as it should, because we will see shortly that the game is actually fair).

Now, *in contrast* to the case of strictly determined games (see p. 484), if player I learns that player II's strategy is to always select column (option) 2, then player I can improve his situation by choosing row 2 instead of row 1, in which case he will now win \$1 instead of losing \$2. This will, in turn, make player II unhappy (as it should) and he will switch to column 1 if he knows that player I will keep selecting row 2. Then player II will win \$3 instead of losing \$1. Obviously, this state of affairs will not last long, as player I will now switch back to row 1 and if player II persists in playing column 1, then player I will, at each turn, win \$6. This argument seems to indicate that the originally suggested solution (player I play option 1 and player II play option 2) is unsatisfactory and that a more suitable solution should be found.

To get an idea of what this more suitable solution should be, we analyze more carefully the problems involved in the originally suggested solution. The crucial fact here, as was already pointed out, is that whenever the strategy of one of the players is predictable, the other player can use this information to his advantage. Consequently, it appears that a more suitable strategy for the players would involve one in which neither player can predict the option that the other player will select.

Example 11.3.1 indicates that for a game which is not strictly determined, a player should vary his selection of options in order that his opponent will not be able to predict what his choice will be. The only really satisfactory way for a player to do this is to select his option at random at the beginning of each play of the game. For example, a player might toss a coin at the beginning of each play and, if it comes up heads, select option 1, whereas if it comes up tails, he will select option 2. In this case, if the coin is fair, this results in the player choosing option 1 50 percent of the time and option 2 50 percent of the time. This, of course, may or may not be an optimal strategy. It might, perhaps, be more preferable for the player to select option 1 30 percent of the time and option 2 70 percent of the time.

With the above comments in mind, we now make the following definition.

Definition

Let $P = [p_1, p_2]$ be a probability row vector of length 2. This means that $p_1, p_2 \geq 0$ and $p_1 + p_2 = 1$. Then P is called a *mixed strategy for player I*. The interpretation is that at each play of the game, player I chooses option 1 with probability p_1 and option 2 with probability p_2. Similarly, let

$$Q = \begin{bmatrix} q_1 \\ q_2 \end{bmatrix}$$

be a probability column vector (i.e., $q_1, q_2, \geq 0, q_1 + q_2 = 1$). Then Q is called a *mixed strategy for player II*. The interpretation is that at each play of the game, player II chooses option 1 with probability q_1 and option 2 with probability q_2.

At this point these several remarks are in order. First, if as in the case of a strictly determined game, the optimal strategy for a player is to always select the same option, this can be considered as a mixed strategy. For example, suppose it is determined that player I should always select option 2. Then his mixed strategy is the probability row vector $P = [0, 1]$. Such mixed strategies are often referred to as *pure strategies*.

The second remark involves the practical method of utilizing a mixed strategy. If, for example, player II uses the mixed strategy

$$Q = \begin{bmatrix} \frac{1}{2} \\ \frac{1}{2} \end{bmatrix}$$

it is a simple matter for him to apply this strategy. At the beginning of each play of the game he tosses a *fair* coin. If it comes up heads he selects option 1, and if it comes up tails he selects option 2. But suppose that player II wishes to use the mixed strategy

$$Q = \begin{bmatrix} \frac{3}{5} \\ \frac{2}{5} \end{bmatrix}$$

so that options 1 and 2 should be played, respectively, 60 and 40 percent of the time. Tossing a (fair) coin will not work. However, several methods will work. One method would be to consult a table of random digits from 0 to 9, at the beginning of each play of the game. If the digit observed is between 0 and 5, inclusive, the player should select option 1, while if the digit observed is between 6 and 9, inclusive, the player should select option 2.

We will learn in Section 11.6 that, if mixed strategies are allowed, each player has an optimal mixed strategy for playing the game. Moreover, the methods of linear programming can be applied to determine these optimal strategies.

When both players use their optimal strategies, then the expected payoff per play of the game is called the *value* of the game and is denoted by v. In particular, then, if $v = 0$, the game is fair; if $v > 0$, the game favors player I; and if $v < 0$, the game favors player II.

At this point we will simply give the formulas for determining the optimal strategies for the players and the value of the game. The methods for obtaining these formulas will be discussed in Section 11.5.

Theorem 11.3.1
Consider a 2 × 2 matrix game with payoff matrix

$$A = \begin{bmatrix} a & b \\ c & d \end{bmatrix}$$

Suppose that the game is not strictly determined so that A has no saddle point. Then the optimal strategies for the players are

$$P^* = [(d - c)/(a - b - c + d), (a - b)/(a - b - c + d)] \qquad (11.3.1)$$

and

$$Q^* = \begin{bmatrix} (d - b)/(a - b - c + d) \\ (a - c)/(a - b - c + d) \end{bmatrix} \qquad (11.3.2)$$

Moreover, the value of the game is

$$v = (ad - bc)/(a - b - c + d) \qquad (11.3.3)$$

The results of this theorem will now be applied to some specific examples.

Example 11.3.2 Consider the 2×2 matrix game of Example 11.3.1. The payoff matrix is

$$A = \begin{bmatrix} 6 & -2 \\ -3 & 1 \end{bmatrix}$$

As was pointed out in Example 11.3.1, this matrix has no saddle point, and consequently Theorem 11.3.1 applies. Here $a = 6$, $b = -2$, $c = -3$, and $d = 1$. Now, we have

$$d - c = 4, \, a - b = 8, \, d - b = 3, \, a - c = 9$$

and $a - b - c + d = 12$. Thus the optimal strategy for player I is

$$P^* = [\tfrac{4}{12}, \tfrac{8}{12}] = [\tfrac{1}{3}, \tfrac{2}{3}]$$

and that for player II is

$$Q^* = \begin{bmatrix} \tfrac{3}{12} \\ \tfrac{9}{12} \end{bmatrix} = \begin{bmatrix} \tfrac{1}{4} \\ \tfrac{3}{4} \end{bmatrix}$$

The value of the game is

$$v = \frac{ad - bc}{12} = \frac{6 \cdot 1 - (-2)(-3)}{12} = \frac{6 - 6}{12} = 0$$

and hence the game is fair, as was suggested in Example 11.3.1.

Example 11.3.3 Consider again the 2×2 matrix game introduced in Example 11.1.1. The payoff matrix for the game is given in Figure 11.1.1. It is

$$A = \begin{bmatrix} 2 & -3 \\ -3 & 4 \end{bmatrix}$$

Many people think that this game is fair. However, as we shall see in a moment, it is not. In the notation of Theorem 11.3.1, $a = 2$, $b = -3$, $c = -3$, $d = 4$. Now

$$d - c = 7, \quad a - b = 5, \quad d - b = 7, \quad a - c = 5$$

and $a - b - c + d = 12$. Consequently, player I's optimal strategy is

$$P^* = [\tfrac{7}{12}, \tfrac{5}{12}]$$

and player II's is

$$Q^* = \begin{bmatrix} \tfrac{7}{12} \\ \tfrac{5}{12} \end{bmatrix}$$

The value of the game is

$$v = \frac{ad - bc}{12} = \frac{2 \cdot 4 - (-3)(-3)}{12} = \frac{8 - 9}{12} = -\frac{1}{12}$$

and therefore the game is biased in favor of player II. On the average player I will lose $\$\tfrac{1}{12}$ to player II. For example, after 120 plays of the game, player II will be about $\$10$ ahead.

There is one other quite interesting aspect of this game. If both players use their optimal strategies, then, although player I will lose money in the long run, he will, nevertheless, win more than half of the games. The problem is that the majority of times that he actually does win he will win $2 and not $4.

To see that the above statements are true, let

$$W = \text{event player I wins at a given trial}$$
$$E_1 = \text{event player I selects option 1}$$
$$E_2 = \text{event player I selects option 2}$$
$$F_1 = \text{event player II selects option 1}$$
$$F_2 = \text{event player II selects option 2}$$

Then $W = (E_1 \cap F_1) \cup (E_2 \cap F_2)$, so, by the addition principle of probability,

$$\Pr(W) = \Pr(E_1 \cap F_1) + \Pr(E_2 \cap F_2)$$

Also the events E_1 and F_1 are independent, as are E_2 and F_2. Thus, by the multiplication principle of probability,

$$\Pr(W) = \Pr(E_1)\Pr(F_1) + \Pr(E_2)\Pr(F_2)$$
$$= (\tfrac{7}{12})(\tfrac{7}{12}) + (\tfrac{5}{12})(\tfrac{5}{12}) = \tfrac{74}{144} \doteq .514 > \tfrac{1}{2}$$

Moreover, given that player I wins at a certain trial, the probability that he wins $2 is

$$\Pr(E_1 \cap F_1 \mid W) = \frac{\Pr(E_1 \cap F_1 \cap W)}{\Pr(W)} = \frac{\Pr(E_1 \cap F_1)}{\Pr(W)} = \frac{(\tfrac{7}{12})^2}{\tfrac{74}{144}} = \tfrac{49}{74} \doteq .662$$

Exercises for 11.3

1. For a two-person, zero-sum, 2×2 matrix game give
   (a) Two examples of mixed strategies for player I.
   (b) Two examples of pure strategies for player I.
   (c) Two examples of mixed strategies for player II.
   (d) Two examples of pure strategies for player II.
2. How many pure strategies are there for player I involved in a 2×2 matrix game? for player II?
3. Determine which of the following vectors are mixed strategies for player I involved in a 2×2 matrix game. For those which are mixed strategies, indicate the ones that are pure strategies.

   (a) $[\tfrac{1}{2}, \tfrac{1}{2}]$ (b) $[\tfrac{3}{4}, \tfrac{1}{4}]$

   (c) $[\tfrac{3}{2}, -\tfrac{1}{2}]$ (d) $[1, 0]$

   (e) $[\tfrac{1}{2}, \tfrac{3}{4}]$ (f) $[0, 1]$

   (g) $[1, 1]$ (h) $\begin{bmatrix} \tfrac{1}{4} \\ \tfrac{3}{4} \end{bmatrix}$

4. Determine which of the following vectors are mixed strategies for player II involved in a 2×2 matrix game. For those which are mixed strategies, indicate the ones that are also pure strategies.

   (a) $[\tfrac{1}{4}, \tfrac{3}{4}]$ (b) $\begin{bmatrix} -\tfrac{1}{8} \\ \tfrac{9}{8} \end{bmatrix}$

   (c) $\begin{bmatrix} 0 \\ 1 \end{bmatrix}$ (d) $\begin{bmatrix} \tfrac{1}{4} \\ \tfrac{3}{4} \end{bmatrix}$

(e) $\begin{bmatrix} \frac{7}{12} \\ \frac{5}{12} \end{bmatrix}$ (f) $\begin{bmatrix} 1 \\ 0 \end{bmatrix}$

(g) $\begin{bmatrix} \frac{3}{4} \\ \frac{1}{2} \end{bmatrix}$ (h) $[.6, .4]$

In each of problems 5–10, determine the optimal strategies for the players involved in the 2×2 matrix game with the given payoff matrix. Also, give the value of the game and indicate which (if any) of the players the game favors.

5. $\begin{bmatrix} 1 & -1 \\ -1 & 1 \end{bmatrix}$

6. $\begin{bmatrix} 2 & -1 \\ -4 & 3 \end{bmatrix}$

7. $\begin{bmatrix} 0 & 2 \\ 1 & -5 \end{bmatrix}$

8. $\begin{bmatrix} 2 & -1 \\ -2 & -5 \end{bmatrix}$

9. $\begin{bmatrix} -1 & 3 \\ -4 & 10 \end{bmatrix}$

10. $\begin{bmatrix} 5 & -8 \\ -1 & 3 \end{bmatrix}$

11. Refer to problem 5, Exercises 11.1. The payoff matrix is

$$\begin{array}{cc} & RA \quad BD \\ \begin{array}{c} RD \\ BT \end{array} & \begin{bmatrix} -1 & 4 \\ 2 & -5 \end{bmatrix} \end{array}$$

where RD = red deuce, BT = black trey, etc.
(a) Use the methods of this section to determine the optimal strategies for the players.
(b) What is the value of the game?
(c) Whom does the game favor?
(d) About how much will the favored player be ahead after 100 plays of the game?

*12. Consider a two-person, zero-sum, 2×2 matrix game with the payoff matrix

$$\begin{bmatrix} a & b \\ c & d \end{bmatrix}$$

(a) Show that the game is *nonstrictly* determined if and only if one of the two following conditions holds:
    (1) $a < b$, $a < c$, $d < b$, and $d < c$
    (2) $a > b$, $a > c$, $d > b$, and $d > c$
(b) What do the above conditions mean in terms of the entries on the two diagonals of the matrix?

13. Suppose that a 2×2 matrix game has the payoff matrix

$$\begin{bmatrix} a & b \\ c & d \end{bmatrix}$$

and assume that the game is nonstrictly determined.
(a) Show that the game is fair if and only if $ad = bc$.
(b) Show that neither of the optimal mixed strategies for the players is a pure strategy. (*Hint:* Problem 12.)

14. Assume that the payoff matrix for a two-person, zero-sum, 2×2 matrix game is given by

$$\begin{bmatrix} a & 0 \\ 0 & d \end{bmatrix}$$

and suppose that the game is *nonstrictly* determined.
(a) What can you conclude about the product ad?
(b) What is the value of the game?
(c) What are the optimal strategies for the players?

Section 11.4 $m \times n$ Matrix Games

In Section 11.3 we analyzed 2×2 matrix games which are not strictly determined. In this section we shall apply similar arguments in order to consider $m \times n$ matrix games that are not strictly determined.

As in the case of 2×2 nonstrictly determined matrix games, the players involved in an $m \times n$ matrix game, which is not strictly determined, should vary their selections of options in order that their opponent will not be able to predict the option to be chosen. In other words, the players should use *mixed strategies* (that are not pure).

Definition

Consider a two-person, zero-sum, $m \times n$ matrix game. Recall that this means that player I has m options and player II has n options. A *mixed strategy for player I* is a probability row vector $P = [p_1, p_2, \ldots, p_m]$ of length m. The interpretation is as before: if player I uses the strategy P, this means that at the beginning of each trial of the game he chooses option 1 with probability p_1, option 2 with probability p_2, and so on. A *mixed strategy for player II* is a probability column vector

$$Q = \begin{bmatrix} q_1 \\ q_2 \\ \vdots \\ q_n \end{bmatrix}$$

of length n.

Example 11.4.1 For a 4×3 matrix game the mixed strategies for player I are probability row vectors of length 4 and those for player II are probability column vectors of length 3. For example, if player I uses the mixed strategy $P = [\frac{1}{4}, 0, \frac{1}{8}, \frac{5}{8}]$, he chooses option 1 with probability $\frac{1}{4}$, never chooses option 2, chooses option 3 with probability $\frac{1}{8}$, and chooses option 4 with probability $\frac{5}{8}$. Two examples of mixed strategies for player II are

$$Q_1 = \begin{bmatrix} \frac{1}{4} \\ \frac{1}{2} \\ \frac{1}{4} \end{bmatrix} \quad \text{and} \quad Q_2 = \begin{bmatrix} 0 \\ 0 \\ 1 \end{bmatrix}$$

If player II employs strategy Q_1, he will choose options 1 and 3 with probability $\frac{1}{4}$ each and option 2 with probability $\frac{1}{2}$. On the other hand, if he uses strategy Q_2, he will always select option 3 (this is an example of a mixed strategy that is pure).

In what follows we will develop a procedure that will allow us to obtain a method for determining optimal (mixed) strategies for the players involved in an $m \times n$ matrix game. The main problem here is to determine what criteria should be used to decide upon whether a particular strategy is "good" or "bad."

Let us return, for the moment, to strictly determined games in which the optimal strategies are pure. That is, each player should always select that option which *minimizes his maximum possible loss.* For player I this means that his optimal (pure) strategy is to always select that option whose resulting payoff, against *any* option chosen by player II, is as large as possible (i.e., he should choose that option which maximizes the minimum payoff). For example, consider the 2×3 strictly determined game whose payoff matrix is shown in Figure 11.4.1. If player I always selects option 1,

Figure 11.4.1

$$\begin{array}{c} \\ 1 \\ 2 \end{array} \begin{array}{ccc} 1 & 2 & 3 \\ \left[\begin{array}{ccc} 3 & 5 & 2 \\ 4 & 7 & 1 \end{array}\right] \end{array}$$

he will win at least \$2 regardless of what player II does. On the other hand, if he always selects option 2, he will win at least \$1, regardless of what player II does. According to the above criterion, player I should always select option 1.

Now, as mentioned above, in the case of a nonstrictly determined game it is necessary for each player to use a strategy that results in his choosing different options at various plays of the game (i.e., each player should use a mixed strategy). However, if a player uses a mixed strategy, then at the beginning of the game he will not know, for certain, which option he will actually choose. Consequently, there is no way in which he will be able to determine what his maximum possible loss will be, because he does not even know which option he will select. Therefore, in contrast to what is done for strictly determined games, the player has no way of minimizing his maximum possible loss because of the fact that he will be considering mixed strategies.

The way around this difficulty is to consider averages. Each player should choose a mixed strategy that minimizes his maximum possible *expected* loss. For player I this means that he should select a mixed strategy that *on the average* will result in the maximum payoff regardless of what player II does. On the other hand, this means that player II should select a mixed strategy that *on the average* will result in the minimum payoff, regardless of what player I decides to do.

To help in the understanding of the above ideas, the following example is presented.

Example 11.4.2 Consider the 2×3 nonstrictly determined matrix game with payoff matrix

$$\begin{array}{c} \\ 1 \\ 2 \end{array} \begin{array}{ccc} 1 & 2 & 3 \\ \left[\begin{array}{ccc} 8 & -3 & 10 \\ -1 & 7 & -2 \end{array}\right] \end{array}$$

Suppose that player I uses the mixed strategy $P_1 = [\frac{1}{4}, \frac{3}{4}]$. That is, he selects option 1 with probability $\frac{1}{4}$ and option 2 with probability $\frac{3}{4}$. If player II selects option 1, then player I's expected gain is

$$8 \cdot \tfrac{1}{4} + (-1) \cdot \tfrac{3}{4} = \tfrac{5}{4} = \$1.25$$

(i.e., he will, on the average, win $1.25). This is because player I selects option 1 with probability $\frac{1}{4}$, which results in a gain of 8, or player I selects option 2 with probability $\frac{3}{4}$, which results in a gain of -1 (see Section 4.16 for the definition of expected value). If player II selects option 2, player I's expected gain is

$$-3 \cdot \frac{1}{4} + 7 \cdot \frac{3}{4} = \frac{18}{4} = \$4.50$$

and if player II selects option 3, player I's expected gain is

$$10 \cdot \frac{1}{4} + (-2) \cdot \frac{3}{4} = \frac{4}{4} = \$1.00$$

The minimum expected gain for player I when he uses the mixed strategy P_1 is, therefore, $1. Thus, if player I uses the mixed strategy $P_1 = [\frac{1}{4}, \frac{3}{4}]$, then, regardless of what player II does, he can be assured that *on the average* he will gain at least $1.

Suppose, on the other hand, that player I uses the mixed strategy $P_2 = [\frac{8}{19}, \frac{11}{19}]$. That is, he selects option 1 with probability $\frac{8}{19}$ and option 2 with probability $\frac{11}{19}$. Then, when player II selects options 1, 2, and 3, respectively, player I's expected gains are

$$8 \cdot \frac{8}{19} + (-1) \cdot \frac{11}{19} = \frac{53}{19} \doteq \$2.79$$
$$-3 \cdot \frac{8}{19} + 7 \cdot \frac{11}{19} = \frac{53}{19} \doteq \$2.79$$

and

$$10 \cdot \frac{8}{19} + (-2) \cdot \frac{11}{19} = \frac{58}{19} \doteq \$3.05$$

respectively. Consequently, if player I uses the mixed strategy $P_2 = [\frac{8}{19}, \frac{11}{19}]$, then, regardless of which option player II selects, he can be certain that on the average he will gain at least $\frac{53}{19}$ ($\doteq \$2.79$).

To summarize the above results, we have seen that player I's minimum expected gain using the mixed strategy P_1 is $1 while his minimum expected gain using the mixed strategy P_2 is $\frac{53}{19}$ ($\doteq \$2.79$). Thus the mixed strategy P_2 is preferable to P_1. We will see later that, in fact, P_2 is the optimal mixed strategy for player I. In other words, $P_2 = [\frac{8}{19}, \frac{11}{19}]$ is the mixed strategy for player I which yields the largest possible minimum expected payoff.

Let us now consider player II. Assume that he uses the mixed strategy

$$Q_1 = \begin{bmatrix} \frac{1}{8} \\ \frac{1}{2} \\ \frac{3}{8} \end{bmatrix}$$

so that he chooses options 1, 2, and 3 with probabilities $\frac{1}{8}$, $\frac{1}{2}$, and $\frac{3}{8}$, respectively. If player I selects option 1, then player II's expected loss is

$$8 \cdot \frac{1}{8} + (-3) \cdot \frac{1}{2} + 10 \cdot \frac{3}{8} = \frac{26}{8} = \$3.25$$

(i.e., he will, on the average, lose $3.25). On the other hand, if player I selects option 2, then player II's expected loss is

$$(-1) \cdot \frac{1}{8} + 7 \cdot \frac{1}{2} + (-2) \cdot \frac{3}{8} = \frac{21}{8} \doteq \$2.62$$

Hence, on the average, the worst loss player II will encounter by using strategy Q_1 is $3.25. That is, if player II uses the mixed strategy Q_1, his maximum expected loss is $3.25.

Now, suppose instead that player II uses the mixed strategy

$$Q_2 = \begin{bmatrix} \frac{10}{19} \\ \frac{9}{19} \\ 0 \end{bmatrix}$$

so that he chooses option 1 with probability $\frac{10}{19}$, option 2 with probability $\frac{9}{19}$, and option 3 with probability 0 (i.e., he never chooses option 3). Then, when player I selects option 1, player II's expected loss is

$$8 \cdot \tfrac{10}{19} + (-3) \cdot \tfrac{9}{19} + 10 \cdot 0 = \tfrac{53}{19} \doteq \$2.79$$

and when player I selects option 2, player II's expected loss is

$$(-1) \cdot \tfrac{10}{19} + 7 \cdot \tfrac{9}{19} + (-2) \cdot 0 = \tfrac{53}{19} \doteq \$2.79$$

Thus, if player II uses the mixed strategy Q_2, then, regardless of what action player I takes, his expected loss is at most $\$\frac{53}{19}$.

In summary, then, if player II uses the mixed strategy Q_1, his expected loss is at most \$3.25, whereas if he uses the mixed strategy Q_2, his expected loss is at most $\$\frac{53}{19}$ ($\doteq \$2.79$). Consequently, the mixed strategy Q_2 is preferable to Q_1 as far as player II is concerned. We shall see later that the mixed strategy Q_2 is optimal for player II in the sense that by using it, the maximum expected payoff, against any strategy of player I, is kept to a minimum.

Exercises for 11.4

1. For a two-person, zero-sum, 5×4 matrix game, give
    (a) Two examples of mixed strategies for player I.
    (b) Two examples of mixed strategies for player II.
    (c) All pure strategies for player I.
    (d) All pure strategies for player II.
2. How many pure strategies are there for player I involved in an $m \times n$ matrix game? for player II?

In problems 3 and 4, determine which of the following are mixed strategies for player I, which are mixed strategies for player II, and which are neither. For those which are mixed strategies, indicate the ones that are also pure strategies.

3. The payoff matrix is 3×4:

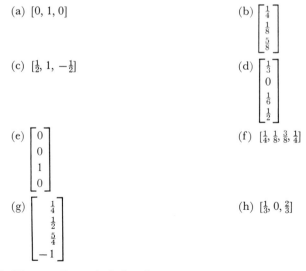

(a) $[0, 1, 0]$

(b) $\begin{bmatrix} \frac{1}{4} \\ \frac{1}{8} \\ \frac{5}{8} \end{bmatrix}$

(c) $[\frac{1}{2}, 1, -\frac{1}{2}]$

(d) $\begin{bmatrix} \frac{1}{3} \\ 0 \\ \frac{1}{6} \\ \frac{1}{2} \end{bmatrix}$

(e) $\begin{bmatrix} 0 \\ 0 \\ 1 \\ 0 \end{bmatrix}$

(f) $[\frac{1}{4}, \frac{1}{8}, \frac{3}{8}, \frac{1}{4}]$

(g) $\begin{bmatrix} \frac{1}{4} \\ \frac{1}{2} \\ \frac{5}{4} \\ -1 \end{bmatrix}$

(h) $[\frac{1}{3}, 0, \frac{2}{3}]$

4. The payoff matrix is 5×2.
    (a) $[\frac{1}{3}, \frac{2}{3}]$

    (b) $\begin{bmatrix} \frac{2}{3} \\ \frac{1}{3} \\ \frac{1}{2} \end{bmatrix}$

(c) $[0, 1, 0, 0, 0]$

(d) $\begin{bmatrix} \frac{3}{4} \\ \frac{1}{4} \end{bmatrix}$

(e) $[\frac{1}{5}, \frac{2}{5}, 0, 0, \frac{2}{5}]$

(f) $\begin{bmatrix} 0 \\ 1 \end{bmatrix}$

(g) $[\frac{1}{4}, \frac{1}{8}, \frac{2}{8}, \frac{1}{2}, -\frac{1}{8}]$

(h) $\begin{bmatrix} \frac{1}{6} \\ \frac{1}{6} \\ \frac{1}{3} \\ \frac{1}{2} \end{bmatrix}$

In each of problems 5–9, determine the minimum expected gain for player I when he uses the specified mixed strategy for the given matrix game (see Example 11.4.2).

5. $P = [\frac{1}{3}, \frac{2}{3}]$ and

$$A = \begin{array}{c} \\ 1 \\ 2 \end{array} \begin{array}{cc} 1 & 2 \\ \left[\begin{array}{cc} 9 & -3 \\ -3 & 6 \end{array} \right] \end{array}$$

6. $P = [\frac{2}{5}, \frac{3}{5}]$ and

$$A = \begin{array}{c} \\ 1 \\ 2 \end{array} \begin{array}{ccc} 1 & 2 & 3 \\ \left[\begin{array}{ccc} -5 & 10 & 5 \\ 20 & -5 & 10 \end{array} \right] \end{array}$$

7. $P = [\frac{1}{4}, \frac{1}{2}, \frac{1}{4}]$ and

$$A = \begin{array}{c} \\ 1 \\ 2 \\ 3 \end{array} \begin{array}{cc} 1 & 2 \\ \left[\begin{array}{cc} 4 & -2 \\ -8 & 10 \\ 4 & -8 \end{array} \right] \end{array}$$

8. $P = [\frac{1}{3}, 0, \frac{1}{6}, \frac{1}{2}]$ and

$$A = \begin{array}{c} \\ 1 \\ 2 \\ 3 \\ 4 \end{array} \begin{array}{ccc} 1 & 2 & 3 \\ \left[\begin{array}{ccc} 6 & 3 & -3 \\ 4 & -2 & 1 \\ -12 & 3 & 6 \\ 1 & 0 & 2 \end{array} \right] \end{array}$$

9. $P = [\frac{1}{8}, \frac{1}{4}, \frac{5}{8}]$ and

$$A = \begin{array}{c} \\ 1 \\ 2 \\ 3 \end{array} \begin{array}{cccc} 1 & 2 & 3 & 4 \\ \left[\begin{array}{cccc} 1 & 0 & -4 & 2 \\ 3 & 6 & -5 & -4 \\ -2 & -1 & 3 & 7 \end{array} \right] \end{array}$$

In each of problems 10–14, determine the maximum expected loss for player II when he uses the specified mixed strategy for the given matrix game (see Example 11.4.2).

10. $Q = \begin{bmatrix} \frac{1}{3} \\ \frac{2}{3} \end{bmatrix}$ and $A = \begin{array}{c} \\ 1 \\ 2 \end{array} \begin{array}{cc} 1 & 2 \\ \left[\begin{array}{cc} 9 & -3 \\ -3 & 6 \end{array} \right] \end{array}$

11. $Q = \begin{bmatrix} \frac{2}{5} \\ \frac{1}{5} \\ \frac{2}{5} \end{bmatrix}$ and $A = \begin{array}{c} \\ 1 \\ 2 \end{array} \begin{array}{ccc} 1 & 2 & 3 \\ \left[\begin{array}{ccc} -5 & 10 & 5 \\ 20 & -5 & 10 \end{array} \right] \end{array}$

12.
$$Q = \begin{bmatrix} \frac{1}{4} \\ \frac{3}{4} \end{bmatrix} \quad \text{and} \quad A = \begin{array}{c} \\ 1 \\ 2 \\ 3 \end{array} \begin{array}{c} \begin{array}{cc} 1 & 2 \end{array} \\ \begin{bmatrix} 4 & -2 \\ -8 & 10 \\ 4 & -8 \end{bmatrix} \end{array}$$

13.
$$Q = \begin{bmatrix} \frac{1}{8} \\ \frac{1}{2} \\ \frac{3}{8} \end{bmatrix} \quad \text{and} \quad A = \begin{array}{c} \\ 1 \\ 2 \\ 3 \end{array} \begin{array}{c} \begin{array}{ccc} 1 & 2 & 3 \end{array} \\ \begin{bmatrix} 1 & -4 & 0 \\ -6 & 2 & -1 \\ 3 & -8 & 2 \end{bmatrix} \end{array}$$

14.
$$Q = \begin{bmatrix} \frac{1}{4} \\ \frac{1}{8} \\ \frac{1}{2} \\ \frac{1}{8} \end{bmatrix} \quad \text{and} \quad A = \begin{array}{c} \\ 1 \\ 2 \\ 3 \end{array} \begin{array}{c} \begin{array}{cccc} 1 & 2 & 3 & 4 \end{array} \\ \begin{bmatrix} 1 & 0 & -4 & 2 \\ 3 & 6 & -5 & -4 \\ -2 & -1 & 3 & 7 \end{bmatrix} \end{array}$$

15. Refer to Example 11.3.2. The payoff matrix is

$$A = \begin{bmatrix} 6 & -2 \\ -3 & 1 \end{bmatrix}$$

In Example 11.3.2 it was shown that the optimal mixed strategies for the players are

$$P^* = [\tfrac{1}{3}, \tfrac{2}{3}] \quad \text{and} \quad Q^* = \begin{bmatrix} \frac{1}{4} \\ \frac{3}{4} \end{bmatrix}$$

It was also indicated that the value of the game is 0. Find the minimum expected gain for player I when he uses P^* and the maximum expected loss for player II when he uses Q^*.

16. Refer to Example 11.1.1, where the payoff matrix is

$$A = \begin{bmatrix} 2 & -3 \\ -3 & 4 \end{bmatrix}$$

In Example 11.3.3 we found that the optimal strategies for players I and II are given by

$$P^* = [\tfrac{7}{12}, \tfrac{5}{12}] \quad \text{and} \quad Q^* = \begin{bmatrix} \frac{7}{12} \\ \frac{5}{12} \end{bmatrix}$$

The value of the game was determined to be $-\frac{1}{12}$. Find the minimum expected gain for player I when he uses P^* and also find the maximum expected loss for player II when he uses Q^*.

17. Let

$$A = \begin{bmatrix} a & b \\ c & d \end{bmatrix}$$

be the payoff matrix for a nonstrictly determined 2×2 matrix game. Let P^* and Q^* be the optimal mixed strategies for players I and II, respectively. Also, let v be the value of the game. Use Theorem 11.3.1 to determine

(a) The minimum expected gain for player I when he uses P^*.
(b) The maximum expected loss for player II when he uses Q^*.
(c) P^*A
(d) AQ^*
(e) P^*AQ^*

Section 11.5   Determination of Optimal Strategies

In Section 11.4 we indicated that an optimal mixed strategy for a player involved in an $m \times n$ matrix game is one that minimizes his maximum expected loss against any strategy which his opponent chooses to employ. The fact that there always exist such optimal strategies is not easy to prove and we postpone its proof until Section 11.6.

In this section we shall present an algorithm (method) for determining the optimal mixed strategies for the players involved in an $m \times n$ matrix game. As a by-product of this we will obtain the value of the game, which is just the expected gain of player I (or the expected loss of player II) if both players use their optimal strategies. Clearly, if $v = 0$, the game is fair; if $v > 0$, the game favors player I; and if $v < 0$, the game favors player II.

Basically, the algorithm for determining the optimal strategies for the players and the value of the game is just the simplex algorithm for solving linear programs. This is not surprising, because the problem involves determining the values of unknowns that optimize certain quantities. Specifically there are two problems:

1. Determine the values $p_1, p_2, \ldots, p_m$ such that the mixed strategy $P = [p_1, p_2, \ldots, p_m]$ for player I *maximizes* the minimum expected payoff.
2. Determine the values $q_1, q_2, \ldots, q_n$ such that the mixed strategy

$$Q = \begin{bmatrix} q_1 \\ q_2 \\ \vdots \\ q_n \end{bmatrix}$$

for player II *minimizes* the maximum expected payoff.

The problems, as they stand, are not directly solvable by the simplex algorithm, because they are not in the required form (the form of a linear program). However, a suitable modification will put them in such a form.

The description of the algorithm for determining optimal strategies is presented below. The explanation of why this algorithm works will be given in Section 11.6. Consider an $m \times n$ matrix game with payoff matrix $A = [a_{ij}]_{mn}$. Throughout, $P = [p_1, p_2, \ldots, p_m]$ and

$$Q = \begin{bmatrix} q_1 \\ q_2 \\ \vdots \\ q_n \end{bmatrix}$$

will refer, respectively, to mixed strategies for players I and II. In solving linear programs the first step in the simplex algorithm is to set up the problem in tableau form (the Tucker tableau). For matrix games the initial step is, similarly, to put the problem in tableau form, called the *game tableau*. Its general form is given in Figure 11.5.1.

Figure 11.5.1

	v	q_1	q_2	$\cdots$	q_n	
$-u$	0	1	1	$\cdots$	1	$= -(-1)$
p_1	-1	a_{11}	a_{12}	$\cdots$	a_{1n}	$= -t_1$
p_2	-1	a_{21}	a_{22}	$\cdots$	a_{2n}	$= -t_2$
$\vdots$	$\vdots$	$\vdots$	$\vdots$	$\ddots$	$\vdots$	$\vdots$
p_m	-1	a_{m1}	a_{m2}	$\cdots$	a_{mn}	$= -t_m$
$\|$	$\|$	$\|$	$\|$		$\|$	
	-1	s_1	s_2	$\cdots$	s_n	

Example 11.5.1 Consider the 2×3 matrix game of Example 11.4.2. Its payoff matrix is

$$A = \begin{array}{c} \\ 1 \\ 2 \end{array}\begin{array}{ccc} 1 & 2 & 3 \\ \left[\begin{array}{ccc} 8 & -3 & 10 \\ -1 & 7 & -2 \end{array}\right] \end{array}$$

The game tableau for this game is shown in Figure 11.5.2.

Figure 11.5.2

	v	q_1	q_2	q_3	
$-u$	0	1	1	1	$= -(-1)$
p_1	-1	8	-3	10	$= -t_1$
p_2	-1	-1	7	-2	$= -t_2$
$\|$	$\|$	$\|$	$\|$	$\|$	
	-1	s_1	s_2	s_3	

Now, as stated, the game tableau is not in the specific form required for the application of the simplex algorithm. To put it in the desired form it is necessary to perform the following steps:

---

1. Rearrange the rows (if necessary) so that the lower right-hand entry of the game tableau is a maximum in the last column of the payoff matrix. In terms of the notation, this means that the rows of the tableau should be rearranged so that

$$a_{mn} \geq a_{in} \qquad (11.5.1)$$

for $i = 1, 2, \ldots, m - 1$. We emphasize that it is also required that the corresponding labels of the tableau be interchanged.
2. Pivot on the upper right-hand entry of the tableau.
3. Pivot on the lower left-hand entry of the tableau.

Example 11.5.2 Consider again the 2×3 matrix game of Example 11.5.1, whose game tableau is given in Figure 11.5.2. We apply steps 1–3 to put the tableau in the form of a linear programming tableau.

1. The lower right-hand entry of the game tableau is -2. Since $-2 < 10$, the first and second rows of the tableau are interchanged so that Eq. (11.5.1) holds:

	v	q_1	q_2	q_3	
$-u$	0	1	1	1*	$= -(-1)$
p_2	-1	-1	7	-2	$= -t_2$
p_1	-1	8	-3	10	$= -t_1$
	$\parallel$	$\parallel$	$\parallel$	$\parallel$	
	-1	s_1	s_2	s_3	

2. Next we pivot on the upper right-hand entry of the tableau. The resulting tableau (with the interior lines suppressed) is

	v	q_1	q_2	-1	
s_3	0	1	1	1	$= -q_3$
p_2	-1	1	9	2	$= -t_2$
p_1	-1*	-2	-13	-10	$= -t_1$
	$\parallel$	$\parallel$	$\parallel$	$\parallel$	
	-1	s_1	s_2	$-u$	

3. Finally, we pivot on the lower left-hand entry of the tableau and insert new interior lines in the resulting tableau, to obtain Figure 11.5.3. Thus, by using steps 1–3 we have transformed the initial game tableau given in Figure 11.5.2 into the Tucker tableau in Figure 11.5.3.

Figure 11.5.3

	t_1	q_1	q_2	-1	
s_3	0	1	1	1	$= -q_3$
p_2	-1	3	22	12	$= -t_2$
-1	-1	2	13	10	$= -v$
	$\parallel$	$\parallel$	$\parallel$	$\parallel$	
	p_1	s_1	s_2	$-u$	

Now that the game tableau has been transformed into a linear programming tableau, we can use the simplex algorithm. The steps in the simplex algorithm yield the following sequence of tableaux:

	t_1	q_1	q_2	-1	
s_3	0	1^*	1	1	$= -q_3$
p_2	-1	3	22	12	$= -t_2$
-1	-1	2	13	10	$= -v$

	$\|\|$	$\|\|$	$\|\|$	$\|\|$
	p_1	s_1	s_2	$-u$

	t_1	q_3	q_2	-1	
s_1	0	1	1	1	$= -q_1$
p_2	-1	-3	19^*	9	$= -t_2$
-1	-1	-2	11	8	$= -v$

	$\|\|$	$\|\|$	$\|\|$	$\|\|$
	p_1	s_3	s_2	$-u$

	t_1	q_3	t_2	-1	
s_1	$\frac{1}{19}$	$\frac{22}{19}$	$-\frac{1}{19}$	$\frac{10}{19}$	$= -q_1$
s_2	$-\frac{1}{19}$	$-\frac{3}{19}$	$\frac{1}{19}$	$\frac{9}{19}$	$= -q_2$
-1	$-\frac{8}{19}$	$-\frac{5}{19}$	$-\frac{11}{19}$	$\frac{53}{19}$	$= -v$

	$\|\|$	$\|\|$	$\|\|$	$\|\|$
	p_1	s_3	p_2	$-u$

Reading this final tableau in the usual way gives the following results: $p_1 = \frac{8}{19}, p_2 = \frac{11}{19}, q_1 = \frac{10}{19}, q_2 = \frac{9}{19}, q_3 = 0$, and $v = \frac{53}{19}$. These are the desired values: the optimal mixed strategy for player I is

$$P^* = [\tfrac{8}{19}, \tfrac{11}{19}]$$

That for player II is

$$Q^* = \begin{bmatrix} \frac{10}{19} \\ \frac{9}{19} \\ 0 \end{bmatrix}$$

Finally, the value of the game is $\frac{53}{19}$. These results verify the contentions of Example 11.4.2.

Example 11.5.3   Solve the 2×2 matrix game of Example 11.1.1 by using the simplex algorithm.

The payoff matrix for the game is given in Figure 11.1.1. It is

$$\begin{bmatrix} 2 & -3 \\ -3 & 4 \end{bmatrix}$$

The corresponding game tableau is therefore given by Figure 11.5.4.

Figure 11.5.4

	v	q_1	q_2	
$-u$	0	1	1*	$= -(-1)$
p_1	-1	2	-3	$= -t_1$
p_2	-1	-3	4	$= -t_2$
	$\parallel$	$\parallel$	$\parallel$	
	-1	s_1	s_2	

We now apply steps 1–3 to transform the game tableau into a linear programming tableau.

1. The lower right-hand entry in the game tableau is 4. Since $4 > -3$, no interchanging of rows is required. We thus proceed to step 2.
2. Pivoting on the upper right-hand entry yields the tableau

	v	q_1	-1	
s_2	0	1	1	$= -q_2$
p_1	-1	5	3	$= -t_1$
p_2	-1*	-7	-4	$= -t_2$
	$\parallel$	$\parallel$	$\parallel$	
	-1	s_1	$-u$	

3. After pivoting on the lower left-hand entry of the preceding tableau we obtain the Tucker tableau

	t_2	q_1	-1	
s_2	0	1	1	$= -q_2$
p_1	-1	12*	7	$= -t_1$
-1	-1	7	4	$= -v$
	$\parallel$	$\parallel$	$\parallel$	
	p_2	s_1	$-u$	

Applying the simplex algorithm beginning with this tableau yields

	t_2	t_1	-1	
s_2	$\frac{1}{12}$	$-\frac{1}{12}$	$\frac{5}{12}$	$= -q_2$
s_1	$-\frac{1}{12}$	$\frac{1}{12}$	$\frac{7}{12}$	$= -q_1$
-1	$-\frac{5}{12}$	$-\frac{7}{12}$	$-\frac{1}{12}$	$= -v$
	$\parallel$	$\parallel$	$\parallel$	
	p_2	p_1	$-u$	

Reading this tableau we find that $p_1 = \frac{7}{12}$, $p_2 = \frac{5}{12}$, $q_1 = \frac{7}{12}$, $q_2 = \frac{5}{12}$, and $v = -\frac{1}{12}$. In other words, the optimal strategies are

$$P^* = [\tfrac{7}{12}, \tfrac{5}{12}] \qquad Q^* = \begin{bmatrix} \frac{7}{12} \\ \frac{5}{12} \end{bmatrix}$$

and the value of the game is $-\frac{1}{12}$. This agrees with the solution given in Example 11.3.3.

Example 11.5.4 As our final illustration of the simplex method for solving matrix games we apply it to the strictly determined 4×3 matrix game of Example 11.2.1. The payoff matrix is

$$\begin{bmatrix} 2 & -1 & 2 \\ -3 & -4 & -1 \\ 3 & 1 & 2 \\ 3 & 1 & -2 \end{bmatrix}$$

and so the initial game tableau is

	v	q_1	q_2	q_3	
$-u$	0	1	1	1	$=-(-1)$
p_1	-1	2	-1	2	$=-t_1$
p_2	-1	-3	-4	-1	$=-t_2$
p_3	-1	3	1	2	$=-t_3$
p_4	-1	3	1	-2	$=-t_4$
	‖	‖	‖	‖	
	-1	s_1	s_2	s_3	

1. The lower right-hand entry is -2 and is not a maximum in its column. Thus we interchange the last two rows at step 1. This gives

	v	q_1	q_2	q_3	
$-u$	0	1	1	1^*	$=-(-1)$
p_1	-1	2	-1	2	$=-t_1$
p_2	-1	-3	-4	-1	$=-t_2$
p_4	-1	3	1	-2	$=-t_4$
p_3	-1	3	1	2	$=-t_3$
	‖	‖	‖	‖	
	-1	s_1	s_2	s_3	

2. Pivoting on the upper right-hand entry yields

	v	q_1	q_2	-1	
s_3	0	1	1	1	$= -q_3$
p_1	-1	0	-3	-2	$= -t_1$
p_2	-1	-2	-3	1	$= -t_2$
p_4	-1	5	3	2	$= -t_4$
p_3	$-1*$	1	-1	-2	$= -t_3$
	$\parallel$	$\parallel$	$\parallel$	$\parallel$	
	-1	s_1	s_2	$-u$	

3. Pivoting on the lower left-hand entry we get the Tucker tableau

	t_3	q_1	q_2	-1	
s_3	0	1	$1*$	1	$= -q_3$
p_1	-1	-1	-2	0	$= -t_1$
p_2	-1	-3	-2	3	$= -t_2$
p_4	-1	4	4	4	$= -t_4$
-1	-1	-1	1	2	$= -v$
	$\parallel$	$\parallel$	$\parallel$	$\parallel$	
	p_3	s_1	s_2	$-u$	

Applying the simplex algorithm to this last tableau yields

	t_3	q_1	q_3	-1	
s_2	0	1	1	1	$= -q_2$
p_1	-1	1	2	2	$= -t_1$
p_2	-1	-1	2	5	$= -t_2$
p_4	-1	0	-4	0	$= -t_4$
-1	-1	-2	-1	1	$= -v$
	$\parallel$	$\parallel$	$\parallel$	$\parallel$	
	p_3	s_1	s_3	$-u$	

Since this tableau has only nonpositive indicators, we have the final solution: $p_1 = 0$, $p_2 = 0, p_3 = 1, p_4 = 0, q_1 = 0, q_2 = 1, q_3 = 0$, and $v = 1$. In other words, the optimal strategies are

$$P^* = [0, 0, 1, 0] \quad \text{and} \quad Q^* = \begin{bmatrix} 0 \\ 1 \\ 0 \end{bmatrix}$$

and the value of the game is 1. Notice that the optimal strategies are pure—player I always chooses option 3 and player II always chooses option 2. This is because the game is strictly determined (see Figure 11.2.1).

Exercises for 11.5

In each of problems 1–6, form the game tableau for the game with the given payoff matrix and then use steps 1–3 of this section to transform the game tableau into a Tucker tableau.

1. $\begin{bmatrix} 2 & -3 \\ 4 & 5 \end{bmatrix}$

2. $\begin{bmatrix} -2 & 3 \\ 5 & -4 \end{bmatrix}$

3. $\begin{bmatrix} 1 & -3 & -6 \\ 2 & 4 & 5 \end{bmatrix}$

4. $\begin{bmatrix} -4 & 5 \\ 3 & -7 \\ 0 & 1 \end{bmatrix}$

5. $\begin{bmatrix} 1 & 0 & -1 & 2 \\ -3 & -2 & 5 & 1 \end{bmatrix}$

6. $\begin{bmatrix} 5 & -1 \\ -3 & 4 \\ 6 & 2 \\ -7 & 3 \end{bmatrix}$

In each of problems 7–16, use the methods of this section to find the optimal strategies for the players and the value of the game. Indicate which (if any) of the players the game favors.

7. $\begin{bmatrix} 2 & -3 \\ -4 & 5 \end{bmatrix}$

8. $\begin{bmatrix} -2 & 3 \\ 5 & -4 \end{bmatrix}$

9. $\begin{bmatrix} 1 & -1 \\ -1 & 1 \end{bmatrix}$

10. $\begin{bmatrix} 2 & -1 \\ -2 & -5 \end{bmatrix}$

11. $\begin{bmatrix} -1 & 3 \\ -4 & 10 \end{bmatrix}$

12. $\begin{bmatrix} -5 & 10 & 5 \\ 20 & -5 & 10 \end{bmatrix}$

13. $\begin{bmatrix} 1 & -3 & -6 \\ 2 & 4 & 5 \end{bmatrix}$

14. $\begin{bmatrix} -4 & 5 \\ 3 & -7 \\ 0 & 1 \end{bmatrix}$

15. $\begin{bmatrix} 1 & 0 & -1 & 2 \\ -3 & -2 & 5 & 1 \end{bmatrix}$

16. $\begin{bmatrix} 5 & 3 & -7 & -5 \\ 3 & 4 & 3 & 3 \\ -3 & 6 & 0 & 3 \end{bmatrix}$

17. In the rock–paper–scissors game of problem 4, Exercises 11.1, determine the optimal strategies for the players and the value of the game. Is the game fair? (See problem 12, Exercises 11.2.)

18. Refer to problem 3, Exercises 11.1. Determine the optimal strategies for the players. Is the game fair? (See problem 11, Exercises 11.2.)

19. Use the methods of this section to solve the Mississippi gambler game of problem 5, Exercises 11.1. (See problem 13, Exercises 11.2.)

20. Apply the methods of this section to Example 11.1.1 to find the optimal strategies and the value of the game. Is the game fair?

*21. Use the methods of this section to prove Theorem 11.3.1. If

$$\begin{bmatrix} a & b \\ c & d \end{bmatrix}$$

is the payoff matrix for a *nonstrictly* determined 2×2 matrix game, the optimal strategies for the players are

$$P^* = [(d - c)/(a - b - c + d), (a - b)/(a - b - c + d)]$$

and

$$Q^* = \begin{bmatrix} (d - b)/(a - b - c + d) \\ (a - c)/(a - b - c + d) \end{bmatrix}$$

Moreover, the value of the game is

$$v = (ad - bc)/(a - b - c + d)$$

(*Hint:* Consider two cases, $b \le d$ and $b > d$.)

22. Consider a *strictly determined* 2×2 matrix game with payoff matrix

$$\begin{array}{cc} & \begin{array}{cc} 1 & 2 \end{array} \\ \begin{array}{c} 1 \\ 2 \end{array} & \begin{bmatrix} a & b \\ c & d \end{bmatrix} \end{array}$$

where b is a saddle point. Use the methods of this section to show that the optimal strategies are

$$P^* = [1, 0] \quad \text{and} \quad Q^* = \begin{bmatrix} 0 \\ 1 \end{bmatrix}$$

and that b is the value of the game.

Section 11.6[1] von Neumann's Minimax Theorem

In this section we present the proof of the existence of optimal strategies for the players involved in a two-person, zero-sum, $m \times n$ matrix game. In the course of the proof the reader will find the justification for the method introduced in Section 11.5 for determining the optimal strategies and the value of the game.

The notation is as before. Let $A = [a_{ij}]_{mn}$ be the payoff matrix of an $m \times n$ matrix game. A mixed strategy for player I is a probability row vector $P = [p_1, p_2, \ldots, p_m]$ of length m and a mixed strategy for player II is a probability column vector

$$Q = \begin{bmatrix} q_1 \\ q_2 \\ \vdots \\ q_n \end{bmatrix}$$

[1]This section is optional.

of length n. The interpretation of such mixed strategies is given in Section 11.4. In that section we gave the reasoning involved for the selection of a strategy by a player: the player should attempt to minimize his maximum expected loss against any strategy that his opponent chooses to employ.

Since the entries in the payoff matrix represent payments from player II to player I, this means that player I should try to maximize the minimum expected payoff. We now proceed to state this objective precisely in terms of the entries of the mixed strategy P for player I and the payoff matrix A.

So, assume that player I employs the mixed strategy P. If player II selects option (column) j, the expected payoff is given by

$$g_j = p_1 a_{1j} + p_2 a_{2j} + \cdots + p_m a_{mj} \tag{11.6.1}$$

This is because player I selects option 1 with probability p_1, which results in a payoff of a_{1j}, or player I selects option 2 with probability p_2, which results in a payoff a_{2j}, and so on. Let u be the minimum value of the g_js. That is,

$$u = \text{minimum } \{g_j | 1 \leq j \leq n\} \tag{11.6.2}$$

Notice that u *depends on the mixed strategy P.*

Now, suppose that player II chooses the mixed strategy Q and player I employs the mixed strategy P. Then the expected payoff on any given play is

$$q_1 g_1 + q_2 g_2 + \cdots + q_n g_n \tag{11.6.3}$$

This is because player II selects option 1 with probability q_1, in which case the expected payoff is g_1, or player II selects option 2 with probability q_2, in which case the expected payoff is g_2, and so on.

By the definition of u we have that $u \leq g_j$ for $j = 1, 2, \ldots, n$, so

$$q_1 g_1 + q_2 g_2 + \cdots + q_n g_n \geq q_1 u + q_2 u + \cdots + q_n u$$
$$= u(q_1 + q_2 + \cdots + q_n)$$

But since Q is a probability vector, $q_1 + q_2 + \cdots + q_n = 1$, and consequently,

$$q_1 g_1 + q_2 g_2 + \cdots + q_n g_n \geq u \tag{11.6.4}$$

The inequality (11.6.4) simply indicates that if player I uses strategy P, then, regardless of the strategy player II employs, the expected payoff is at least u. Consequently, *player I's objective is to choose the mixed strategy P so that u is as large as possible.* This choice will result in player I minimizing his maximum expected loss against any strategy that player II chooses to employ.

Next, we analyze player II's objectives. Because the entries in the payoff matrix correspond to payments from player II to player I, the objective of player II is to minimize the maximum expected payoff (this is equivalent to player II minimizing his maximum expected loss).

So suppose that player II uses the mixed strategy Q. If player I selects option i, the expected payoff is

$$l_i = q_1 a_{i1} + q_2 a_{i2} + \cdots + q_n a_{in} \tag{11.6.5}$$

The reasoning behind Eq. (11.6.5) is analogous to that of Eq. (11.6.1). Let v be the maximum value of the l_is. That is,

$$v = \text{maximum } \{l_i | 1 \leq i \leq m\} \tag{11.6.6}$$

Notice that v *depends on Q.*

Now, if player I uses strategy P, the expected payoff when player I uses strategy Q is

$$p_1 l_1 + p_2 l_2 + \cdots + p_m l_m \tag{11.6.7}$$

by the same argument used to get Eq. (11.6.3). Because of Eq. (11.6.6) $l_i \leq v$ for $i = 1, 2, \ldots, m$, so

$$p_1 l_1 + p_2 l_2 + \cdots + p_m l_m \leq p_1 v + p_2 v + \cdots + p_m v$$
$$= v(p_1 + p_2 + \cdots + p_m)$$

Consequently, since $p_1 + p_2 + \cdots + p_m = 1$, we have

$$p_1 l_1 + p_2 l_2 + \cdots + p_m l_m \leq v \tag{11.6.8}$$

Thus if player II employs the mixed strategy Q, then no matter which strategy player I uses, the expected payoff is at most v. Therefore, *player II's objective is to choose the mixed strategy Q so that v is as small as possible.* By doing this player II will minimize his maximum expected loss against any strategy selected by player I.

It is often quite useful to express the above results in vector-matrix form. To do this, first define the expected gain and expected loss vectors by

$$G = [g_1, g_2, \ldots, g_n] \qquad \text{and} \qquad L = \begin{bmatrix} l_1 \\ l_2 \\ \vdots \\ l_m \end{bmatrix}$$

Using Eq. (11.6.1) and the definition of matrix multiplication, we get that

$$G = PA \tag{11.6.9}$$

and, by Eq. (11.6.5),

$$L = AQ \tag{11.6.10}$$

Moreover, we can express Eqs. (11.6.4) and (11.6.8) in the form

$$GQ \geq u \qquad \text{and} \qquad PL \leq v$$

In other words,

$$(PA)Q \geq u \qquad \text{and} \qquad P(AQ) \leq v \tag{11.6.11}$$

Since $(PA)Q = P(AQ)$ by the associative law for multiplication of matrices, we have proved the following important fact.

Theorem 11.6.1

Let the notation be as before. Assume that players I and II use the mixed strategies P and Q, respectively. Then the expected payoff (which is the expected gain for player I and the expected loss for player II) is PAQ. Moreover,

$$u \leq PAQ \leq v \tag{11.6.12}$$

Because of the meanings of u and v, it follows from Eq. (11.6.12) that if strategies P^* and Q^* can be found such that $\boxed{u = v}$, they must be optimal in the sense that P^* maximizes u and Q^* minimizes v (see problem 18, Exercises 11.6).

We now proceed to prove that for any matrix game, such optimal strategies can be found. This fact is known as *von Neumann's minimax theorem*. Concurrent with the development of the proof will be an examination of the relationship between matrix games and linear programming which will justify the use of the algorithm presented in Section 11.5 for obtaining the optimal strategies of the players and the value of the game.

To begin with, we subtract u from both sides of Eq. (11.6.1) to get the system of equations

$$g_1 - u = p_1 a_{11} + p_2 a_{21} + \cdots + p_m a_{m1} - u$$
$$g_2 - u = p_1 a_{12} + p_2 a_{22} + \cdots + p_m a_{m2} - u$$
$$\vdots \qquad \qquad \vdots$$
$$g_n - u = p_1 a_{1n} + p_2 a_{2n} + \cdots + p_m a_{mn} - u$$

Then we define the slack variables s_j, for $j = 1, 2, \ldots, n$ by

$$s_j = g_j - u \tag{11.6.13}$$

for $j = 1, 2, \ldots, n$. Notice that the quantity s_j represents the excess expected gain which player I will obtain playing strategy P if player II always selects option j.

In a similar manner we define t_i, for $i = 1, 2, \ldots, m$, by

$$t_i = v - l_i \tag{11.6.14}$$

Recall that v is player II's maximum expected loss playing strategy Q. Consequently, t_i is the improvement over this maximum loss which player II can expect playing strategy Q, if player I always selects option i. It will be more convenient for us to multiply all the equations represented by (11.6.14) on both sides by -1. This results in the equivalent system

$$-t_i = l_i - v \tag{11.6.15}$$

where $i = 1, 2, \ldots, m$.

Our problem now is to find vectors P and Q and a common value $u = v$ (called the *value* of the game) such that $P \geq \theta$, $Q \geq \theta$, and

$$S \geq \theta \tag{11.6.16}$$

$$T \geq \theta \tag{11.6.17}$$

where

$$S = \begin{bmatrix} s_1 \\ s_2 \\ \vdots \\ s_n \end{bmatrix} \qquad \text{and} \qquad T = [t_1, t_2, \ldots, t_m]$$

Notice that Eqs. (11.6.16) and (11.6.17) must hold because of Eqs. (11.6.2) and (11.6.6), respectively. Also because the strategies are probability vectors, it is necessary that

$$p_1 + p_2 + \cdots + p_m = 1 \tag{11.6.18}$$

and

$$q_1 + q_2 + \cdots + q_n = 1 \tag{11.6.19}$$

The conditions in Eqs. (11.6.13), (11.6.15), (11.6.18), and (11.6.19) can be put into a game tableau, as shown in Figure 11.6.1.

Figure 11.6.1

	v	q_1	q_2	$\cdots$	q_n	
$-u$	0	1	1	$\cdots$	1	$= -(-1)$
p_1	-1	a_{11}	a_{12}	$\cdots$	a_{1n}	$= -t_1$
p_2	-1	a_{21}	a_{22}	$\cdots$	a_{2n}	$= -t_2$
$\vdots$	$\vdots$	$\vdots$	$\vdots$	$\ddots$	$\vdots$	$\vdots$
p_m	-1	a_{m1}	a_{m2}	$\cdots$	a_{mn}	$= -t_m$
	$\|$	$\|$	$\|$		$\|$	
	-1	s_1	s_2	$\cdots$	s_n	

This is the same tableau as given in Figure 11.5.1. The constraint given by a row of the tableau is obtained by "dropping down" the v and the q_js to that row, multiplying each one by the corresponding entry in the row, adding all these terms together, and setting them equal to the appropriate entry outside the tableau at the right. For example, the constraint given by the first row of the tableau is

$$v \cdot 0 + q_1 \cdot 1 + q_2 \cdot 1 + \cdots + q_n \cdot 1 = -(-1)$$

In other words,

$$q_1 + q_2 + \cdots + q_n = 1$$

which is Eq. (11.6.19). As another example, the equation given by the third row of the tableau is

$$v \cdot (-1) + q_1 a_{21} + q_2 a_{22} + \cdots + q_n a_{2n} = -t_2$$

or, in other words [see Eq. (11.6.5)],

$$-v + l_2 = -t_2$$

This is just the second equation ($i = 2$) in Eq. (11.6.15). The equations given by the columns of the tableau are obtained in a similar manner.

Specifically, the first row of the tableau gives Eq. (11.6.19); the remaining rows yield the system of equations (11.6.15). Moreover, the first column in the tableau represents the condition (11.6.18) and the remaining columns give the system (11.6.13). The problem is to find a common value $u = v$ and nonnegative values for the p_is and q_js that make all the t_is and s_js nonnegative and satisfy the constraints given by the first row and first column of the tableau.

As mentioned in Section 11.5, the game tableau in Figure 11.6.1 is not in the required form to apply the simplex algorithm. However, as was also stated in Section 11.5, the game tableau can be transformed into a Tucker tableau by performing a rearrangement of the rows, if necessary, and two pivots (see page 501):

1. First the rows of the tableau are rearranged, if necessary, so that the lower right-hand entry of the tableau is a maximum in the last column of the payoff matrix. The new tableau will then be of the form shown in Figure 11.6.2, where the a'_{ij}s, p'_is, and t'_is represent the entries obtained after the (possible) rearrangement of the rows of Figure 11.6.1.

Figure 11.6.2

	v	q_1	q_2	$\cdots$	q_n	
$-u$	0	1	1	$\cdots$	1^*	$= -(-1)$
p'_1	-1	a'_{11}	a'_{12}	$\cdots$	a'_{1n}	$= -t'_1$
p'_2	-1	a'_{21}	a'_{22}	$\cdots$	a'_{2n}	$= -t'_2$
$\vdots$	$\vdots$	$\vdots$	$\vdots$	$\ddots$	$\vdots$	$\vdots$
p'_m	-1	a'_{m1}	a'_{m2}	$\cdots$	a'_{mn}	$= -t'_m$

	$\parallel$	$\parallel$	$\parallel$		$\parallel$
	-1	s_1	s_2	$\cdots$	s_n

2. The next step is to pivot on the upper right-hand entry of the tableau. The resulting tableau is as shown in Figure 11.6.3, where $a''_{ij} = a'_{ij} - a'_{in}$, for $i = 1, 2, \ldots, m$ and $j = 1, 2, \ldots, n - 1$.

Figure 11.6.3

	v	q_1	q_2	$\cdots$	q_{n-1}	-1	
s_n	0	1	1	$\cdots$	1	1	$= -q_n$
p'_1	-1	a''_{11}	a''_{12}	$\cdots$	$a''_{1,n-1}$	$-a'_{1n}$	$= -t'_1$
p'_2	-1	a''_{21}	a''_{22}	$\cdots$	$a''_{2,n-1}$	$-a'_{2n}$	$= -t'_2$
$\vdots$	$\vdots$	$\vdots$	$\vdots$	$\ddots$	$\vdots$	$\vdots$	$\vdots$
p'_m	-1^*	a''_{m1}	a''_{m2}	$\cdots$	$a''_{m,n-1}$	$-a'_{mn}$	$= -t'_m$

	$\parallel$	$\parallel$	$\parallel$		$\parallel$	$\parallel$
	-1	s_1	s_2	$\cdots$	s_{n-1}	$-u$

3. Finally, we pivot on the lower left-hand entry of the tableau in Figure 11.6.3 to obtain the Tucker tableau of Figure 11.6.4, where for $i = 1, 2, \ldots, m - 1$ and $j = 1, 2, \ldots, n - 1$,

$$\alpha_{ij} = a'_{ij} + a'_{mn} - a'_{in} - a'_{mj} \tag{11.6.20}$$

and

$$b_i = a'_{mn} - a'_{in} \tag{11.6.21}$$

for $i = 1, 2, \ldots, m - 1$,

$$c_j = a'_{mn} - a'_{mj} \tag{11.6.22}$$

for $j = 1, 2, \ldots, n - 1$, and

$$d = a'_{mn} \tag{11.6.23}$$

In this form (Figure 11.6.4) we are maximizing $-v$ and minimizing $-u$, which is, of course, equivalent to minimizing v and maximizing u.

Figure 11.6.4

	t'_m	q_1	q_2	$\cdots$	q_{n-1}	-1	
s_n	0	1	1	$\cdots$	1	1	$= -q_n$
p'_1	-1	α_{11}	α_{12}	$\cdots$	$\alpha_{1,n-1}$	b_1	$= -t'_1$
p'_2	-1	α_{21}	α_{22}	$\cdots$	$\alpha_{2,n-1}$	b_2	$= -t'_2$
$\vdots$	$\vdots$	$\vdots$	$\vdots$	$\ddots$	$\vdots$	$\vdots$	
p'_{m-1}	-1	$\alpha_{m-1,1}$	$\alpha_{m-1,2}$	$\cdots$	$\alpha_{m-1,n-1}$	b_{m-1}	$= -t'_{m-1}$
-1	-1	c_1	c_2	$\cdots$	c_{n-1}	d	$= -v$
	$\parallel$	$\parallel$	$\parallel$		$\parallel$	$\parallel$	
	p'_m	s_1	s_2	$\cdots$	s_{n-1}	$-u$	

The only question remaining is whether we can actually carry out the steps of the simplex algorithm, beginning with the Tucker tableau in Figure 11.6.4, to obtain a tableau whose indicators are all nonpositive. Indeed, if this can be done, we know from our work with linear programming that a solution of the linear program represented by the tableau in Figure 11.6.4 (and hence of the original matrix game problem) will exist and can be obtained by reading the final tableau.

We simply state, without proof, that the answer to the above question is affirmative. The two results required for the proof are:

1. The linear programming problems represented by the Tucker tableau in Figure 11.6.4 have a solution.
2. The solution can be obtained from the Tucker tableau by applying the simplex algorithm.

Exercises for 11.6

In each of problems 1–6, determine
(a) The expected gain vector G if player I uses strategy P [see Eq. (11.6.9)].
(b) The minimum expected gain, u, for player I if he uses the mixed strategy P [see Eq. (11.6.2)].
(c) The expected loss vector L if player II uses strategy Q [see Eq. (11.6.10)].
(d) The maximum expected loss, v, for player II if he uses the mixed strategy Q [see Eq. (11.6.6)].
(e) The expected gain for player I (and hence the expected loss for player II) when the players use the mixed strategies P and Q (see Theorem 11.6.1). Also, verify that $u \leq v$.

1. $P = [\frac{1}{3}, \frac{2}{3}]$,

$$A = \begin{bmatrix} 9 & -3 \\ -3 & 6 \end{bmatrix} \quad \text{and} \quad Q = \begin{bmatrix} \frac{2}{3} \\ \frac{1}{3} \end{bmatrix}$$

2. $P = [\frac{2}{5}, \frac{3}{5}]$,

$$A = \begin{bmatrix} -5 & 10 & 5 \\ 20 & -5 & 10 \end{bmatrix} \quad \text{and} \quad Q = \begin{bmatrix} \frac{2}{5} \\ \frac{1}{5} \\ \frac{2}{5} \end{bmatrix}$$

3. $P = [\frac{1}{4}, \frac{1}{2}, \frac{1}{4}]$,

$$A = \begin{bmatrix} 4 & -2 \\ -8 & 10 \\ 4 & -8 \end{bmatrix} \quad \text{and} \quad Q = \begin{bmatrix} \frac{1}{4} \\ \frac{3}{4} \end{bmatrix}$$

4. $P = [\frac{1}{3}, 0, \frac{1}{6}, \frac{1}{2}]$,

$$A = \begin{bmatrix} 6 & 3 & -3 \\ 4 & -2 & 1 \\ -12 & 3 & 6 \\ 1 & 0 & 2 \end{bmatrix} \quad \text{and} \quad Q = \begin{bmatrix} \frac{1}{6} \\ \frac{2}{3} \\ \frac{1}{6} \end{bmatrix}$$

5. $P = [\frac{1}{8}, \frac{1}{4}, \frac{5}{8}]$,

$$A = \begin{bmatrix} 1 & 0 & -4 & 2 \\ 3 & 6 & -5 & -4 \\ -2 & -1 & 3 & 7 \end{bmatrix} \quad \text{and} \quad Q = \begin{bmatrix} \frac{1}{4} \\ \frac{1}{8} \\ \frac{1}{2} \\ \frac{1}{8} \end{bmatrix}$$

6. $P = [0, 0, 0, 1, 0]$,

$$A = \begin{bmatrix} 4 & 3 & -6 & -4 \\ -3 & 7 & 0 & 1 \\ 2 & -6 & 1 & 0 \\ 1 & 2 & 7 & -2 \\ 5 & -1 & -3 & 4 \end{bmatrix} \quad \text{and} \quad Q = \begin{bmatrix} 0 \\ 1 \\ 0 \\ 0 \end{bmatrix}$$

In each of problems 7–15, show that the given mixed strategies for the players are optimal by establishing the fact that $u = v$. Also, verify that $PAQ = u(= v)$.

7. $P = [\frac{1}{3}, \frac{2}{3}]$,

$$A = \begin{bmatrix} 6 & -2 \\ -3 & 1 \end{bmatrix} \quad \text{and} \quad Q = \begin{bmatrix} \frac{1}{4} \\ \frac{3}{4} \end{bmatrix}$$

8. $P = [\frac{7}{12}, \frac{5}{12}]$,

$$A = \begin{bmatrix} 2 & -3 \\ -3 & 4 \end{bmatrix} \quad \text{and} \quad Q = \begin{bmatrix} \frac{7}{12} \\ \frac{5}{12} \end{bmatrix}$$

9. $P = [\frac{8}{19}, \frac{11}{19}]$,

$$A = \begin{bmatrix} 8 & -3 & 10 \\ -1 & 7 & -2 \end{bmatrix} \quad \text{and} \quad Q = \begin{bmatrix} \frac{10}{19} \\ \frac{9}{19} \\ 0 \end{bmatrix}$$

10. $P = [0, 0, 1, 0]$,

$$A = \begin{bmatrix} 2 & -1 & 2 \\ -3 & -4 & -1 \\ 3 & 1 & 2 \\ 3 & 1 & -2 \end{bmatrix} \quad \text{and} \quad Q = \begin{bmatrix} 0 \\ 1 \\ 0 \end{bmatrix}$$

11. $P = [\frac{1}{3}, \frac{1}{3}, \frac{1}{3}]$,

$$A = \begin{bmatrix} 0 & -1 & 1 \\ 1 & 0 & -1 \\ -1 & 1 & 0 \end{bmatrix} \quad \text{and} \quad Q = \begin{bmatrix} \frac{1}{3} \\ \frac{1}{3} \\ \frac{1}{3} \end{bmatrix}$$

12. $P = [0, \frac{1}{5}, \frac{4}{5}]$,

$$A = \begin{bmatrix} 6 & -1 \\ 0 & 4 \\ 4 & 3 \end{bmatrix} \quad \text{and} \quad Q = \begin{bmatrix} \frac{1}{5} \\ \frac{4}{5} \end{bmatrix}$$

13. $P = [\frac{3}{4}, \frac{1}{4}]$,

$$A = \begin{bmatrix} 1 & 0 & -1 & 0 \\ -3 & -2 & 1 & 2 \end{bmatrix} \quad \text{and} \quad Q = \begin{bmatrix} 0 \\ \frac{1}{2} \\ \frac{1}{2} \\ 0 \end{bmatrix}$$

14. $P = [\frac{1}{2}, \frac{1}{2}]$,

$$A = \begin{bmatrix} -1 & 5 & -1 & -2 & 8 & 10 \\ 3 & -6 & 0 & 8 & -9 & -8 \end{bmatrix} \quad \text{and} \quad Q = \begin{bmatrix} 0 \\ \frac{1}{12} \\ \frac{11}{12} \\ 0 \\ 0 \\ 0 \end{bmatrix}$$

15. $P = [\frac{1}{6}, \frac{1}{2}, 0, \frac{1}{3}]$,

$$A = \begin{bmatrix} 6 & 5 & -2 & 3 \\ 2 & 2 & 1 & -2 \\ 1 & 1 & 0 & -3 \\ 1 & -5 & 0 & 2 \end{bmatrix} \quad \text{and} \quad Q = \begin{bmatrix} 0 \\ \frac{7}{78} \\ \frac{47}{78} \\ \frac{24}{78} \end{bmatrix}$$

16. Recall from page 510 that P and Q are optimal strategies if and only if $u = v$. Show that if P and Q are optimal, the expected gain of player I (and hence the expected loss of player II) is equal to v when the players use these optimal strategies (this is why v is called the value of the game).

*17. Suppose that A is the payoff matrix for an $m \times n$ matrix game. Let P and Q be mixed strategies for the players. Let ω be a real number and define U to be the row vector of length n all of whose entries are ω and V to be the column vector of length m all of whose entries are ω. Assume that

$$PA \geq U \quad \text{and} \quad AQ \leq V$$

Prove that ω is the value of the game and that P and Q are optimal strategies. (*Hint:* You must verify that $u = v = \omega$.)

18. Prove that the statement that P^* and Q^* are optimal strategies if $u = v$ is legitimate by using the following argument.

(a) Indicate the dependence of u on P and v on Q by writing

$$u = u(P) \quad \text{and} \quad v = v(Q)$$

(b) Show that if $u(P^*) = v(Q^*)$, then $u(P^*) \geq u(P)$ for all mixed strategies P for player I. (This shows that P^* maximizes the minimum expected payoff.)

(c) Show that if $u(P^*) = v(Q^*)$, then $v(Q^*) \leq v(Q)$ for all mixed strategies Q for player II. (This shows that Q^* minimizes the maximum expected payoff.)
[*Hint:* By Theorem 11.6.1, we have that $u(P) \leq v(Q)$ for all mixed strategies P and Q.]

Section 11.7 Applications and Illustrations

In this final section of the chapter we shall present some applications and illustrations of matrix games.

Example 11.7.1 Two gasoline companies are planning to build a number of gas stations in a new suburb. At each of several intersections, each of the two companies plans to put a gas station on one of the corners (see Figure 11.7.1). At each intersection company A has a choice of locating at either the northern or eastern corner, and company B may select either the southern or western location.

Figure 11.7.1

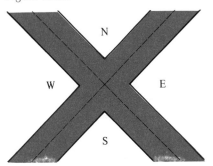

Because of the various factors involved (e.g., traffic flow, signal length) the companies have estimated the relative advantages and disadvantages of locating at a particular corner. The results obtained are:

1. If companies A and B locate at the northern and southern corners, respectively, company A will get 60 percent of the business and company B, 40 percent.
2. If they locate at the northern and western corners, respectively, company A will get 30 percent of the business and company B, 70 percent.
3. Also, if company A selects the eastern corner and company B chooses the southern corner, the business will be divided 45 percent for A and 55 percent for B.
4. Finally, if the companies select the eastern and western locations, respectively, the business will be split 65 percent for A and 35 percent for B.

Both companies are required to make their decisions in writing at the same time so that neither company will have prior knowledge of the other's choices. What strategy should each of the companies choose to assure itself of the best percentage of the business?

To solve this problem we consider it as a two-person, zero-sum, 2×2 matrix game. Company A will be player I and company B will be player II. The entries in the payoff matrix will represent the percentage above 50 percent which company B sacrifices to company A because of the particular selections of locations that are made. As usual, if company B obtains more than 50 percent of the business because of the selections, the corresponding entry in the payoff matrix will be negative.

Keeping 1–4 in mind, we see that the payoff matrix is as shown in Figure 11.7.2.

Figure 11.7.2

$$\begin{array}{c} & \begin{array}{cc} S & W \end{array} \\ \begin{array}{c} N \\ E \end{array} & \left[\begin{array}{cc} 10 & -20 \\ -5 & 15 \end{array}\right] \end{array}$$

Notice that the game corresponding to this payoff matrix is not strictly determined. To obtain the optimal strategies for the companies we apply the methods of Section 11.5. The game tableau is as shown in Figure 11.7.3. Applying the usual procedure we get the following sequence of tableaux:

Figure 11.7.3

	v	q_1	q_2	
$-u$	0	1	1*	$= -(-1)$
p_1	-1	10	-20	$= -t_1$
p_2	-1	-5	15	$= -t_2$
	$\parallel$	$\parallel$	$\parallel$	
	-1	s_1	s_2	

	v	q_1	-1	
s_2	0	1	1	$= -q_2$
p_1	-1	30	20	$= -t_1$
p_2	$-1*$	-20	-15	$= -t_2$
	$\parallel$	$\parallel$	$\parallel$	
	-1	s_1	$-u$	

	t_2	q_1	-1	
s_2	0	1	1	$= -q_2$
p_1	-1	50*	35	$= -t_1$
-1	-1	20	15	$= -v$
	$\parallel$	$\parallel$	$\parallel$	
	p_2	s_1	$-u$	

	t_2	t_1	-1	
s_2	$\frac{1}{50}$	$-\frac{1}{50}$	$\frac{3}{10}$	$= -q_2$
s_1	$-\frac{1}{50}$	$\frac{1}{50}$	$\frac{7}{10}$	$= -q_1$
-1	$-\frac{3}{5}$	$-\frac{2}{5}$	1	$= -v$
	$\parallel$	$\parallel$	$\parallel$	
	p_2	p_1	$-u$	

Since all the indicators in this last tableau are nonpositive, this is the final tableau. Reading it we see that $p_1 = \frac{2}{5}$, $p_2 = \frac{3}{5}$, $q_1 = \frac{7}{10}$, $q_2 = \frac{3}{10}$, and $v = 1$. In other words, the optimal strategies are

$$P^* = [\tfrac{2}{5}, \tfrac{3}{5}] \quad \text{and} \quad Q^* = \begin{bmatrix} \frac{7}{10} \\ \frac{3}{10} \end{bmatrix}$$

and the value of the game is 1.

The interpretation of these results to the original problem is as follows: company A should choose the northern and eastern locations with probabilities .4 and .6, respectively. Company B should select the southern and western locations with probabilities .7 and .3, respectively. The situation is biased in favor of company A, whose expected percentage of the business is 51 percent (this is because $v = 1$).

Example 11.7.2[2] Two politicians are running for the same office. The politicians must now make plans for the last 2 days of campaigning. The polls indicate that at the present time the two opponents have an equal chance of winning. Both politicians plan to spend the last 2 days of the campaign in two critical areas. The first town has a voting population of 30,000, the second has a voting population of 20,000. The politicians plan to spend an integer number of days (0, 1, or 2) in each town. At the present time they are uncertain how many days to spend in each area.

It has been estimated that if both politicians spend the same number of days in an area, they each will get 50 percent of the vote. Also, it appears that if one politician spends no time in one of the towns, his opponent will get 60 or 70 percent of the vote in that town if he spends 1 or 2 days there, respectively. Finally, it seems likely that if one of the politicians spends 1 day in a given town, the other will receive 55 percent of the vote in that town by spending 2 days there.

Because of the fact that the travel arrangements must be made in advance, neither politician will know the other's schedule until after he has decided on his own. What campaign schedules should the politicians select to maximize their chances of winning the election?

To solve this problem we rephrase it in terms of a two-person, zero-sum, 3×3 matrix game in the following way. Player I refers to one of the politicians and player II refers to the other. Each of the three options of each player represents the number of days the corresponding politician decides to stay in the town with 30,000 voters. Finally, each entry of the payoff matrix gives the *net gain in votes over 25,000* ($= 50$ percent of the total 50,000) *by player I* given the number of days that each politician plans to campaign in the town with 30,000 voters.

For convenience the towns with 30,000 and 20,000 voters will be referred to as towns A and B, respectively. The information concerning percentages is displayed in Table 11.7.1. This gives the percentage division of votes when the politicians remain

Table 11.7.1

No. days for:		Percentage of votes for:	
I	II	I	II
0	0	50	50
0	1	40	60
0	2	30	70
1	0	60	40
1	1	50	50
1	2	45	55
2	0	70	30
2	1	55	45
2	2	50	50

[2]This is a modification of a problem presented in F. S. Hillier and G. J. Lieberman, *Introduction to Operations Research*, Holden-Day, Inc., San Francisco, 1967.

in a particular town the stated number of days. Using the table together with the facts that town A has 30,000 voters and town B has 20,000 voters, we obtain Table 11.7.2.

Table 11.7.2

No. days in town A		No. days in town B		No. votes in A	No. votes in B	Total votes	Net gain (over 25,000)
I	II	I	II	I	I	I	I
0	0	2	2	15,000	10,000	25,000	0
0	1	2	1	12,000	11,000	23,000	−2,000
0	2	2	0	9,000	14,000	23,000	−2,000
1	0	1	2	18,000	9,000	27,000	2,000
1	1	1	1	15,000	10,000	25,000	0
1	2	1	0	13,500	12,000	25,500	500
2	0	0	2	21,000	6,000	27,000	2,000
2	1	0	1	16,500	8,000	24,500	−500
2	2	0	0	15,000	10,000	25,000	0

It is now evident that the payoff matrix for the "game" in question is given by Figure 11.7.4. Note that this matrix has a saddle point, the entry in the second row

Figure 11.7.4

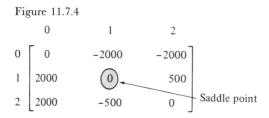

and second column. Consequently, we know from the results on strictly determined games that the optimal strategy for player I is to always select the option labeling the second row, and the optimal strategy for player II is to always select the option labeling the second column. Also the value of the game is 0 (the saddle-point entry), and therefore the game is fair.

Interpreting these results in terms of the original problem, we conclude that each politician should spend 1 day in each town and that by doing so neither will gain an advantage.

Incidentally, if the populations of the towns are changed, it may no longer be optimal for the politicians to stay in each town for 1 day. For example, if town A has 30,000 voters and town B has 10,000 voters, both politicians should spend both days in town A (see problem 3, Exercises 11.7).

Exercises for 11.7

1. Two companies are planning to locate in one of two towns. Call the companies I and II and the towns A and B. If both companies locate in the same town, I will get 60 percent of the total business and II will receive 40 percent of the total business. If they locate in different towns, they will each get 50 percent of the total business. Neither company can determine what the other will do until both have made commitments.

(a) Determine the optimal strategies for the companies.

(b) Which company has the advantage? How much of an advantage does this company have?

2. This exercise refers to the situation of problem 7, Exercises 11.1 (also, see problem 15, Exercises 11.2).

   (a) Determine the optimal strategies for the clothing manufacturers.

   (b) Which company (if any) has the advantage?

3. Suppose that in Example 11.7.2 town A has 30,000 voters and town B has 10,000 voters.

   (a) Find the optimal strategies for the politicians and the value of the "game."

   (b) Interpret the results in (a) in terms of the campaign schedules and election returns.

4. At a carnival booth the operator charges $1 to play the following game. He places behind his back either one $1 bill, two $1 bills, one silver dollar, or two silver dollars. The customer guesses what the operator has behind his back. If he guesses correctly he gets the money, and if he guesses incorrectly he gets nothing.

   (a) What are the optimal strategies for the operator and the customer?

   (b) Is the game fair? If it is not fair, whom does it favor and by how much?

5. Assume that two companies (I and II) compete for the sale of a given product, and that these are the only two companies that manufacture the product. At the beginning of each month each of the companies must decide on which medium it will use for advertising that month; either television, radio, or magazines. The following payoff matrix gives the additional units of revenue (that over 50 percent of the total revenue) earned by company I during a given month for the various possible choices by the companies.

$$
\begin{array}{c}
 & \begin{array}{ccc} T & R & M \end{array} \\
\begin{array}{c} T \\ R \\ M \end{array} &
\left[\begin{array}{ccc}
0 & -1 & 2 \\
1 & 0 & -1 \\
-2 & 1 & 0
\end{array} \right]
\end{array}
$$

(a) Find the optimal strategies for the companies.

(b) Which, if any, of the companies has the advantage.

(c) Interpret your results.

Appendix A
The Real Number System

In this chapter we give a brief introduction to the real number system and some important related concepts. It is intended to be an *algebra review* which should be adequate preparation for the main body of the text.

Section A.1   The Real Numbers

All of us have some familiarity with the real numbers and, in fact, we use them regularly in our day-to-day lives. In this respect, an informal point of view with regard to the real numbers is often sufficient. However, when studying or applying mathematics it is usually necessary to take a more formal attitude. To begin with, we will give names to certain sets of numbers and then develop certain rules and methods for working with them.

The most frequently encountered numbers are the counting numbers: 1, 2, 3, 4, ... Mathematicians call these the *positive integers*. From these numbers we are led naturally to consider the number 0 and the *negative integers* $-1, -2, -3, -4, \ldots$. The positive integers, negative integers, and 0 are collectively referred to as the *integers*.

It does not take long before we discover that the integers themselves are inadequate for handling problems that arise even in day-to-day occurrences. For example, in measuring the length of a board, in inches, we frequently find that it is not an integral number of inches (e.g., it may be 10 and $\frac{3}{4}$ inches long). Thus we must consider fractions, such as, $\frac{1}{2}, \frac{7}{4}, -\frac{3}{5}$, and $\frac{15}{16}$. Formally, fractions are just quotients of integers. In mathematics the fractions are referred to as *rational numbers*. Notice that each integer is also a rational number (e.g., $8 = \frac{8}{1}$).

At first glance it might appear that the rational numbers should be sufficient for describing quantitative measurements. However, this is not the case, as is illustrated by the following two examples.

Example A.1.1 Consider an inclined road, as in Figure A.1.1. By the Pythagorean theorem it follows that the length, l, of the road is $\sqrt{2}$ miles. It can be shown that $\sqrt{2}$ is *not* a rational number; that is, $\sqrt{2}$ cannot be expressed as the quotient of two integers.

Figure A.1.1

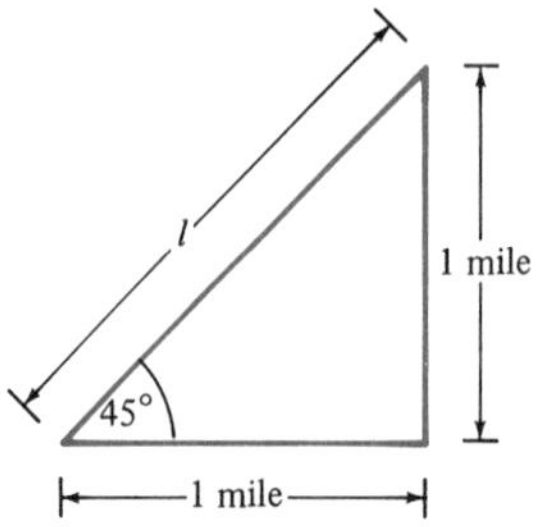

Example A.1.2 Suppose that a farmer has a circular plot of land that is 2 miles in diameter (see Figure A.1.2). Then it is known that the area of the plot is π square miles. The number π is another example of a nonrational number. However, it is approximately equal to $\frac{22}{7}$.

Figure A.1.2

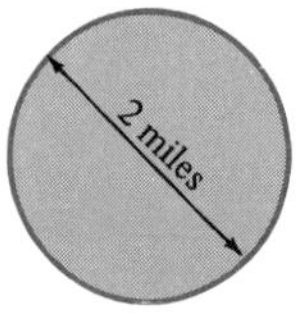

The above two examples illustrate clearly that it is worthwhile considering numbers other than the rational numbers. Numbers that are not rational are called *irrational numbers*. Finally, the rational and irrational numbers are collectively referred to as the *real numbers*.

The most important arithmetic properties of the real numbers are summarized below.

Addition of Real Numbers: If a, b, and c are real numbers:

A1: $a + b$ is a real number (closure)
A2: $a + b = b + a$ (commutative law)
A3: $(a + b) + c = a + (b + c)$ (associative law)
A4: $a + 0 = a$ (property of 0)
A5: $a + (-a) = 0$ (property of negatives)

Multiplication of Real Numbers: If a, b, and c are real numbers:

M1: $a \cdot b$ is a real number (closure)
M2: $a \cdot b = b \cdot a$ (commutative law)
M3: $(a \cdot b) \cdot c = a \cdot (b \cdot c)$ (associative law)
M4: $a \cdot 1 = a$ (property of 1)
M5: $a \cdot \dfrac{1}{a} = 1$, for $a \neq 0$ (property of reciprocals)

Distributive Laws for Real Numbers: If a, b, and c are real numbers:

D1: $a \cdot (b + c) = a \cdot b + a \cdot c$

D2: $(a + b) \cdot c = a \cdot c + b \cdot c$

Addition, multiplication, and division of fractions are dealt with throughout the text. Therefore, we list here the rules for dealing with such operations. Notice that the notations $\dfrac{a}{b}$, a/b, and $a \div b$ are all interchangeable.

Arithmetic of Fractions

F1: $\dfrac{a}{b} + \dfrac{c}{d} = \dfrac{ad + bc}{bd}$

F2: $\dfrac{a}{b} \cdot \dfrac{c}{d} = \dfrac{a \cdot c}{b \cdot d}$

F3: $\dfrac{a}{b} \bigg/ \dfrac{c}{d} = \dfrac{a \cdot d}{b \cdot c}$

Example A.1.3 Arithmetic of Fractions

1. $\dfrac{3}{4} + \dfrac{5}{8} = \dfrac{3 \cdot 8 + 4 \cdot 5}{4 \cdot 8} = \dfrac{44}{32} = \dfrac{11}{8}$

2. $6 + \dfrac{2}{3} = \dfrac{6}{1} + \dfrac{2}{3} = \dfrac{6 \cdot 3 + 1 \cdot 2}{1 \cdot 3} = \dfrac{20}{3}$

3. $-\dfrac{3}{5} + \dfrac{8}{7} = \dfrac{-3 \cdot 7 + 5 \cdot 8}{5 \cdot 7} = \dfrac{19}{35}$

4. $\dfrac{5}{6} \cdot \dfrac{3}{2} = \dfrac{5 \cdot 3}{6 \cdot 2} = \dfrac{15}{12} = \dfrac{5}{4}$

5. $\dfrac{13}{5} \cdot 2 = \dfrac{13}{5} \cdot \dfrac{2}{1} = \dfrac{13 \cdot 2}{5 \cdot 1} = \dfrac{26}{5}$

6. $\dfrac{5}{7} \cdot \left(-\dfrac{12}{11}\right) = \dfrac{5 \cdot (-12)}{7 \cdot 11} = -\dfrac{60}{77}$

7. $\dfrac{7}{8} \bigg/ \dfrac{3}{5} = \dfrac{7 \cdot 5}{8 \cdot 3} = \dfrac{35}{24}$

8. $5 \bigg/ \dfrac{18}{13} = \dfrac{5}{1} \bigg/ \dfrac{18}{13} = \dfrac{5 \cdot 13}{1 \cdot 18} = \dfrac{65}{18}$

9. $-\dfrac{4}{3} \bigg/ \dfrac{22}{7} = \dfrac{-4 \cdot 7}{3 \cdot 22} = \dfrac{-28}{66} = -\dfrac{14}{33}.$

The final concept to be discussed in this section is that of *exponents*. This is a mathematical shorthand that is convenient for representing repeated multiplication.

Definition

If a is a real number and n is a positive integer, we define

$$a^n = \underbrace{a \cdot a \cdot \, \cdots \, a}_{n \text{ times}}$$

For example, we have

1. $4^2 = 4 \cdot 4 = 16$
2. $3^4 = 3 \cdot 3 \cdot 3 \cdot 3 = 81$

3. $(-6)^3 = (-6) \cdot (-6) \cdot (-6) = -216$

4. $(\frac{1}{2})^5 = \frac{1}{2} \cdot \frac{1}{2} \cdot \frac{1}{2} \cdot \frac{1}{2} \cdot \frac{1}{2} = \frac{1}{32}$

5. $(-\frac{2}{3})^4 = (-\frac{2}{3}) \cdot (-\frac{2}{3}) \cdot (-\frac{2}{3}) \cdot (-\frac{2}{3}) = \frac{16}{81}$

By convention we define

$$a^0 = 1$$

for a a nonzero real number. Moreover, if n is a negative integer and a is a *nonzero* real number, we define

$$a^n = \frac{1}{a^{-n}}$$

For example,

1. $8^{-2} = \dfrac{1}{8^2} = \dfrac{1}{64}$

2. $(-5)^{-3} = \dfrac{1}{(-5)^3} = -\dfrac{1}{125}$

3. $\left(\dfrac{1}{3}\right)^{-4} = \dfrac{1}{(\frac{1}{3})^4} = \dfrac{1}{\frac{1}{81}}$

$$= \frac{1}{1}\Big/\frac{1}{81} = \frac{1 \cdot 81}{1 \cdot 1} = 81$$

Some of the important properties of exponents are as follows:

E1: $a^n a^m = a^{n+m}$

E2: $a^n/a^m = a^{n-m}$

E3: $(ab)^n = a^n b^n$

E4: $(a/b)^n = a^n/b^n$

E5: $a^{-n} = 1/a^n$

E6: $(a^n)^m = a^{nm}$

These properties follow directly from the above definitions.

Exercises for A.1

1. Evaluate the following.
   (a) $\frac{1}{3} + \frac{1}{2}$
   (b) $-\frac{1}{8} + \frac{3}{4}$
   (c) $\frac{1}{5} + 7$
   (d) $\frac{5}{6} + (-\frac{1}{5})$
   (e) $(-\frac{7}{11}) + (-\frac{1}{2})$
   (f) $\frac{2}{3} \cdot \frac{4}{5}$
   (g) $3 \cdot \frac{7}{8}$
   (h) $\frac{2}{3} \cdot (-\frac{1}{8})$
   (i) $-5 \cdot (-\frac{1}{3})$
   (j) $\frac{2}{3}/\frac{3}{5}$
   (k) $-\frac{4}{5}/\frac{3}{8}$
   (l) $\frac{7}{16}/3$
   (m) $\frac{2}{1}/\frac{5}{8}$
   (n) $-\frac{1}{3}/-\frac{2}{5}$

2. Evaluate the following.
   (a) $\frac{7}{2} + 2$
   (b) $-1 + \frac{13}{5}$
   (c) $\frac{3}{4} + \frac{23}{8}$
   (d) $\frac{7}{3} + \frac{13}{4}$
   (e) $\frac{35}{8} - \frac{2}{3}$
   (f) $\frac{15}{4} + \frac{47}{8}$
   (g) $-\frac{5}{2} + \frac{27}{5}$
   (h) $-\frac{71}{9} - \frac{13}{4}$

3. Identify the property (or properties) of the real numbers that justifies each of the following.
   (a) $(\frac{1}{3} \cdot 5) \cdot \sqrt{2} = \frac{1}{3} \cdot (5 \cdot \sqrt{2})$
   (b) $(-1) + 7 = 7 + (-1)$
   (c) $a \cdot 1 = a$, where a is any real number

(d) $-\frac{2}{3} + 0 = -\frac{2}{3}$

(e) $(a \cdot b) \cdot c = a \cdot (c \cdot b)$, where a, b, and c are real numbers

(f) $2 \cdot (3 + 4) = 2 \cdot 3 + 2 \cdot 4$

4. Property A2 of the real numbers states that the real numbers are commutative under the operation of addition. That is, if a and b are any real numbers, then $a + b = b + a$. Are the real numbers commutative under the operation of subtraction? That is, is $a - b = b - a$?

5. (a) Are the integers closed under addition? That is, if a and b are any integers, is $a + b$ an integer?

   (b) Are the integers closed under division? That is, if a and b are any integers with $b \neq 0$, is $a \div b$ an integer?

6. Are the real numbers closed under the operation of division? That is, if a and b are any real numbers with $b \neq 0$, is $a \div b$ a real number?

7. (a) Is the operation of division of real numbers commutative? That is, is $a \div b = b \div a$, where a and b are any real numbers with $a \neq 0$ and $b \neq 0$?

   (b) Is the operation of division associative? That is, if a, b, and c are any real numbers with $b \neq 0$ and $c \neq 0$, is $a \div (b \div c) = (a \div b) \div c$?

8. Evaluate each of the following.

   (a) 4^3 (b) $(\frac{1}{3})^4$

   (c) $(-2)^3$ (d) $(5)^{-3}$

   (e) $(\frac{1}{4})^{-2}$ (f) $(-6)^{-3}$

   (g) $\dfrac{2^{-3}}{3^{-2}}$ (h) $(\frac{2}{3})^0$

   (i) $(3^{-1})(3^{-2})$ (j) $(5^{-1})^2$

   (k) $(3^2)^{-1}(2^2)^{-1}$ (l) $(2^{-2}4^3)^{-3}$

9. Simplify each of the following.

   (a) $x^0 y^2$ (b) $(3x^2 y^3)(\frac{2}{3}xy^5)$

   (c) $(2a^3 b^2 c)^4$ (d) $\left(\dfrac{3a^3}{6}\right)^2 \left(\dfrac{b}{a^3}\right)^3$

   (e) $\dfrac{(2x^2)^3}{4x^4}$ (f) $(3x^2)(-\frac{1}{6}x^5)$

   (g) $\left(\dfrac{3x^0 y^3}{x^4 y}\right)^2$ (h) $\left(\dfrac{3a^2}{2bc}\right)^3 \left(\dfrac{cb^2}{a}\right)^4$

10. By use of negative exponents, write the following without denominators and simplify whenever possible.

   (a) $\dfrac{4x^2}{y^3}$ (b) $\dfrac{2a^2}{6}$

   (c) $\dfrac{3a^2 b}{b^2 c^3}$ (d) $\dfrac{4a^2 b^3}{2cd^2}$

   (e) $\dfrac{x^3}{3x^5 y^2}$ (f) $\dfrac{4a^2 b}{3b^3 c^2}$

   (g) $\dfrac{3x^2 y^4}{4^0 x^3 y^5}$ (h) $\dfrac{7a^3 b^2}{3a^5 b^3}$

   (i) $\dfrac{3a^2 b^3 c}{2^{-1}a^{-1}b^4 c^{-2}}$ (j) $\dfrac{2x^3 y^2 z^4}{3^{-2}x^4 yz^{-2}}$

   (k) $\dfrac{4a^3 b^{-1} c^2}{2^{-1}a^4 b^{-2} c^{-1}}$ (l) $\dfrac{8x^3 y^{-3} z}{4^{-1}x^4 y^{-2} z^3}$

11. Simplify each of the following and write in a form free of negative exponents.

   (a) $(-2a^4)(\frac{1}{4}a^{-5})$ (b) $(\frac{1}{2}a^4 b^{-3})^{-2}$

   (c) $\dfrac{3x^{-3}y^2}{(x^2 y^{-1})^3}$ (d) $\left(\dfrac{4a^2}{b^{-3}}\right)^{-1}\left(\dfrac{a^{-1}}{2b^2}\right)^2$

(e) $\left(\dfrac{8x^2y^{-3}}{5x^{-5}y^4}\right)^0$

(f) $\dfrac{a^{-2} + b^{-2}}{(ab)^{-1}}$

(g) $\dfrac{x^{-1} + y^{-1}}{(x + y)^{-1}}$

(h) $\dfrac{a}{b^{-1}} + \dfrac{b}{a^{-1}}$

12. Note that $2 \cdot (3 + 4) = 2 + (3 \cdot 4)$. Is this true for any three real numbers a, b, and c? That is, is $a \cdot (b + c) = a + (b \cdot c)$?

13. (a) Find real numbers a, b, and c to illustrate that the following is not always true:

$$\frac{a}{b} + \frac{a}{c} = \frac{a}{b + c}$$

(b) Is it ever true?

14. Use the properties of the real numbers to show that if a and b are real numbers, then $-a + (a + b) = b$.

15. Let a and b be real numbers with $a \neq 0$ and $b \neq 0$. Show that $[(1/a)(1/b)](ab) = 1$.

16. Let a, b, c, and d be real numbers. Show that $(ac + ad) + (bc + bd) = (a + b)(c + d)$.

17. Let a, b, and c be real numbers with $c \neq 0$. Show that $-(ab) + (ca)[b(1/c)] = 0$.

18. Supply the missing reasons for the proof of the following: "There is no rational number r such that $r^2 = 2$; thus $\sqrt{2}$ is not a rational number."

   Proof: Suppose there is a rational number r such that $r^2 = 2$. Then $r = p/q$, where p and q are integers and $q \neq 0$. (Why?) Furthermore, it is always possible to take integers p and q so that p and q have no common integral factor (other than 1 and -1). (Why?) We have, then,

$$\left(\frac{p}{q}\right)^2 = r^2 = 2$$

That is,

$$\frac{p^2}{q^2} = 2 \qquad \text{(why?)}$$

or

$$p^2 = 2q^2$$

Since q is an integer, so is q^2. Thus we have p^2 represented as an even integer $2q^2$. But this implies that p itself must be an even integer. (Why?) So we may write

$$p = 2m \qquad \text{for some integer } m$$

Then, returning to our previous equality, we have

$$(2m)^2 = p^2 = 2q^2$$

That is, $4m^2 = 2q^2$ or $2m^2 = q^2$. But m^2 is an integer, so that now we have q^2 written as an even integer, $2m^2$. Thus q is also an even integer. However, if p and q are both even integers, they must have a common integral factor other than 1 or -1. (Why?) This is a contradiction to our previous requirement that p and q have no common integral factor different from 1 or -1. Hence there is no rational number r which has the property that $r^2 = 2$.

Section A.2 Order Properties of Real Numbers

In our study of linear programming (Chapters 7 and 8) we require a knowledge of the order properties of the real numbers. The idea of one number being less than (or greater than) another number is certainly not strange to any of us. For example, we all agree that 15 is less than 20 and that 100 is not less than 50. However, as is usual in mathematics, a precise definition of this concept is necessary to exploit its full value.

We begin by dividing the real numbers into three subclasses: the positive real numbers, the number 0, and the negative real numbers. For example,

$$17, \tfrac{1}{5}, \sqrt{2}, .34, \text{ and } \tfrac{75}{8}$$

are examples of positive real numbers, while

$$-35, -\tfrac{7}{8}, -\pi, -.62$$

are examples of negative real numbers.

Some of the important arithmetic properties of these subclasses of real numbers are as follows:

O1: The sum of two positive real numbers is a positive real number.
O2: The product of two positive real numbers is a positive real number.
O3: The sum of two negative real numbers is a negative real number.
O4: The product of two negative real numbers is a *positive* real number.
O5: The product of a positive and negative real number is a negative real number.

For convenience we use the notation $a > 0$ to represent the fact that a is a positive real number and the notation $a < 0$ to represent the fact that a is a negative real number. So, for example,

$$6 > 0, \tfrac{1}{5} > 0, .2 > 0, \sqrt{7} > 0$$

while

$$-1 < 0, -\tfrac{8}{3} < 0, -\sqrt{2} < 0$$

With this notation the properties O1–O5 can be expressed more compactly in the following way:

O1. If $a > 0$ and $b > 0$, then $a + b > 0$.
O2. If $a > 0$ and $b > 0$, then $a \cdot b > 0$.
O3. If $a < 0$ and $b < 0$, then $a + b < 0$.
O4. If $a < 0$ and $b < 0$, then $a \cdot b > 0$.
O5. If $a < 0$ and $b > 0$ or if $a > 0$ and $b < 0$, then $a \cdot b < 0$.

We are now in a position to give precise definitions of the notions of "less than" and "greater than."

Definition

If a and b are real numbers, we say that $a < b$ (read "a is less than b") if $b - a$ is a positive real number. Thus

$$a < b \quad \text{means} \quad b - a > 0$$

Similarly, we say that $b > a$ (read "b is greater than a") if $b - a$ is a positive real number. Thus

$$b > a \quad \text{means} \quad b - a > 0$$

Notice, of course, that saying that $a < b$ is precisely the same thing as saying that $b > a$.

Example A.2.1

1. $15 < 20$ since $20 - 15 = 5 > 0$
2. $50 < 100$ since $100 - 50 = 50 > 0$
3. $8 > 6$ since $8 - 6 = 2 > 0$
4. $\frac{3}{4} > \frac{1}{2}$ since $\frac{3}{4} - \frac{1}{2} = \frac{1}{4} > 0$
5. $-2 < 1$ since $1 - (-2) = 3 > 0$
6. $-2 > -5$ since $-2 - (-5) = 3 > 0$
7. $\frac{1}{6} > -3$ since $\frac{1}{6} - (-3) = \frac{19}{6} > 0$

Notice, for example, that $4 \not< 4$ (i.e., 4 is *not* less than 4) since $4 - 4 = 0 \not> 0$, and similarly $4 \not> 4$ since $4 - 4 = 0 \not> 0$.

It is convenient to also define the concepts "less than or equal to" and "greater than or equal to." We use the notation $a \geq 0$ to represent the fact that a is a non-negative real number; that is, a is either 0 or a positive real number.

Definition

If a and b are real numbers, we say that $a \leq b$ (read "a is less than or equal to b") if $b - a$ is a nonnegative real number, that is, if it is either a positive real number or 0. Thus

$$a \leq b \quad \text{means} \quad b - a \geq 0$$

Similarly, we say that $b \geq a$ (read "b is greater than or equal to a") if $b - a$ is a nonnegative real number. Thus

$$b \geq a \quad \text{means} \quad b - a \geq 0$$

Notice that the statements $a \leq b$ and $b \geq a$ are equivalent. Also notice that if $a < b$, then $a \leq b$, but not necessarily vice versa. For example, $4 \leq 4$ (since $4 - 4 = 0 \geq 0$) but $4 \not< 4$ (since $4 - 4 = 0 \not> 0$).

Example A.2.2

1. $15 \leq 20$ since $20 - 15 = 5 \geq 0$
2. $-\frac{1}{5} \leq -\frac{1}{10}$ since $-\frac{1}{10} - (-\frac{1}{5}) = \frac{1}{10} \geq 0$
3. $6 \leq 6$ since $6 - 6 = 0 \geq 0$
4. $-3 \geq -7$ since $-3 - (-7) = 4 \geq 0$
5. $\frac{1}{2} \geq \frac{2}{5}$ since $\frac{1}{2} - \frac{2}{5} = \frac{1}{10} \geq 0$
6. $-35 \geq -35$ since $-35 - (-35) = 0 \geq 0$

In solving linear inequalities (see Section A.3) we will need the basic properties involving inequalities as related to arithmetic operations. These properties are as follows:

I1: If $a \leq b$ and c is any real number, then $a + c \leq b + c$. That is, any real number can be added to both sides of an inequality without affecting the inequality.

I2: (a) If $a \leq b$ and $c > 0$, then $a \cdot c \leq b \cdot c$. That is, if both sides of an inequality are multiplied by a *positive* real number, the inequality is unaffected.

(b) If $a \leq b$ and $c < 0$, then $a \cdot c \geq b \cdot c$. That is, if both sides of an inequality are multiplied by a *negative* real number, the inequality is *reversed*.

I3: If a and b are *positive* real numbers and $a \leq b$, then $1/a \geq 1/b$.

The same rules apply when the $\leq$ and $\geq$ signs are replaced by the $<$ and $>$ signs.

Example A.2.3

1. Since $3 \leq 6$, we have
$$3 + 4 \leq 6 + 4 \qquad (7 \leq 10)$$
and
$$3 - 4 \leq 6 - 4 \qquad (-1 \leq 2)$$

2. Since $3 \leq 6$ and $4 > 0$, we have
$$3 \cdot 4 \leq 6 \cdot 4 \qquad (12 \leq 24)$$

   On the other hand, since $3 \leq 6$ and $-4 < 0$, we have
$$3 \cdot (-4) \geq 6 \cdot (-4) \qquad (-12 \geq -24)$$

3. Since 2 and 3 are positive real numbers and $2 \leq 3$, we have
$$\tfrac{1}{2} \geq \tfrac{1}{3}$$

Exercises for A.2

1. Fill in the blanks with the appropriate symbol, $<$ or $>$.
   (a) $6 \underline{\quad} 13$
   (b) $\frac{1}{4} \underline{\quad} \frac{2}{5}$
   (c) $\frac{8}{3} \underline{\quad} \frac{11}{4}$
   (d) $-5 \underline{\quad} 0$
   (e) $-2 \underline{\quad} -1$
   (f) $-\frac{5}{3} \underline{\quad} \frac{1}{3}$
   (g) $\frac{1}{5} \underline{\quad} -2$
   (h) $3^0 \underline{\quad} (-2)^2$
   (i) $\frac{16}{5} \underline{\quad} \frac{22}{7}$
   (j) $\frac{11}{3} \underline{\quad} \frac{29}{8}$

2. Fill in the blanks with the appropriate symbol, $\leq$ or $\geq$ (or both).
   (a) $14 \underline{\quad} 10$
   (b) $-6 \underline{\quad} \frac{2}{3}$
   (c) $\frac{1}{2} \underline{\quad} \frac{2}{3}$
   (d) $5 \underline{\quad} 5$
   (e) $3 \underline{\quad} (-1)^2$
   (f) $(-2)^3 \underline{\quad} (-2)^4$
   (g) $7^2 \underline{\quad} (\frac{13}{2})^2$
   (h) $\frac{3}{4} \underline{\quad} \frac{6}{8}$
   (i) $1^2 \underline{\quad} (-2)^2$
   (j) $1^3 \underline{\quad} (-2)^3$
   (k) $(-\frac{1}{2})^3 \underline{\quad} (-\frac{2}{3})^2$
   (l) $(\frac{5}{3})^3 \underline{\quad} (-\frac{1}{2})^3$

3. Suppose that a is a real number. Why is it impossible to have $a > a$?

4. Let a, b, and c be real numbers with $a \geq b$ and $c \leq b$. What possible relations can exist between a and c? Illustrate by numerical examples.

5. Let a and b be real numbers with $b > 0$. Prove that $a - b < a$.

6. Let a be a real number with $0 < a < 1$. Prove that $1/a > 1$.

7. Suppose that a and b are real numbers with $a < b$. Prove that $a < (a + b)/2 < b$. (*Hint:* Add a to both sides of the given inequality; then add b to both sides of the given inequality.)

8. Suppose that a, b, and c are real numbers with $a < b$ and $b < c$. Show that $a < c$.

9. Let a, b, c, and d be real numbers with $a < b$ and $c < d$. Show that $a + c < b + d$.

10. Suppose that a, b, c, and d are real numbers with $0 < a < b$ and $0 < c < d$. Prove that $ac < bd$.

11. Let a and b be *positive* real numbers. Prove that $a^2 < b^2$ if and only if $a < b$. [*Hint:* $b^2 - a^2 = (b - a)(b + a)$.]

Section A.3   The Real Line and Linear Inequalities

It is often useful to have a geometric interpretation of the real numbers. This is obtained by associating with each real number a point on a line.

We begin by specifying a particular point as the *origin*. This point will correspond to the number 0. Through this point we draw a straight line (usually horizontal). Then we introduce a scale by specifying a unit length. Finally, we introduce an *orientation* by specifying a positive and negative direction on the line drawn. At this time we have the picture in Figure A.3.1.

Figure A.3.1

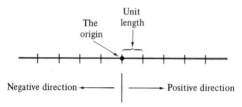

As mentioned previously, the origin will correspond to the real number 0. Next we associate the real number 1 with the point one unit from the origin in the positive direction. Now that this is done it is clear how to associate the real numbers with the points on the line. We illustrate the procedure in Figure A.3.2. The line obtained in the figure, whose points are associated with real numbers as indicated, is called the *real line*.

Figure A.3.2

Note that the geometric interpretation of $a < b$ is simply that the point on the real line corresponding to the real number a lies to the left of the point on the real line corresponding to the real number b. In particular, the positive real numbers correspond to the points on the real line to the right of the origin, and the negative real numbers correspond to the points on the real line to the left of the origin.

The next topic to be considered is that of solving linear inequalities in one variable. However, before doing this we recall the notion of linear equations in one variable and the solution method for such equations.

Definition

A *linear equation* in one variable, x, is an equation of the form

$$ax + b = c \tag{A.3.1}$$

where a, b, and c are given real numbers and $a \neq 0$.

Example A.3.1

1. The equation

$$5x - 2 = 13 \tag{A.3.2}$$

is a linear equation in the one variable x. In the notation of Eq. (A.3.1) we have $a = 5$, $b = -2$, and $c = 13$.

2. The equation

$$-\tfrac{3}{2}x = 4 \tag{A.3.3}$$

is a linear equation in the one variable x. In the notation of Eq. (A.3.1) we have $a = -\tfrac{3}{2}$, $b = 0$, and $c = 4$.

In considering a linear equation in one variable, x, the problem is to determine what real number, when substituted in place of x, will make the equation true. This is referred to as *solving for x*. The method of solution involves utilizing the arithmetic properties of real numbers to "isolate" x on one side of the equation. The crucial fact is that adding a real number to both sides of an equation or multiplying both sides of an equation by a nonzero real number does not affect the equality.

Example A.3.2 Solve the equation in (A.3.2) for x. Adding 2 to both sides of the equation gives the equivalent equation

$$5x = 15$$

By multiplying both sides of this last equation by $\tfrac{1}{5}$ we obtain the equation

$$x = 3$$

Thus $x = 3$ is the solution to the linear equation $5x - 2 = 13$.

We can check to see that this is, in fact, the case by substituting 3 for x in the equation and verifying that the resulting equation is true:

$$5 \cdot 3 - 2 = 15 - 2 = 13$$

as desired.

Example A.3.3 Solve the linear equation

$$-\tfrac{3}{4}x + 7 = -11$$

Proceeding as in Example A.3.2, we obtain the following sequence of equations:

$$-\tfrac{3}{4}x = -18$$
$$x = 24$$

and so the solution is $x = 24$.

A linear inequality in one variable, x, is basically a linear equation in one variable x, with the equal sign replaced by one of the inequality signs.

Definition

A *linear inequality* in one variable, x, is an expression of one of the following four forms:

1. $ax + b < c$
2. $ax + b > c$

3. $ax + b \leq c$
4. $ax + b \geq c$

where a, b, and c are real numbers with $a \neq 0$.

Example A.3.4 The following are examples of linear inequalities in the one variable, x.

1. $2x + 4 < 5$
2. $-8x + 7 > 13$
3. $3x \leq 24$
4. $-\frac{2}{5}x + 8 \geq 0$

As in the case for a linear equation in x, the problem for a linear inequality in x is to determine real numbers that when substituted in for x render the inequality true. Such values are called *solutions* of the linear inequality, and the collection of all such values is called the *solution set* of the linear inequality.

The method for solving linear inequalities is similar to the method used for solving linear equations. However, a bit more care must be taken, because the inequality can be *reversed* by multiplying both sides of the original linear inequality by a *negative* real number [see I2(b) of Section A.2].

Example A.3.5 Determine the solution set of the linear inequality

$$2x + 3 \leq 13 \qquad\qquad\qquad (A.3.4)$$

First we add -3 to both sides of the inequality, to obtain

$$2x \leq 10$$

Then both sides of this last inequality are multiplied by $\frac{1}{2}$ to give

$$x \leq 5$$

[*Note:* Since $\frac{1}{2} > 0$, the inequality sign remains the same, by I2(a) of Section A.2.]

Hence the solution set to the linear inequality (A.3.4) consists of all real numbers less than or equal to 5. The "graph" of this solution set on the real line is illustrated in Figure A.3.3. The solid dot at 5 is used to indicate that 5 is a member of the solution set.

Figure A.3.3

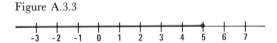

Example A.3.6 Determine the solution set of the linear inequality

$$-4x + 5 < 13 \qquad\qquad\qquad (A.3.5)$$

First we add -5 to both sides of the inequality. The result is

$$-4x < 8$$

Next, we multiply both sides of this inequality by $-\frac{1}{4}$. Since $-\frac{1}{4} < 0$, the resulting inequality has the "reverse" inequality sign [see I2(b) of Section A.2]:

$$x > -2$$

Hence the solution set to the linear inequality (A.3.5) consists of all real numbers greater than -2. The graph of this solution set is as shown in Figure A.3.4. The hollow dot at -2 is used to indicate that -2 is *not* a member of the solution set.

Figure A.3.4

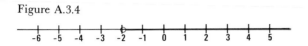

Exercises for A.3

1. Solve the following equations for x.
   (a) $x + 3 = 0$
   (b) $2x - 5 = 3$
   (c) $3x + 4 = 13$
   (d) $7 + 5x = 22$
   (e) $8 = 11 + 3x$
   (f) $25 = 31 - 3x$
   (g) $3x - 10 = 14$
   (h) $11 - 8x = -5$
   (i) $3(5 - x) = 0$
   (j) $ax + b = 0 \quad (a \neq 0)$

2. Solve each of the following equations for x.
   (a) $3x + 5 = x + 17$
   (b) $4x + 3 = x + 18$
   (c) $2x + 3 = 5x - 4$
   (d) $\frac{2}{3}x - 5 = 4 + \frac{1}{2}x$
   (e) $\frac{1}{2}x - 3 = \frac{3}{4}x + 1$
   (f) $\frac{2x}{3} + \frac{x}{4} = 2$
   (g) $8 - \frac{x+1}{3} = \frac{2x-5}{4} + 7$
   (h) $15 - (2 + 3x) = 9x + 1$

3. For what value of a is $x = -2$ the solution of the equation $2x + a = x - 8 - a$?

4. Find the solution set of each of the following inequalities and represent the set by a graph.
   (a) $x + 5 > 10$
   (b) $x - 16 \le 15$
   (c) $2x - 3 \le 5$
   (d) $5x + 1 > 2x - 6$
   (e) $\frac{3}{2}x + \frac{5}{3} \ge \frac{1}{2}x + \frac{14}{3}$
   (f) $2x - 1 \ge 5x + 3$
   (g) $4 - 3x > 7 + 2x$
   (h) $\frac{1}{2}x - \frac{3}{4} < 2 - \frac{1}{3}x$
   (i) $\frac{2x - 5}{3} \le 0$
   (j) $\frac{8 - 3x}{-4} \le 8$
   (k) $2x - 1 < 5x + 3$
   (l) $1 - 7x \le x - 1$

5. Find the solution set of each of the following inequalities and represent the set by a graph.
   (a) $1 < 2x - 3 < 2$†
   (b) $-3 < 1 - 2x < 4$
   (c) $3 \le 2x + 1 < 7$
   (d) $1 < 3 - 2x < 2$
   (e) $5 \le 3x + 3 \le 15$
   (f) $-5 < \frac{4 - 3x}{2} < 1$

   †*Note:* $1 < 2x - 3 < 2$ represents *two* inequalities, $2x - 3 > 1$ and $2x - 3 < 2$. The problem is to find the values for x which satisfy *both* inequalities.

6. Show that if x is a real number such that $x < -2$, then $(x + 2)(x - 1) > 0$.
7. Show that if $-2 < x$ and $x < 1$, then $(x + 2)(x - 1) < 0$.
8. If $x > 1$, show that $(x + 2)(x - 1) > 0$.
9. The point on the real number line corresponding to the irrational number $\sqrt{2}$ can be found by striking off a circular arc, as indicated in the figure. Use a similar method to find the point on the real line corresponding to the irrational number $\sqrt{5}$.

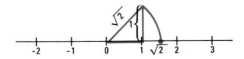

Appendix B
Tables

Table 1

The Binomial Coefficients—$\binom{n}{k}$

Note: $\binom{n}{k} = {}_nC_k$

and

$$\binom{n}{k} = \binom{n}{n-k}$$

	n												
k	1	2	3	4	5	6	7	8	9	10	11	12	13
0	1	1	1	1	1	1	1	1	1	1	1	1	1
1		2	3	4	5	6	7	8	9	10	11	12	13
2			6	10	15	21	28	36	45	55	66	78
3					20	35	56	84	120	165	220	286
4						70	126	210	330	495	715
5							252	462	792	1,287
6								924	1,716

k	14	15	16	17	18	19	20	21	22
0	1	1	1	1	1	1	1	1	1
1	14	15	16	17	18	19	20	21	22
2	91	105	120	136	153	171	190	210	231
3	364	455	560	680	816	969	1,140	1,330	1,540
4	1,001	1,365	1,820	2,380	3,060	3,876	4,845	5,985	7,315
5	2,002	3,003	4,368	6,188	8,568	11,628	15,504	20,349	26,334
6	3,003	5,005	8,008	12,376	18,564	27,132	38,760	54,264	74,613
7	3,432	6,435	11,440	19,448	31,824	50,388	77,520	116,280	170,544
8			12,870	24,310	43,758	75,582	125,970	203,490	319,770
9					48,620	92,378	167,960	293,930	497,420
10							184,756	352,716	646,646
11									705,432

537

k	23	24	25	26	27	28
				n		
0	1	1	1	1	1	1
1	23	24	25	26	27	28
2	253	276	300	325	351	378
3	1,771	2,024	2,300	2,600	2,925	3,276
4	8,855	10,626	12,650	14,950	17,550	20,475
5	33,649	42,504	53,130	65,780	80,730	98,280
6	100,947	134,596	177,100	230,230	296,010	376,740
7	245,157	346,104	480,700	657,800	888,030	1,184,040
8	490,314	735,471	1,081,575	1,562,275	2,220,075	3,108,105
9	817,190	1,307,504	2,042,975	3,124,550	4,686,825	6,906,900
10	1,144,066	1,961,256	3,268,760	5,311,735	8,436,285	13,123,110
11	1,352,078	2,496,144	4,457,400	7,726,160	13,037,895	21,474,180
12		2,704,156	5,200,300	9,657,700	17,383,860	30,421,755
13				10,400,600	20,058,300	37,442,160
14						40,116,600

k	29	30	31	32	33
0	1	1	1	1	1
1	29	30	31	32	33
2	406	435	465	496	528
3	3,654	4,060	4,495	4,960	5,456
4	23,751	27,405	31,465	35,960	40,920
5	118,755	142,506	169,911	201,376	237,336
6	475,020	593,775	736,281	906,192	1,107,568
7	1,560,780	2,035,800	2,629,575	3,365,856	4,272,048
8	4,292,145	5,852,925	7,888,725	10,518,300	13,884,156
9	10,015,005	14,307,150	20,160,075	28,048,800	38,567,100
10	20,030,010	30,045,015	44,352,165	64,512,240	92,561,040
11	34,597,290	54,627,300	84,672,315	129,024,480	193,536,720
12	51,895,935	86,493,225	141,120,525	225,792,840	354,817,320
13	67,863,915	119,759,850	206,253,075	347,373,600	573,166,440
14	77,558,760	145,422,675	265,182,525	471,435,600	818,809,200
15		155,117,520	300,540,195	565,722,720	1,037,158,320
16				601,080,390	1,166,803,110
17					

			n		
k	34	35	36	37	38
0	1	1	1	1	1
1	34	35	36	37	38
2	561	595	630	666	703
3	5,984	6,545	7,140	7,770	8,436
4	46,376	52,360	58,905	66,045	73,815
5	278,256	324,632	376,992	435,897	501,942
6	1,344,904	1,623,160	1,947,792	2,324,784	2,760,681
7	5,379,616	6,724,520	8,347,680	10,295,472	12,620,256
8	18,156,204	23,535,820	30,260,340	38,608,020	48,903,492
9	52,451,256	70,607,460	94,143,280	124,403,620	163,011,640
10	131,128,140	183,579,396	254,186,856	348,330,136	472,733,756
11	286,097,760	417,225,900	600,805,296	854,992,152	1,203,322,288
12	548,354,040	834,451,800	1,251,677,700	1,852,482,996	2,707,475,148
13	927,983,760	1,476,337,800	2,310,789,600	3,562,467,300	5,414,950,296
14	1,391,975,640	2,319,959,400	3,796,297,200	6,107,086,800	9,669,554,100
15	1,855,967,520	3,247,943,160	5,567,902,560	9,364,199,760	15,471,286,560
16	2,203,961,430	4,059,928,950	7,307,872,110	12,875,774,670	22,239,974,430
17	2,333,606,220	4,537,567,650	8,597,496,600	15,905,368,710	28,781,143,380
18			9,075,135,300	17,672,631,900	33,578,000,610
19					35,345,263,800

k	39	40	41	42
0	1	1	1	1
1	39	40	41	42
2	741	780	820	861
3	9,139	9,880	10,660	11,480
4	82,251	91,390	101,270	111,930
5	575,757	658,008	749,398	850,668
6	3,262,623	3,838,380	4,496,388	5,245,786
7	15,380,937	18,643,560	22,481,940	26,978,328
8	61,523,748	76,904,685	95,548,245	118,030,185
9	211,915,132	273,438,880	350,343,565	445,891,810
10	635,745,396	847,660,528	1,121,099,408	1,471,442,973
11	1,676,056,044	2,311,801,440	3,159,461,968	4,280,561,376
12	3,910,797,436	5,586,853,480	7,898,654,920	11,058,116,888
13	8,122,425,444	12,033,222,880	17,620,076,360	25,518,731,280
14	15,084,504,396	23,206,929,840	35,240,152,720	52,860,229,080
15	25,140,840,660	40,225,345,056	63,432,274,896	98,672,427,616
16	37,711,260,990	62,852,101,650	103,077,446,706	166,509,721,602
17	51,021,117,810	88,732,378,800	151,584,480,450	254,661,927,156
18	62,359,143,990	113,380,261,800	202,112,640,600	353,697,121,050
19	68,923,264,410	131,282,408,400	244,662,670,200	446,775,310,800
20		137,846,528,820	269,128,937,220	513,791,607,420
21				538,257,874,440

Table 1   The Binomial Coefficients   539

k	n			
	43	44	45	46
0	1	1	1	1
1	43	44	45	46
2	903	946	990	1,035
3	12,341	13,244	14,190	15,180
4	123,410	135,751	148,995	163,185
5	962,598	1,086,008	1,221,759	1,370,754
6	6,096,454	7,059,052	8,145,060	9,366,819
7	32,224,114	38,320,568	45,379,620	53,524,680
8	145,008,513	177,232,627	215,553,195	260,932,815
9	563,921,995	708,930,508	886,163,135	1,101,716,330
10	1,917,334,783	2,481,256,778	3,190,187,286	4,076,350,421
11	4,752,004,349	7,669,339,132	10,150,595,910	13,340,783,196
12	15,338,678,264	21,090,682,613	28,760,021,745	38,910,617,655
13	36,576,848,168	51,915,526,432	73,006,209,045	101,766,230,790
14	78,378,960,360	114,955,808,528	166,871,334,960	239,877,544,005
15	151,532,656,696	229,911,617,056	344,867,425,584	511,738,760,544
16	265,182,149,218	416,714,805,914	646,626,422,970	991,493,848,554
17	421,171,648,758	686,353,797,976	1,103,068,603,890	1,749,695,026,860
18	608,359,048,206	1,029,530,696,964	1,715,884,494,940	2,818,953,098,830
19	800,472,431,850	1,408,831,480,056	2,438,362,177,020	4,154,246,671,960
20	960,566,918,220	1,761,039,350,070	3,169,870,830,126	5,608,233,007,146
21	1,052,049,481,860	2,012,616,400,080	3,773,655,750,150	6,943,526,580,276
22		2,104,098,963,720	4,116,715,363,800	7,890,371,113,950
23				8,233,430,727,600

k	n		
	47	48	49
0	1	1	1
1	47	48	49
2	1,081	1,128	1,176
3	16,215	17,296	18,424
4	178,365	194,580	211,876
5	1,533,939	1,712,304	1,906,884
6	10,737,573	12,271,512	13,983,816
7	62,891,499	73,629,072	85,900,584
8	314,457,495	377,348,994	450,978,066
9	1,362,649,145	1,677,106,640	2,054,455,634
10	5,178,066,751	6,540,715,897	8,217,822,536
11	17,417,133,617	22,595,200,368	29,135,916,264
12	52,251,400,851	69,668,534,468	92,263,734,836
13	140,676,848,445	192,928,249,296	262,596,783,764
14	341,643,774,795	482,320,623,240	675,248,872,536
15	751,616,304,549	1,093,260,079,344	1,575,580,702,584
16	1,503,232,609,098	2,254,848,913,647	3,348,108,992,991
17	2,741,188,875,414	4,244,421,484,512	6,499,270,398,159
18	4,568,648,125,690	7,309,837,001,104	11,554,258,485,616
19	6,973,199,770,790	11,541,847,896,480	18,851,684,897,584
20	9,762,479,679,106	16,735,679,449,896	28,277,527,346,376
21	12,551,759,587,422	22,314,239,266,528	39,049,918,716,424
22	14,833,897,694,226	27,385,657,281,648	49,699,896,548,176
23	16,123,801,841,550	30,957,699,535,776	58,343,356,817,424
24		32,247,603,683,100	63,205,303,218,876
25			

Table 1 The Binomial Coefficients 541

	n		
k	50	51	52
0	1	1	1
1	50	51	52
2	1,225	1,275	1,326
3	19,600	20,825	22,100
4	230,300	249,900	270,725
5	2,118,760	2,349,060	2,598,960
6	15,890,700	18,009,460	20,358,520
7	99,884,400	115,775,100	133,784,560
8	536,878,650	636,763,050	752,538,150
9	2,505,433,700	3,042,312,350	3,679,075,400
10	10,272,278,170	12,777,711,870	15,820,024,220
11	37,353,738,800	47,626,016,970	60,403,728,840
12	121,399,651,100	158,753,389,900	206,379,406,870
13	354,860,518,600	476,260,169,700	635,013,559,600
14	937,845,656,300	1,292,706,174,900	1,768,966,344,600
15	2,250,829,575,120	3,188,675,231,420	4,481,381,406,320
16	4,923,689,695,575	7,174,519,270,695	10,363,194,502,115
17	9,847,379,391,150	14,771,069,086,725	21,945,588,357,420
18	18,053,528,883,775	27,900,908,274,925	42,671,977,361,650
19	30,405,943,383,200	48,459,472,266,975	76,360,380,541,900
20	47,129,212,243,960	77,535,155,627,160	125,994,627,894,135
21	67,327,446,062,800	114,456,658,306,760	191,991,813,933,920
22	88,749,815,264,600	156,077,261,327,400	270,533,919,634,160
23	108,043,253,365,600	196,793,068,630,200	352,870,329,957,600
24	121,548,660,036,300	229,591,913,401,900	426,384,982,032,100
25	126,410,606,437,752	247,959,266,474,052	477,551,179,875,952
26			495,918,532,948,104

Table 2

Binomial Probabilities—$\binom{n}{k}p^k(1-p)^{n-k}$

Note: $\binom{n}{k}p^k(1-p)^{n-k} = \binom{n}{n-k}(1-p)^{n-k}p^k$

						p				
n	k	.01	.05	.10	.15	.20	.25	.30	.40	.50
1	0	.9900	.9500	.9000	.8500	.8000	.7500	.7000	.6000	.5000
	1	.0100	.0500	.1000	.1500	.2000	.2500	.3000	.4000	.5000
2	0	.9801	.9025	.8100	.7225	.6400	.5625	.4900	.3600	.2500
	1	.0198	.0950	.1800	.2550	.3200	.3750	.4200	.4800	.5000
	2	.0001	.0025	.0100	.0225	.0400	.0625	.0900	.1600	.2500
3	0	.9703	.8574	.7290	.6141	.5120	.4219	.3430	.2160	.1250
	1	.0294	.1354	.2430	.3251	.3840	.4219	.4410	.4320	.3750
	2	.0003	.0071	.0270	.0574	.0960	.1406	.1890	.2880	.3750
	3	.0000	.0001	.0010	.0034	.0080	.0156	.0270	.0640	.1250
4	0	.9606	.8145	.6561	.5220	.4096	.3164	.2401	.1296	.0625
	1	.0388	.1715	.2916	.3685	.4096	.4219	.4116	.3456	.2500
	2	.0006	.0135	.0486	.0975	.1536	.2109	.2646	.3456	.3750
	3	.0000	.0005	.0036	.0115	.0256	.0469	.0756	.1536	.2500
	4	.0000	.0000	.0001	.0005	.0016	.0039	.0081	.0256	.0625
5	0	.9510	.7738	.5905	.4437	.3277	.2373	.1681	.0778	.0313
	1	.0430	.2036	.3280	.3915	.4096	.3955	.3602	.2592	.1563
	2	.0010	.0214	.0729	.1382	.2048	.2637	.3087	.3456	.3125
	3	.0000	.0011	.0081	.0244	.0512	.0879	.1323	.2304	.3125
	4	.0000	.0000	.0004	.0022	.0064	.0146	.0284	.0768	.1563
	5	.0000	.0000	.0000	.0001	.0003	.0010	.0024	.0102	.0313
6	0	.9415	.7351	.5314	.3771	.2621	.1780	.1176	.0467	.0156
	1	.0571	.2321	.3543	.3993	.3932	.3560	.3025	.1866	.0938
	2	.0014	.0305	.0984	.1762	.2458	.2966	.3241	.3110	.2344
	3	.0000	.0021	.0146	.0415	.0819	.1318	.1852	.2765	.3125
	4	.0000	.0001	.0012	.0055	.0154	.0330	.0595	.1382	.2344
	5	.0000	.0000	.0001	.0004	.0015	.0044	.0102	.0369	.0938
	6	.0000	.0000	.0000	.0000	.0001	.0002	.0007	.0041	.0156
7	0	.9321	.6983	.4783	.3206	.2097	.1335	.0824	.0280	.0078
	1	.0659	.2573	.3720	.3960	.3670	.3115	.2471	.1306	.0547
	2	.0020	.0406	.1240	.2097	.2753	.3115	.3177	.2613	.1641
	3	.0000	.0036	.0230	.0617	.1147	.1730	.2269	.2903	.2734
	4	.0000	.0002	.0026	.0109	.0287	.0577	.0972	.1935	.2734
	5	.0000	.0000	.0002	.0012	.0043	.0115	.0250	.0774	.1641
	6	.0000	.0000	.0000	.0001	.0004	.0013	.0036	.0172	.0547
	7	.0000	.0000	.0000	.0000	.0000	.0001	.0002	.0016	.0078

543

						p				
n	k	.01	.05	.10	.15	.20	.25	.30	.40	.50
8	0	.9227	.6634	.4305	.2725	.1678	.1001	.0576	.0168	.0039
	1	.0746	.2793	.3826	.3847	.3355	.2670	.1977	.0896	.0313
	2	.0026	.0515	.1488	.2376	.2936	.3115	.2965	.2090	.1094
	3	.0001	.0054	.0331	.0839	.1468	.2076	.2541	.2787	.2188
	4	.0000	.0004	.0046	.0185	.0459	.0865	.1361	.2322	.2734
	5	.0000	.0000	.0004	.0026	.0092	.0231	.0467	.1239	.2188
	6	.0000	.0000	.0000	.0002	.0011	.0038	.0100	.0413	.1094
	7	.0000	.0000	.0000	.0000	.0001	.0004	.0012	.0079	.0313
	8	.0000	.0000	.0000	.0000	.0000	.0000	.0001	.0007	.0039
9	0	.9135	.6302	.3874	.2316	.1342	.0751	.0404	.0101	.0020
	1	.0830	.2985	.3874	.3679	.3020	.2253	.1556	.0605	.0176
	2	.0034	.0629	.1722	.2597	.3020	.3003	.2668	.1612	.0703
	3	.0001	.0077	.0446	.1069	.1762	.2336	.2668	.2508	.1641
	4	.0000	.0006	.0074	.0283	.0661	.1168	.1715	.2508	.2461
	5	.0000	.0000	.0008	.0050	.0165	.0389	.0735	.1672	.2461
	6	.0000	.0000	.0001	.0006	.0028	.0087	.0210	.0743	.1641
	7	.0000	.0000	.0000	.0000	.0003	.0012	.0039	.0212	.0703
	8	.0000	.0000	.0000	.0000	.0000	.0001	.0004	.0035	.0176
	9	.0000	.0000	.0000	.0000	.0000	.0000	.0000	.0003	.0020
10	0	.9044	.5987	.3487	.1969	.1074	.0563	.0282	.0060	.0010
	1	.0914	.3151	.3874	.3474	.2684	.1877	.1211	.0403	.0098
	2	.0042	.0746	.1937	.2759	.3020	.2816	.2335	.1209	.0439
	3	.0001	.0105	.0574	.1298	.2013	.2503	.2668	.2150	.1172
	4	.0000	.0010	.0112	.0401	.0881	.1460	.2001	.2508	.2051
	5	.0000	.0001	.0015	.0085	.0264	.0584	.1029	.2007	.2461
	6	.0000	.0000	.0001	.0012	.0055	.0162	.0368	.1115	.2051
	7	.0000	.0000	.0000	.0001	.0008	.0031	.0090	.0425	.1172
	8	.0000	.0000	.0000	.0000	.0001	.0004	.0014	.0106	.0439
	9	.0000	.0000	.0000	.0000	.0000	.0000	.0001	.0016	.0098
	10	.0000	.0000	.0000	.0000	.0000	.0000	.0000	.0001	.0010
11	0	.8953	.5688	.3138	.1673	.0859	.0422	.0198	.0036	.0005
	1	.0995	.3293	.3835	.3248	.2362	.1549	.0932	.0266	.0054
	2	.0050	.0867	.2131	.2866	.2953	.2581	.1998	.0887	.0269
	3	.0002	.0137	.0710	.1517	.2215	.2581	.2568	.1774	.0806
	4	.0000	.0014	.0158	.0536	.1107	.1721	.2201	.2365	.1611
	5	.0000	.0001	.0025	.0132	.0388	.0803	.1321	.2207	.2256
	6	.0000	.0000	.0003	.0023	.0097	.0268	.0566	.1471	.2256
	7	.0000	.0000	.0000	.0003	.0017	.0064	.0173	.0701	.1611
	8	.0000	.0000	.0000	.0000	.0002	.0011	.0037	.0234	.0806
	9	.0000	.0000	.0000	.0000	.0000	.0001	.0005	.0052	.0269
	10	.0000	.0000	.0000	.0000	.0000	.0000	.0000	.0007	.0054
	11	.0000	.0000	.0000	.0000	.0000	.0000	.0000	.0000	.0005
12	0	.8864	.5404	.2824	.1422	.0687	.0317	.0138	.0022	.0002
	1	.1074	.3413	.3766	.3012	.2062	.1267	.0712	.0174	.0029
	2	.0060	.0988	.2301	.2924	.2835	.2323	.1678	.0639	.0161

					p					
n	k	.01	.05	.10	.15	.20	.25	.30	.40	.50
12	3	.0002	.0173	.0852	.1720	.2362	.2581	.2397	.1419	.0537
	4	.0000	.0021	.0213	.0683	.1329	.1936	.2311	.2128	.1208
	5	.0000	.0002	.0038	.0193	.0532	.1032	.1585	.2270	.1934
	6	.0000	.0000	.0005	.0040	.0155	.0401	.0792	.1766	.2256
	7	.0000	.0000	.0000	.0006	.0033	.0115	.0291	.1009	.1934
	8	.0000	.0000	.0000	.0001	.0005	.0024	.0078	.0420	.1208
	9	.0000	.0000	.0000	.0000	.0001	.0004	.0015	.0125	.0537
	10	.0000	.0000	.0000	.0000	.0000	.0000	.0002	.0025	.0161
	11	.0000	.0000	.0000	.0000	.0000	.0000	.0000	.0003	.0029
	12	.0000	.0000	.0000	.0000	.0000	.0000	.0000	.0000	.0002
13	0	.8775	.5133	.2542	.1209	.0550	.0238	.0097	.0013	.0001
	1	.1152	.3512	.3672	.2774	.1787	.1029	.0540	.0113	.0016
	2	.0070	.1109	.2448	.2987	.2680	.2059	.1388	.0453	.0095
	3	.0003	.0214	.0997	.1900	.2457	.2517	.2181	.1107	.0349
	4	.0000	.0028	.0277	.0838	.1535	.2097	.2337	.1845	.0873
	5	.0000	.0003	.0055	.0266	.0691	.1258	.1803	.2214	.1571
	6	.0000	.0000	.0008	.0063	.0230	.0559	.1030	.1968	.2095
	7	.0000	.0000	.0001	.0011	.0058	.0186	.0442	.1312	.2095
	8	.0000	.0000	.0000	.0001	.0011	.0047	.0142	.0656	.1571
	9	.0000	.0000	.0000	.0000	.0001	.0009	.0034	.0243	.0873
	10	.0000	.0000	.0000	.0000	.0000	.0001	.0006	.0065	.0349
	11	.0000	.0000	.0000	.0000	.0000	.0000	.0001	.0012	.0095
	12	.0000	.0000	.0000	.0000	.0000	.0000	.0000	.0001	.0016
	13	.0000	.0000	.0000	.0000	.0000	.0000	.0000	.0000	.0001
14	0	.8687	.4877	.2288	.1028	.0440	.0178	.0068	.0008	.0001
	1	.1229	.3593	.3559	.2539	.1539	.0832	.0407	.0073	.0009
	2	.0081	.1229	.2570	.2912	.2501	.1802	.1134	.0317	.0056
	3	.0003	.0259	.1142	.2056	.2501	.2402	.1943	.0845	.0222
	4	.0000	.0037	.0349	.0998	.1720	.2202	.2290	.1549	.0611
	5	.0000	.0004	.0078	.0352	.0860	.1468	.1963	.2066	.1222
	6	.0000	.0000	.0013	.0093	.0322	.0734	.1262	.2066	.1833
	7	.0000	.0000	.0002	.0019	.0092	.0280	.0618	.1574	.2095
	8	.0000	.0000	.0000	.0003	.0020	.0082	.0232	.0918	.1833
	9	.0000	.0000	.0000	.0000	.0003	.0018	.0066	.0408	.1222
	10	.0000	.0000	.0000	.0000	.0000	.0003	.0014	.0136	.0611
	11	.0000	.0000	.0000	.0000	.0000	.0000	.0002	.0033	.0222
	12	.0000	.0000	.0000	.0000	.0000	.0000	.0000	.0005	.0056
	13	.0000	.0000	.0000	.0000	.0000	.0000	.0000	.0001	.0009
	14	.0000	.0000	.0000	.0000	.0000	.0000	.0000	.0000	.0001
15	0	.8601	.4633	.2059	.0874	.0352	.0134	.0047	.0005	.0000
	1	.1303	.3658	.3432	.2312	.1319	.0668	.0305	.0047	.0005
	2	.0092	.1348	.2669	.2856	.2309	.1559	.0916	.0219	.0032
	3	.0004	.0307	.1285	.2184	.2501	.2252	.1700	.0634	.0139
	4	.0000	.0049	.0428	.1156	.1876	.2252	.2186	.1268	.0417
	5	.0000	.0006	.0105	.0449	.1032	.1651	.2061	.1859	.0916
	6	.0000	.0000	.0019	.0132	.0430	.0917	.1472	.2066	.1527

Table 2   Binomial Probabilities   545

					p				
n	k	.01	.05	.10	.15	.20	.25	.30	.40	.50
15	7	.0000	.0000	.0003	.0030	.0138	.0393	.0811	.1771	.1964
	8	.0000	.0000	.0000	.0005	.0035	.0131	.0348	.1181	.1964
	9	.0000	.0000	.0000	.0001	.0007	.0034	.0116	.0612	.1527
	10	.0000	.0000	.0000	.0000	.0001	.0007	.0030	.0245	.0916
	11	.0000	.0000	.0000	.0000	.0000	.0001	.0006	.0074	.0417
	12	.0000	.0000	.0000	.0000	.0000	.0000	.0001	.0016	.0139
	13	.0000	.0000	.0000	.0000	.0000	.0000	.0000	.0003	.0032
	14	.0000	.0000	.0000	.0000	.0000	.0000	.0000	.0000	.0005
	15	.0000	.0000	.0000	.0000	.0000	.0000	.0000	.0000	.0000
16	0	.8515	.4401	.1853	.0743	.0281	.0100	.0033	.0003	.0000
	1	.1376	.3706	.3294	.2097	.1126	.0535	.0228	.0030	.0002
	2	.0104	.1463	.2745	.2775	.2111	.1336	.0732	.0150	.0018
	3	.0005	.0359	.1423	.2285	.2463	.2079	.1465	.0468	.0085
	4	.0000	.0061	.0514	.1311	.2001	.2252	.2040	.1014	.0278
	5	.0000	.0008	.0137	.0555	.1201	.1802	.2099	.1623	.0667
	6	.0000	.0001	.0028	.0180	.0550	.1101	.1649	.1983	.1222
	7	.0000	.0000	.0004	.0045	.0197	.0524	.1010	.1889	.1746
	8	.0000	.0000	.0001	.0009	.0055	.0197	.0487	.1417	.1964
	9	.0000	.0000	.0000	.0001	.0012	.0058	.0185	.0840	.1746
	10	.0000	.0000	.0000	.0000	.0002	.0014	.0056	.0392	.1222
	11	.0000	.0000	.0000	.0000	.0000	.0002	.0013	.0142	.0667
	12	.0000	.0000	.0000	.0000	.0000	.0000	.0002	.0040	.0278
	13	.0000	.0000	.0000	.0000	.0000	.0000	.0000	.0008	.0085
	14	.0000	.0000	.0000	.0000	.0000	.0000	.0000	.0001	.0018
	15	.0000	.0000	.0000	.0000	.0000	.0000	.0000	.0000	.0002
	16	.0000	.0000	.0000	.0000	.0000	.0000	.0000	.0000	.0000
17	0	.8429	.4181	.1668	.0631	.0225	.0075	.0023	.0002	.0000
	1	.1447	.3741	.3150	.1893	.0957	.0426	.0169	.0019	.0001
	2	.0117	.1575	.2800	.2673	.1914	.1136	.0581	.0102	.0010
	3	.0006	.0415	.1556	.2359	.2393	.1893	.1245	.0341	.0052
	4	.0000	.0076	.0605	.1457	.2093	.2209	.1868	.0796	.0182
	5	.0000	.0010	.0175	.0668	.1361	.1914	.2081	.1379	.0472
	6	.0000	.0001	.0039	.0236	.0680	.1276	.1784	.1839	.0944
	7	.0000	.0000	.0007	.0065	.0267	.0668	.1201	.1927	.1484
	8	.0000	.0000	.0001	.0014	.0084	.0279	.0644	.1606	.1855
	9	.0000	.0000	.0000	.0003	.0021	.0093	.0276	.1070	.1855
	10	.0000	.0000	.0000	.0000	.0004	.0025	.0095	.0571	.1484
	11	.0000	.0000	.0000	.0000	.0001	.0005	.0026	.0242	.0944
	12	.0000	.0000	.0000	.0000	.0000	.0001	.0006	.0081	.0472
	13	.0000	.0000	.0000	.0000	.0000	.0000	.0001	.0021	.0182
	14	.0000	.0000	.0000	.0000	.0000	.0000	.0000	.0004	.0052
	15	.0000	.0000	.0000	.0000	.0000	.0000	.0000	.0001	.0010
	16	.0000	.0000	.0000	.0000	.0000	.0000	.0000	.0000	.0001
	17	.0000	.0000	.0000	.0000	.0000	.0000	.0000	.0000	.0000
18	0	.8345	.3972	.1501	.0536	.0180	.0056	.0016	.0001	.0000
	1	.1517	.3763	.3002	.1704	.0811	.0338	.0126	.0012	.0001
	2	.0130	.1683	.2835	.2556	.1723	.0958	.0458	.0069	.0006

		p								
n	k	.01	.05	.10	.15	.20	.25	.30	.40	.50
18	3	.0007	.0473	.1680	.2406	.2297	.1704	.1046	.0246	.0031
	4	.0000	.0093	.0700	.1592	.2153	.2130	.1681	.0614	.0117
	5	.0000	.0014	.0218	.0787	.1507	.1988	.2017	.1146	.0327
	6	.0000	.0002	.0052	.0301	.0816	.1436	.1873	.1655	.0708
	7	.0000	.0000	.0010	.0091	.0350	.0820	.1376	.1892	.1214
	8	.0000	.0000	.0002	.0022	.0120	.0376	.0811	.1734	.1669
	9	.0000	.0000	.0000	.0004	.0033	.0139	.0386	.1284	.1855
	10	.0000	.0000	.0000	.0001	.0008	.0042	.0149	.0771	.1669
	11	.0000	.0000	.0000	.0000	.0001	.0010	.0046	.0374	.1214
	12	.0000	.0000	.0000	.0000	.0000	.0002	.0012	.0145	.0708
	13	.0000	.0000	.0000	.0000	.0000	.0000	.0002	.0045	.0327
	14	.0000	.0000	.0000	.0000	.0000	.0000	.0000	.0011	.0117
	15	.0000	.0000	.0000	.0000	.0000	.0000	.0000	.0002	.0031
	16	.0000	.0000	.0000	.0000	.0000	.0000	.0000	.0000	.0006
	17	.0000	.0000	.0000	.0000	.0000	.0000	.0000	.0000	.0001
	18	.0000	.0000	.0000	.0000	.0000	.0000	.0000	.0000	.0000
19	0	.8262	.3774	.1351	.0456	.0144	.0042	.0011	.0001	.0000
	1	.1586	.3774	.2852	.1529	.0685	.0268	.0093	.0008	.0000
	2	.0144	.1787	.2852	.2428	.1540	.0803	.0358	.0046	.0003
	3	.0008	.0533	.1796	.2428	.2182	.1517	.0869	.0175	.0018
	4	.0000	.0112	.0798	.1714	.2182	.2023	.1491	.0467	.0074
	5	.0000	.0018	.0266	.0907	.1636	.2023	.1916	.0933	.0222
	6	.0000	.0002	.0069	.0374	.0955	.1574	.1916	.1451	.0518
	7	.0000	.0000	.0014	.0122	.0443	.0974	.1525	.1797	.0961
	8	.0000	.0000	.0002	.0032	.0166	.0487	.0981	.1797	.1442
	9	.0000	.0000	.0000	.0007	.0051	.0198	.0514	.1464	.1762
	10	.0000	.0000	.0000	.0001	.0013	.0066	.0220	.0976	.1762
	11	.0000	.0000	.0000	.0000	.0003	.0018	.0077	.0532	.1442
	12	.0000	.0000	.0000	.0000	.0000	.0004	.0022	.0237	.0961
	13	.0000	.0000	.0000	.0000	.0000	.0001	.0005	.0085	.0518
	14	.0000	.0000	.0000	.0000	.0000	.0000	.0001	.0024	.0222
	15	.0000	.0000	.0000	.0000	.0000	.0000	.0000	.0005	.0074
	16	.0000	.0000	.0000	.0000	.0000	.0000	.0000	.0001	.0018
	17	.0000	.0000	.0000	.0000	.0000	.0000	.0000	.0000	.0003
	18	.0000	.0000	.0000	.0000	.0000	.0000	.0000	.0000	.0000
	19	.0000	.0000	.0000	.0000	.0000	.0000	.0000	.0000	.0000
20	0	.8179	.3585	.1216	.0388	.0115	.0032	.0008	.0000	.0000
	1	.1652	.3774	.2702	.1368	.0576	.0211	.0068	.0005	.0000
	2	.0159	.1887	.2852	.2293	.1369	.0669	.0278	.0031	.0002
	3	.0010	.0596	.1901	.2428	.2054	.1339	.0716	.0123	.0011
	4	.0000	.0133	.0898	.1821	.2182	.1897	.1304	.0350	.0046
	5	.0000	.0022	.0319	.1028	.1746	.2023	.1789	.0746	.0148
	6	.0000	.0003	.0089	.0454	.1091	.1686	.1916	.1244	.0370
	7	.0000	.0000	.0020	.0160	.0545	.1124	.1643	.1659	.0739
	8	.0000	.0000	.0004	.0046	.0222	.0609	.1144	.1797	.1201
	9	.0000	.0000	.0001	.0011	.0074	.0271	.0654	.1597	.1602
	10	.0000	.0000	.0000	.0002	.0020	.0099	.0308	.1171	.1762
	11	.0000	.0000	.0000	.0000	.0005	.0030	.0120	.0710	.1602

Table 2 Binomial Probabilities 547

		p								
n	k	.01	.05	.10	.15	.20	.25	.30	.40	.50
20	12	.0000	.0000	.0000	.0000	.0001	.0008	.0039	.0355	.1201
	13	.0000	.0000	.0000	.0000	.0000	.0002	.0010	.0146	.0739
	14	.0000	.0000	.0000	.0000	.0000	.0000	.0002	.0049	.0370
	15	.0000	.0000	.0000	.0000	.0000	.0000	.0000	.0013	.0148
	16	.0000	.0000	.0000	.0000	.0000	.0000	.0000	.0003	.0046
	17	.0000	.0000	.0000	.0000	.0000	.0000	.0000	.0000	.0011
	18	.0000	.0000	.0000	.0000	.0000	.0000	.0000	.0000	.0002
	19	.0000	.0000	.0000	.0000	.0000	.0000	.0000	.0000	.0000
	20	.0000	.0000	.0000	.0000	.0000	.0000	.0000	.0000	.0000

Appendix C
Answers to Selected Exercises

Chapter 1

Exercises for 1.1
1. (a), (b), (c), (f), and (h) are propositions; (d), (e), and (g) are not.
3. (a) All roses are red or some tulips are yellow.
   (b) Some lines are parallel or these lines intersect.
   (c) Philadelphia is in New Jersey, or Texas is one of the New England states.
   (d) Ray has gone fishing, or Judy is swimming.
   (e) This is a good steak, or he is hungry.
5. (a), (b), and (c) are true; (d) is false.
7. (a) He is not a good student.
   (b) The steak was not tender.
   (c) Some stock is not listed on the New York Stock Exchange.
   (d) No person owns two cars.
   (e) Someone enjoyed the book.
   (f) Not everyone is different.
9. (a) The sun is shining, and it is cold.
   (b) The sun is shining, or it is cold.
   (c) The sun is not shining.
   (d) The sun is shining, or it is not cold.
   (e) The sun is not shining, and it is cold.
   (f) The sun is not shining, and it is not cold.
11. (a), (c), (e), (g), (i), and (j) are true; (b), (d), (f), and (h) are false.
13. $(p \lor q) \land [\sim(p \land q)]$

Exercises for 1.2

1. (a)

p	q	$\sim p$	$\sim p \vee q$
T	T	F	T
T	F	F	F
F	T	T	T
F	F	T	T

(b)

p	q	$\sim p$	$\sim q$	$\sim p \wedge \sim q$
T	T	F	F	F
T	F	F	T	F
F	T	T	F	F
F	F	T	T	T

(c)

p	q	$\sim p$	$\sim q$	$\sim p \vee \sim q$
T	T	F	F	F
T	F	F	T	T
F	T	T	F	T
F	F	T	T	T

(d)

p	q	$\sim q$	$p \wedge \sim q$	$\sim(p \wedge \sim q)$
T	T	F	F	T
T	F	T	T	F
F	T	F	F	T
F	F	T	F	T

(e)

p	q	$\sim p$	$\sim p \vee q$	$(\sim p \vee q) \wedge q$
T	T	F	T	T
T	F	F	F	F
F	T	T	T	T
F	F	T	T	F

(f)

p	q	$\sim p$	$\sim p \vee q$	$(\sim p \vee q) \wedge p$
T	T	F	T	T
T	F	F	F	F
F	T	T	T	F
F	F	T	T	F

(g)

p	q	$\sim p$	$\sim q$	$p \wedge \sim q$	$\sim p \vee (p \wedge \sim q)$
T	T	F	F	F	F
T	F	F	T	T	T
F	T	T	F	F	T
F	F	T	T	F	T

(h)

p	q	$\sim p$	$\sim q$	$q \wedge \sim p$	$(q \wedge \sim p) \vee \sim q$
T	T	F	F	F	F
T	F	F	T	F	T
F	T	T	F	T	T
F	F	T	T	F	T

(i)

p	q	$\sim q$	$p \vee q$	$p \wedge \sim q$	$(p \vee q) \vee (p \wedge \sim q)$
T	T	F	T	F	T
T	F	T	T	T	T
F	T	F	T	F	T
F	F	T	F	F	F

(j)

p	q	$\sim p$	$\sim q$	$p \wedge \sim q$	$\sim p \wedge q$	$(p \wedge \sim q) \vee (\sim p \wedge q)$
T	T	F	F	F	F	F
T	F	F	T	T	F	T
F	T	T	F	F	T	T
F	F	T	T	F	F	F

3. (a)

p	q	r	$p \wedge q$	$(p \wedge q) \wedge r$
T	T	T	T	T
T	T	F	T	F
T	F	T	F	F
T	F	F	F	F
F	T	T	F	F
F	T	F	F	F
F	F	T	F	F
F	F	F	F	F

(b)

p	q	r	$p \wedge q$	$(p \wedge q) \vee r$
T	T	T	T	T
T	T	F	T	T
T	F	T	F	T
T	F	F	F	F
F	T	T	F	T
F	T	F	F	F
F	F	T	F	T
F	F	F	F	F

(c)

p	q	r	$\sim p$	$\sim r$	$\sim p \vee q$	$(\sim p \vee q) \wedge \sim r$
T	T	T	F	F	T	F
T	T	F	F	T	T	T
T	F	T	F	F	F	F
T	F	F	F	T	F	F
F	T	T	T	F	T	F
F	T	F	T	T	T	T
F	F	T	T	F	T	F
F	F	F	T	T	T	T

(d)

p	q	r	$\sim p$	$\sim q$	$\sim q \wedge r$	$\sim p \vee (\sim q \wedge r)$
T	T	T	F	F	F	F
T	T	F	F	F	F	F
T	F	T	F	T	T	T
T	F	F	F	T	F	F
F	T	T	T	F	F	T
F	T	F	T	F	F	T
F	F	T	T	T	T	T
F	F	F	T	T	F	T

(e)

p	q	r	$\sim p$	$\sim p \wedge q$	$(\sim p \wedge q) \vee r$
T	T	T	F	F	T
T	T	F	F	F	F
T	F	T	F	F	T
T	F	F	F	F	F
F	T	T	T	T	T
F	T	F	T	T	T
F	F	T	T	F	T
F	F	F	T	F	F

(f)

p	q	r	$p \wedge q$	$p \wedge r$	$(p \wedge q) \vee (p \wedge r)$
T	T	T	T	T	T
T	T	F	T	F	T
T	F	T	F	T	T
T	F	F	F	F	F
F	T	T	F	F	F
F	T	F	F	F	F
F	F	T	F	F	F
F	F	F	F	F	F

(g)

p	q	r	$\sim r$	$p \vee \sim r$	$q \vee \sim r$	$(p \vee \sim r) \wedge (q \vee \sim r)$
T	T	T	F	T	T	T
T	T	F	T	T	T	T
T	F	T	F	T	F	F
T	F	F	T	T	T	T
F	T	T	F	F	T	F
F	T	F	T	T	T	T
F	F	T	F	F	F	F
F	F	F	T	T	T	T

(h)

p	q	r	$\sim p$	$\sim q$	$\sim p \vee q$	$\sim q \vee r$	$\sim(\sim p \vee q)$	$\sim(\sim p \vee q) \wedge (\sim q \vee r)$
T	T	T	F	F	T	T	F	F
T	T	F	F	F	T	F	F	F
T	F	T	F	T	F	T	T	T
T	F	F	F	T	F	T	T	T
F	T	T	T	F	T	T	F	F
F	T	F	T	F	T	F	F	F
F	F	T	T	T	T	T	F	F
F	F	F	T	T	T	T	F	F

5.

p	q	r	$p \wedge q$	$(p \wedge q) \wedge r$
T	T	T	T	T
T	T	F	T	F
T	F	T	F	F
T	F	F	F	F
F	T	T	F	F
F	T	F	F	F
F	F	T	F	F
F	F	F	F	F

p	q	r	$q \wedge r$	$p \wedge (q \wedge r)$
T	T	T	T	T
T	T	F	F	F
T	F	T	F	F
T	F	F	F	F
F	T	T	T	F
F	T	F	F	F
F	F	T	F	F
F	F	F	F	F

7. (a) $\sim(p \wedge \sim q)$

p	q	$\sim q$	$p \wedge \sim q$	$\sim(p \wedge \sim q)$
T	T	F	F	T
T	F	T	T	F
F	T	F	F	T
F	F	T	F	T

(b) The compound proposition is true unless it is raining and it is not cold.

9.

p	q	$p \downarrow q$
T	T	F
T	F	F
F	T	F
F	F	T

Exercises for 1.3

1.

p	q	$p \vee q$	$q \vee p$
T	T	T	T
T	F	T	T
F	T	T	T
F	F	F	F

Since the last two columns of this truth table are identical, we have that $p \vee q \equiv q \vee p$.

3.

p	q	$\sim p$	$\sim q$	$p \vee q$	$\sim(p \vee q)$	$\sim p \wedge \sim q$
T	T	F	F	T	F	F
T	F	F	T	T	F	F
F	T	T	F	T	F	F
F	F	T	T	F	T	T

Since the last two columns of this truth table are identical, we have $\sim(p \vee q) \equiv \sim p \wedge \sim q$.

5. (a)

p	$p \vee p$
T	T
F	F

Thus $p \vee p \equiv p$.

(b)

p	$p \wedge p$
T	T
F	F

Thus $p \wedge p \equiv p$.

7.

p	q	$\sim p$	$p \vee q$	$(p \vee q) \wedge \sim p$	$\sim p \wedge q$
T	T	F	T	F	F
T	F	F	T	F	F
F	T	T	T	T	T
F	F	T	F	F	F

Since the last two columns of this truth table are identical, we have that $(p \vee q) \wedge \sim p \equiv \sim p \wedge q$.

9. (a)

p	t	$p \wedge t$
T	T	T
F	T	F

Thus $p \wedge t \equiv p$.

(b)

p	f	$p \wedge f$
T	F	F
F	F	F

Thus $p \wedge f \equiv f$.

(c)

p	t	$p \vee t$
T	T	T
F	T	T

Thus $p \vee t \equiv t$.

(d)

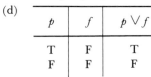

p	f	$p \vee f$
T	F	T
F	F	F

Thus $p \vee f \equiv p$.

(e)

p	$\sim p$	t	$p \vee \sim p$
T	F	T	T
F	T	T	T

Thus $p \vee \sim p \equiv t$.

(f)

p	$\sim p$	f	$p \wedge \sim p$
T	F	F	F
F	T	F	F

Thus $p \wedge \sim p \equiv f$.

11. $\sim[p \vee \sim(q \vee \sim r)] \equiv \sim p \wedge \sim[\sim(q \vee \sim r)]$, by Eq. (1.3.4)
$\equiv \sim p \wedge (q \vee \sim r)$, by problem 4
$\equiv (\sim p \wedge q) \vee (\sim p \wedge \sim r)$, by Eq. (1.3.2)
$\equiv (\sim p \wedge q) \vee \sim(p \vee r)$, by Eq. (1.3.4)
$\equiv \sim(p \vee r) \vee (\sim p \wedge q)$, by problem 1

13. $\sim p \wedge \sim(\sim q \wedge r) \equiv \sim[p \vee (\sim q \wedge r)]$, by Eq. (1.3.4)
$\equiv \sim[(p \vee \sim q) \wedge (p \vee r)]$, by problem 2

15. (a)

p	q	$\sim p$	$\sim q$	$p \downarrow q$	$\sim p \wedge \sim q$
T	T	F	F	F	F
T	F	F	T	F	F
F	T	T	F	F	F
F	F	T	T	T	T

Thus $\sim p \wedge \sim q \equiv p \downarrow q$.

(b)

p	$\sim p$	$p \downarrow p$
T	F	F
F	T	T

Thus $\sim p \equiv p \downarrow p$.

(c)

p	q	$p \downarrow p$	$q \downarrow q$	$(p \downarrow p) \downarrow (q \downarrow q)$	$p \wedge q$
T	T	F	F	T	T
T	F	F	T	F	F
F	T	T	F	F	F
F	F	T	T	F	F

Thus $p \wedge q \equiv (p \downarrow p) \downarrow (q \downarrow q)$.

(d)

p	q	$p \downarrow q$	$(p \downarrow q) \downarrow (p \downarrow q)$	$p \vee q$
T	T	F	T	T
T	F	F	T	T
F	T	F	T	T
F	F	T	F	F

Thus $p \vee q \equiv (p \downarrow q) \downarrow (p \downarrow q)$.

Exercises for 1.4

1. (a) $p \rightarrow q$ (b) $q \rightarrow p$
   (c) $\sim p \rightarrow \sim q$ (d) $\sim q \rightarrow \sim p$
   (e) $p \rightarrow \sim q$

3. (a) $(p \wedge q) \rightarrow r$ (b) $(p \vee q) \rightarrow r$
   (c) $\sim r \rightarrow (\sim p \vee \sim q)$ (d) $r \rightarrow (p \vee q)$
   (e) $(\sim p \vee \sim q) \rightarrow \sim r$ (f) $(q \wedge \sim p) \rightarrow r$

5. (a)

p	q	$p \rightarrow q$	$p \vee q$	$(p \rightarrow q) \rightarrow (p \vee q)$
T	T	T	T	T
T	F	F	T	T
F	T	T	T	T
F	F	T	F	F

(b)

p	q	$\sim q$	$p \rightarrow q$	$\sim q \rightarrow (p \rightarrow q)$
T	T	F	T	T
T	F	T	F	F
F	T	F	T	T
F	F	T	T	T

7. (a) If I wear my coat, then it is snowing.
   (b) If wages do not rise, then productivity does not increase.
   (c) If I get nervous, then I am taking an examination.

(d) If -1 is larger than 0, then 2 is larger than 3.

(e) If a triangle is equiangular, then it is equilateral.

9.

	Converse	Contrapositive	Inverse
(a)	$\sim q \to p$	$q \to \sim p$	$\sim p \to q$
(b)	$q \to \sim p$	$\sim q \to p$	$p \to \sim q$
(c)	$\sim q \to \sim p$	$q \to p$	$p \to q$
(d)	$\sim p \to \sim q$	$p \to q$	$q \to p$

11. The converse of $p \to q$ is $q \to p$ and the contrapositive of $q \to p$ is $\sim p \to \sim q$, which is the inverse of $p \to q$.

13.

p	q	r	$q \wedge r$	$p \to q$	$p \to r$	$(p \to q) \wedge (p \to r)$	$p \to (q \wedge r)$
T	T	T	T	T	T	T	T
T	T	F	F	T	F	F	F
T	F	T	F	F	T	F	F
T	F	F	F	F	F	F	F
F	T	T	T	T	T	T	T
F	T	F	F	T	T	T	T
F	F	T	F	T	T	T	T
F	F	F	F	T	T	T	T

Exercises for 1.5

1. (a) I will come if and only if it is not raining.
   (b) I will come if and only if it is raining.
   (c) I will not come if and only if it is not raining.
   (d) I will not come if and only if it is raining.

3. (a)

p	q	$\sim q$	$p \wedge \sim q$	$(p \wedge \sim q) \leftrightarrow p$
T	T	F	F	F
T	F	T	T	T
F	T	F	F	T
F	F	T	F	T

(b)

p	q	$\sim q$	$p \vee q$	$\sim q \leftrightarrow (p \vee q)$
T	T	F	T	F
T	F	T	T	T
F	T	F	T	F
F	F	T	F	F

(c)

p	q	$\sim q$	$p \to \sim q$	$(p \to \sim q) \leftrightarrow q$
T	T	F	F	F
T	F	T	T	F
F	T	F	T	T
F	F	T	T	F

(d)

p	q	$\sim p$	$\sim p \vee q$	$(\sim p \vee q) \leftrightarrow \sim p$
T	T	F	T	F
T	F	F	F	T
F	T	T	T	T
F	F	T	T	T

(e)

p	q	$\sim p$	$p \wedge q$	$\sim p \leftrightarrow (p \wedge q)$
T	T	F	T	F
T	F	F	F	T
F	T	T	F	F
F	F	T	F	F

(f)

p	q	$\sim p$	$\sim q$	$\sim p \vee \sim q$	$p \leftrightarrow q$	$(\sim p \vee \sim q) \rightarrow (p \leftrightarrow q)$
T	T	F	F	F	T	T
T	F	F	T	T	F	F
F	T	T	F	T	F	F
F	F	T	T	T	T	T

(g)

p	q	$\sim p$	$\sim q$	$\sim p \leftrightarrow q$	$\sim(\sim p \leftrightarrow q)$	$p \rightarrow q$	$(p \rightarrow q) \wedge \sim(\sim p \leftrightarrow q)$
T	T	F	F	F	T	T	T
T	F	F	T	T	F	F	F
F	T	T	F	T	F	T	F
F	F	T	T	F	T	T	T

(h)

p	q	$\sim q$	$p \leftrightarrow \sim q$	$q \rightarrow p$	$(p \leftrightarrow \sim q) \leftrightarrow (q \rightarrow p)$
T	T	F	F	T	F
T	F	T	T	T	T
F	T	F	T	F	F
F	F	T	F	T	F

5.

p	q	$\sim p$	$\sim q$	$\sim p \vee q$	$\sim q \vee p$	$(\sim p \vee q) \wedge (\sim q \vee p)$	$p \leftrightarrow q$
T	T	F	F	T	T	T	T
T	F	F	T	F	T	F	F
F	T	T	F	T	F	F	F
F	F	T	T	T	T	T	T

Since the last two columns of the truth table are identical, we have

$$p \leftrightarrow q \equiv (\sim p \vee q) \wedge (\sim q \vee p)$$

Exercises for 1.6

1. (a)

p	$\sim p$	$p \wedge \sim p$	$\sim(p \wedge \sim p)$
T	F	F	T
F	T	F	T

(b)

p	q	$p \wedge q$	$\sim(p \wedge q)$	$p \vee \sim(p \wedge q)$
T	T	T	F	T
T	F	F	T	T
F	T	F	T	T
F	F	F	T	T

3. (a)

p	q	$p \vee q$	$p \wedge (p \vee q)$	$[p \wedge (p \vee q)] \leftrightarrow p$
T	T	T	T	T
T	F	T	T	T
F	T	T	F	T
F	F	F	F	T

(b)

p	q	$p \wedge q$	$p \vee (p \wedge q)$	$[p \vee (p \wedge q)] \leftrightarrow p$
T	T	T	T	T
T	F	F	T	T
F	T	F	F	T
F	F	F	F	T

(c)

p	q	$\sim p$	$\sim q$	$p \rightarrow q$	$q \rightarrow p$	$\sim p \leftrightarrow \sim q$	$(p \rightarrow q) \wedge (q \rightarrow p)$	$(\sim p \leftrightarrow \sim q) \leftrightarrow [(p \rightarrow q) \wedge (q \rightarrow p)]$
T	T	F	F	T	T	T	T	T
T	F	F	T	F	T	F	F	T
F	T	T	F	T	F	F	F	T
F	F	T	T	T	T	T	T	T

(d)

p	q	r	$q \vee r$	$p \vee q$	$p \vee (q \vee r)$	$(p \vee q) \vee r$	$[p \vee (q \vee r)] \leftrightarrow [(p \vee q) \vee r]$
T	T	T	T	T	T	T	T
T	T	F	T	T	T	T	T
T	F	T	T	T	T	T	T
T	F	F	F	T	T	T	T
F	T	T	T	T	T	T	T
F	T	F	T	T	T	T	T
F	F	T	T	F	T	T	T
F	F	F	F	F	F	F	T

5. (a)

p	$\sim p$	$p \vee \sim p$	$\sim(p \vee \sim p)$
T	F	T	F
F	T	T	F

(b)

p	q	$p \vee q$	$\sim(p \vee q)$	$\sim(p \vee q) \wedge p$
T	T	T	F	F
T	F	T	F	F
F	T	T	F	F
F	F	F	T	F

(c)

p	q	$p \wedge q$	$p \vee q$	$\sim(p \vee q)$	$(p \wedge q) \wedge \sim(p \vee q)$
T	T	T	T	F	F
T	F	F	T	F	F
F	T	F	T	F	F
F	F	F	F	T	F

7. (a), (b), (c), and (e) are valid; (d) is invalid.
9. (c) and (d) are valid; (a), (b), and (e) are invalid.
13.

p	q	r	$\sim p$	$\sim q$	$q \vee \sim p$	$r \vee \sim q$	$(q \vee \sim p) \wedge (r \vee \sim q) \wedge p$	$[(q \vee \sim p) \wedge (r \vee \sim q) \wedge p] \rightarrow r$
T	T	T	F	F	T	T	T	T
T	T	F	F	F	T	F	F	T
T	F	T	F	T	F	T	F	T
T	F	F	F	T	F	T	F	T
F	T	T	T	F	T	T	F	T
F	T	F	T	F	T	F	F	T
F	F	T	T	T	T	T	F	T
F	F	F	T	T	T	T	F	T

Chapter 2

Exercises for 2.1

1. (a) $\in$
   (c) $\notin$
   (e) $\in$

   (b) $\notin$
   (d) $\in$

3. (a) $d \notin B$
   (c) $x \notin S$

   (b) $a \in A$
   (d) $e \in E$

5. (a) true
   (c) false
   (e) true

   (b) true
   (d) false
   (f) false

7. (a) true
   (b) false
   (c) false

9. (a) false   (b) false
   (c) true   (d) false
   (e) true   (f) false
11. (a) $\{2, 4\}$
   (b) {California, Colorado, Connecticut}
   (c) {v, a, n, i, 1}
   (d) {catcher, pitcher, first baseman, second baseman, third baseman, shortstop, left fielder, right fielder, center fielder}
   (e) $\{1, 0, -1, -2, -3, \ldots\}$
   (f) $\{\ldots, -12, -9, -6, -3, 0, 3, 6, 9, 12, \ldots\}$
   (g) $\{-2, 2\}$
13. The set of all rational numbers between 0 and 1.
15. $\{rrw, rwr, rww, wwr, wrw, wrr\}$, where, for example, rrw means that the first two balls selected are red and the third selected is white.

Exercises for 2.2

1. They are all equal.
3. (a) $\subsetneqq$ (b) $\subsetneqq$
   (c) $=$ (d) $\subsetneqq$
   (e) $=$ (f) $=$
5. (a) $\{x \mid x^2 = 4\} = \{2, -2\}$. Thus the subsets are $\emptyset$, $\{2, -2\}$, $\{2\}$, and $\{-2\}$.
   (b) $\{a, b, c\}$, $\emptyset$, $\{a\}$, $\{b\}$, $\{c\}$, $\{a, b\}$, $\{b, c\}$, $\{a, c\}$
   (c) $\{1, 2, 3, 4\}$, $\emptyset$, $\{1\}$, $\{2\}$, $\{3\}$, $\{4\}$, $\{1, 2\}$, $\{1, 3\}$, $\{1, 4\}$, $\{3, 4\}$, $\{2, 3\}$, $\{2, 4\}$, $\{1, 2, 3\}$, $\{1, 2, 4\}$, $\{1, 3, 4\}$, $\{2, 3, 4\}$
   (d) $\{1, \{2, 3\}, 4\}$, $\emptyset$, $\{1\}$, $\{\{2, 3\}\}$, $\{4\}$, $\{1, \{2, 3\}\}$, $\{1, 4\}$, $\{\{2, 3\}, 4\}$
   (e) $\emptyset$
7. Only (d).
9. No; the empty set has no proper subsets.
11. Both 2 and 4 are members of the set A but are not members of the set B. Thus $A \not\subset B$.
15. No; $S = \{4\}$.
17. (a) true   (b) true
   (c) false   (d) true
   (e) false

Exercises for 2.3

1. (a) $\bar{A} = \{1, 5, 8, 10, 11, 45\}$
   (b) $\bar{A} = \{3, 15, 45\}$
   (c) $\bar{A} = \{1, 3, 5, 7, 11, 15, 21, 45\}$
   (d) $\bar{A} = \{3, 8, 10, 11, 21, 45\}$
   (e) $\bar{A} = \emptyset$
3. (a) $\emptyset$ (b) U
5. (a) $A \cup B = \{1, 2, 3, 4, 6, 8\}$ (b) $A \cup C = \{1, 2, 3, 4, 5, 6\}$
   (c) $B \cup C = \{2, 3, 4, 5, 6, 8\}$ (d) $B \cup B = \{2, 4, 6, 8\} = B$
7. (a) $C \cap E = \{\text{Connecticut}\}$
   (b) $C \cap B = \{\text{California}\}$
   (c) $E \cap \bar{C} = \{\text{Maine, New Hampshire, Vermont, Massachusetts, Rhode Island}\}$
   (d) $E \cup B = \{\text{Maine, New Hampshire, Vermont, Massachusetts, Connecticut, Rhode Island, California, Oregon, Washington, Alaska, Hawaii}\}$
   (e) $B \cap E = \emptyset$
   (f) $B \cap \bar{E} = B$, since $B \cap E = \emptyset$
9. Company C can be accused of taking advantage of the foreign market.
11. Let $x \in A$. Then $A \subset B$ implies that $x \in B$. Thus $x \in A \cap B$. Therefore, $A \subset A \cap B$. So, since we already know from problem 10 that $A \cap B \subset A$, we have $A = A \cap B$.

Similarly, let $x \in A \cup B$. Then $x \in A$ or $x \in B$. If $x \in A$, then $A \subset B$ implies that $x \in B$. If $x \in B$, then $x \in B$. Hence, in any case, $x \in A \cup B$ implies that $x \in B$. Thus $A \cup B \subset B$. By problem 10, $B \subset A \cup B$. Therefore, $A \cup B = B$.

13. Let $x \in \bar{B}$. Then $x \notin B$. Thus, since $A \subset B$, $x \notin A$. So $x \in \bar{A}$. Thus $\bar{B} \subset \bar{A}$.

15. (a) $A - B = \{1, 3\}$ (b) $B - A = \{6, 8\}$
    (c) $B - C = \{2, 8\}$ (d) $C - A = \{5, 6\}$
    (e) $A - A = \emptyset$

17. Let $x \in A - B$. Then, by definition, $x \in A$ and $x \notin B$. In particular, $x \in A$. Thus $A - B \subset A$.

19. Let $x \in A - B$. Then $x \in A$ and $x \notin B$. Thus $x \in A$ and $x \in \bar{B}$. So, $x \in A \cap \bar{B}$. Therefore, $A - B \subset A \cap \bar{B}$. On the other hand, suppose that $x \in A \cap \bar{B}$. Then $x \in A$ and $x \in \bar{B}$. Thus $x \in A$ and $x \notin B$. But this implies that $x \in A - B$. So $A \cap \bar{B} \subset A - B$. Therefore, $A - B = A \cap \bar{B}$.

21. (a) Let $x \in A \cup B$. Then, by definition, $x \in A$ or $x \in B$. Thus $x \in B \cup A$. Therefore, $A \cup B \subset B \cup A$. Similarly, $B \cup A \subset A \cup B$. Thus $A \cup B = B \cup A$.
    (b) Let $x \in A \cap B$. Then, by definition, $x \in A$ and $x \in B$. Thus $x \in B \cap A$. Therefore, $A \cap B \subset B \cap A$. Similarly, $B \cap A \subset A \cap B$. Thus $A \cap B = B \cap A$.

Exercises for 2.4

1. (a)   (b)

   (c)   (d)

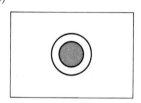   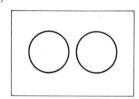

Nothing to be shaded, because $A \cap B = \emptyset$.

3. (a)   (b)

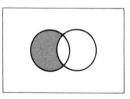   

   (c)   (d)

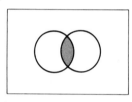   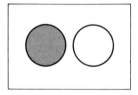

Nothing to be shaded, because $A - B = A \cap \bar{B} = \emptyset$.

5. (a) $\{1, 3, 5, 6, 7, 8, 9\}$ (b) $\{9\}$
(c) $\{2, 4, 5, 6, 7, 8, 9\}$ (d) $\{1, 2, 3, 4, 5, 7\}$
(e) $\{1, 2, 3, 5, 6, 7, 8, 9\}$ (f) $\{1, 2, 3, 4, 5, 7, 9\}$

11. By problem 19, Exercises 2.3, $A - B = \widetilde{A \cap B}$. But, by De Morgan's law, $\widetilde{A \cap \tilde{B}} = \tilde{A} \cup B$.

Now, by problem 14, Exercises 2.3, $\tilde{\tilde{B}} = B$. Thus $A - B = \widetilde{A \cap \tilde{B}} = \tilde{A} \cup \tilde{\tilde{B}} = \tilde{A} \cup B$.

13.

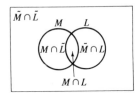

$M \cap L =$ males who like the show
$\tilde{M} \cap \tilde{L} =$ females who do not like the show
$M \cap \tilde{L} =$ males who do not like the show
$\tilde{M} \cap L =$ females who like the show

Exercises for 2.5
1. (a) $\{4\}$ (b) U
   (c) $\{3, 4\}$ (d) $\{1, 2, 3, 4, 8\}$
3. (a)   (b)

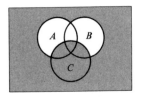
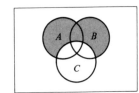

   (c)   (d)

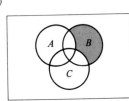
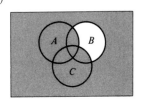

5. (a) All female residents of the United States who smoke.
(b) All residents of the United States over the age of 65 who smoke.
(c) All female residents of the United States who either smoke or are over the age of 65.
(d) All females over the age of 65 who smoke.
(e) All males over the age of 65 who smoke.
(f) All people who are either female or smoke or are over the age of 65.
(g) All female nonsmokers over the age of 65.
(h) All female residents of the United States over the age of 65 who smoke.
7. (a) U (b) $\tilde{A} \cap B$
   (c) $\emptyset$ (d) $A \cap B$
   (e) $\emptyset$

9. (a)

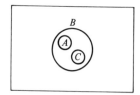

(b)

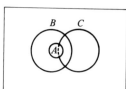

(c)

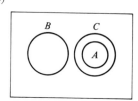

(d)

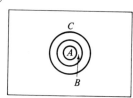

13. $(A \cap B) \cap (A \cap \bar{B}) = [(A \cap B) \cap A] \cap \bar{B}$
$= [A \cap (A \cap B)] \cap \bar{B}$
$= A \cap [(A \cap B) \cap \bar{B}] = A \cap [A \cap (B \cap \bar{B})]$
$= A \cap [A \cap \varnothing] = A \cap \varnothing = \varnothing$

17. (a) $A \triangle B = (A \cup B) \cap \overline{(A \cap B)} = (A \cup B) \cap (\bar{A} \cup \bar{B})$
$= [(A \cup B) \cap \bar{A}] \cup [(A \cup B) \cap \bar{B}]$
$= [(A \cap \bar{A}) \cup (B \cap \bar{A})] \cup [(A \cap \bar{B}) \cup (B \cap \bar{B})]$
$= [\varnothing \cup (B \cap \bar{A})] \cup [(A \cap \bar{B}) \cup \varnothing] = (B \cap \bar{A}) \cup (A \cap \bar{B})$
$= (A \cap \bar{B}) \cup (B \cap \bar{A})$

(b) Yes; $A \triangle B = (A \cap \bar{B}) \cup (B \cap \bar{A})$, by part (a)
$= (B \cap \bar{A}) \cup (A \cap \bar{B})$, by problem 21(b), Exercises 2.3
$= B \triangle A$, by part (a)

Exercises for 2.6
1. (a) 4
   (c) 6
   (e) 0
   (b) 4
   (d) 1
   (f) 50
3. (a) 4
   (c) 5
   (e) 1
   (b) 2
   (d) 1
   (f) 3
7. (a) 85
   (c) 60
   (b) 152
   (d) 72
9. (a) 22
   (c) 9
   (b) 10
   (d) 4

Exercises for 2.7
1. (a) Let $D = A \cap B$. Then, by Eq. (2.5.10),

$$A \cap B = D = (D \cap C) \cup (D \cap \bar{C})$$
$$= (A \cap B \cap C) \cup (A \cap B \cap \bar{C})$$

(b) Let $D = A \cap B$. Then, by Eq. (2.5.11),

$$(D \cap C) \cap (D \cap \bar{C}) = \varnothing$$

In other words,

$$(A \cap B \cap C) \cap (A \cap B \cap \bar{C}) = \varnothing$$

Using this fact along with part (a) and Corollary 2.6.2, we get the desired conclusion.
3. (a) 58
   (c) 7
   (b) 19
   (d) yes

Chapter 3

Exercises for 3.1
1. (a) HH, HT, TH, TT
   (b)

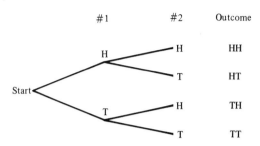

3. (a) $NU1$, $NU2$, $NU3$, $ND1$, $ND2$, $ND3$, $SU1$, $SU2$, $SU3$, $SD1$, $SD2$, $SD3$
   (b)

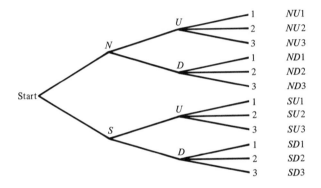

   (c) $NU3$, $ND1$, $ND2$, $ND3$, $SU3$, $SD1$, $SD2$, $SD3$
5. (a) ARC, ACR, RAC, RCA, CAR, CRA
   (b)

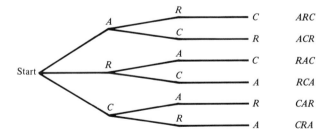

   (c) ACR, RAC, RCA, CAR

7. Let the models be denoted by M_1, M_2, M_3; the elevations by E_1, E_2; and the locations by L_1, L_2.
   (a) 12
   (b)

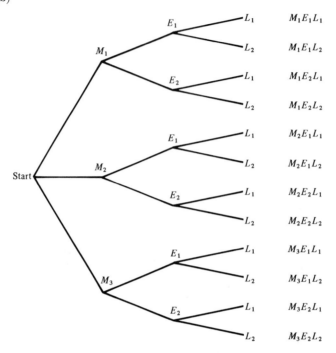

Exercises for 3.2

1. $2 \cdot 2 = 4$
3. $2 \cdot 2 \cdot 3 = 12$
5. $3 \cdot 2 \cdot 1 = 6$
7. $3 \cdot 2 \cdot 2 = 12$
9. $6 \cdot 6 = 36$
11. $6 \cdot 5 \cdot 4 \cdot 3 = 360$
13. (a) $2 \cdot 2 \cdot 2 = 8$
    (b) $2 + 2 \cdot 2 + 2 \cdot 2 \cdot 2 = 14$
15. $10 \cdot 9 \cdot 8 \cdot 8 \cdot 7 = 40,320$
17. $2 \cdot 2 \cdot 2 \cdot 2 \cdot 2 \cdot 4 \cdot 4 \cdot 4 = 2,048$
19. $\underbrace{2 \cdot 2 \cdots 2}_{n \text{ times}} = 2^n$

21. $n \cdot (n - 1) \cdots (n - r + 1)$

Exercises for 3.3

1. (a) ab, ac, ad, ba, bc, bd, ca, cb, cd, da, db, dc
   (b) $\{a, b\}$, $\{a, c\}$, $\{a, d\}$, $\{b, c\}$, $\{b, d\}$, $\{c, d\}$
3. (a) abc, abd, abe, acb, acd, ace,
       adb, adc, ade, aeb, aec, aed,
       bac, bad, bae, bca, bcd, bce,
       bda, bdc, bde, bea, bec, bed,
       cab, cad, cae, cba, cbd, cbe,
       cda, cdb, cde, cea, ceb, ced,
       dab, dac, dae, dba, dbc, dbe,
       dca, dcb, dce, dea, deb, dec,

eab, eac, ead, eba, ebc, ebd,

eca, ecb, ecd, eda, edb, edc

(b) $\{a, b, c\}$, $\{a, b, d\}$, $\{a, b, e\}$, $\{a, c, d\}$, $\{a, c, e\}$

$\{a, d, e\}$, $\{b, c, d\}$, $\{b, c, e\}$, $\{b, d, e\}$, $\{c, d, e\}$

5. Denote the suits by S_1, S_2, S_3, S_4 and the pairs of shoes by P_1, P_2, P_3. Then the possible selections are

$$\{S_1, S_2, P_1, P_2\}, \{S_1, S_2, P_1, P_3\},$$
$$\{S_1, S_2, P_2, P_3\}, \{S_1, S_3, P_1, P_2\},$$
$$\{S_1, S_3, P_1, P_3\}, \{S_1, S_3, P_2, P_3\},$$
$$\{S_1, S_4, P_1, P_2\}, \{S_1, S_4, P_1, P_3\},$$
$$\{S_1, S_4, P_2, P_3\}, \{S_2, S_3, P_1, P_2\},$$
$$\{S_2, S_3, P_1, P_3\}, \{S_2, S_3, P_2, P_3\},$$
$$\{S_2, S_4, P_1, P_2\}, \{S_2, S_4, P_1, P_3\},$$
$$\{S_2, S_4, P_2, P_3\}, \{S_3, S_4, P_1, P_2\},$$
$$\{S_3, S_4, P_1, P_3\}, \{S_3, S_4, P_2, P_3\}$$

Exercises for 3.4

1. (a) (1) $\{a\}$, $\{b\}$, $\{c\}$, $\{d\}$

(2) $\{a, b\}$, $\{a, c\}$, $\{a, d\}$, $\{b, c\}$, $\{b, d\}$, $\{c, d\}$

(3) $\{a, b, c\}$, $\{a, b, d\}$, $\{a, c, d\}$, $\{b, c, d\}$

(4) $\{a, b, c, d\}$

(b) (1) a, b, c, d

(2) ab, ac, ad, ba, bc, bd, ca, cb, cd, da, db, dc

(3) abc, abd, acb, acd, adb, adc,

bac, bad, bca, bcd, bda, bdc,

cab, cad, cba, cbd, cda, cdb,

dab, dac, dba, dbc, dca, dcb

(4) $abcd$, $abdc$, $acbd$, $acdb$,

$adbc$, $adcb$, $bacd$, $badc$,

$bcad$, $bcda$, $bdac$, $bdca$,

$cabd$, $cadb$, $cbad$, $cbda$,

$cdab$, $cdba$, $dabc$, $dacb$,

$dbac$, $dbca$, $dcab$, $dcba$

3. (a) 1   (b) 2

(c) 1   (d) 3

(e) 3   (f) 1

(g) 4   (h) 6

(i) 4   (j) 1

7. $_{25}C_8$

9. $_6P_6$

11. $_{52}C_5$

13. $_{203}C_4$

15. $_{100}P_3$

Exercises for 3.5

1. (a) 1   (b) 2

(c) 2   (d) 3

(e) 6   (f) 6

(g) 4   (h) 12

(i) 24   (j) 24

3. $_5P_5 = 120$

5. $_{15}P_3 = 2,730$

7. $_{26}P_3 = 15,600$

Exercises for 3.6

1. (a) 1   (b) 2
   (c) 1   (d) 3
   (e) 3   (f) 1
   (g) 4   (h) 6
   (i) 4   (j) 1

3. $_6C_4 = 15$

5. $_{52}C_5 = 2{,}598{,}960$

7. $_{25}C_5 = 53{,}130$

9. $_{12}C_3 = 220$

11. $_{80}C_{10} = 1{,}646{,}492{,}110{,}120$

Exercises for 3.7

1. (a) $_{18}C_4 = 3{,}060$
   (b) $_{10}C_2 \cdot {_8}C_2 = 1{,}260$

3. $_4C_4 \cdot {_4}C_3 \cdot {_4}C_2 \cdot {_4}C_2 \cdot {_{36}}C_2 = 90{,}720$

5. (a) $_{80}C_{15} = 6{,}635{,}869{,}816{,}740{,}560$
   (b) $_{70}C_{15} \cdot {_{10}}C_0 = 721{,}480{,}692{,}460{,}864$
   (c) $_{70}C_5 \cdot {_{10}}C_{10} = 12{,}103{,}014$
   (d) $_{70}C_{12} \cdot {_{10}}C_3 = 1{,}276{,}667{,}287{,}022{,}400$

7. (a) $_{52}C_5 = 2{,}598{,}960$
   (b) $_4C_3 \cdot {_4}C_2 \cdot {_{44}}C_0 = 24$
   (c) $_4C_3 \cdot {_4}C_1 \cdot {_{44}}C_1 = 704$
   (d) $_{13}C_2 \cdot {_{11}}C_1 \cdot {_4}C_2 \cdot {_4}C_2 \cdot {_4}C_1 \cdot {_{40}}C_0 = 123{,}552$
   (e) $_4C_1 \cdot {_{13}}C_5 \cdot {_{39}}C_0 = 5{,}148$ (this includes straight flushes)

9. $_{100}C_{10} \cdot {_{90}}C_7 \cdot {_{83}}C_{15} \cdot {_{68}}C_8$

11. (a) $_{10}C_3 \cdot {_7}C_3 \cdot {_4}C_4 = 4{,}200$
   (b) $_{10}P_3 \cdot {_7}C_3 \cdot {_4}C_4 = 25{,}200$
   (c) $_{10}P_3 \cdot {_7}P_3 \cdot {_4}C_4 = 151{,}200$

13. (a) $_{130}C_{25}$
   (b) $_{50}C_{13} \cdot {_{80}}C_{12}$
   (c) $_{50}C_{25}$

Exercises for 3.8

1. (a) 1   (b) 2
   (c) 720   (d) 1
   (e) 5,040   (f) 40,320

3. (a) 120   (b) 120
   (c) 120   (d) 2,880
   (e) 17,280   (f) 120

5. (a) $\dfrac{5!}{2!}$ (b) $\dfrac{6!}{1!}$

   (c) $\dfrac{6!}{0!}$ (d) $\dfrac{100!}{80!}$

   (e) $\dfrac{1{,}000!}{950!}$ (f) $\dfrac{10!}{6!}$

7. (a) 10   (b) 15
   (c) 28   (d) 28
   (e) 6   (f) 4
   (g) 1,000   (h) 1,000
   (i) 1   (j) 1

9. $_nP_k > \binom{n}{k}$ for $k \geq 2$

11. (a) $\dfrac{7!}{2!3!2!}$

   (b) $\dfrac{10!}{3!2!1!4!}$

   (c) $\dfrac{15!}{2!4!5!1!2!1!}$

Exercises for 3.9

1. (a) $(a + b)^5 = a^5 + 5a^4b + 10a^3b^2 + 10a^2b^3 + 5ab^4 + b^5$
   (b) $(x + y)^6 = x^6 + 6x^5y + 15x^4y^2 + 20x^3y^3 + 15x^2y^4 + 6xy^5 + y^6$
3. (a) $(x - y)^3 = x^3 - 3x^2y + 3xy^2 - y^3$
   (b) $(1 - x)^3 = 1 - 3x + 3x^2 - x^3$
   (c) $(2 - x)^4 = 16 - 32x + 24x^2 - 8x^3 + x^4$
   (d) $(x - 2)^4 = x^4 - 8x^3 + 24x^2 - 32x + 16$

5. $\binom{6}{4} = 15$

7. $\binom{10}{7} \cdot 2^3 = 960$

9. $\binom{7}{3} \cdot 2^4 \cdot \left(-\tfrac{1}{3}\right)^3 = -\tfrac{560}{27}$

11. 2^n

Chapter 4

Exercises for 4.1

1. (a), (c), and (d) are random; (b) and (e) are nonrandom.
3. 5,000
5. $\tfrac{1}{50} = .02$
7. (a) p (b) (1) $100p$ percent, (2) $500,000p$

Exercises for 4.2

1. (a) 2
   (b) $\{H, T\}$
   (c) $\Pr(\{H\}) = \Pr(\{T\}) = \tfrac{1}{2}$
   (d) $\Pr(\{H\}) = \tfrac{1}{5}$, $\Pr(\{T\}) = \tfrac{4}{5}$
   (e) $\Pr(\{H\}) = \tfrac{3}{5}$, $\Pr(\{T\}) = \tfrac{2}{5}$
3. (a) 1 and 2
   (b) 1
   (c) 2
5. (a) 52   (b) $\Pr(\{\omega\}) = \tfrac{1}{52}$ for all $\omega \in \Omega$
7. (a) $\Omega = \{d, r, o\}$, where d, r, o correspond to Democrat, Republican, Other, respectively.
   (b) $\Pr(\{d\}) = .45$, $\Pr(\{r\}) = .42$, $\Pr(\{o\}) = .13$
9. (a) $\Omega = \{r, w, b\}$, where r, w, b correspond to red, white, blue, respectively. $\Pr(\{r\}) = .5$,
     $\Pr(\{w\}) = .3$, $\Pr(\{b\}) = .2$.
   (b) $\Omega = \{r_1, r_2, r_3, r_4, r_5, w_1, w_2, w_3, b_1, b_2\}$, where, for example, r_1 denotes red chip 1, w_2
     denotes white chip 2. $\Pr(\{\omega\}) = .1$ for all $\omega \in \Omega$.

Exercises for 4.3

1. (a) (1) $\{2, 4, 6\}$ (2) $\{1, 3, 5\}$
      (3) $\{3, 4, 5, 6\}$ (4) $\{1, 2, 3, 4\}$
      (5) $\{5\}$
   (b) (1) $\frac{1}{2}$ (2) $\frac{1}{2}$
      (3) $\frac{2}{3}$ (4) $\frac{2}{3}$
      (5) $\frac{1}{6}$
   (c) (1) $.40 = \frac{2}{5}$ (2) $.60 = \frac{3}{5}$
      (3) $.75 = \frac{3}{4}$ (4) $.70 = \frac{7}{10}$
      (5) $.10 = \frac{1}{10}$

3. (a) $\Omega = \{\omega_1, \omega_2, \omega_3, \omega_4\}$, where $\omega_1, \omega_2, \omega_3, \omega_4$ correspond, respectively, to the possibilities in (1)–(4).
   (b) $\Pr(\{\omega_2, \omega_3\}) = \frac{1}{16} + \frac{3}{16} = \frac{1}{4}$
   (c) $\Pr(\{\omega_2, \omega_3, \omega_4\}) = \frac{1}{16} + \frac{3}{16} + \frac{1}{8} = \frac{3}{8}$

5. (a) (1) $\{0, 1, 2\}$ (2) $\{4, 5, 6+\}$
      (3) $\{2, 3, 4\}$ (4) $\varnothing$
   (b) (1) $.65$ (2) $.20$
      (3) $.60$ (4) 0

7. (a) (1) $\{[4, 1], [4, 2], [4, 3], [4, 4], [4, 5], [4, 6]\}$
      (2) $\{[1, 6], [2, 6], [3, 6], [4, 6], [5, 6], [6, 6]\}$
      (3) $\{[2, 1], [3, 1], [4, 1], [5, 1], [6, 1], [3, 2], [4, 2], [5, 2], [6, 2], [4, 3], [5, 3], [6, 3], [5, 4],$
          $[6, 4], [6, 5]\}$
      (4) $\{[1, 1], [2, 2], [3, 3], [4, 4], [5, 5], [6, 6]\}$
      (5) $\{[1, 6], [2, 5], [3, 4], [4, 3], [5, 2], [6, 1]\}$
      (6) $\{[5, 6], [6, 5]\}$
   (b) (1) $\frac{1}{6}$ (2) $\frac{1}{6}$
      (3) $\frac{15}{36}$ (4) $\frac{1}{6}$
      (5) $\frac{1}{6}$ (6) $\frac{1}{18}$

9. (a) $\Omega = \{r_1, r_2, r_3, r_4, r_5, w_1, w_2, w_3, b_1, b_2\}$
      (1) $\Pr(\{\omega\}) = \frac{1}{10}$ for all $\omega \in \Omega$ (2) $\frac{4}{5}$
   (b) $\Omega = \{r, w, b\}$
      (1) $\Pr(\{r\}) = \frac{1}{2}$, $\Pr(\{w\}) = \frac{3}{10}$, $\Pr(\{b\}) = \frac{1}{5}$
      (2) $\frac{4}{5}$

Exercises for 4.4

1. (a) (1) Either the second toss is a head or at least one of the two tosses is a tail.
      (2) The second toss is a head and at least one of the two tosses is a tail (i.e., the first toss is a tail and the second toss is a head).
      (3) The second toss is not a head (i.e., the second toss is a tail).
      (4) Neither of the tosses yields tails (i.e., both tosses are heads).
   (b) (1) $\{HH, TH, HT, TT\} = \Omega$ (2) $\{TH\}$
      (3) $\{HT, TT\}$ (4) $\{HH\}$
   (c) no

3. (a) (1) The third toss is a head and exactly two of the four tosses yield heads (i.e., the third and exactly one other toss yield heads).
      (2) The third toss is a head and less than two of the four tosses yield heads (i.e., the third toss is a head and the other three tosses are tails).
      (3) Exactly two of the four tosses yield heads and at least two of the four tosses yield heads (i.e., exactly two of the four tosses yield heads).
      (4) The third toss is a head and not exactly two of the four tosses yield heads (i.e., the third toss is a head and the total number of heads is one, three, or four).
      (5) Exactly two of the four tosses yield heads or at least two of the four tosses yield heads (i.e., at least two of the four tosses yield heads).

(b) (1) {HTHT, THHT, TTHH}

(2) {TTHT}

(3) {HHTT, HTHT, HTTH, THHT, THTH, TTHH}

(4) {TTHT, HHHT, HTHH, THHH, HHHH}

(5) {HHHH, HHHT, HHTH, HTHH, THHH, HHTT, HTHT, HTTH, THHT, THTH, TTHH}

(c) no

5. (a) The bolt is defective in both length and width.

(b) The bolt is defective in either length or width (or both).

(c) The bolt is defective in length but not in width.

(d) The bolt is defective in width but not in length.

(e) The bolt is not defective in both length and width.

7. (a), (c), and (e) are mutually exclusive.

9. (a) 0   (b) 1

Exercises for 4.5

1. $\frac{5}{18}$

3. $\frac{19}{24}$

5. $\frac{5}{6} \neq \frac{2}{3} + \frac{1}{4}$

7. (a) $\frac{2}{3}$ (b) $\frac{1}{3}$ (c) $\frac{5}{6}$

9. $\frac{11}{12}$

11. (a) $\frac{11}{12}$ (b) $\frac{1}{6}$

(c) $\frac{1}{6}$ (d) $\frac{5}{6}$

Exercises for 4.6

1. $\frac{3}{6} = \frac{1}{2}$

3. 7; 2 and 12

5. (a) $\frac{1}{2}$ (b) $\frac{1}{4}$

(c) $\frac{3}{8}$ (d) $\frac{7}{8}$

7. $\frac{3}{5}$

9. (a) $\binom{13}{4}\binom{2}{1}\Big/\binom{15}{5} = \frac{10}{21}$ (b) $\binom{13}{3}\binom{2}{2}\Big/\binom{15}{5} = \frac{2}{21}$

Exercises for 4.7

1. $\binom{30}{20}\binom{10}{0}\Big/\binom{40}{20} \doteq .0002$

3. (a) $\binom{13}{5}\binom{39}{0}\Big/\binom{52}{5} \doteq .0004$ (b) $\binom{13}{2}\binom{39}{3}\Big/\binom{52}{5} \doteq .274$

(c) $\binom{13}{3}\binom{39}{2}\Big/\binom{52}{5} \doteq .082$ (d) $\binom{26}{5}\binom{26}{0}\Big/\binom{52}{5} \doteq .025$

5. (a) $\binom{4}{4}\binom{48}{9}\Big/\binom{52}{13} \doteq .002$

(b) $\binom{4}{4}\binom{4}{2}\binom{44}{7}\Big/\binom{52}{13} \doteq .0004$

(c) $4 \cdot 3 \cdot 2 \cdot \binom{13}{6}\binom{13}{5}\binom{13}{2}\binom{13}{0}\Big/\binom{52}{13} \doteq .006$

(d) $4 \cdot \binom{13}{4}\binom{13}{3}\binom{13}{3}\binom{13}{3}\Big/\binom{52}{13} \doteq .105$

(e) $\binom{4}{2} \cdot 2 \cdot 1 \cdot \binom{13}{5}\binom{13}{5}\binom{13}{2}\binom{13}{1}\Big/\binom{52}{13} \doteq .032$

7. (a) $\dbinom{13}{2}\dbinom{11}{1}\dbinom{4}{2}\dbinom{4}{2}\dbinom{4}{1}\Big/\dbinom{52}{5} \doteq .04754$

(b) $13 \cdot 12 \cdot \dbinom{4}{4}\dbinom{4}{1}\Big/\dbinom{52}{5} \doteq .00024$

9. $1 - \dfrac{\dbinom{30}{20}\dbinom{10}{0} + \dbinom{30}{19}\dbinom{10}{1} + \dbinom{30}{18}\dbinom{10}{2}}{\dbinom{40}{20}} \doteq .968$

11. $\dfrac{\dbinom{6}{3}\dbinom{4}{1} + \dbinom{6}{4}\dbinom{4}{0}}{\dbinom{10}{4}} \doteq .452$

13. (a) $\dbinom{10}{0}\dbinom{10}{6}\Big/\dbinom{20}{6} \doteq .005$ (b) $\dbinom{10}{2}\dbinom{8}{4}\dbinom{2}{0}\Big/\dbinom{20}{6} \doteq .081$

Exercises for 4.8

1. $\dfrac{\dbinom{10}{4}}{2^{10}} = \dfrac{210}{1,024} \doteq .205$

3. $\dfrac{\dbinom{30}{5}}{2^{30}} \doteq .0001$

5. $\dfrac{\dbinom{10}{3}}{2^{10}} = \dfrac{120}{1,024} \doteq .117$

7. (a) $\dfrac{\dbinom{6}{5}}{2^6} = \dfrac{6}{64} \doteq .094$

(b) $1 - \dfrac{\dbinom{6}{0}}{2^6} = \dfrac{63}{64} \doteq .984$

9. (a) $\dfrac{\dbinom{7}{4}}{2^7} = \dfrac{35}{128} \doteq .273$

(b) $1 - \dfrac{\dbinom{7}{0} + \dbinom{7}{1}}{2^7} = \dfrac{120}{128} \doteq .938$

11. $\dfrac{\dbinom{15}{7}}{2^{15}} = \dfrac{6,435}{32,768} \doteq .196$

Exercises for 4.9

1. $\frac{1}{2}$
3. $\frac{1}{6}$
5. (a) $\frac{1}{2}$ (b) $\frac{2}{3}$
7. (a) $\frac{1}{2}$ (b) $\frac{3}{4}$
9. (a), (c), and (d) are true; (b) and (e) are false.

11. no

13. $\frac{16}{41}$

15. (a) $\frac{5}{6}$ (b) $\frac{5}{8}$

Exercises for 4.10

1. $\frac{2}{11}$

3. $\frac{1}{8}$

5. (a) $\frac{1}{2}$ (b) $\frac{1}{5}$

7. $\frac{1}{9}$

9. (a) $\dfrac{\binom{4}{4}\binom{48}{1}}{\binom{4}{2}\binom{48}{3} + \binom{4}{3}\binom{48}{2} + \binom{4}{4}\binom{48}{1}} \doteq .0004$

   (b) $\dfrac{\binom{13}{5}\binom{39}{0}}{\binom{13}{4}\binom{39}{1} + \binom{13}{5}\binom{39}{0}} \doteq .044$

13. (a) $\dfrac{\binom{3}{2}\binom{36}{11}}{\binom{39}{13}} \doteq .222$ (b) $\dfrac{\binom{6}{3}\binom{20}{10}}{\binom{26}{13}} \doteq .355$

Exercises for 4.11

1. (a) .3   (b) .28

3. $\frac{17}{132} \doteq .129$

5. both equal $\Pr(E \cap F)$

7. $\frac{1}{18}$

9. $\frac{19}{30}$

11. .885

13. $\frac{3}{10}$

Exercises for 4.12

1. $\frac{9}{19} \doteq .474$

3. $\frac{2}{59} \doteq .034$

5. (a) $\frac{1}{3}$ (b) $\frac{1}{4}$

7. (a) 18.75 percent   (b) 40 percent

11. (a) $\frac{205}{378} \doteq .542$ (b) $\frac{14}{41} \doteq .341$

13. (a) 11 percent   (b) $\left(\frac{450}{11}\right)$ percent $\doteq 40.9$ percent

15. $\frac{9}{20} = .45$

Exercises for 4.13

1. yes

3. (a) yes   (b) yes

5. $\Pr(E) = \Pr(F) = \frac{1}{2}$; $\Pr(E \cap F) = \frac{1}{4}$

7. (a) $\Pr(E \cap F) = \Pr(E)\Pr(F) > 0$, so $E \cap F \neq \emptyset$

   (b) $\Pr(\emptyset \,|\, F) = \dfrac{\Pr(\emptyset \cap F)}{\Pr(F)} = \dfrac{\Pr(\emptyset)}{\Pr(F)}$

   $= \dfrac{0}{\Pr(F)} = 0 = \Pr(\emptyset)$

9. (a) $\frac{1}{52}$

   (b) $\frac{1}{169}$

   (c) $\frac{24}{169}$

11. no
13. There seems to be a "positive correlation" between driving while intoxicated and having accidents, whereas sex appears to have no influence on (i.e., be independent of) having accidents.
15. By the law of total probability $\Pr(B) = \Pr(B|A)\Pr(A) + \Pr(B|\bar{A})\Pr(\bar{A})$. Since A and B are independent, $\Pr(B|A) = \Pr(B)$, so we get

$$\Pr(B) = \Pr(B)\Pr(A) + \Pr(B|\bar{A})\Pr(\bar{A})$$

or

$$\Pr(B)(1 - \Pr(A)) = \Pr(B|\bar{A})\Pr(\bar{A})$$

But $1 - \Pr(A) = \Pr(\bar{A})$, and hence

$$\Pr(B)\Pr(\bar{A}) = \Pr(B|\bar{A})\Pr(\bar{A})$$

which implies that $\Pr(B) = \Pr(B|\bar{A})$, so $\bar{A}$ and B are independent.

Exercises for 4.14

1.

Sample point	SSS	SSF	SFS	SFF	FSS	FSF	FFS	FFF
Probability	$\frac{1}{27}$	$\frac{2}{27}$	$\frac{2}{27}$	$\frac{4}{27}$	$\frac{2}{27}$	$\frac{4}{27}$	$\frac{4}{27}$	$\frac{8}{27}$

$\Omega = \{SSS, SSF, SFS, SFF, FSS, FSF, FFS, FFF\}$

3.

Sample point	HHH	HHT	HTH	HTT	THH	THT	TTH	TTT
Probability	$\frac{1}{6}$	$\frac{1}{12}$	$\frac{1}{6}$	$\frac{1}{12}$	$\frac{1}{6}$	$\frac{1}{12}$	$\frac{1}{6}$	$\frac{1}{12}$

$\Omega = \{HHH, HHT, HTH, HTT, THH, THT, TTH, TTT\}$

5. no

7. (a) $\Omega = \{GGGG,\ GGGB,\ GGBG,\ GGBB,\ GBGG,\ GBGB,\ GBBG,\ GBBB,\ BGGG,\ BGGB,$ $BGBG,\ BGBB,\ BBGG,\ BBGB,\ BBBG,\ BBBB\}$

(b)

ω	$\Pr(\{\omega\})$	ω	$\Pr(\{\omega\})$
$GGGG$	$\frac{30}{576}$	$BGGG$	$\frac{15}{576}$
$GGGB$	$\frac{60}{576}$	$BGGB$	$\frac{30}{576}$
$GGBG$	$\frac{50}{576}$	$BGBG$	$\frac{25}{576}$
$GGBB$	$\frac{100}{576}$	$BGBB$	$\frac{50}{576}$
$GBGG$	$\frac{18}{576}$	$BBGG$	$\frac{9}{576}$
$GBGB$	$\frac{36}{576}$	$BBGB$	$\frac{18}{576}$
$GBBG$	$\frac{30}{576}$	$BBBG$	$\frac{15}{576}$
$GBBB$	$\frac{60}{576}$	$BBBB$	$\frac{30}{576}$

9. no

11. $\Omega = \{FF, FO, FN, OF, OO, ON, NF, NO, NN\}$

ω	FF	FO	FN	OF	OO	ON	NF	NO	NN
$\Pr(\{\omega\})$	.36	.18	.06	.18	.09	.03	.06	.03	.01

Exercises for 4.15

1. $\binom{6}{4}\left(\frac{1}{2}\right)^4\left(\frac{1}{2}\right)^{6-4} = \frac{15}{64}$

3. $\binom{6}{4}\left(\frac{1}{2}\right)^4\left(\frac{1}{2}\right)^{6-4} + \binom{6}{5}\left(\frac{1}{2}\right)^5\left(\frac{1}{2}\right)^{6-5} + \binom{6}{6}\left(\frac{1}{2}\right)^6\left(\frac{1}{2}\right)^{6-6} = \frac{11}{32}$

5. (a) $\binom{7}{5}\left(\frac{2}{3}\right)^5\left(\frac{1}{3}\right)^{7-5} = \frac{224}{729} \doteq .307$ (b) no

7. (a) $\binom{5}{5}\left(\frac{1}{10}\right)^5\left(\frac{9}{10}\right)^{5-5} = .00001$

    (b) $\binom{5}{3}\left(\frac{1}{10}\right)^3\left(\frac{9}{10}\right)^{5-3} + \binom{5}{4}\left(\frac{1}{10}\right)^4\left(\frac{9}{10}\right)^{5-4} + \binom{5}{5}\left(\frac{1}{10}\right)^5\left(\frac{9}{10}\right)^{5-5} = .00856$

9. $\binom{5}{3}\left(\frac{3}{10}\right)^3\left(\frac{7}{10}\right)^{5-3} + \binom{5}{4}\left(\frac{3}{10}\right)^4\left(\frac{7}{10}\right)^{5-4} + \binom{5}{5}\left(\frac{3}{10}\right)^5\left(\frac{7}{10}\right)^{5-5} = .16308$

11. $\binom{10}{0}\left(\frac{1}{4}\right)^0\left(\frac{3}{4}\right)^{10-0} + \binom{10}{1}\left(\frac{1}{4}\right)^1\left(\frac{3}{4}\right)^{10-1} + \binom{10}{2}\left(\frac{1}{4}\right)^2\left(\frac{3}{4}\right)^{10-2} + \binom{10}{3}\left(\frac{1}{4}\right)^3\left(\frac{3}{4}\right)^{10-3} \doteq .776$

13. $\binom{10}{7}\left(\frac{4}{5}\right)^7\left(\frac{1}{5}\right)^{10-7} \doteq .201$

15. (a) $\binom{8}{0}\left(\frac{1}{20}\right)^0\left(\frac{19}{20}\right)^{8-0} + \binom{8}{1}\left(\frac{1}{20}\right)^1\left(\frac{19}{20}\right)^{8-1} \doteq .943$

    (b) at least 5.

Exercises for 4.16

1. $\frac{3}{4}$
3. $\frac{12}{5}$
5. $-\frac{18}{25}$
7. 7
9. $\frac{1}{2}$
11. $87,500

Chapter 5

Exercises for 5.1

1. (a) 12   (b) 70
   (c) 174   (d) 42
   (e) 48   (f) 16
3. (a) 8   (b) 19.5
   (c) 6   (d) 14
5. (a) $\frac{20}{3}$
   (b) 93.5
   (c) 31.5
7. (a) $\frac{7}{6}$
   (b) $\frac{137}{30}$
   (c) $\frac{137}{30}$
9. (a) 4
   (b) 3
   (c) 3

Exercises for 5.2

1. (a) $\frac{15}{4} = 3.75$
   (b) $\frac{74}{5} = 14.8$
   (c) $\frac{20}{7}$

3. (a) 4   (b) 4

    (c) 3   (d) 3.5

5. (a) $\frac{755}{11} \doteq 68.64$ inches   (b) 68 inches

7. (a) $3{,}026/14 \doteq 216.14$ hours   (b) 175 hours

9. (a) $28{,}953/20 = 1{,}447.65$ cm^3 (b) 1,446.50 cm^3

11. $\dfrac{m\bar{x} + n\bar{y}}{m + n}$

13. $4{,}998{,}000/505 \doteq 9{,}897.03$ dollars

15. 70 inches

17. 245.50 hours

19. 67 inches

21. 5

Exercises for 5.3

1. (1) $R = 2$ (2) $\bar{x} = 2$

    (3) m.d. $= \frac{2}{3}$ (4) $s^2 = 1$

    (5) $s = 1$

3. (1) $R = 4$ (2) $\bar{x} = 3$

    (3) m.d. $= 1.2$ (4) $s^2 = 2.5$

    (5) $s \doteq 1.58$

5. (1) $R = 11$ (2) $\bar{x} = 1.4$

    (3) m.d. $= 3.52$ (4) $s^2 = 19.3$

    (5) $s \doteq 4.39$

7. (1) $R = 80$ (2) $\bar{x} = 15$

    (3) m.d. $= 24$ (4) $s^2 = 1{,}000$

    (5) $s \doteq 31.62$

9. (a) They are all equal.   (b) They are all equal.

11. $s \doteq 10.12$ pounds

13. $s \doteq 1.6$

Exercises for 5.4

1. (1)

Class	Class limits	Tallies	Frequency
1	40–48	|||	3
2	49–57			1
3	58–66	||||	5
4	67–75	|||| |||| |||| ||	17
5	76–84	|||| |||| |||	13
6	85–93	||||		6
7	94–102	||||	5
			50

(2)

Class	Class limits	Class frequency	Class mark	Relative frequency	Percentage of observations
1	40–48	3	44	.06	6.0
2	49–57	1	53	.02	2.0
3	58–66	5	62	.10	10.0
4	67–75	17	71	.34	34.0
5	76–84	13	80	.26	26.0
6	85–93	6	89	.12	12.0
7	94–102	5	98	.10	10.0
		50		1.00	100.0

(3)

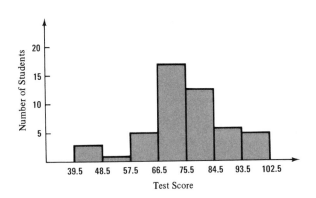

(4)

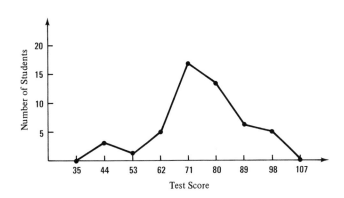

3. (1)

Class	Class limits	Tallies	Frequency
1	240–250	||	2
2	251–261	||	2
3	262–272	|||	3
4	273–283	ЦНТ ||	7
5	284–294	ЦНТ ЦНТ ЦНТ ||	17
6	295–305	ЦНТ ЦНТ ЦНТ ЦНТ ЦНТ ||	27
7	306–316	ЦНТ ЦНТ ЦНТ ЦНТ ||||	24
8	317–327	ЦНТ ||||	9
9	328–338	||||	4
10	339–349	||||	4
11	350–360	|	1
			100

(2)

Class	Class limits	Class frequency	Class mark	Relative frequency	Percentage of observations
1	240–250	2	245	.02	2
2	251–261	2	256	.02	2
3	262–272	3	267	.03	3
4	273–283	7	278	.07	7
5	284–294	17	289	.17	17
6	295–305	27	300	.27	27
7	306–316	24	311	.24	24
8	317–327	9	322	.09	9
9	328–338	4	333	.04	4
10	339–349	4	344	.04	4
11	350–360	1	355	.01	1
		100		1.00	100

(3)

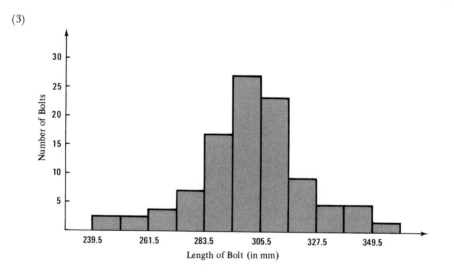

(4)

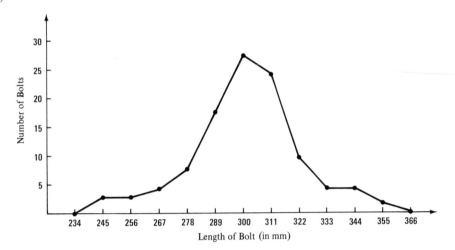

Length of Bolt (in mm)

5. (1)

Class	Class limits	Tallies	Frequency
1	66–68	||||	4
2	69–71	ⅬⅣⅠ |	6
3	72–74	ⅬⅣⅠ ⅬⅣⅠ	10
4	75–77	ⅬⅣⅠ ||||	9
5	78–80	ⅬⅣⅠ ||	7
6	81–83	ⅬⅣⅠ ⅬⅣⅠ |	11
7	84–86	ⅬⅣⅠ ⅬⅣⅠ	10
8	87–89		0
9	90–92	||	2
10	93–95	||	2
			61

(2)

Class	Class limits	Class frequency	Class mark	Relative frequency	Percentage of observations
1	66–68	4	67	.066	6.6
2	69–71	6	70	.098	9.8
3	72–74	10	73	.164	16.4
4	75–77	9	76	.147	14.7
5	78–80	7	79	.115	11.5
6	81–83	11	82	.180	18.0
7	84–86	10	85	.164	16.4
8	87–89	0	88	.000	0.0
9	90–92	2	91	.033	3.3
10	93–95	2	94	.033	3.3
		61		1.000	100.0

(3)

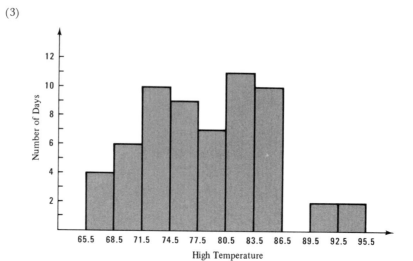

(4)

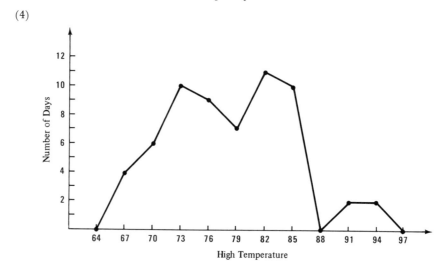

Exercises for 5.5

1. $\bar{x} \doteq 47.22,$ $s^2 \doteq 35.29$
   $\hat{x} \doteq 48.83,$ $s \doteq 5.94$
3. $\bar{x} \doteq 30.46,$ $s^2 \doteq 71.08$
   $\hat{x} \doteq 30.30,$ $s \doteq 8.43$
5. $\bar{x} = 21.00,$ $s^2 \doteq 127.07$
   $\hat{x} \doteq 22.83,$ $s \doteq 11.27$
7. $\bar{x} \doteq 3.49,$ $s^2 \doteq 3.93$
   $\hat{x} \doteq 3.26,$ $s \doteq 1.98$
9. $\bar{x} \doteq 5.85,$ $s^2 \doteq 46.47$
   $\hat{x} = 3.50,$ $s \doteq 6.82$
11. $\bar{x} \doteq 19.87,$ $s^2 \doteq 23.12$
   $\hat{x} = 19.65,$ $s \doteq 4.81$

Exercises for 5.6

1. $\bar{x} = 276.25;\ s_x^2 \doteq 6.92;\ s_x \doteq 2.63$
3. $\bar{x} = 427.24;\ s_x^2 \doteq .89;\ s_x \doteq .94$
5. $\bar{x} \doteq .03;\ s_x^2 \doteq .0002;\ s_x \doteq .01$

7. $\bar{x} = 47,640;\ s_x^2 = 293,000;\ s_x \doteq 541.29$
9. $\bar{x} \doteq 178.69;\ s_x^2 \doteq 102.50;\ s_x \doteq 10.12$
11. $\bar{x} = 11,900;\ s_x^2 \doteq 7,336,111.13;\ s_x \doteq 2,708.53$
13. $\bar{x} = 75.32;\ s_x^2 \doteq 176.02;\ s_x \doteq 13.27$
15. $\bar{x} = 301.87;\ s_x^2 \doteq 410.80;\ s_x \doteq 20.27$

Chapter 6

Exercises for 6.1

1. Some possible answers are
   (a) $3x_1 + 4x_2 = 5$
      $6x_1 - 3x_2 = 8$
   (b) $2y_1 - 5y_2 + \frac{1}{2}y_3 = -7$
      $-y_1 + 7y_2 + 6y_3 = 12$
   (c) $u_1 + 6u_2 - 7u_3 + 4u_4 = \frac{1}{3}$
      $5u_1 - 2u_2 + 6u_3 + u_4 = 18$
   (d) $4x_1 + 2x_2 - 3x_3 + \quad x_4 + 6x_5 - 2x_6 = 8$
      $2x_1 + 3x_2 + 8x_3 - 12x_4 + 5x_5 - \quad x_6 = 10$
3. (a), (d), and (e) give solutions
5. (a) $c = -13$ (b) $d = -\frac{14}{3}$
7. (a) Four solutions are given in the following table:

x_1	x_2	x_3	x_4	x_5
21	4	0	0	0
11	0	4	0	0
20	0	0	1	0
9	0	0	0	4

(b) Four solutions are given in the following table:

x_1	x_2	x_3
-6	1	0
-11	0	3
$-\frac{15}{2}$	0	0
$-\frac{5}{2}$	1	-3

9. (a) $.01x_1 + .05x_2 + .10x_3 + .25x_4 + .50x_5 = 2.35$
   or
   $x_1 + 5x_2 + 10x_3 + 25x_4 + 50x_5 = 235$
   (b) Four possibilities are:

Pennies	x_1	235	10	85	10
Nickels	x_2	0	1	4	10
Dimes	x_3	0	2	3	5
Quarters	x_4	0	4	2	1
Half-dollars	x_5	0	2	1	2

11. $\begin{aligned} x_1 + x_2 + x_3 + x_4 &= 7 \\ x_1 + x_2 &= 4 \\ x_1 - x_2 - x_3 &= 0 \\ \tfrac{1}{2}x_1 + \tfrac{1}{2}x_2 + \tfrac{1}{2}x_3 + \tfrac{1}{4}x_4 &= 3 \end{aligned}$

13. $n = 1$.

Exercises for 6.2

1. Three examples are

$\begin{aligned} 2x_1 + 3x_2 &= 8 \\ 4x_1 + 6x_2 &= 7 \end{aligned} \qquad \begin{aligned} -4x_1 + x_2 &= -12 \\ 2x_1 + 5x_2 &= 16 \end{aligned} \qquad \begin{aligned} x_1 + x_2 &= 1 \\ x_1 - x_2 &= 0 \end{aligned}$

3. An example of such a system is

$\begin{aligned} 2y_1 + y_2 - 4y_3 &= 7 \\ y_1 - y_2 + y_3 &= 2 \\ 4y_1 - 3y_3 &= 0 \\ 6y_1 + 7y_2 - 8y_3 &= 5 \\ 4y_2 + 2y_3 &= -4 \end{aligned}$

5. Only (d) is a simultaneous solution.

7. None are simultaneous solutions.

9. $\begin{aligned} .01x_1 + .05x_2 + .10x_3 + .25x_4 + .50x_5 &= 2.35 \\ x_3 - x_4 - x_5 &= 0 \\ x_1 - x_3 &= 0 \\ x_1 - 15x_2 + x_3 + x_4 + x_5 &= 0 \\ x_1 - 2x_2 + x_3 - 2x_4 - x_5 &= 0 \end{aligned}$

11. $x_1 = 6,\ x_2 = -1$ is the unique simultaneous solution.

13. $x_1 = \tfrac{1}{2},\ x_2 = 0;\ x_1 = 0,\ x_2 = -\tfrac{1}{3};$ and $x_1 = 2,\ x_2 = 1$ are solutions. There are many others.

Exercises for 6.3

1. $x_1 = \tfrac{7}{2} + \tfrac{5}{2}x_2$ for both equations.

3. (a) $\begin{aligned} 2x_1 - 3x_2 + 4x_3 &= 6 \\ 3x_1 + 5x_2 - 6x_3 &= 7 \\ 2x_1 - x_2 + 3x_3 &= -1 \\ 5x_1 + 4x_2 - 7x_3 &= 0 \end{aligned}$

(b) $\begin{aligned} 2x_1 - 3x_2 + 4x_3 &= 6 \\ 5x_1 + 4x_2 - 7x_3 &= 0 \\ 4x_1 - 2x_2 + 6x_3 &= -2 \\ 3x_1 + 5x_2 - 6x_3 &= 7 \end{aligned}$

(c) $\begin{aligned} 2x_1 - 3x_2 + 4x_3 &= 6 \\ 3x_1 + 5x_2 - 6x_3 &= 7 \\ 4x_2 - 2x_3 &= -14 \\ 5x_1 + 4x_2 - 7x_3 &= 0 \end{aligned}$

(d) $\begin{aligned} \tfrac{23}{4}x_1 - \tfrac{5}{4}x_3 &= 6 \\ 3x_1 + 5x_2 - 6x_3 &= 7 \\ 4x_1 - 2x_2 + 6x_3 &= -2 \\ 5x_1 + 4x_2 - 7x_3 &= 0 \end{aligned}$

(e)
$$2x_1 - 3x_2 + 4x_3 = 6$$
$$x_1 + \tfrac{5}{3}x_2 - 2x_3 = \tfrac{7}{3}$$
$$4x_1 - 2x_2 + 6x_3 = -2$$
$$5x_1 + 4x_2 - 7x_3 = 0$$

(f)
$$2x_1 - 3x_2 + 4x_3 = 6$$
$$3x_1 + 5x_2 - 6x_3 = 7$$
$$4x_1 - 2x_2 + 6x_3 = -2$$
$$\tfrac{58}{6}x_1 + \tfrac{10}{6}x_2 = -\tfrac{14}{6}$$

5. (a)
$$-4x_1 + 8x_2 = 12$$
$$2x_1 - 3x_2 = -2$$

(b)
$$x_1 - 2x_2 = -3$$
$$2x_1 - 3x_2 = -2$$

(c)
$$x_1 - 2x_2 = -3$$
$$x_2 = 4$$

(d)
$$x_1 = 5$$
$$x_2 = 4$$

The simultaneous solution to (*) is $x_1 = 5$, $x_2 = 4$.

7. (a)
$$x_1 + x_2 = 2$$
$$2x_1 + 3x_2 = 5$$
$$3x_1 + 4x_2 = 4$$

(b)
$$x_1 + x_2 = 2$$
$$x_2 = 1$$
$$3x_1 + 4x_2 = 4$$

(c)
$$x_1 + x_2 = 2$$
$$x_2 = 1$$
$$x_2 = -2$$

(d)
$$x_1 = 1$$
$$x_2 = 1$$
$$x_2 = -2$$

(e)
$$x_1 = 1$$
$$x_2 = 1$$
$$0 = -3$$

The last equation in the last system is $0 = -3$, or $0x_1 + 0x_2 = -3$, which has no solutions. Hence the solution set of the last system is $\varnothing$, and consequently the solution set of (*) is $\varnothing$.

Exercises for 6.4

1. $x_1 = 1$, $x_2 = 2$ is the only solution.
3. The system has the unique solution $x_1 = 8$, $x_2 = 6$.
5. $x_1 = 10$, $x_2 = -20$ is the unique solution.
7. The system has the unique solution $x_1 = 3$, $x_2 = 2$, $x_3 = 1$.
9. $x_1 = 3$, $x_2 = \tfrac{1}{3}$, $x_3 = 1$ is the unique solution.
11. The system has the unique solution $x_1 = 0$, $x_2 = 1$, $x_3 = -1$, $x_4 = 2$.

Exercises for 6.5

1. Solution set contains one solution: $x_1 = 2$, $x_2 = -1$.
3. The system has no solutions; that is, its solution set is $\varnothing$.
5. Solution set contains one solution: $x_1 = \tfrac{5}{7}$, $x_2 = \tfrac{2}{7}$.
7. The solution set consists of all values for x_1, x_2, x_3 satisfying

$$x_1 = 11 + 7x_3$$
$$x_2 = 1 - 2x_3$$

9. The solution set of the system consists of the unique solution $x_1 = 1$, $x_2 = 0$, $x_3 = -1$.
11. The solution set consists of all values for the variables x_1, x_2, x_3 satisfying

$$x_1 = \tfrac{16}{11} - \tfrac{10}{11}x_3$$
$$x_2 = \tfrac{7}{11} - \tfrac{3}{11}x_3$$

13. The system has no simultaneous solutions. That is, its solution set is $\varnothing$.
15. Television: $2,500,000
    Magazines: $1,000,000
    Radio: $1,500,000
    Direct mail: $2,000,000
17. 1,125 units of the vaccine and 375 units of the glucose must be prepared.

Exercises for 6.6

1. (a) Some examples are [1, 2, 3, 4, 5], [1, 2, 3, 4, 5, 6], [1, 2, 3, 4, 5, 6, 7]
   (b) Some examples are

$$\begin{bmatrix} 1 \\ -1 \\ 1 \\ -1 \\ 1 \end{bmatrix} \quad \begin{bmatrix} 1 \\ -1 \\ 1 \\ -1 \\ 1 \\ -1 \end{bmatrix} \quad \begin{bmatrix} 1 \\ -1 \\ 1 \\ -1 \\ 1 \\ -1 \\ 1 \end{bmatrix}$$

3. (a), (b), and (f) unequal; (c), (d), and (e) equal.
5. impossible
7. [6, 4, −8]

9. $\begin{bmatrix} 2 \\ 33 \end{bmatrix}$

11. $\begin{bmatrix} 2 \\ -2 \end{bmatrix}$

13. $\begin{bmatrix} -\frac{1}{4} \\ \frac{25}{4} \\ \frac{9}{2} \end{bmatrix}$

15. [−15, −11, 31]

17. $X = \begin{bmatrix} 1 \\ 3 \\ -5 \end{bmatrix}$

19. $X = [0, \frac{10}{3}, \frac{14}{3}]$

21. $X = \begin{bmatrix} 1 \\ 1 \\ 2 \end{bmatrix}$

23. $X = \begin{bmatrix} 0 \\ 0 \end{bmatrix}$

29. $W = V$

Exercises for 6.7

1. Some possible examples are

(a) $\begin{bmatrix} 1 & 2 & 3 \\ 4 & 5 & 6 \end{bmatrix}$

(b) $\begin{bmatrix} 1 & 2 & 3 & 4 \\ 5 & 6 & 7 & 8 \\ 9 & 10 & 11 & 12 \\ 13 & 14 & 15 & 16 \\ 17 & 18 & 19 & 20 \end{bmatrix}$

(c) $[-1, 3, 4, 2, 5, \frac{1}{2}]$

(d) $\begin{bmatrix} 1 \\ 2 \\ -5 \end{bmatrix}$

(e) $$\begin{bmatrix} 1 & 3 & 4 & 5 & 2 & 1 & 0 \\ 4 & -6 & 3 & 4 & 1 & 2 & 8 \\ 6 & -5 & 1 & 0 & 0 & 4 & 1 \\ 8 & 6 & 3 & 5 & 2 & 0 & 4 \\ 5 & 2 & 8 & 3 & 7 & 1 & 2 \\ 0 & 0 & 4 & 1 & 0 & 3 & 0 \\ 2 & 6 & 4 & 1 & 8 & 9 & 5 \end{bmatrix}$$ (f) [4]

3. $\begin{bmatrix} 1 & 1 \\ 2 & 4 \end{bmatrix}$

5. $\begin{bmatrix} 3 & 3 & 0 \\ -3 & \frac{3}{2} & 15 \\ 5 & 9 & 3 \end{bmatrix}$

7. $\begin{bmatrix} -4 & 5 & 15 \\ 5 & -1 & \frac{17}{2} \\ -3 & 1 & -7 \end{bmatrix}$

9. $\begin{bmatrix} 3 & 11 & -16 \\ -1 & 13 & -8 \end{bmatrix}$

11. $\begin{bmatrix} 11 & 14 \\ 2 & -2 \\ 1 & 4 \end{bmatrix}$

13. impossible

15. $\begin{bmatrix} 0 & 0 & 0 & 0 \\ 1 & 2 & 1 & 4 \\ 2 & 4 & 2 & 8 \\ 3 & 6 & 3 & 12 \end{bmatrix}$

17. $[7, 28, 14, -21]$

19. impossible

21. $\begin{bmatrix} 2 & -9 & 11 & 7 \\ 24 & -6 & 30 & 1 \\ 40 & 0 & 40 & 14 \\ -25 & \frac{27}{2} & -\frac{77}{2} & 5 \end{bmatrix}$

23. (a) $A = \begin{bmatrix} 6 & 5 & 7 \\ 4 & 3 & 5 \\ 1 & 2 & 1 \\ 10 & 11 & 8 \end{bmatrix}$

(b) $B = \begin{bmatrix} 20 & 10 & 5 & 6 \\ 4 & 1 & 7 & 18 \end{bmatrix}$

(c) $BA = \begin{bmatrix} 225 & 206 & 243 \\ 215 & 235 & 184 \end{bmatrix}$

(d) The i–j entry of the matrix BA represents the cost to the contractor of job i if he buys from distributor j. In other words, the three entries of the first row of BA give the costs of materials for job 1 if the contractor buys from distributors 1, 2, and 3, respectively. Similarly for the second row.

(e) The second distributor. The third distributor.

Exercises for 6.8

1. $a_{11} = 3$, $a_{12} = \pi$, $a_{13} = \frac{1}{2}$, $a_{21} = 2$, $a_{22} = .5$, $a_{23} = 7$, $a_{31} = -1$, $a_{32} = \frac{3}{4}$, $a_{33} = 1$, $a_{41} = 0$, $a_{42} = .3$, $a_{43} = \frac{1}{3}$

3. $A = \begin{bmatrix} \frac{1}{2} & -\frac{1}{2} & -\frac{3}{2} \\ 2 & 1 & 0 \end{bmatrix}$

5. $\begin{bmatrix} 6 & 18 \\ 24 & 62 \end{bmatrix}$

7. impossible

9. $\begin{bmatrix} \frac{45}{2} & -2 & -13 \\ -\frac{155}{2} & 9 & 49 \\ -100 & 11 & 62 \end{bmatrix}$

11. $\begin{bmatrix} -41 & 69 \\ 33 & 25 \end{bmatrix}$

13. $X = \begin{bmatrix} -3 & 2 \\ 2 & -7 \end{bmatrix}$

15. $X = \begin{bmatrix} -\frac{10}{3} & -\frac{2}{3} & 1 \\ -\frac{14}{3} & -2 & \frac{4}{3} \\ \frac{1}{6} & \frac{1}{3} & -\frac{2}{3} \end{bmatrix}$

17. $\begin{aligned} 3x_1 + x_2 &= -1 \\ -2x_1 + 4x_2 &= 0 \\ 6x_1 + 5x_2 &= 8 \end{aligned}$

23. (a) $\begin{bmatrix} 3 & 2 \\ 1 & -1 \\ 6 & 8 \\ 5 & 2 \end{bmatrix}$
(b) $\begin{bmatrix} 8 & 5 & 3 \\ 2 & 6 & \frac{1}{2} \\ -1 & 1 & 4 \end{bmatrix}$

(c) $\begin{bmatrix} 1 \\ 3 \\ 5 \\ -7 \end{bmatrix}$
(d) $\begin{bmatrix} 3 & 1 & 8 \\ 1 & 0 & -5 \\ 8 & -5 & 2 \end{bmatrix}$

Exercises for 6.9

1. $\begin{bmatrix} 3 & 2 \\ 4 & -8 \end{bmatrix} \begin{bmatrix} x_1 \\ x_2 \end{bmatrix} = \begin{bmatrix} 7 \\ -3 \end{bmatrix}$

3. $\begin{bmatrix} 3 & -2 & 7 \\ 1 & 0 & -6 \end{bmatrix} \begin{bmatrix} y_1 \\ y_2 \\ y_3 \end{bmatrix} = \begin{bmatrix} 10 \\ -4 \end{bmatrix}$

5. $\begin{bmatrix} 3 & 7 & -4 & 8 \\ 1 & 0 & -1 & 2 \\ .6 & 3 & -.4 & 1 \end{bmatrix} \begin{bmatrix} x_1 \\ x_2 \\ x_3 \\ x_4 \end{bmatrix} = \begin{bmatrix} 12 \\ 7 \\ \frac{1}{2} \end{bmatrix}$

7. $x_1 = 2$, $x_2 = -1$
9. $x_1 = 1$, $x_2 = -3$, $x_3 = 4$
11. $x_1 = 1$, $x_2 = 0$, $x_3 = -2$
13. This system has infinitely many solutions: any values for the variables x_1, x_2 that satisfy

$$x_1 = -1 + 3x_2$$

15. This system has infinitely many solutions: any values for the variables x_1, x_2, x_3 that satisfy

$$x_1 = -13 + 7x_3$$
$$x_2 = -9 + 4x_3$$

17. The solution to the first system is $x_1 = 3$, $x_2 = 1$ and that to the second is $x_1 = 5$, $x_2 = -2$.

19. The solutions to the first and second systems are given respectively by

$$x_1 = 1, \quad x_2 = 0, \quad x_3 = -2$$
$$x_1 = 3, \quad x_2 = -4, \quad x_3 = 5$$

21. The solution for test group I is

$$x_1 = 2, x_2 = 6, x_3 = 2$$

and that for test group II is

$$x_1 = 5, x_2 = 0, x_3 = 5$$

23. (a) The solutions to the two systems are given by

$$x_1 = \quad a_{22}/d \qquad x_2 = -a_{21}/d$$
$$y_1 = -a_{12}/d \qquad y_2 = \quad a_{11}/d$$

where $d = a_{11}a_{22} - a_{12}a_{21}$.

Exercises for 6.10

3. $\begin{bmatrix} \frac{2}{7} & -\frac{3}{7} \\ -\frac{1}{7} & \frac{5}{7} \end{bmatrix}$

5. Only square matrices can possibly have inverses. Hence this matrix cannot have an inverse.

7. $\begin{bmatrix} -\frac{89}{5} & \frac{7}{5} & -4 \\ \frac{46}{5} & -\frac{3}{5} & 2 \\ -\frac{24}{5} & \frac{2}{5} & -1 \end{bmatrix}$

9. Since A has an inverse and $AE = A$, we get

(*) $\qquad A^{-1}(AE) = A^{-1}A = I_n$

But, by the associative law for matrix multiplication,

(**) $\qquad A^{-1}(AE) = (A^{-1}A)E = I_nE = E$

Thus, by (*) and (**), $E = I_n$.

11. Claim that $(AB)^{-1} = B^{-1}A^{-1}$. Indeed,

$$(B^{-1}A^{-1})(AB) = B^{-1}(A^{-1}A)B$$
$$= B^{-1}I_nB = B^{-1}B = I_n$$

and

$$(AB)(B^{-1}A^{-1}) = A(BB^{-1})A^{-1}$$
$$= AI_nA^{-1} = AA^{-1} = I_n$$

Chapter 7

Exercises for 7.1

1. (a) Some possibilities are
   (1) $f(x_1, x_2) = 8x_1 - 3x_2$ (2) $g(x_1, x_2) = 7x_1 + 5x_2$
   (b) Some possibilities are
   (1) $f(y_1, y_2) = 3y_1 + 5y_2$ (2) $g(y_1, y_2) = 2y_1 - y_2$

3. (a) 45
   (b) 40
   (c) -20
5. (a), (c), and (d) are linear functions; (b) and (e) are not.
7. $f(x_1, x_2) = 10x_1 + 25x_2$

Exercises for 7.2

1.

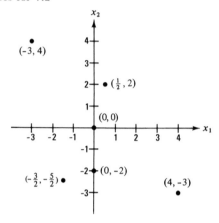

3. (1) $x_2 = 1 - 2x_1$

(2)

x_1	x_2
0	1
1	-1
-1	3
2	-3

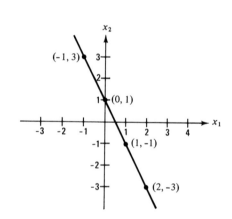

5. (1) $x_1 = 6 - 4x_2$

(2)

x_1	x_2
6	0
2	1
-2	2
4	$\frac{1}{2}$

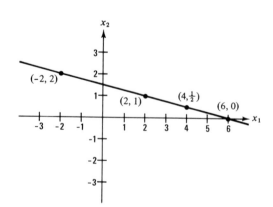

7. (1) $y_2 = 2y_1 + 4$

(2)

y_1	y_2
0	4
-1	2
-2	0
1	6

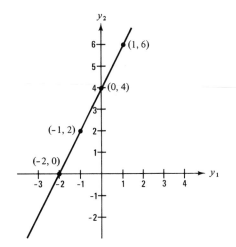

9. (1) $x_1 = 4 + \frac{4}{3}x_2$

(2)

x_1	x_2
4	0
$\frac{16}{3}$	1
$\frac{8}{3}$	-1
0	-3

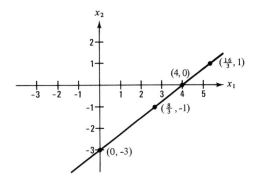

11. (1) $x_1 = 2$

(2)

x_1	x_2
2	-1
2	1
2	-2
2	2

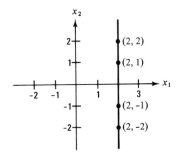

13. (1) $x_2 = 0$

(2)

x_1	x_2
2	0
4	0
-1	0
-3	0

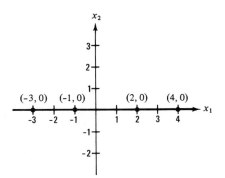

15. (a) 0° centigrade
   (b) 212° Fahrenheit
   (c) Proceeding as usual, we obtain:

x_1	x_2
32	0
212	100
68	20

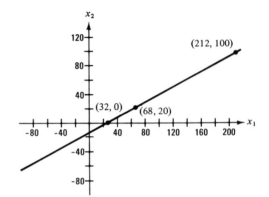

17. $-x_1 + 5x_2 = 7$
19. $-2x_1 + 3x_2 = 12$
21. $x_1 = 2$ (or $x_1 + 0 \cdot x_2 = 2$)

Exercises for 7.3

1. The point of intersection is $(1, 3)$.

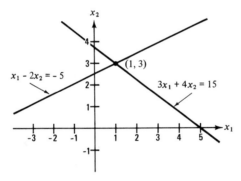

3. The point of intersection is $(-3, -5)$.

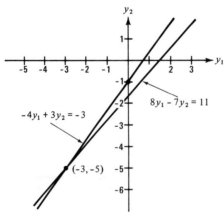

5. The equations represent the same line, so the corresponding lines intersect in infinitely many points.

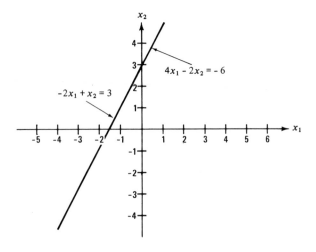

7. The equations represent the same line, so the corresponding lines intersect in infinitely many points.

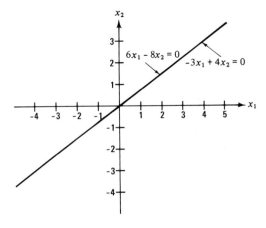

9. The lines intersect at $\left(\frac{50}{7}, \frac{15}{7}\right)$.

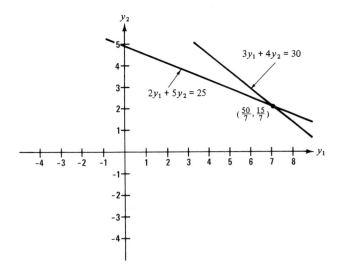

11. The point of intersection is $\left(\frac{75}{2}, 0\right)$.

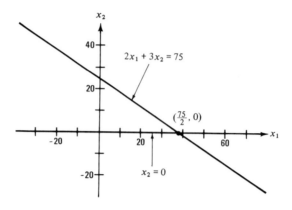

13. The lines are parallel, so there are no points of intersection.

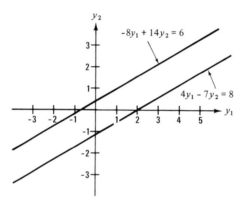

15. The equations represent the same line, and therefore their corresponding straight lines intersect in infinitely many points.

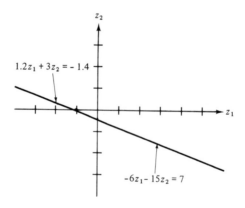

17. (a) $x_1 = 1$ and $x_2 = 1$ is the unique solution to both of the systems.

(b) I: II:

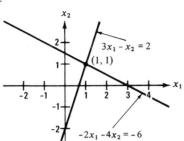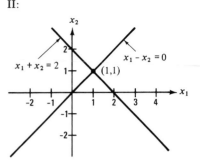

The point of intersection of the straight lines corresponding to the two equations in each system is the same.

(c) Two equivalent systems have the property that the point(s) of intersection of their corresponding straight lines is (are) the same.

Exercises for 7.4

1. (a), (b), (d), and (h)

3. (a) (3), (4), and (6)   (b) (1) and (5)

   (c) (1), (4), and (6)   (d) (2), (3), (4), and (5)

5.

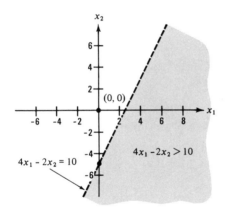

7.

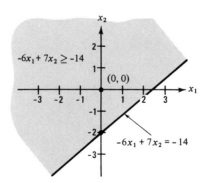

9.

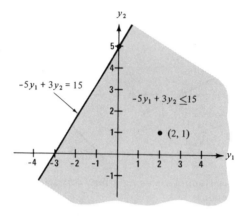

11.

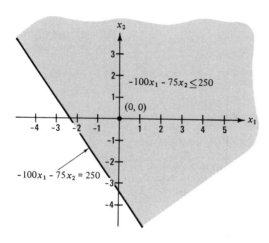

13.

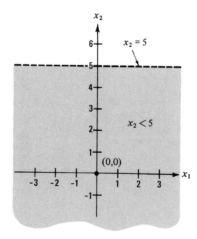

15.

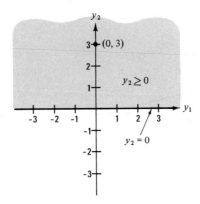

17.

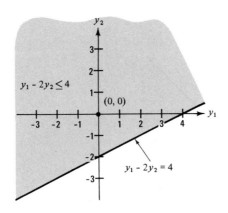

19.

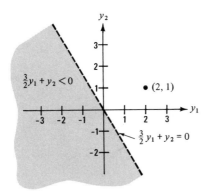

21. (a) $2x_1 + 10x_2 \leq 120$

(b)

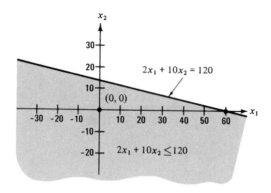

(c) $x_1 - x_2 \geq 0$

(d)

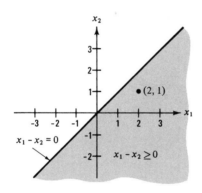

23. (a) $2x_1 + 3x_2 \leq 72$

(b)

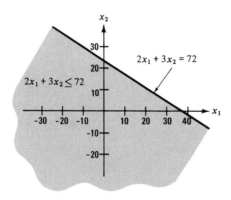

(c) $2x_1 + 10x_2 \leq 100$

(d)

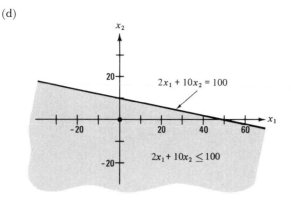

Exercises for 7.5

1. The polyhedral convex set corresponding to this system is

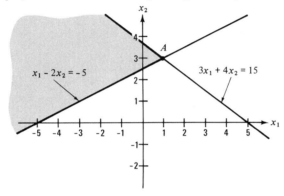

The set has one extreme point, $A = (1, 3)$.

3. The polyhedral convex set is

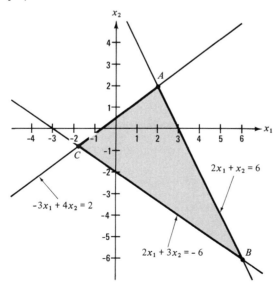

The set has three extreme points: $A = (2, 2)$, $B = (6, -6)$, $C = (-\frac{30}{17}, -\frac{14}{17})$.

5. The polyhedral convex set is

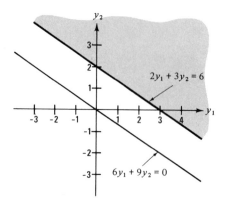

and has no extreme points.

7. The polyhedral convex set is

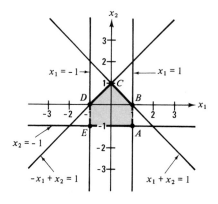

The extreme points are: $A = (1, -1), B = (1, 0), C = (0, 1), D = (-1, 0), E = (-1, -1)$.

9. The polyhedral convex set is

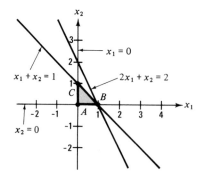

The extreme points are $A = (0, 0), B = (1, 0), C = (0, 1)$.

11. The polyhedral convex set is

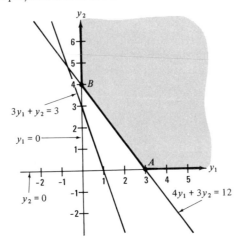

$3y_1 + y_2 = 3$

$y_1 = 0$

$y_2 = 0$

$4y_1 + 3y_2 = 12$

The extreme points are $A = (3, 0)$, $B = (0, 4)$.

13. The polyhedral convex set is

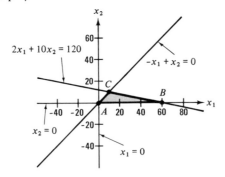

$2x_1 + 10x_2 = 120$

$-x_1 + x_2 = 0$

$x_2 = 0$

$x_1 = 0$

The extreme points are $A = (0, 0)$, $B = (60, 0)$, $C = (10, 10)$.

15. (a), (b), (d), and (f) are convex.

17. (a) yes

   (b) no

   (c) no

Exercises for 7.6

1. minimum value is -5

   maximum value is 3

3. minimum value is -5

   maximum value is 11

5. minimum value is -18

   maximum value is 0

7. minimum value is $-\frac{3}{2}$

   maximum value is 1

9. minimum value is -15 and occurs at $(0, 3)$

   maximum value is 10 and occurs at $(5, 0)$

11. minimum value is 10 and occurs at $(0, 10)$

   no maximum value

13. minimum value is 8 and occurs at $(0, 4)$

   no maximum value

15. no minimum value and no maximum value

17. (a) no   (b) 4

Exercises for 7.7

1. (a) 90 steak and 60 lobster dinners   (b) 110 steak and 40 lobster dinners
3. (a) 10 each per week
    (b) 60 "simple" and none of the "complex" forms should be processed per week
5. $\frac{15}{7}$ cents per unit of the vitamin supplement and $\frac{25}{7}$ cents per unit of the mineral supplement
7. (a) 3 days from refinery I and 1 day from refinery II
    (b) same as in part (a)

Chapter 8

Exercises for 8.1

1. Some possible answers are
    (a) $2x_1$ and $6x_1$
    (b) $3x_1 + 4x_2$ and $-6x_1 + 3x_2$
    (c) $2y_1 - 4y_2 + y_3$ and $3y_1 + 5y_2 + 6y_3$
    (d) $8u_1 + u_2 - u_3 + u_4$ and $7u_1 + 8u_2 - \frac{1}{2}u_3 + 6u_4$
3. (a) 5
    (b) 10
    (c) 11
5. (a) 2
    (b) 2
    (c) $-\frac{17}{6}$
7. (c) and (e) are linear; (a), (b), (d), and (f) are not linear.
9. (a), (b), and (d)
11. Four possibilities are
    (1) $x_1 = 2$, $x_2 = x_3 = x_4 = x_5 = x_6 = 0$
    (2) $x_1 = x_2 = x_3 = x_4 = x_5 = x_6 = 1$
    (3) $x_1 = 1$, $x_2 = 2$, $x_3 = 3$, $x_4 = 4$, $x_5 = 5$, $x_6 = 6$
    (4) $x_1 = 1$, $x_2 = -1$, $x_3 = 1$, $x_4 = -1$, $x_5 = 1$, $x_6 = -1$
    Of course there are many other possibilities.
13. (a) $18x_1^2 - 8x_2^2$ (b) not necessarily, as part (a) shows
15. (a) $c(x_1, x_2, x_3, x_4) = 5x_1 + 2x_2 + 4x_3 + 3x_4$
    (b) $5x_1 + 2x_2 + 4x_3 + 3x_4 \leq 1,030$
    (c) \$1.50 per pound
17. (a) $g(y_1, y_2, y_3, y_4) = 2y_1 + 1.5y_2 + 1.5y_3 + .8y_4$
    (b) $y_1 \geq 700$
        $y_2 + y_4 \leq 400$
        $y_1 + y_2 \geq 1,100$
        $y_2 + y_3 + y_4 \leq 1,100$
        $y_1 + y_2 + y_3 + y_4 \geq 1,700$
    (Of course, we must have $y_1 \geq 0, y_2 \geq 0, y_3 \geq 0, y_4 \geq 0$.)

Exercises for 8.2

1. (a) $\leq$ (b) $\geq$
    (c) $\leq$ (d) $\leq$
3. Maximize: CX
    subject to: $AX \leq B$, $X \geq \theta$
    where

$$A = \begin{bmatrix} 6 & 7 \\ 2 & 1 \end{bmatrix} \quad B = \begin{bmatrix} 10 \\ 4 \end{bmatrix} \quad C = [3, 5] \quad \theta = \begin{bmatrix} 0 \\ 0 \end{bmatrix} \quad X = \begin{bmatrix} x_1 \\ x_2 \end{bmatrix}$$

5. Minimize: YB
   subject to: $YA \geq C, \; Y \geq \theta$
   where

   $$A = \begin{bmatrix} 7 & 3 \\ 4 & -6 \end{bmatrix} \quad B = \begin{bmatrix} 2 \\ 4 \end{bmatrix} \quad C = [15, 5] \quad \theta = [0, 0] \quad Y = [y_1, y_2]$$

7. Maximize: CX
   subject to: $AX \leq B, \; X \geq \theta$
   where

   $$A = \begin{bmatrix} 1 & -1 & 4 \\ 3 & 5 & -2 \\ 2 & 3 & 4 \\ -7 & 6 & 1 \end{bmatrix} \quad B = \begin{bmatrix} 8 \\ 6 \\ 5 \\ -2 \end{bmatrix} \quad C = [7, -5, 3] \quad X = \begin{bmatrix} x_1 \\ x_2 \\ x_3 \end{bmatrix} \quad \theta = \begin{bmatrix} 0 \\ 0 \\ 0 \end{bmatrix}$$

9. Minimize: YB
   subject to: $YA \geq C, \; Y \geq \theta$
   where

   $$A = \begin{bmatrix} 3 & 2 \\ -6 & 4 \\ 4 & -1 \end{bmatrix} \quad B = \begin{bmatrix} 5 \\ 3 \\ -7 \end{bmatrix} \quad C = [-8, 3] \quad Y = [y_1, y_2, y_3] \quad \theta = [0, 0, 0]$$

11. The standard form for the system of linear inequalities is

    $$\begin{aligned} 3x_1 + 5x_2 &\leq 8 \\ 3x_1 - 2x_2 &\leq 0 \\ x_1 &\geq 0 \\ x_2 &\geq 0 \end{aligned}$$

    and so the vector-matrix form is

    Maximize: CX
    subject to: $AX \leq B, \; X \geq \theta$
    where

    $$A = \begin{bmatrix} 3 & 5 \\ 3 & -2 \end{bmatrix} \quad B = \begin{bmatrix} 8 \\ 0 \end{bmatrix} \quad C = [-1, 2] \quad X = \begin{bmatrix} x_1 \\ x_2 \end{bmatrix} \quad \theta = \begin{bmatrix} 0 \\ 0 \end{bmatrix}$$

13. The standard form for the system of linear inequalities is

    $$\begin{aligned} 2y_1 + 4y_2 + 8y_3 &\geq 7 \\ -3y_1 + 6y_2 + y_3 &\geq 5 \\ -2y_2 + y_3 &\geq 0 \\ y_1 &\geq 0 \\ y_2 &\geq 0 \\ y_3 &\geq 0 \end{aligned}$$

    and hence the vector-matrix form is

    Minimize: YB
    subject to: $YA \geq C, \; Y \geq \theta$
    where

    $$A = \begin{bmatrix} 2 & -3 & 0 \\ 4 & 6 & -2 \\ 8 & 1 & 1 \end{bmatrix} \quad B = \begin{bmatrix} 1 \\ 2 \\ -3 \end{bmatrix} \quad C = [7, 5, 0] \quad Y = [y_1, y_2, y_3] \quad \theta = [0, 0, 0]$$

17. false (e.g., $V = [1, -1]$)
19. true

Exercises for 8.3

1. The Tucker tableau is

	x_1	x_2	-1	
y_1	5	2	6	$= -t_1$
y_2	4	-6	1	$= -t_2$
-1	3	-7	0	$= f$
	$\|\|$	$\|\|$	$\|\|$	
	s_1	s_2	g	

and the indicators are 3 and -7.

3. The Tucker tableau is

	x_1	x_2	x_3	-1	
y_1	4	2	-3	1	$= -t_1$
y_2	3	-1	5	4	$= -t_2$
-1	7	-8	1	0	$= f$
	$\|\|$	$\|\|$	$\|\|$	$\|\|$	
	s_1	s_2	s_3	g	

and the indicators are 7, -8, and 1.

5. The Tucker tableau is

	x_1	x_2	x_3	-1	
y_1	2	3	-4	1	$= -t_1$
y_2	1	0	-1	4	$= -t_2$
y_3	6	-5	0	16	$= -t_3$
-1	-5	1	1	0	$= f$
	$\|\|$	$\|\|$	$\|\|$	$\|\|$	
	s_1	s_2	s_3	g	

and the indicators are -5, 1, and 1.

7. We first must rewrite the system of linear inequalities in standard form:

$$3x_1 - 4x_2 + x_3 \leq 2$$
$$x_1 \qquad - 6x_3 \leq 4$$
$$-5x_1 - 4x_2 \qquad \leq 5$$
$$- x_2 + 4x_3 \leq 0$$
$$x_1 \geq 0$$
$$x_2 \geq 0$$
$$x_3 \geq 0$$

The Tucker tableau is

	x_1	x_2	x_3	-1	
y_1	3	-4	1	2	$= -t_1$
y_2	1	0	-6	4	$= -t_2$
y_3	-5	-4	0	5	$= -t_3$
y_4	0	-1	4	0	$= -t_4$
-1	3	1	-6	0	$= f$
	$\parallel$	$\parallel$	$\parallel$	$\parallel$	
	s_1	s_2	s_3	g	

and the indicators are 3, 1, and -6.

9. The standard form for the system of linear inequalities is

$$2y_1 + 5y_2 \geq 7$$
$$-3y_1 + 6y_2 \geq -2$$
$$y_1 + 2y_2 \geq -3$$
$$y_1 \geq 0$$
$$y_2 \geq 0$$

The Tucker tableau is

	x_1	x_2	x_3	-1	
y_1	2	-3	1	5	$= -t_1$
y_2	5	6	2	4	$= -t_2$
-1	7	-2	-3	0	$= f$
	$\parallel$	$\parallel$	$\parallel$	$\parallel$	
	s_1	s_2	s_3	g	

and the indicators are 7, -2, and -3.

11. The Tucker tableaux for both problems are the same:

	x_1	x_2	x_3	x_4	-1	
y_1	2	6	3	-4	3	$= -t_1$
y_2	0	8	-3	1	1	$= -t_2$
y_3	-1	0	4	2	4	$= -t_3$
-1	4	-2	1	5	0	$= f$
	$\parallel$	$\parallel$	$\parallel$	$\parallel$	$\parallel$	
	s_1	s_2	s_3	s_4	g	

and the indicators are 4, -2, 1, and 5.

13. Maximize: $f(x_1, x_2) = -5x_1 + 7x_2$
subject to:

$$2x_1 - 5x_2 \leq 8$$
$$3x_1 + 6x_2 \leq 4$$
$$x_1 \geq 0$$
$$x_2 \geq 0$$

Minimize: $g(y_1, y_2) = 8y_1 + 4y_2$
subject to:

$$2y_1 + 3y_2 \geq -5$$
$$-5y_1 + 6y_2 \geq 7$$
$$y_1 \geq 0$$
$$y_2 \geq 0$$

15. Maximize: $f(x_1, x_2) = 4x_1 + 6x_2$
subject to:

$$\tfrac{1}{4}x_1 - 3x_2 \leq 2$$
$$-5x_1 + \tfrac{2}{3}x_2 \leq 1$$
$$6x_1 - 8x_2 \leq 3$$
$$x_1 \geq 0$$
$$x_2 \geq 0$$

Minimize: $g(y_1, y_2, y_3) = 2y_1 + y_2 + 3y_3$
subject to:

$$\tfrac{1}{4}y_1 - 5y_2 + 6y_3 \geq 4$$
$$-3y_1 + \tfrac{2}{3}y_2 - 8y_3 \geq 6$$
$$y_1 \geq 0$$
$$y_2 \geq 0$$
$$y_3 \geq 0$$

17. Maximize: $f(x_1, x_2, x_3, x_4) = 3x_1 + 2x_2 + 5x_3 - 5x_4$
subject to:

$$\tfrac{3}{4}x_1 + 2x_2 + 6x_3 - 4x_4 \leq 6$$
$$-8x_1 + 3x_2 + x_3 + 5x_4 \leq 4$$
$$x_1 \geq 0$$
$$x_2 \geq 0$$
$$x_3 \geq 0$$
$$x_4 \geq 0$$

Minimize: $g(y_1, y_2) = 6y_1 + 4y_2$
subject to:

$$\tfrac{3}{4}y_1 - 8y_2 \geq 3$$
$$2y_1 + 3y_2 \geq 2$$
$$6y_1 + y_2 \geq 5$$
$$-4y_1 + 5y_2 \geq -5$$
$$y_1 \geq 0$$
$$y_2 \geq 0$$

Exercises for 8.4
1. The maximum value of f is 18 and occurs when $x_1 = 0$, $x_2 = 6$.
3. The maximum value of f is 20 and occurs when $x_1 = 4$, $x_2 = 0$.
5. The maximum value of f is 170 and occurs when $x_1 = 10$, $x_2 = 70$, and $x_3 = 0$.
7. The maximum value of f is 84 and occurs when $x_1 = \tfrac{7}{2}$, $x_2 = 1$, $x_3 = \tfrac{1}{2}$, and $x_4 = 0$.

Exercises for 8.5

1.

	t_2	x_2	-1	
y_1	$-\frac{1}{5}$	$-\frac{28}{5}$	$\frac{7}{5}$	$= -t_1$
s_1	$\frac{1}{5}$	$\frac{8}{5}$	$\frac{3}{5}$	$= -x_1$
-1	$-\frac{4}{5}$	$-\frac{62}{5}$	$-\frac{12}{5}$	$= f$
	$\parallel$	$\parallel$	$\parallel$	
	y_2	s_2	g	

3.

	t_1	x_2	-1	
s_1	$\frac{1}{8}$	$-\frac{1}{4}$	$\frac{1}{8}$	$= -x_1$
y_2	$-\frac{1}{8}$	$\frac{17}{4}$	$\frac{39}{8}$	$= -t_2$
-1	$-\frac{1}{4}$	$-\frac{11}{2}$	$-\frac{1}{4}$	$= f$
	$\parallel$	$\parallel$	$\parallel$	
	y_1	s_2	g	

5.

	x_1	t_2	-1	
y_1	4	$\frac{1}{4}$	$\frac{13}{2}$	$= -t_1$
s_2	2	$\frac{1}{8}$	$\frac{1}{4}$	$= -x_2$
y_3	-2	$-\frac{3}{8}$	$\frac{9}{4}$	$= -t_3$
-1	-13	$-\frac{1}{2}$	-1	$= f$
	$\parallel$	$\parallel$	$\parallel$	
	s_1	y_2	g	

7.

	x_1	t_3	x_3	-1	
y_1	$\frac{5}{4}$	-2	-4	$\frac{3}{4}$	$= -t_1$
y_2	-6	12	$\frac{99}{4}$	$\frac{7}{2}$	$= -t_2$
s_2	-2	4	8	$\frac{1}{2}$	$= -x_2$
-1	12	-20	$-\frac{161}{4}$	$-\frac{5}{2}$	$= f$
	$\parallel$	$\parallel$	$\parallel$	$\parallel$	
	s_1	y_3	s_3	g	

9.

	x_1	t_3	-1	
y_1	$\frac{3}{16}$	$-\frac{1}{4}$	$\frac{15}{16}$	$= -t_1$
y_2	$-\frac{5}{4}$	2	$\frac{5}{2}$	$= -t_2$
s_2	$-\frac{3}{2}$	2	$\frac{1}{2}$	$= -x_2$
y_4	4	-4	3	$= -t_4$
-1	$\frac{9}{2}$	-2	$-\frac{1}{2}$	$= f$

$$\begin{array}{ccc} \| & \| & \| \\ s_1 & y_3 & g \end{array}$$

Exercises for 8.6

1. maximum value is 30 and occurs when $x_1 = 5$ and $x_2 = 0$
3. minimum value is 16 and occurs when $y_1 = 4$ and $y_2 = 2$
5. minimum value is 8 and occurs when $y_1 = 0$ and $y_2 = 4$
7. minimum value is 17 and occurs when $y_1 = 1$ and $y_2 = 3$
9. maximum value is $\frac{279}{2}$ and occurs when $x_1 = 9$, $x_2 = \frac{27}{2}$, and $x_3 = \frac{9}{2}$
11. minimum value is $\frac{176}{3}$ and occurs when $y_1 = \frac{14}{9}$, $y_2 = \frac{8}{9}$, and $y_3 = 0$
13. no solution
15. maximum value is $\frac{33}{4}$ and occurs when $x_1 = \frac{15}{4}$ and $x_2 = \frac{3}{4}$; minimum value is $\frac{33}{4}$ and occurs when $y_1 = \frac{7}{12}$ and $y_2 = \frac{1}{12}$
17. maximum value is 13 and occurs when $x_1 = 1$ and $x_2 = 5$; minimum value is 13 and occurs when $y_1 = \frac{13}{6}$, $y_2 = 0$, and $y_3 = \frac{1}{6}$
19. maximum value is 170 and occurs when $x_1 = 10$, $x_2 = 70$, and $x_3 = 0$; minimum value is 170 and occurs when $y_1 = \frac{1}{4}$ and $y_2 = 2$
21. maximum value is 1,480 and occurs when $x_1 = 14$, $x_2 = 0$, and $x_3 = 5$; minimum value is 1,480 and occurs when $y_1 = 1$, $y_2 = \frac{20}{3}$, and $y_3 = 0$
23. maximum value is $\frac{166}{19}$ and occurs when $x_1 = \frac{16}{19}$, $x_2 = 0$, $x_3 = 0$, and $x_4 = \frac{5}{19}$; minimum value is $\frac{166}{19}$ and occurs when $y_1 = \frac{53}{57}$, $y_2 = 0$, and $y_3 = \frac{1}{19}$

Exercises for 8.7

1. (a) The restaurant should prepare 90 steak dinners and 60 lobster dinners.
   (b) The restaurant should prepare 110 steak dinners and 40 lobster dinners.
3. The manufacturer should produce 75 of the XL-25, none of the XL-40, and 25 of the XL-85 per week.
7. (1) Factory I should be operational 4 days and factory II 2 days per week.
   (2) Factory I should be inoperative and factory II should be operated 7 days per week.
   (3) same as in (1)
9. The diet should consist of $\frac{1}{2}$ pound of meat, 1 pound of salad, and no bread per day.
11. The manufacturer should purchase 1,300 units of item I, 0 units of item II, 0 units of item III, and 250 units of item IV per month.

Chapter 9

Exercises for 9.1

1. (a) Given the total number of heads tossed up to and including a given time, the total number of heads tossed up to and including the next time period is independent of the total number of heads tossed at past times.
   (b) (1) $\frac{1}{2}$ (2) $\frac{1}{2}$
       (3) 0   (4) 0

3. (a) (1) 0
      (2) 1
   (b) (1) $\frac{1}{2}$
      (2) $\frac{1}{2}$
      (3) 0
5. (a) yes
   (b) (1) $\frac{1}{2}$
      (2) 0
      (3) $\frac{1}{2}$
   (c) (1) 1
      (2) 0
      (3) 0
7. yes
9. The future state of the system depends not only on the present state of the system but also on past states. For example, suppose that the present state of the system is H. Then the probability that the state of the system at the next time period is H is equal to $\frac{1}{2}$ if all previous states of the system were H and is equal to $\frac{1}{3}$ if at any previous time the state of the system was T.
11. The future state of the system depends not only on the present state of the system but also on past states. For example, suppose that the state of the system at time 50 is F (female). If the states of the system from times 1–49 have always been F, the probability that the state of the system at time 51 is M is .5 ($= \frac{100}{200}$). On the other hand, if the states of the system from times 1–49 have always been M, the probability that the state of the system at time 51 is M is .255 ($= \frac{51}{200}$).

Exercises for 9.2

1. (a) .6   (b) .1
  (c) .1   (d) .7

3. $p_{00} = 0$, $p_{01} = 1$, $p_{02} = 0$, $p_{03} = 0$, $p_{04} = 0$
   $p_{10} = \frac{1}{4}$, $p_{11} = 0$, $p_{12} = \frac{3}{4}$, $p_{13} = 0$, $p_{14} = 0$
   $p_{20} = 0$, $p_{21} = \frac{1}{2}$, $p_{22} = 0$, $p_{23} = \frac{1}{2}$, $p_{24} = 0$
   $p_{30} = 0$, $p_{31} = 0$, $p_{32} = \frac{3}{4}$, $p_{33} = 0$, $p_{34} = \frac{1}{4}$
   $p_{40} = 0$, $p_{41} = 0$, $p_{42} = 0$, $p_{43} = 1$, $p_{44} = 0$

5. $p_{11} = 0$, $p_{12} = 1$, $p_{13} = 0$
   $p_{21} = 0$, $p_{22} = 0$, $p_{23} = 1$
   $p_{31} = \frac{1}{2}$, $p_{32} = \frac{1}{2}$, $p_{33} = 0$

7. (a) $p_{00} = 0$, $p_{01} = 1$, $p_{02} = 0$, $p_{03} = 0$
      $p_{10} = \frac{1}{9}$, $p_{11} = \frac{4}{9}$, $p_{12} = \frac{4}{9}$, $p_{13} = 0$
      $p_{20} = 0$, $p_{21} = \frac{4}{9}$, $p_{22} = \frac{4}{9}$, $p_{23} = \frac{1}{9}$
      $p_{30} = 0$, $p_{31} = 0$, $p_{32} = 1$, $p_{33} = 0$

   (b)

Next State

	State	0	1	2	3
	0	0	1	0	0
Present State	1	$\frac{1}{9}$	$\frac{4}{9}$	$\frac{4}{9}$	0
	2	0	$\frac{4}{9}$	$\frac{4}{9}$	$\frac{1}{9}$
	3	0	0	1	0

9. $p_{11} = .3,$ $\quad p_{12} = .15,$ $\quad p_{13} = .05,$ $\quad p_{14} = .5$
$p_{21} = .05,$ $\quad p_{22} = .4,$ $\quad p_{23} = .05,$ $\quad p_{24} = .5$
$p_{31} = .05,$ $\quad p_{32} = .1,$ $\quad p_{33} = .35,$ $\quad p_{34} = .5$
$p_{41} = 0,$ $\quad p_{42} = 0,$ $\quad p_{43} = 0,$ $\quad p_{44} = 1$

11. $p_{00} = 0,$ $\quad p_{01} = \frac{1}{4},$ $\quad p_{02} = \frac{1}{4},$ $\quad p_{03} = \frac{1}{4},$ $\quad p_{04} = \frac{1}{4}$
$p_{10} = \frac{1}{3},$ $\quad p_{11} = \frac{1}{3},$ $\quad p_{12} = \frac{1}{3},$ $\quad p_{13} = 0,$ $\quad p_{14} = 0$
$p_{20} = 0,$ $\quad p_{21} = \frac{1}{3},$ $\quad p_{22} = \frac{1}{3},$ $\quad p_{23} = \frac{1}{3},$ $\quad p_{24} = 0$
$p_{30} = 0,$ $\quad p_{31} = 0,$ $\quad p_{32} = \frac{1}{3},$ $\quad p_{33} = \frac{1}{3},$ $\quad p_{34} = \frac{1}{3}$
$p_{40} = \frac{1}{4},$ $\quad p_{41} = \frac{1}{4},$ $\quad p_{42} = \frac{1}{4},$ $\quad p_{43} = \frac{1}{4},$ $\quad p_{44} = 0$

13.
$$p_{ij} = \begin{cases} i/d & \text{if } j = i - 1 \\ (d - i)/d & \text{if } j = i + 1 \\ 0 & \text{otherwise} \end{cases}$$

Exercises for 9.3

1. (a) $\frac{1}{4}$ (b) 0
   (c) $\frac{1}{4}$ (d) $\frac{3}{16}$

3.

$$\begin{array}{c} \\ 1 \\ 2 \end{array} \begin{array}{cc} 1 & 2 \\ \left[\begin{matrix} \frac{1}{3} & \frac{2}{3} \\ \frac{1}{8} & \frac{7}{8} \end{matrix}\right] \end{array}$$

5.

$$\begin{array}{c} \\ 1 \\ 2 \\ 3 \end{array} \begin{array}{ccc} 1 & 2 & 3 \\ \left[\begin{matrix} 0 & 1 & 0 \\ 0 & 0 & 1 \\ \frac{1}{2} & \frac{1}{2} & 0 \end{matrix}\right] \end{array}$$

7.

$$\begin{array}{c} \\ 0 \\ 1 \\ 2 \\ 3 \\ 4 \end{array} \begin{array}{ccccc} 0 & 1 & 2 & 3 & 4 \\ \left[\begin{matrix} 0 & 1 & 0 & 0 & 0 \\ \frac{1}{4} & 0 & \frac{3}{4} & 0 & 0 \\ 0 & \frac{1}{2} & 0 & \frac{1}{2} & 0 \\ 0 & 0 & \frac{3}{4} & 0 & \frac{1}{4} \\ 0 & 0 & 0 & 1 & 0 \end{matrix}\right] \end{array}$$

9.

$$\begin{array}{c} \\ 1 \\ 2 \\ 3 \\ 4 \\ 5 \\ 6 \end{array} \begin{array}{cccccc} 1 & 2 & 3 & 4 & 5 & 6 \\ \left[\begin{matrix} \frac{1}{6} & \frac{1}{6} & \frac{1}{6} & \frac{1}{6} & \frac{1}{6} & \frac{1}{6} \\ 0 & \frac{1}{3} & \frac{1}{6} & \frac{1}{6} & \frac{1}{6} & \frac{1}{6} \\ 0 & 0 & \frac{1}{2} & \frac{1}{6} & \frac{1}{6} & \frac{1}{6} \\ 0 & 0 & 0 & \frac{2}{3} & \frac{1}{6} & \frac{1}{6} \\ 0 & 0 & 0 & 0 & \frac{5}{6} & \frac{1}{6} \\ 0 & 0 & 0 & 0 & 0 & 1 \end{matrix}\right] \end{array}$$

11. $\frac{1}{4}$

13. (a) and (h)

15.

$$\begin{array}{c} \\ 1 \\ 2 \\ 3 \\ 4 \end{array} \begin{array}{cccc} 1 & 2 & 3 & 4 \\ \left[\begin{matrix} .30 & .15 & .05 & .50 \\ .05 & .40 & .05 & .50 \\ .05 & .10 & .35 & .50 \\ 0 & 0 & 0 & 1 \end{matrix}\right] \end{array}$$

Exercises for 9.4

1. (a) $\frac{2}{3}$ (b) 0
   (c) $\frac{7}{9}$ (d) $\frac{2}{9}$
   (e) $\frac{1}{3}$ (f) 0

3. $P^{(2)} = \begin{bmatrix} 1 & 0 \\ 0 & 1 \end{bmatrix}$

5. (a) $\begin{bmatrix} p^2 & 1 - p^2 \\ 0 & 1 \end{bmatrix}$

7. (a) $\begin{bmatrix} \frac{7}{36} & \frac{29}{36} \\ \frac{29}{192} & \frac{163}{192} \end{bmatrix}$

   (b) $\frac{29}{192} \doteq .151$

9. (a) $\begin{bmatrix} 1 & 0 & 0 \\ \frac{1}{2} & \frac{1}{3} & \frac{1}{6} \\ \frac{1}{3} & \frac{2}{9} & \frac{4}{9} \end{bmatrix}$

   (b) $\frac{1}{3}$
   (c) $\frac{1}{3}$

11. $\begin{bmatrix} 1 & 0 & 0 \\ \frac{2}{3} & \frac{1}{6} & \frac{1}{6} \\ \frac{1}{6} & \frac{1}{3} & \frac{1}{2} \end{bmatrix}$

13. $\begin{bmatrix} \frac{1}{4} & 0 & \frac{3}{4} & 0 & 0 \\ 0 & \frac{5}{8} & 0 & \frac{3}{8} & 0 \\ \frac{1}{8} & 0 & \frac{3}{4} & 0 & \frac{1}{8} \\ 0 & \frac{3}{8} & 0 & \frac{5}{8} & 0 \\ 0 & 0 & \frac{3}{4} & 0 & \frac{1}{4} \end{bmatrix}$

15. $P^{(2)} = P^2 = PP$, so $P^{(2)}$ is a 3×3 matrix. By problem 14, Exercises 9.3, it follows that $P^{(2)} = PP$ is stochastic because P is.

17. $P^{(2)} = [p_{ij}^{(2)}]$, where

$$p_{ij}^{(2)} = \begin{cases} (i^2 - i)/d^2 & \text{if } j = i - 2 \\ (2id - 2i^2 + d)/d^2 & \text{if } j = i \\ (d^2 - 2id + i^2 - d + i)/d^2 & \text{if } j = i + 2 \\ 0 & \text{otherwise} \end{cases}$$

Exercises for 9.5

1. (a) $\frac{7}{9}$ (b) 0
   (c) $\frac{7}{27}$ (d) 0
   (e) $\frac{20}{27}$ (f) $\frac{7}{9}$

3. (a) .54444   (b) .19375
   (c) .23056   (d) .30832
   (Answers given to five decimal places.)

5. (a) $\begin{bmatrix} 1 & 0 \\ 0 & 1 \end{bmatrix}$ (b) $\begin{bmatrix} 1 & 0 \\ 0 & 1 \end{bmatrix}$

7. (a) $\begin{bmatrix} p^3 & 1 - p^3 \\ 0 & 1 \end{bmatrix}$ (b) $\begin{bmatrix} p^n & 1 - p^n \\ 0 & 1 \end{bmatrix}$

9. (a) $\begin{bmatrix} .781 & .219 \\ .438 & .562 \end{bmatrix}$ (b) .219

11. (a)
$$\begin{bmatrix} \dfrac{1{,}601}{5{,}400} & \dfrac{1{,}893}{5{,}400} & \dfrac{1{,}906}{5{,}400} \\[2mm] \dfrac{701}{2{,}250} & \dfrac{743}{2{,}250} & \dfrac{806}{2{,}250} \\[2mm] \dfrac{827}{2{,}700} & \dfrac{911}{2{,}700} & \dfrac{962}{2{,}700} \end{bmatrix}$$

(b) $\dfrac{1{,}601}{5{,}400} \doteq .296$

13. (a) $\begin{bmatrix} 1 & 0 \\ \frac{7}{8} & \frac{1}{8} \end{bmatrix}$

(b) $\begin{bmatrix} 1 & 0 \\ 1 - \dfrac{1}{2^n} & \dfrac{1}{2^n} \end{bmatrix}$

15. (a) $\begin{bmatrix} 0 & \frac{1}{2} & \frac{1}{2} \\ \frac{1}{3} & \frac{1}{3} & \frac{1}{3} \\ \frac{1}{4} & \frac{1}{2} & \frac{1}{4} \end{bmatrix}$

(b)
$$P^{(2)} = \begin{bmatrix} \frac{7}{24} & \frac{5}{12} & \frac{7}{24} \\ \frac{7}{36} & \frac{4}{9} & \frac{13}{36} \\ \frac{11}{48} & \frac{5}{12} & \frac{17}{48} \end{bmatrix}$$

$$P^{(3)} = \begin{bmatrix} \frac{61}{288} & \frac{124}{288} & \frac{103}{288} \\ \frac{103}{432} & \frac{184}{432} & \frac{145}{432} \\ \frac{131}{576} & \frac{248}{576} & \frac{197}{576} \end{bmatrix}$$

(c) $\frac{5}{12} \doteq .417$

(d) $\frac{145}{432} \doteq .336$

Exercises for 9.6

1. $\frac{181}{640} \doteq .283$
3. (a) $\frac{1}{8}$ (b) $\frac{7}{8}$
5. $\frac{3}{7}$
7. $\frac{5}{12}$
9. $\frac{89}{200} = .445$
11. approximately 64 percent

Exercises for 9.7

1. $[\frac{9}{10}, \frac{1}{10}]$
3. .3352
5. (a) $[p^2/2, 1 - p^2/2]$
  (b) $[p^3/2, 1 - p^3/2]$
  (c) $[p^n/2, 1 - p^n/2]$
7. (a) $[\frac{1}{3}, \frac{1}{3}, \frac{1}{3}]$
  (b) $\frac{11}{24}$
  (c) $\frac{1}{4}$
9. $\frac{13}{81} \doteq .160$
11. (a) $\frac{1}{4}$ (b) $\frac{1}{24}$
13. $\frac{16}{729} \doteq .022$

Exercises for 9.8

1. $[\frac{1}{2}, \frac{1}{2}]$
3. $[\frac{49}{149}, \frac{100}{149}] \doteq [.329, .671]$

Exercises for 9.9

1. (a), (b), and (g) are regular; the others are not regular.
3. no
5. no
7. (a), (c), and (d) are probability vectors; (b) is not.

9. (a) $VP = [v_1 p_{11} + v_2 p_{21}, v_1 p_{12} + v_2 p_{22}]$

Since the v_is and p_{ij}s are nonnegative, it follows (see Appendix A) that the entries of VP are nonnegative. Also, we have

$$(v_1 p_{11} + v_2 p_{21}) + (v_1 p_{12} + v_2 p_{22})$$
$$= v_1(p_{11} + p_{12}) + v_2(p_{21} + p_{22})$$
$$= v_1 \cdot 1 + v_2 \cdot 1 = v_1 + v_2 = 1$$

so VP is a probability vector.

(b) If P is an $N \times N$ transition matrix and V is a probability vector of length N, then VP is a probability vector of length N.

11. First note that since V is a fixed vector and $\lambda \neq 0$, λV is a nonzero vector. Also,

$$(\lambda V)A = \lambda(VA) = \lambda(V) = \lambda V$$

so λV is a fixed vector for A.

13. (a) Note that $p_{22} = 1$. This means that the probability of going from 2 to 2 in one transition is equal to 1. That is, if the chain is ever in state 2, it remains there. So $p_{22}^{(n)} = 1$ for all n. But since P^n is stochastic, this implies that $p_{21}^{(n)} = 0$ for all n. Hence P is not regular.

(b) $[0, 1]$ is the unique fixed probability vector.

Exercises for 9.10

1. $[\frac{1}{3}, \frac{2}{3}]$

3. $[\frac{4}{15}, \frac{2}{5}, \frac{1}{3}]$

5. (a) 1 2
$[\frac{8}{23}, \frac{15}{23}]$

where 1 corresponds to studying and 2 corresponds to not studying

(b) about 35 percent of the time

7. (a) 1 2
$[\frac{1}{3}, \frac{2}{3}]$

where 1 corresponds to eating steak and 2 corresponds to not eating steak

(b) $33\frac{1}{3}$ percent of the time

9. (a) 1 2
$[\frac{8}{13}, \frac{5}{13}]$

where 1 corresponds to drinking Scotch and 2 to drinking bourbon

(b) about 62 percent of the time

11. (a) W L D
$[\frac{10}{37}, \frac{12}{37}, \frac{15}{37}]$

where W = win, L = lose, D = draw

(b) In the long run he wins about 27 percent of the time, loses about 32 percent of the time, and breaks even about 41 percent of the time.

13. (a) 1 2
$[\frac{1}{3}, \frac{2}{3}]$

where 1 corresponds to driving and 2 corresponds to riding the bus

(b) In the long run he rides the bus about 67 percent of the time and drives about 33 percent of the time.

15. (a) F C D
$[\frac{39}{91}, \frac{28}{91}, \frac{24}{91}]$

(b) In the long run he leases a Ford about 43 percent of the time, a Chevrolet about 31 percent of the time, and a Dodge about 26 percent of the time.

17. (a) The equilibrium distribution for a regular Markov chain is the unique probability vector V satisfying $VP = V$. Now, $V = [\frac{1}{3}, \frac{1}{3}, \frac{1}{3}]$ is a probability vector. Moreover,

$$VP = [\tfrac{1}{3}, \tfrac{1}{3}, \tfrac{1}{3}] \begin{bmatrix} p_{11} & p_{12} & p_{13} \\ p_{21} & p_{22} & p_{23} \\ p_{31} & p_{32} & p_{33} \end{bmatrix}$$

$$= [\tfrac{1}{3}p_{11} + \tfrac{1}{3}p_{21} + \tfrac{1}{3}p_{31}, \tfrac{1}{3}p_{12} + \tfrac{1}{3}p_{22} + \tfrac{1}{3}p_{32}, \tfrac{1}{3}p_{13} + \tfrac{1}{3}p_{23} + \tfrac{1}{3}p_{33}]$$

$$= [\tfrac{1}{3}(p_{11} + p_{21} + p_{31}), \tfrac{1}{3}(p_{12} + p_{22} + p_{32}), \tfrac{1}{3}(p_{13} + p_{23} + p_{33})]$$

Since the column sums equal 1, by assumption, we see that

$$VP = [\tfrac{1}{3}, \tfrac{1}{3}, \tfrac{1}{3}] = V$$

Hence V is the equilibrium distribution for the Markov chain.

(b) The equilibrium distribution for a regular Markov chain whose transition matrix is doubly stochastic and $N \times N$ is given by the following row vector of length N:

$$V = [1/N, 1/N, \ldots, 1/N]$$

Exercises for 9.11

1. States 2 and 5 are absorbing.
3. (a), (b), (c), (d), and (f)
5. (a) 0 and 4+, where 4+ stands for the state where the total capital of the gambler is at least \$4.
   (b) yes
7. (a) yes   (b) yes
9. $p = 0$ or $q = 0$ (or both)

Exercises for 9.12

1. (a) State 2 is absorbing and since $p_{12} = \frac{1}{4} > 0$ and $p_{32} = \frac{1}{3} > 0$, it is possible to go from each nonabsorbing state to the absorbing state 2. Hence P is the transition matrix for an absorbing Markov chain.

   (b) The canonical matrix is

$$P* = \begin{array}{c} \\ 2 \\ 1 \\ 3 \end{array} \begin{array}{ccc} 2 & 1 & 3 \\ \begin{bmatrix} 1 & 0 & 0 \\ \frac{1}{4} & \frac{1}{4} & \frac{1}{2} \\ \frac{1}{3} & \frac{1}{3} & \frac{1}{3} \end{bmatrix} \end{array}$$

   and

$$Q = \begin{bmatrix} \frac{1}{4} & \frac{1}{2} \\ \frac{1}{3} & \frac{1}{3} \end{bmatrix}$$

3. (a) The canonical matrix is

$$P* = \begin{array}{c} \\ 2 \\ 5 \\ 1 \\ 3 \\ 4 \end{array} \begin{array}{ccccc} 2 & 5 & 1 & 3 & 4 \\ \begin{bmatrix} 1 & 0 & 0 & 0 & 0 \\ 0 & 1 & 0 & 0 & 0 \\ 0 & 0 & \frac{1}{3} & \frac{2}{3} & 0 \\ 0 & 0 & \frac{1}{2} & \frac{1}{4} & \frac{1}{4} \\ 1 & 0 & 0 & 0 & 0 \end{bmatrix} \end{array}$$

   and

$$Q = \begin{bmatrix} \frac{1}{3} & \frac{2}{3} & 0 \\ \frac{1}{2} & \frac{1}{4} & \frac{1}{4} \\ 0 & 0 & 0 \end{bmatrix}$$

(b)
$$F = \begin{bmatrix} \frac{9}{2} & 4 & 1 \\ 3 & 4 & 1 \\ 0 & 0 & 1 \end{bmatrix}$$

5. (a) The transition matrix is

$$P = \begin{array}{c} \\ 0 \\ 1 \\ 2 \\ 3 \\ 4 \end{array}\begin{array}{c} \begin{array}{ccccc} 0 & 1 & 2 & 3 & 4 \end{array} \\ \begin{bmatrix} 1 & 0 & 0 & 0 & 0 \\ \frac{2}{3} & 0 & \frac{1}{3} & 0 & 0 \\ 0 & \frac{2}{3} & 0 & \frac{1}{3} & 0 \\ 0 & 0 & \frac{2}{3} & 0 & \frac{1}{3} \\ 0 & 0 & 0 & 0 & 1 \end{bmatrix} \end{array}$$

The states 0 and 4 are absorbing and from each nonabsorbing state it is possible to reach 0 and 4. Hence the Markov chain is absorbing.

(b) The canonical matrix is

$$P* = \begin{array}{c} \\ 0 \\ 4 \\ 1 \\ 2 \\ 3 \end{array}\begin{array}{c} \begin{array}{ccccc} 0 & 4 & 1 & 2 & 3 \end{array} \\ \begin{bmatrix} 1 & 0 & 0 & 0 & 0 \\ 0 & 1 & 0 & 0 & 0 \\ \frac{2}{3} & 0 & 0 & \frac{1}{3} & 0 \\ 0 & 0 & \frac{2}{3} & 0 & \frac{1}{3} \\ 0 & \frac{1}{3} & 0 & \frac{2}{3} & 0 \end{bmatrix} \end{array}$$

and

$$Q = \begin{bmatrix} 0 & \frac{1}{3} & 0 \\ \frac{2}{3} & 0 & \frac{1}{3} \\ 0 & \frac{2}{3} & 0 \end{bmatrix}$$

(c)
$$F = \begin{bmatrix} \frac{7}{5} & \frac{3}{5} & \frac{1}{5} \\ \frac{6}{5} & \frac{9}{5} & \frac{3}{5} \\ \frac{4}{5} & \frac{6}{5} & \frac{7}{5} \end{bmatrix}$$

7. (a)

$$P = \begin{array}{c} \\ 1 \\ 2 \\ 3 \\ 4 \\ 5 \\ 6 \end{array}\begin{array}{c} \begin{array}{cccccc} 1 & 2 & 3 & 4 & 5 & 6 \end{array} \\ \begin{bmatrix} 1 & 0 & 0 & 0 & 0 & 0 \\ 0 & 1 & 0 & 0 & 0 & 0 \\ \frac{1}{5} & \frac{7}{10} & \frac{1}{10} & 0 & 0 & 0 \\ \frac{1}{5} & 0 & \frac{7}{10} & \frac{1}{10} & 0 & 0 \\ \frac{1}{5} & 0 & 0 & \frac{7}{10} & \frac{1}{10} & 0 \\ \frac{1}{5} & 0 & 0 & 0 & \frac{7}{10} & \frac{1}{10} \end{bmatrix} \end{array}$$

(b) States 1 and 2 are absorbing and from each nonabsorbing state it is possible to go to state 2 (and also to state 1). Thus the Markov chain is absorbing.

(c) The canonical matrix is

$$P* = \begin{array}{c} \\ 1 \\ 2 \\ 3 \\ 4 \\ 5 \\ 6 \end{array}\begin{array}{c} \begin{array}{cccccc} 1 & 2 & 3 & 4 & 5 & 6 \end{array} \\ \begin{bmatrix} 1 & 0 & 0 & 0 & 0 & 0 \\ 0 & 1 & 0 & 0 & 0 & 0 \\ \frac{1}{5} & \frac{7}{10} & \frac{1}{10} & 0 & 0 & 0 \\ \frac{1}{5} & 0 & \frac{7}{10} & \frac{1}{10} & 0 & 0 \\ \frac{1}{5} & 0 & 0 & \frac{7}{10} & \frac{1}{10} & 0 \\ \frac{1}{5} & 0 & 0 & 0 & \frac{7}{10} & \frac{1}{10} \end{bmatrix} \end{array}$$

and

$$Q = \begin{bmatrix} \frac{1}{10} & 0 & 0 & 0 \\ \frac{7}{10} & \frac{1}{10} & 0 & 0 \\ 0 & \frac{7}{10} & \frac{1}{10} & 0 \\ 0 & 0 & \frac{7}{10} & \frac{1}{10} \end{bmatrix}$$

(d)

$$F = \begin{bmatrix} \frac{10}{9} & 0 & 0 & 0 \\ \frac{70}{81} & \frac{10}{9} & 0 & 0 \\ \frac{490}{729} & \frac{70}{81} & \frac{10}{9} & 0 \\ \frac{3,430}{6,561} & \frac{490}{729} & \frac{70}{81} & \frac{10}{9} \end{bmatrix}$$

Exercises for 9.13

1.   1   3

   2 $[\frac{1}{2} \quad \frac{1}{2}]$

3. (a)   2   4

   $\begin{array}{c} 1 \\ 3 \end{array} \begin{bmatrix} \frac{2}{5} & \frac{3}{5} \\ \frac{1}{5} & \frac{4}{5} \end{bmatrix}$

   (b) $\frac{4}{5}$

   (c) $\frac{2}{5}$

5. (a) $\frac{7}{31}$

   (b) $\frac{28}{31}$

   (c) $\frac{15}{31}$

7. (a)   1   2

   $A = \begin{array}{c} 3 \\ 4 \\ 5 \\ 6 \end{array} \begin{bmatrix} \frac{2}{9} & \frac{7}{9} \\ \frac{32}{81} & \frac{49}{81} \\ \frac{386}{729} & \frac{343}{729} \\ \frac{4,160}{6,561} & \frac{2,401}{6,561} \end{bmatrix}$

   (b) $\frac{4,160}{6,561} \doteq .634$

   (c) $\frac{343}{729} \doteq .470$

   (d) junior year

Chapter 10

Exercises for 10.1

1. (a) (1) $\frac{1}{2}$ (2) $\frac{1}{2}$

   (b) The offspring must be (1) H, (2) D, (3) R.

3. (a)   D   H   R

   $P^3 = \begin{array}{c} D \\ H \\ R \end{array} \begin{bmatrix} \frac{5}{16} & \frac{1}{2} & \frac{3}{16} \\ \frac{1}{4} & \frac{1}{2} & \frac{1}{4} \\ \frac{3}{16} & \frac{1}{2} & \frac{5}{16} \end{bmatrix}$

   (b) (1) $\frac{1}{4}$

       (2) $\frac{1}{2}$

       (3) $\frac{1}{4}$

5. (a) $\Pi^{(0)} = [\frac{1}{4}, 0, \frac{3}{4}]$

   (b) (1) $\frac{3}{16}$

       (2) $\frac{1}{2}$

       (3) $\frac{5}{16}$

   (c) $\Pi^{(3)} = [\frac{7}{32}, \frac{1}{2}, \frac{9}{32}]$

7. (a)

$$P = \begin{array}{c} \\ D \\ H \\ R \end{array}\begin{array}{c} D \quad H \quad R \end{array} \begin{bmatrix} 0 & 1 & 0 \\ 0 & \frac{1}{2} & \frac{1}{2} \\ 0 & 0 & 1 \end{bmatrix}$$

(b)

$$P^2 = \begin{array}{c} \\ D \\ H \\ R \end{array}\begin{array}{c} D \quad H \quad R \end{array} \begin{bmatrix} 0 & \frac{1}{2} & \frac{1}{2} \\ 0 & \frac{1}{4} & \frac{3}{4} \\ 0 & 0 & 1 \end{bmatrix}$$

$$P^3 = \begin{array}{c} \\ D \\ H \\ R \end{array}\begin{array}{c} D \quad H \quad R \end{array} \begin{bmatrix} 0 & \frac{1}{4} & \frac{3}{4} \\ 0 & \frac{1}{8} & \frac{7}{8} \\ 0 & 0 & 1 \end{bmatrix}$$

(c) R is an absorbing state and it is possible to go from either D or H to R.

(d) (1) 0

   (2) $\frac{1}{4}$

   (3) $\frac{3}{4}$

(e) (1) 0

   (2) $\frac{1}{10}$

   (3) $\frac{9}{10}$

9. (a)

$$P^* = \begin{array}{c} \\ 1 \\ 6 \\ 2 \\ 3 \\ 4 \\ 5 \end{array} \begin{array}{c} 1 \quad\; 6 \quad\; 2 \quad\; 3 \quad\; 4 \quad\; 5 \end{array} \begin{bmatrix} 1 & 0 & 0 & 0 & 0 & 0 \\ 0 & 1 & 0 & 0 & 0 & 0 \\ \frac{1}{4} & 0 & \frac{1}{2} & 0 & \frac{1}{4} & 0 \\ 0 & 0 & 0 & 0 & 1 & 0 \\ \frac{1}{16} & \frac{1}{16} & \frac{1}{4} & \frac{1}{8} & \frac{1}{4} & \frac{1}{4} \\ 0 & \frac{1}{4} & 0 & 0 & \frac{1}{4} & \frac{1}{2} \end{bmatrix}$$

(b)

$$F = \begin{bmatrix} \frac{8}{3} & \frac{1}{6} & \frac{4}{3} & \frac{2}{3} \\ \frac{4}{3} & \frac{4}{3} & \frac{8}{3} & \frac{4}{3} \\ \frac{4}{3} & \frac{1}{3} & \frac{8}{3} & \frac{4}{3} \\ \frac{2}{3} & \frac{1}{6} & \frac{4}{3} & \frac{8}{3} \end{bmatrix}$$

(c)

$$A = \begin{array}{c} \\ 2 \\ 3 \\ 4 \\ 5 \end{array} \begin{array}{c} 1 \quad\; 6 \end{array} \begin{bmatrix} \frac{3}{4} & \frac{1}{4} \\ \frac{1}{2} & \frac{1}{2} \\ \frac{1}{2} & \frac{1}{2} \\ \frac{1}{4} & \frac{3}{4} \end{bmatrix}$$

(d) $\frac{1}{4}$

Exercises for 10.2

1. (a) $d_1 = \frac{81}{256}$, $h_1 = \frac{126}{256}$, $r_1 = \frac{49}{256}$ (b) The same as in part (a).

3. $d_0 = 1$, $h_0 = 0$, $r_0 = 0$ is one possibility. Another possibility is $d_0 = \frac{1}{4}$, $h_0 = \frac{1}{2}$, $r_0 = \frac{1}{4}$.

5. We have by problem 4 that

$$d_2 = [d_1 + (h_1/2)]^2$$

$$= \left[\left(d_0 + \frac{h_0}{2}\right)^2 + \left\{2\left(d_0 + \frac{h_0}{2}\right)\left(r_0 + \frac{h_0}{2}\right)\right\}/2\right]^2$$

$$= \left[\left(d_0 + \frac{h_0}{2}\right)\left\{\left(d_0 + \frac{h_0}{2}\right) + \left(r_0 + \frac{h_0}{2}\right)\right\}\right]^2$$

$$= \left[\left(d_0 + \frac{h_0}{2}\right)(d_0 + h_0 + r_0)\right]^2$$

$$= \left[\left(d_0 + \frac{h_0}{2}\right) \cdot 1\right]^2 = [d_0 + (h_0/2)]^2 = d_1$$

Similar arguments show that $h_2 = h_1$ and $r_2 = r_1$.

Exercises for 10.3

1. (a)

$$
\begin{array}{c c}
& \begin{array}{ccccc} 0 & 1 & 2 & 3 & 4 \end{array} \\
\begin{array}{c} 0 \\ 1 \\ 2 \\ 3 \\ 4 \end{array} &
\left[\begin{array}{ccccc}
\frac{2}{5} & \frac{3}{5} & 0 & 0 & 0 \\
\frac{3}{10} & \frac{11}{20} & \frac{3}{20} & 0 & 0 \\
0 & \frac{3}{10} & \frac{11}{20} & \frac{3}{20} & 0 \\
0 & 0 & \frac{3}{10} & \frac{11}{20} & \frac{3}{20} \\
0 & 0 & 0 & \frac{3}{4} & \frac{1}{4}
\end{array}\right]
\end{array}
$$

The equilibrium distribution is

$$V = [\tfrac{5}{23}, \tfrac{10}{23}, \tfrac{5}{23}, \tfrac{5}{46}, \tfrac{1}{46}]$$
$$\doteq [.217, .435, .217, .109, .022]$$

(b) approximately 21.7 percent of the time
(c) approximately 2.2 percent of the time

Exercises for 10.4

1. (a)

$$P = \begin{array}{c} 1 \\ 2 \end{array}\begin{array}{c} \begin{array}{cc} 1 & 2 \end{array} \\ \left[\begin{array}{cc} 1 & 0 \\ .2 & .8 \end{array}\right] \end{array}$$

(b) State 1 is absorbing and it is possible to go from the nonabsorbing state 2 to the absorbing state 1. Hence the Markov chain is absorbing.

(c) 1   2
[0, 1]

(d) .5904

3. (a)

$$P = \begin{array}{c} 1 \\ 2 \end{array}\begin{array}{c} \begin{array}{cc} 1 & 2 \end{array} \\ \left[\begin{array}{cc} 1 & 0 \\ .4 & .6 \end{array}\right] \end{array}$$

(b) 1   2
[0, 1]

(c) $.92224 \doteq .92$

5. 7

Exercises for 10.5

1. (a)

$$
\begin{array}{c} \\ 1 \\ P = 2 \\ 3 \end{array}
\begin{array}{ccc} 1 & 2 & 3 \\ \begin{bmatrix} 1 & 0 & 0 \\ \frac{1}{2} & \frac{1}{3} & \frac{1}{6} \\ \frac{1}{2} & \frac{1}{3} & \frac{1}{6} \end{bmatrix} \end{array}
$$

(b)

$$
\begin{array}{c} \quad\quad\quad 1\ 2\ 3 \\ \Pi^{(0)} = [0, \tfrac{2}{3}, \tfrac{1}{3}] \end{array}
$$

(c) $\frac{4}{3}$

3. (a)

$$
\begin{array}{c} \\ 1 \\ P = 2 \\ 3 \end{array}
\begin{array}{ccc} 1 & 2 & 3 \\ \begin{bmatrix} 1 & 0 & 0 \\ \frac{1}{5} & \frac{8}{15} & \frac{4}{15} \\ \frac{1}{5} & \frac{8}{15} & \frac{4}{15} \end{bmatrix} \end{array}
$$

(b)

$$
\begin{array}{c} \quad\quad\quad 1\ 2\ 3 \\ \Pi^{(0)} = [0, \tfrac{2}{3}, \tfrac{1}{3}] \end{array}
$$

(c) .5904

(d) $\frac{10}{3}$

5. 5

Exercises for 10.6

1. $\frac{1}{2}$
3. (a) $\frac{76}{211} \doteq .36$
(b) $\frac{3}{5} = .60$
5. approximately .581
7. The probability that company A survives is $\frac{960}{1,023} \doteq .938$; the probability that company B survives is $\frac{63}{1,023} \doteq .062$.

Exercises for 10.7

1. (a) $\frac{10}{19} \doteq .526$
   (b) approximately .604
   (c) approximately .552
3. (a) $\frac{10}{19} \doteq .526$
   (c) approximately .892

(b) almost 1 (larger than .99999)
(d) approximately .552

Chapter 11

Exercises for 11.1

1. (a) Player II pays player I 3.
   (c) Player I pays player II 4.
   (e) There is no payment.

(b) Player II pays player I 5.
(d) Player II pays player I 1.
(f) Player I pays player II 7.

3. Let H stand for hearts and D for diamonds. The payoff matrix is

$$
\begin{array}{c} \\ 2H \\ 3H \\ 4H \end{array}
\begin{array}{cccc} 3D & 4D & 5D & 6D \\ \begin{bmatrix} -5 & 6 & -7 & 8 \\ 6 & -7 & 8 & -9 \\ -7 & 8 & -9 & 10 \end{bmatrix} \end{array}
$$

5. Let RD = red deuce, BT = black trey, RA = red ace, and BD = black deuce. The payoff matrix is

$$
\begin{array}{c} \\ RD \\ BT \end{array}
\begin{array}{cc} RA & BD \\ \begin{bmatrix} -1 & 4 \\ 2 & -5 \end{bmatrix} \end{array}
$$

7.

$$
\begin{array}{c c c c}
 & 1 & 2 & 3 \\
1 & \begin{bmatrix} 10 \\ 1 \\ 3 \end{bmatrix} & \begin{matrix} -1 \\ 10 \\ -4 \end{matrix} & \begin{matrix} -3 \\ 4 \\ 10 \end{matrix} \end{array}
$$

Exercises for 11.2

1. Strictly determined, with saddle point the 1–1 entry. Both players should always choose option 1. The value of the game is -1.
3. Not strictly determined.
5. Strictly determined, with saddle point the 3–4 entry. Player I should always choose option 3; player II should always choose option 4. The value of the game is 0.
7. Strictly determined, with two saddle points, the 2–3 and 2–4 entries. Player I should always choose option 2; player II should choose either option 3 or 4. The value of the game is 3.
9. (a)

$$
\begin{array}{c c c}
 & 1 & 2 \\
1 & \begin{bmatrix} 2 \\ -3 \end{bmatrix} & \begin{matrix} -3 \\ 4 \end{matrix} \end{array}
$$

(b) no
11. No, it is not strictly determined.
13. No, it is not strictly determined.
15. No, it is not strictly determined.

Exercises for 11.3

1. (a) $[\frac{1}{4}, \frac{3}{4}], [\frac{1}{2}, \frac{1}{2}]$ (b) $[1, 0], [0, 1]$

(c) $\begin{bmatrix} \frac{1}{4} \\ \frac{3}{4} \end{bmatrix}, \begin{bmatrix} \frac{7}{8} \\ \frac{1}{8} \end{bmatrix}$ (d) $\begin{bmatrix} 1 \\ 0 \end{bmatrix}, \begin{bmatrix} 0 \\ 1 \end{bmatrix}$

3. (a) mixed strategy for player I
(b) mixed strategy for player I
(c) not a mixed strategy
(d) mixed strategy for player I, and it is also a pure strategy
(e) not a mixed strategy
(f) mixed strategy for player I, and it is also a pure strategy
(g) not a mixed strategy
(h) not a mixed strategy for player I, because it is not a row vector

5. $P^* = [\frac{1}{2}, \frac{1}{2}]$, $Q^* = \begin{bmatrix} \frac{1}{2} \\ \frac{1}{2} \end{bmatrix}$, and $v = 0$. The game is fair.

7. $P^* = [\frac{3}{4}, \frac{1}{4}]$, $Q^* = \begin{bmatrix} \frac{7}{8} \\ \frac{1}{8} \end{bmatrix}$, and $v = \frac{1}{4}$. The game favors player I.

9. The game is strictly determined. $P^* = [1, 0]$, $Q^* = \begin{bmatrix} 1 \\ 0 \end{bmatrix}$, and $v = -1$. The game favors player II.

11. (a) $P^* = [\frac{7}{12}, \frac{5}{12}]$, $Q^* = \begin{bmatrix} \frac{3}{4} \\ \frac{1}{4} \end{bmatrix}$ (b) $v = \frac{1}{4}$

(c) player I (d) about \$25

1. (a) $[\frac{1}{4}, 0, \frac{1}{4}, \frac{1}{2}, 0]$, $[\frac{1}{10}, \frac{2}{5}, \frac{1}{5}, \frac{1}{20}, \frac{1}{4}]$

(b) $\begin{bmatrix} \frac{1}{3} \\ \frac{1}{6} \\ 0 \\ \frac{1}{2} \end{bmatrix}$ $\begin{bmatrix} \frac{1}{5} \\ \frac{2}{5} \\ \frac{1}{10} \\ \frac{3}{10} \end{bmatrix}$

(c) $[1, 0, 0, 0, 0]$, $[0, 1, 0, 0, 0]$, $[0, 0, 1, 0, 0]$, $[0, 0, 0, 1, 0]$, $[0, 0, 0, 0, 1]$

(d) $\begin{bmatrix} 1 \\ 0 \\ 0 \\ 0 \end{bmatrix}$ $\begin{bmatrix} 0 \\ 1 \\ 0 \\ 0 \end{bmatrix}$ $\begin{bmatrix} 0 \\ 0 \\ 1 \\ 0 \end{bmatrix}$ $\begin{bmatrix} 0 \\ 0 \\ 0 \\ 1 \end{bmatrix}$

3. (a) mixed strategy for player I; also pure
   (b) Since player II has 4 options (not 3), this is not a mixed strategy for player II. On the other hand, since it is not a row vector, it cannot be a mixed strategy for player I.
   (c) not a mixed strategy
   (d) mixed strategy for player II
   (e) mixed strategy for player II; also pure
   (f) Since player I has 3 options (not 4), this is not a mixed strategy for player I. On the other hand, since it is not a column vector, it cannot be a mixed strategy for player II.
   (g) not a mixed strategy
   (h) mixed strategy for player I

5. 1

7. -2

9. $-\frac{3}{8}$

11. 11

13. $-\frac{1}{8}$

15. Player I's minimum expected gain using P^* is 0. Player II's maximum expected loss using Q^* is 0.

17. (a) v (b) v

(c) $[v, v]$ (d) $\begin{bmatrix} v \\ v \end{bmatrix}$

(e) v

Exercises for 11.5

1. The game tableau is

	v	q_1	q_2	
$-u$	0	1	1	$= -(-1)$
p_1	-1	2	-3	$= -t_1$
p_2	-1	4	5	$= -t_2$
	$\parallel$	$\parallel$	$\parallel$	
	-1	s_1	s_2	

and the Tucker tableau is

	t_2	q_1	-1	
s_2	0	1	1	$= -q_2$
p_1	-1	6	8	$= -t_1$
-1	-1	1	5	$= -v$

$$\begin{array}{ccc} \| & \| & \| \\ p_2 & s_1 & -u \end{array}$$

3. The game tableau is

	v	q_1	q_2	q_3	
$-u$	0	1	1	1	$= -(-1)$
p_1	-1	1	-3	-6	$= -t_1$
p_2	-1	2	4	5	$= -t_2$

$$\begin{array}{cccc} \| & \| & \| & \| \\ -1 & s_1 & s_2 & s_3 \end{array}$$

and the Tucker tableau is

	t_2	q_1	q_2	-1	
s_3	0	1	1	1	$= -q_3$
p_1	-1	10	4	11	$= -t_1$
-1	-1	3	1	5	$= -v$

$$\begin{array}{cccc} \| & \| & \| & \| \\ p_2 & s_1 & s_2 & -u \end{array}$$

5. The game tableau is

	v	q_1	q_2	q_3	q_4	
$-u$	0	1	1	1	1	$= -(-1)$
p_1	-1	1	0	-1	2	$= -t_1$
p_2	-1	-3	-2	5	1	$= -t_2$

$$\begin{array}{ccccc} \| & \| & \| & \| & \| \\ -1 & s_1 & s_2 & s_3 & s_4 \end{array}$$

and the Tucker tableau is

	t_1	q_1	q_2	q_3	-1	
s_4	0	1	1	1	1	$= -q_4$
p_2	-1	-3	-1	7	1	$= -t_2$
-1	-1	1	2	3	2	$= -v$
	$\|\|$	$\|\|$	$\|\|$	$\|\|$	$\|\|$	
	p_1	s_1	s_2	s_3	$-u$	

7. $P^* = [\frac{9}{14}, \frac{5}{14}]$, $Q^* = \begin{bmatrix} \frac{4}{7} \\ \frac{3}{7} \end{bmatrix}$, and $v = -\frac{1}{7}$. The game favors player II.

9. $P^* = [\frac{1}{2}, \frac{1}{2}]$, $Q^* = \begin{bmatrix} \frac{1}{2} \\ \frac{1}{2} \end{bmatrix}$, and $v = 0$. The game is fair.

11. $P^* = [1, 0]$, $Q^* = \begin{bmatrix} 1 \\ 0 \end{bmatrix}$, and $v = -1$. The game favors player II.

13. $P^* = [0, 1]$, $Q^* = \begin{bmatrix} 1 \\ 0 \\ 0 \end{bmatrix}$, and $v = 2$. The game favors player I.

15. $P^* = [\frac{7}{8}, \frac{1}{8}]$, $Q^* = \begin{bmatrix} 0 \\ \frac{3}{4} \\ \frac{1}{4} \\ 0 \end{bmatrix}$, and $v = -\frac{1}{4}$. The game favors player II.

17. $P^* = [\frac{1}{3}, \frac{1}{3}, \frac{1}{3}]$, $Q^* = \begin{bmatrix} \frac{1}{3} \\ \frac{1}{3} \\ \frac{1}{3} \end{bmatrix}$, and $v = 0$. The game is fair.

19. $P^* = [\frac{7}{12}, \frac{5}{12}]$, $Q^* = \begin{bmatrix} \frac{3}{4} \\ \frac{1}{4} \end{bmatrix}$, and $v = \frac{1}{4}$. The game favors player I.

Exercises for 11.6

1. (a) $[1, 3]$
   (c) $\begin{bmatrix} 5 \\ 0 \end{bmatrix}$
   (e) $\frac{5}{3}$

   (b) $u = 1$
   (d) $v = 5$

3. (a) $[-2, \frac{3}{2}]$
   (c) $\begin{bmatrix} -\frac{1}{2} \\ \frac{11}{2} \\ -5 \end{bmatrix}$
   (e) $\frac{11}{8}$

   (b) $u = -2$
   (d) $v = \frac{11}{2}$

5. (a) $[-\frac{3}{8}, \frac{7}{8}, \frac{1}{8}, \frac{29}{8}]$
   (c) $\begin{bmatrix} -\frac{3}{2} \\ -\frac{3}{2} \\ \frac{7}{4} \end{bmatrix}$
   (e) $\frac{17}{32}$

   (b) $u = -\frac{3}{8}$
   (d) $v = \frac{7}{4}$

7. $u = v = 0$

9. $u = v = \frac{53}{19}$

11. $u = v = 0$

13. $u = v = -\frac{1}{2}$

15. $u = v = \frac{1}{6}$

Exercises for 11.7

1. (a) $P^* = [\frac{1}{2}, \frac{1}{2}], Q^* = \begin{bmatrix} \frac{1}{2} \\ \frac{1}{2} \end{bmatrix}$

   (b) Company I has a 5 percent advantage.

3. (a) $P^* = [0, 0, 1], Q^* = \begin{bmatrix} 0 \\ 0 \\ 1 \end{bmatrix}$, and $v = 0$.

   (b) Each politician should spend both days in town A. By doing so, neither will gain an advantage.

5. (a) $P^* = [\frac{1}{4}, \frac{1}{2}, \frac{1}{4}], Q^* = \begin{bmatrix} \frac{1}{4} \\ \frac{1}{2} \\ \frac{1}{4} \end{bmatrix}$

   (b) The value of the game is 0, so neither company has an advantage.
   (c) At the beginning of each month each company should choose television as its advertising medium with probability $\frac{1}{4}$, radio with probability $\frac{1}{2}$, and magazines with probability $\frac{1}{4}$.

Appendix A

Exercises for A.1

1. (a) $\frac{5}{6}$
   (b) $\frac{5}{8}$
   (c) $\frac{36}{5}$
   (d) $\frac{19}{30}$
   (e) $-\frac{25}{22}$
   (f) $\frac{8}{15}$
   (g) $\frac{21}{8}$
   (h) $-\frac{1}{12}$
   (i) $\frac{5}{3}$
   (j) $\frac{10}{9}$
   (k) $-\frac{32}{15}$
   (l) $\frac{7}{48}$
   (m) $\frac{16}{5}$
   (n) $\frac{5}{6}$

3. (a) M3
   (b) A2
   (c) M4
   (d) A4
   (e) M3 and M2
   (f) D1

5. (a) yes
   (b) no

7. (a) no
   (b) no

9. (a) y^2
   (b) $2x^3y^8$
   (c) $16a^{12}b^8c^4$
   (d) $b^3/(4a^3)$
   (e) $2x^2$
   (f) $-x^7/2$
   (g) $9y^4/x^8$
   (h) $27a^2b^5c/8$

11. (a) $-1/(2a)$
    (b) $4b^6/a^8$
    (c) $3y^5/x^9$
    (d) $1/(16a^4b^7)$

    (e) 1
    (f) $\frac{b}{a} + \frac{a}{b}$

    (g) $2 + \frac{y}{x} + \frac{x}{y}$
    (h) $2ab$

13. (a) For example, take $a = b = c = 1$.
    (b) Yes; for example, take $a = 0, b = c = 1$.

15. We have

$$\left[\left(\tfrac{1}{a}\right)\left(\tfrac{1}{b}\right)\right](ab) = \left(\tfrac{1}{a}\right)\left[\left(\tfrac{1}{b}\right)(ab)\right], \text{ by M3}$$
$$= \left(\tfrac{1}{a}\right)\left[(ab)\left(\tfrac{1}{b}\right)\right], \text{ by M2}$$
$$= \left(\tfrac{1}{a}\right)\left[a\left(b \cdot \tfrac{1}{b}\right)\right], \text{ by M3}$$
$$= \left(\tfrac{1}{a}\right)[a \cdot 1], \text{ by M5}$$
$$= \tfrac{1}{a} \cdot a, \text{ by M4}$$
$$= a \cdot \tfrac{1}{a}, \text{ by M2}$$
$$= 1, \text{ by M5}$$

17. We have

$$(ca)\left[b\left(\tfrac{1}{c}\right)\right] = (ac)\left[\left(\tfrac{1}{c}\right)b\right], \text{ by M2}$$
$$= a\left(c\left[\left(\tfrac{1}{c}\right)b\right]\right), \text{ by M3}$$
$$= a\left(\left[c\left(\tfrac{1}{c}\right)\right](b)\right), \text{ by M3}$$
$$= a(1 \cdot b), \text{ by M5}$$
$$= a(b \cdot 1), \text{ by M2}$$
$$= ab, \text{ by M4}$$

Therefore,

$$-(ab) + (ca)\left[b\left(\tfrac{1}{c}\right)\right] = -(ab) + ab = 0$$

Exercises for A.2

1. (a) $<$ (b) $<$
   (c) $<$ (d) $<$
   (e) $<$ (f) $<$
   (g) $>$ (h) $<$
   (i) $>$ (j) $>$

3. $a - a = 0 \not> 0$.

5. $a - (a - b) = (a - a) + b = 0 + b = b > 0$, so $a - b < a$.

7. Since $a < b$, $2a < a + b$, so $a < (a + b)/2$. Also, since $a < b$, $a + b < 2b$, so $(a + b)/2 < b$. Thus

$$a < \frac{a + b}{2} < b$$

9. We have

$(*) \quad (b + d) - (a + c) = (b - a) + (d - c)$

Since $a < b$, $b - a > 0$ and since $c < d$, $d - c > 0$. Thus, by O1, $(b - a) + (d - c) > 0$, and therefore, by $(*)$, $(b + d) - (a + c) > 0$, which implies that $a + c < b + d$.

11. First assume that $a < b$. Then $b - a > 0$. By assumption $a > 0$ and $b > 0$, so, by O1, $b + a > 0$. Hence

$$b^2 - a^2 = (b - a)(b + a) > 0$$

by O2. Consequently, $a^2 < b^2$.

Conversely, assume that $a^2 < b^2$. Then $b^2 - a^2 > 0$. But

$$(b - a)(b + a) = b^2 - a^2 > 0$$

so

$$(b - a)(b + a) > 0$$

Since $b + a > 0$, it must be that $b - a > 0$. (Why?) Hence $a < b$.

Exercises for A.3

1. (a) -3 (b) 4
   (c) 3   (d) 3
   (e) -1 (f) 2
   (g) 8   (h) 2
   (i) 5   (j) $-b/a$

3. $a = -3$

5. (a) $2 < x < \frac{5}{2}$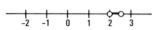

   (b) $-\frac{3}{2} < x < 2$

   (c) $1 \le x < 3$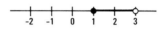

   (d) $\frac{1}{2} < x < 1$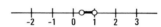

   (e) $\frac{2}{3} \le x \le 4$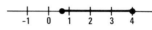

   (f) $\frac{2}{3} < x < \frac{14}{3}$

7. Since $x > -2$, it follows that $x + 2 > 0$. Also, $x < 1$ implies that $x - 1 < 0$. Hence $(x + 2)(x - 1) < 0$, by O5.

Index